Automatic Feedback Control System Synthesis

McGRAW-HILL ELECTRICAL AND ELECTRONIC ENGINEERING SERIES

FREDERICK EMMONS TERMAN, *Consulting Editor*
W. W. HARMAN, HUBERT HEFFNER, AND
J. G. TRUXAL, *Associate Consulting Editors*

AHRENDT AND SAVANT · Servomechanism Practice
ANGELO · Electronic Circuits
ASELTINE · Transform Method in Linear System Analysis
ATWATER · Introduction to Microwave Theory
BAILEY AND GAULT · Alternating-current Machinery
BERANEK · Acoustics
BRENNER AND JAVID · Analysis of Electric Circuits
BROWN · Analysis of Linear Time-invariant Systems
BRUNS AND SAUNDERS · Analysis of Feedback Control Systems
CAGE · Theory and Application of Industrial Electronics
CAUER · Synthesis of Linear Communication Networks
CHEN · The Analysis of Linear Systems
CHEN · Linear Network Design and Synthesis
CHIRLIAN AND ZEMANIAN · Electronics
CLEMENT AND JOHNSON · Electrical Engineering Science
COTE AND OAKES · Linear Vacuum-tube and Transistor Circuits
CUCCIA · Harmonics, Sidebands, and Transients in Communication Engineering
CUNNINGHAM · Introduction to Nonlinear Analysis
EASTMAN · Fundamentals of Vacuum Tubes
EVANS · Control-system Dynamics
FEINSTEIN · Foundations of Information Theory
FITZGERALD AND HIGGINBOTHAM · Basic Electrical Engineering
FITZGERALD AND KINGSLEY · Electric Machinery
FRANK · Electrical Measurement Analysis
FRIEDLAND, WING, AND ASH · Principles of Linear Networks
GEPPERT · Basic Electron Tubes
GHOSE · Microwave Circuit Theory and Analysis
GREINER · Semiconductor Devices and Applications
HAMMOND · Electrical Engineering
HANCOCK · An Introduction to the Principles of Communication Theory
HAPPELL AND HESSELBERTH · Engineering Electronics
HARMAN · Fundamentals of Electronic Motion
HARMAN · Principles of the Statistical Theory of Communication
HARMAN AND LYTLE · Electrical and Mechanical Networks
HARRINGTON · Introduction to Electromagnetic Engineering
HARRINGTON · Time-harmonic Electromagnetic Fields
HAYASHI · Nonlinear Oscillations in Physical Systems
HAYT · Engineering Electromagnetics
HILL · Electronics in Engineering
HUELSMAN · Circuits, Matrices, and Linear Vector Spaces
JAVID AND BRENNER · Analysis, Transmission, and Filtering of Signals
JAVID AND BROWN · Field Analysis and Electromagnetics
JOHNSON · Transmission Lines and Networks
KOENIG AND BLACKWELL · Electromechanical System Theory
KRAUS · Antennas

AUTOMATIC
FEEDBACK CONTROL SYSTEM
SYNTHESIS

PROFESSOR JOHN G. TRUXAL

Head, Department of Electrical Engineering
Polytechnic Institute of Brooklyn
Brooklyn, New York

McGRAW-HILL BOOK COMPANY, INC.

New York   Toronto   London

1955

AUTOMATIC FEEDBACK CONTROL SYSTEM SYNTHESIS

Library of Congress Catalog Card Number 54-9762

XI

65310

To
DORIS

PREFACE

During the years since the end of World War II there have been a number of books published on the subject of feedback theory, with particular emphasis on the analysis and design of feedback control systems. The principal concern of all these books has been with the synthesis of linear feedback control systems, with emphasis on the techniques for system design through inspection of the behavior of the open-loop transfer function at real frequencies. Although almost all the books have employed the Laplace transform liberally, the critical reader continually must question the motive for writing the transfer functions in terms of the complex frequency s. In almost every case, the authors go to considerable length to explain the Laplace transform, go to great pains to use the complex frequency in the process of setting up the equations describing the behavior of the various components of the system, and then blithely replace s by $j\omega$ before launching the design of the compensation networks.

It is true that certain writers emphasize the importance of the dynamic performance of the system. Generally, however, the reader is left with the unsavory choice of determining the transient performance by the depressingly tedious process of taking the exact inverse Laplace transform or of attempting to evaluate an approximate inverse transform by one of the many systematized procedures. If dynamic performance is really of importance in the design of servo systems, neither alternative is appealing. In neither case is any logical method presented for the improvement of the transient response. If the transient performance is unsatisfactory, about the best that the designer can do is to start the entire design over again, proceeding in a slightly different manner toward a final system which meets frequency-domain specifications, and hope that the transient response will be improved.

In view of this widespread emphasis on design in the domain of real frequencies, what justification exists for the use of the Laplace transform? Unfortunately, any exploitation of the advantages of the Laplace transform demands familiarity with aspects of electrical engineering which are not second nature to the majority of engineers. In particular, maximum utilization of the Laplace transform as a design tool depends, on the part of the designer, upon a firm knowledge of the relationships between the Laplace transforms and the transient and frequency responses, the fundamental concepts of feedback theory, the techniques of network synthesis,

vii

the elements of statistical methods of design, and the general concepts used in the analysis of nonlinear systems.

First, the designer must have a working familiarity with the Laplace transform; indeed, a familiarity which goes beyond the simple formal relationships between the time and frequency functions. It is not sufficient to know the mechanical techniques for evaluating direct and inverse transforms. Rather the designer must be conscious of the relationships between time-domain and frequency-domain characteristics, relationships which depend upon the significance of the positions of the poles and zeros of the transfer functions. He must be able to determine the effects, in both time and frequency domains, of varying these pole and zero positions.

Second, the designer must be familiar with the fundamental concepts of feedback theory. Motivation for the use of closed-loop rather than open-loop systems arises from the possibility, with feedback, of controlling sensitivity, output impedance, and subsidiary transmissions while, at the same time, realizing a specified over-all system function. Feedback theory involves a development of the definitions and significances of these controllable quantities and demonstrates system design methods which permit the required control.

Third, if the servo engineer is to appreciate fully the advantages inherent in the use of the Laplace transform, he must be able to synthesize appropriate compensation networks. The familiar lead, lag, and twin-T networks which have so long served as the building blocks of system design fail to support the structure of design when the specifications become stringent, use of isolation amplifiers is denied, or unusual systems are required (such as mechanical or hydraulic networks). It becomes necessary to be able to synthesize networks with prescribed transfer characteristics.

Fourth, the designer must be familiar with the statistical methods of design if he is to cope with the problems associated with realistic signal inputs. A tremendous amount of research effort is being expended in the direction of improving feedback control systems, particularly those systems in which random noise is a primary deterrent to high system performance. Problems associated with the control of corrupting signals which are essentially random in nature are readily handled only with statistical methods.

Fifth, the designer must be acquainted with the basic techniques available for considering nonlinear systems. He must be able to analyze the effects of unwanted nonlinearities present in the system and to synthesize nonlinearities into the system to improve dynamic performance.

This book represents an attempt to organize and unify the background material in these five fields. Emphasis is on the development of the basic theory, although an attempt is made to illustrate the discussion with examples of practical significance. Unfortunately, however, in a book of reasonable length, it is necessary to place most of the emphasis on the theory and allow the reader to use examples from his own experience as illustrations.

The bulk of the material in the book has been taught in a two-semester graduate servomechanisms course in the Electrical Engineering School at Purdue University. This course has followed the introductory course, which has used as texts sections of Brown and Campbell, "Principles of Servomechanisms," Chestnut and Mayer, "Servomechanisms and Regulating System Design," and Ahrendt and Taplin, "Automatic Feedback Control." The author feels that this book, as a text, logically follows any of the three mentioned above. In addition, a serious effort has been made to present the material in a way which will be of value, not only as a textbook, but also as a reference book for industrial engineers. In the contacts which the author has had with industrial problems, he has been impressed by the growing realization on the part of industrial research groups of the necessity for the maximum utilization of available design theory.

In the preparation of the book, an attempt has been made to make as many of the chapters as possible self-contained. Chapter 1 serves as an introduction and a review of the mathematical background. In teaching, the author has usually omitted parts of this chapter until the need for the material arose later in the course. Chapters 2 and 3 present basic theory; in most universities, the material of Chap. 3 is adequately covered in a course on network synthesis. Chapters 4, 5, and 6 describe the important aspects of design in terms of the Laplace transform. Statistical design theory is described in Chaps. 7 and 8, with the former chapter emphasizing the fundamental concepts and the latter chapter describing certain applications of particular interest to the control-systems engineer. Chapter 9 presents the basic characteristics of sampled-data feedback systems, and the book concludes with the two chapters on the analysis of nonlinear feedback systems.

The author is deeply indebted to a number of individuals who assisted in the preparation of the manuscript. In every instance, the author received encouragement and complete cooperation from the electrical engineering staff at Purdue University. Although it is difficult to name all individuals, discussions with Drs. J. R. Burnett and G. R. Cooper were particularly helpful. The proofreading was completely the work of Mr. T. A. Savo, who also contributed encouragement at every stage of the writing and innumerable constructive criticisms for improvement of the presentation. The author's wife typed the complete manuscript and assisted extensively with the figures, etc. Indeed, the book is in every respect the result of the mutual efforts of the author and his wife.

JOHN G. TRUXAL

CONTENTS

CHAPTER 1

INTRODUCTION

During the last decade, feedback systems and active networks have become increasingly important in a number of branches of engineering. Simultaneously, there has been increased interest in the dynamic characteristics of systems, in contrast to the earlier interest in static characteristics. Furthermore, emphasis has been turned toward the performance of systems excited by aperiodic (or transient) signals and signals which can only be described statistically. The combination of these directions of interest has led to the development of refined techniques for the analysis and synthesis of feedback systems.

For example, the dynamic characteristics of feedback systems are of very basic importance for the communications, systems, and instrumentation engineers. The various aspects of the central problem of designing systems for specified dynamic performance are most nearly unified in the field of automatic control, and it is in this field that the greatest part of the research has been done. Only a few years ago, the feedback-control engineer was in many ways a parasite, adapting the methods of the mechanical engineer, the communication engineer, etc., to his problems. Today, as a result of the tremendous research effort of the past decade, the feedback-control engineer has not only brought the various phases of engineering together, but he has assumed at least his share of engineering leadership.

Indeed, in many respects, servomechanisms and automatic control systems today comprise one of the glamorous fields of electrical engineering. The importance and popularity of this field are in no small measure the result of military applications in the development of fire-control systems, missile-control systems, etc. But already the many peacetime applications of feedback control systems are becoming evident. This rapid expansion of feedback-control-system engineering has demonstrated the very fundamental importance of the dynamic characteristics of systems. In the vast majority of servomechanisms, the designer is interested not only in the sinusoidal response of the system, but also in the response to typical or test transient signals.

An aircraft-to-aircraft fire-control system can be used to illustrate the importance of the time-domain characterization of a system. The intelligent design of such a system demands consideration of the actual waveform of the anticipated input signals. A typical target run may last only a short length of time, perhaps 10 sec. During this time interval, the radar must lock on the target and thereafter follow within a specified

1

accuracy.   There are two distinct design problems: the realization of a system which locks on within a very few seconds, even if the decision to lock on is made when the antenna is a considerable distance from the selected target; and the maintenance of suitable tracking accuracy after lock-on, with the probable relative maneuverings of the two aircraft taken into consideration.   If only these factors were involved, the design would resolve simply to the realization of system components with a response sufficiently fast to meet the specifications.   Design is complicated, however, by the presence of noise corrupting the signal.   In a broad sense, design must determine a compromise between speed of response and filtering.   The logical selection of this compromise can be accomplished only in terms of the transient response of the system to typical input signals.   Ultimately, if the specifications are sufficiently difficult to meet, design must yield a system which separates signals from noise, even though both components of the input have the same frequency spectrum.   Such a separation might be accomplished by a nonlinear filter on the basis of the difference in the probability distributions of signal and noise.

This fire-control problem is particularly appropriate for an introductory discussion, because the design problems involved encompass a number of the important aspects of the modern theory of feedback control systems:

(1)   The complexity of the complete system, including the tracking loop (radar, antenna servo, gyros to introduce corrections for own-ship's motion, etc.), the computer (for determining desired gun elevation and bearing from the estimated relative target motion, the ballistics, and the range), and the gun-positioning servos, indicates the need for a systematic approach to analysis and design.   In the design of both the individual components and the over-all, multiloop system, the basic techniques of general network and feedback theory are essential tools.

(2)   The problem emphasizes the importance of the transient response of the final system.   Indeed, all possible input functions can be described by a class of transient signals.   Evaluation of the tracking accuracy (even in the absence of noise) requires characterization of the system in the time domain.

(3)   For a complete design, characteristics of the noise must be known, and the noise power must be determined at various points throughout the system before an evaluation of system performance can be completed. Since the noise is ordinarily random and can be described only in statistical terms, design requires some familiarity with statistical methods of measurement and analysis.

(4)   The effects of the noise are most readily analyzed in the frequency domain, *i.e.*, in terms of the noise power spectrum (measuring the noise power in certain frequency bands) and the gain-frequency characteristics of the physical components.

(5)   Considerations (2) and (4) indicate clearly that design is most effective if system components are described in such a way that both time-domain and frequency-domain characteristics are evident.   The Laplace transform, with the concept of complex frequency $s = \sigma + j\omega$,

provides the required correlation between transient and frequency responses, but only if the transfer functions are considered as functions of s, not if the components are characterized by the gain and phase versus frequency.

(6) The fire-control problem is one in which the ultimate design must be for a nonlinear system, particularly if the system performance is improved to the point where significant errors are introduced by considering the noise characteristics to be constant (when in actuality these characteristics change rather markedly with range). Appropriate methods for the logical design of nonlinear systems are certainly not general at the present time, but, once the properties and limitations of the linear system are clearly understood, a variety of special procedures for analyzing and (in part) designing nonlinear systems is available.

Thus, one of the most important changes in communication and control engineering during the last decade has been the broadening of interest from the frequency characteristics to the performance characteristics with the system excited by transient inputs or by actual, typical inputs described statistically. Techniques for the design and synthesis of networks and feedback systems have been extended to admit control over both time-domain and frequency-domain characteristics. The increased interest in nonlinear systems has provided further impetus to the development of such time-domain characterization. Since superposition does not apply in a nonlinear system, it is no longer possible in the design to justify the use of frequency characteristics by stating that the Fourier integral permits any aperiodic signal to be represented as the sum of sine waves, and, accordingly, design cannot be carried through in terms of frequency characteristics.

The necessity for correlation between time-domain and frequency-domain characteristics has been met in the design of linear systems by exploiting the Laplace transform and the associated complex-function theory as a mathematical tool in synthesis. The characterization of a linear system by a transfer function depending on the complex frequency s permits the designer to consider simultaneously both transient and frequency characteristics. The elements of Laplace-transform theory and complex-function theory are presented in almost all texts on feedback control systems. In this introductory chapter, certain aspects of these theories are considered in detail, and aspects of particular interest in the analysis and synthesis procedures are presented in subsequent chapters.[†] To a very large extent, the power of the theory presented throughout this book depends on a familiarity with the introductory mathematics of this chapter.

† At the outset, a knowledge of the very elementary aspects of Laplace-transform theory is assumed. Appropriate discussions are presented in G. S. Brown and D. P. Campbell, "Principles of Servomechanisms," Chap. 3, John Wiley & Sons, Inc., New York, 1948; in W. R. Ahrendt and J. F. Taplin, "Automatic Feedback Control," Chap. 2, McGraw-Hill Book Company, Inc., New York, 1951; and in H. Chestnut and R. W. Mayer, "Servomechanisms and Regulating System Design," Vol. I, Chap. 4, John Wiley & Sons, Inc., New York, 1951.

1.1. Functions of a Complex Variable. If the transfer function of the network shown in Fig. 1.1 is written as a function of the complex frequency s,

$$\frac{E_2}{E_1}(s) = \frac{1/Cs}{R + 1/Cs} = \frac{1}{RCs + 1} \tag{1.1}$$

The value of the voltage ratio at any sinusoidal angular frequency ω is found by replacing s by $j\omega$; the gain and phase characteristics are then given by the magnitude and angle of $\dfrac{E_2}{E_1}(j\omega)$. Since $\dfrac{E_2}{E_1}(s)$ is also the ratio of the Laplace transforms of the output and input voltages, Eq. (1.1) contains not only the gain and phase characteristics, but also the transient response of the network.

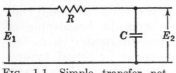

FIG. 1.1. Simple transfer network.

The analysis of more complicated networks follows the same pattern: by means of conventional techniques (loop equations, node equations, etc.), the transfer function is determined in terms of the complex frequency s. If the network is linear and consists of lumped-constant elements, the resulting transfer function, whether it be a voltage ratio, a current ratio, an impedance, or an admittance, is always a *rational algebraic* function of s (that is, the ratio of two polynomials in s). Indeed, this rational algebraic nature is realized regardless of the type of system: *i.e.*, whether electrical, mechanical, hydraulic, etc.

As a consequence of the use of the complex frequency $s = \sigma + j\omega$, analysis of the characteristics of transfer functions can draw upon the mathematicians' well-developed theory of functions of a complex variable. Indeed, the analysis and synthesis of networks and feedback systems are to a very large extent the application of complex-function theory. A few particularly useful aspects of this theory, described briefly in this section, form the basis for the network and feedback theory presented in subsequent chapters.†

Definition. The functions of a complex variable of principal interest are those which possess a unique derivative. The derivative of a real function of a single variable x is defined by the equation

$$f'(x) = \lim_{\Delta x \to 0} \left[\frac{f(x + \Delta x) - f(x)}{\Delta x} \right] \tag{1.2}$$

† Fortunately, a wide variety of excellent texts are available to present the material with more rigor and in considerably more detail. Complex-function theory is considered at least briefly in almost all texts on advanced mathematics for electrical engineers: *e.g.*, E. A. Guillemin, "Mathematics of Circuit Analysis," Chap. 6, John Wiley & Sons, Inc., New York, 1949; and A. Bronwell, "Advanced Mathematics in Physics and Engineering," Chap. 15, McGraw-Hill Book Company, Inc., New York, 1953. Mathematical texts on complex-function theory are numerous. Two that the author has particularly liked are K. Knopp, "Theory of Functions," Dover Publications, New York, 1945; and E. T. Copson, "Theory of Functions of a Complex Variable," Oxford University Press, London, 1935.

If this definition is extended to functions of the complex variable s,

$$G'(s) = \lim_{\Delta s \to 0} \left[\frac{G(s + \Delta s) - G(s)}{\Delta s} \right] \tag{1.3}$$

If the $G(s)$ is an arbitrary function of s, it is clear that the value of $G'(s)$ at any point s_1 may depend on the Δs used: for example, on the angle of Δs (i.e., the direction from s_1 along which the increment is considered). If such a nonuniqueness exists, $G(s)$ is not ordinarily of interest.

A simple example illustrates the difficulty here. The $G(s)$ considered is

$$G(s) = |s| \tag{1.4}$$

or

$$G(s) = \sqrt{\sigma^2 + \omega^2} \tag{1.5}$$

If an attempt is made to evaluate the derivative $G'(s)$ by considering the change in the function as s changes by a real increment $\Delta\sigma$,

$$G'(s) = \lim_{\Delta\sigma \to 0} \left[\frac{\sqrt{(\sigma + \Delta\sigma)^2 + \omega^2} - \sqrt{\sigma^2 + \omega^2}}{\Delta\sigma} \right] \tag{1.6}$$

The numerator can be rewritten to give

$$G'(s) = \lim_{\Delta\sigma \to 0} \left[\sqrt{\sigma^2 + \omega^2} \frac{\sqrt{1 + \dfrac{2\sigma\,\Delta\sigma + (\Delta\sigma)^2}{\sigma^2 + \omega^2}} - 1}{\Delta\sigma} \right] \tag{1.7}$$

As $\Delta\sigma$ tends to zero, Eq. (1.7) becomes

$$G'(s) = \lim_{\Delta\sigma \to 0} \left[\sqrt{\sigma^2 + \omega^2} \frac{\sigma\,\Delta\sigma/(\sigma^2 + \omega^2)}{\Delta\sigma} \right] \tag{1.8}$$

$$G'(s) = \frac{\sigma}{\sqrt{\sigma^2 + \omega^2}} \tag{1.9}$$

If a Δs of $j\Delta\omega$ is used instead of $\Delta\sigma$, Eq. (1.3) gives the relation

$$G'(s) = \frac{-j\omega}{\sqrt{\sigma^2 + \omega^2}} \tag{1.10}$$

In general, Eqs. (1.9) and (1.10) indicate two entirely different values of $G'(s)$. This difficulty in defining a derivative limits severely the permissible mathematical manipulations on $G(s)$. Consequently, in order that a unified theory may be constructed, such $G(s)$ functions are not considered.

The usual functions encountered in network theory and control-system analysis possess a unique derivative at almost all points in the s plane. If $G(s)$ is a rational algebraic function, the derivative exists in the entire s

plane except at the isolated points representing the zeros of the denominator, where $G(s)$ and all derivatives become infinite.

Analyticity. $G(s)$ is analytic in a region if the function and all its derivatives exist in the region. For example, the function $G(s) = 1/(s + 1)$ is analytic in any region of the s plane not including the point -1. The function $\sqrt{s}$ is analytic in any region not including the origin, since at $s = 0$ the first and all higher derivatives do not exist.

In exceptional cases in which doubt exists as to whether a given $G(s)$ is an analytic function of a complex variable, the Cauchy-Riemann equations provide a useful test. $G(s)$ is an analytic function of the complex variable s if

$$\frac{\partial(\operatorname{Re} G)}{\partial \sigma} = \frac{\partial(\operatorname{Im} G)}{\sigma \omega}$$

$$\frac{\partial(\operatorname{Im} G)}{\partial \sigma} = -\frac{\partial(\operatorname{Re} G)}{\partial \omega} \qquad (1.11)$$

and all four partial derivatives are continuous functions of s. Throughout the remainder of this section, all functions considered satisfy these conditions except at isolated points in the s plane.

Singularities. The points at which a function (or its derivatives) does not exist are termed the singularities of the function. In this section, the functions of interest are those with only isolated singularities in the finite part of the plane: *i.e.*, in any finite region there are only a finite number of singularities, or, more rigorously, the singularities do not possess a limit point in the finite part of the s plane.

The singularities are of fundamental importance in characterizing the function of a complex variable, for the location and nature of the singularities determine the behavior of the function throughout the entire plane. Because of this importance, the singularities are the basis for the classification of functions. For example, a function with no singularities in the s plane (including the point at infinity) must be a constant. A function with no finite singularities, but possibly with a singularity at infinity, is termed an *entire function*. Functions with finite singularities are divided according to the nature and number of singularities.

There are three types of singularities of importance in the analysis and design of feedback systems:

(1) Poles
(2) Essential singularities
(3) Branch points

The classification indicates the manner in which the function (or a derivative) behaves as s approaches the singularity, although ordinarily the various types are defined in analytical terms.

The simplest type of singularity, a pole, is defined as follows: if a positive *integer* n can be found such that

$$\lim_{s \to s_1} [(s - s_1)^n G(s)]$$

has a nonzero, finite value, s_1 is a pole of $G(s)$, and the pole is of order n.†
In other words, the denominator of $G(s)$ must include, at least implicitly,
the multiplicative factor $(s - s_1)^n$. Since any rational algebraic function
can be written as the ratio of factored polynomials,

$$\frac{(s - a)(s - b) \cdots (s - m)}{(s - \alpha)(s - \beta) \cdots (s - \nu)}$$

all singularities of rational algebraic functions are poles. In the form
above, the poles are at $\alpha, \beta, \ldots, \nu$. If j of the denominator factors are
identical, one of the poles is of order
j.

An essential singularity can be
viewed as a pole of infinite order.
Rigorously, an essential singularity
should be defined in terms of the
Laurent expansion.‡ For the applications here, however, the rigorous
definition is not especially important, since most essential singularities encountered in network theory
are associated with exponential functions. The function e^{-s}, for example, possesses an essential singularity
at infinity, while $e^{-1/s}$ has an essential singularity at the origin.

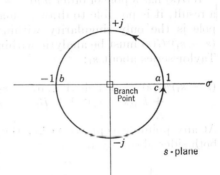

FIG. 1.2. Closed path around a branch
point. $G(s) = \sqrt{s}$.

Branch points are singularities characterized by the phenomenon that
complete traversal of a path enclosing a branch point does not result in a
return to the original value of the function. $\sqrt{s}$ is the simplest function
with a branch point, in this case at the origin. If the path shown in
Fig. 1.2 is followed, the value of $\sqrt{s}$ starts as $\sqrt{e^{j0}} = e^{j0}$, or $+1$; when
point b is reached, the value is $\sqrt{e^{j\pi}}$, or $+j$; as point c is approached, the
value tends to $\sqrt{e^{j2\pi}}$, or -1, and the multivalued character of the function is apparent. A single encirclement of the branch point at the origin
results in a change in the value of $G(s)$. In this case, a second encirclement would result in the original value of the function; consequently, the
branch point is of order two. The logarithmic function $\ln s$ is an example
of a function with a branch point of infinite order, since every positive
encirclement of the origin increases the imaginary part of $\ln s$ by 2π.
Branch points also may be characterized by the behavior of $G(s)$ as s
approaches the singularity. Thus, $\sqrt{s}$ has a zero-type branch point at

† A pole is an isolated singularity. In other words, if the pole is at s_1, it is always
possible to find a small circular region around s_1 such that no other singularities lie
within this region.

‡ The Laurent expansion about an essential singularity contains an infinite number
of terms. As ordinarily defined, an essential singularity need not be an isolated
singularity but may, for example, be the limit point of a sequence of poles.

the origin since $\sqrt{s}$ tends to zero as s approaches zero; on the other hand, the origin is a pole-type branch point for the function $1/\sqrt{s}$.

Behavior of a Function in the Vicinity of a Pole. Since the singularities characterize the function, the analysis and synthesis procedures emphasize the singularities, and the behavior of the function in the vicinity of a singularity is of fundamental importance. The majority of functions to be considered throughout the succeeding chapters are transfer functions of linear, lumped-constant systems and, hence, are rational algebraic functions with poles as the only singularities. Accordingly, the behavior of a function in the vicinity of a pole is of considerable interest.

If $G(s)$ has a pole of order n at $s = s_1$, the singularity is isolated, and, as a result, it is possible to draw a small circle centered at s_1 such that the pole is the only singularity within the circular region. The function $(s - s_1)^n G(s)$ must be analytic within this circle and can be expanded in a Taylor series about s_1:

$$(s - s_1)^n G(s) = A_{-n} + A_{-n+1}(s - s_1) + \cdots + A_{-2}(s - s_1)^{n-2}$$
$$+ k_{s_1}(s - s_1)^{n-1} + B_0(s - s_1)^n + B_1(s - s_1)^{n+1} + \cdots \quad (1.12)$$

At any point (except s_1) within the region, $G(s)$ is given by division of both sides above by $(s - s_1)^n$:

$$G(s) = \frac{A_{-n}}{(s - s_1)^n} + \frac{A_{-(n-1)}}{(s - s_1)^{n-1}} + \cdots + \frac{A_{-2}}{(s - s_1)^2} + \frac{k_{s_1}}{s - s_1}$$
$$+ B_0 + B_1(s - s_1) + \cdots \quad (1.13)$$

Equation (1.13) presents the Laurent series for $G(s)$, a series which is valid in the vicinity of the pole at s_1. Actually, the series is a description of $G(s)$ within a circular region around s_1 and extending to the nearest singularity [*i.e.*, except for s_1, the series has the same region of validity as the Taylor series of Eq. (1.12)].

The series consists of two quite distinct parts: the first, termed the *principal part*, includes all terms with $s - s_1$ raised to negative powers; the second part, including terms in $(s - s_1)$ with zero or positive exponents, is analytic in the vicinity of s_1, and assumes the value B_0 at s_1. The letter A is used for the coefficients of the principal part; B for the analytic part. The importance of the coefficient A_{-1} has led to a special name for this term: the *residue* of the function in the pole at s_1. Throughout this text, the symbol k_{s_1} is used to denote this residue.†

The Laurent series indicates that, if a region sufficiently near the singularity is considered, the behavior of the function is given by the equation,

$$G(s) \xrightarrow[s \to s_1]{} \frac{A_{-n}}{(s - s_1)^n} \quad (1.14)$$

---

† The importance of the residue arises primarily from the fact that integration of the function along a closed path encircling the pole results in a value $2\pi j k_{s_1}$. The integral is independent of the other coefficients in the Laurent expansion.

All other terms in the Laurent series become small compared to this term if $|s - s_1|$ is taken sufficiently small. Thus, the behavior of a function in the vicinity of an nth-order pole can be described by a single term. In circuit applications, this single term is ordinarily divided into two components: the magnitude and phase of $G(s)$, or the real and imaginary parts.

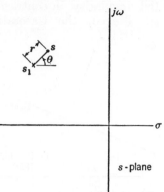

The magnitude and phase are conveniently investigated by introduction of the substitution

$$s = s_1 + re^{j\theta} \qquad (1.15)$$

As indicated in Fig. 1.3, the value of s of interest is specified by r, the radial distance from the pole, and θ, the angle of the

Fig. 1.3. Definition of r and θ coordinates.

vector from the pole to s. Substitution of Eq. (1.15) in (1.14) gives

$$G(s) \xrightarrow[s \to s_1]{} \frac{A_{-n}}{r^n} e^{-jn\theta} \qquad (1.16)$$

Thus,

$$|G(s)| \xrightarrow[s \to s_1]{} \frac{|A_{-n}|}{r^n} \qquad (1.17)$$

$$\underline{/G(s)} \xrightarrow[s \to s_1]{} \underline{/A_{-n}} - n\theta$$

As s approaches s_1 along any radial line emanating from s_1, r decreases monotonically, and the magnitude of $G(s)$ increases monotonically and

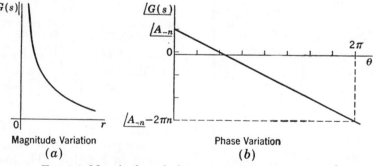

Magnitude Variation
(a)

Phase Variation
(b)

Fig. 1.4. Magnitude and phase near a pole of order n.

independently of the angle θ. The variation in magnitude of $G(s)$ is shown in Fig. 1.4(a). Correspondingly, as θ, the angle of $s - s_1$, increases from 0 to 2π, the angle of $G(s)$ decreases monotonically from $\underline{/A_{-n}}$ to $\underline{/A_{-n}} - 2\pi n$, as indicated in Fig. 1.4(b).

Thus, in the vicinity of s_1 the magnitude of $G(s)$ behaves in a precisely defined way. The monotonic increase of $|G(s)|$ with decreasing r is an important characteristic of the pole type of singularity. If s_1 is an essential singularity, in contrast, the value of $|G(s)|$ varies wildly as s tends to s_1. Indeed, the Casorati-Weierstrasse theorem of complex-function theory states that within *any* small circle around an essential singularity, the function must assume at least once every value except possibly one (for example, $e^{1/s}$ takes on every value except zero inside any small circle around the origin).

The behavior of the real and imaginary parts of $G(s)$ in the vicinity of the nth-order pole at s_1 is clear if Eq. (1.16) is used to write $G(s)$ in rectangular form:

$$G(s) = \frac{|A_{-n}|}{r^n} \cos \left[\underline{/A_{-n}} - n\theta \right]$$

$$- j \frac{|A_{-n}|}{r^n} \sin \left[\underline{/A_{-n}} - n\theta \right] \quad (1.18)$$

Equation (1.18) states that for an nth-order pole the real part of $G(s)$ is positive in n sectors around the pole, negative in the other n sectors. Figure 1.5, showing the regions of positive and negative real parts for poles of order one, two, and three, clarifies this interpretation. Figure 1.5(a), drawn for a simple pole, illustrates the most important of the three cases. If $\underline{/A_{-n}}$ (in this case, k_{s_1}) is zero (k_{s_1} real and positive), the real part is positive everywhere to the right of the pole, negative to the left.†

In a similar fashion, the regions of the positive and negative imaginary part can be determined, as shown in Fig. 1.5. The lines representing the zero imaginary part are $90/n$ degrees from the loci of the zero real part. Of some interest,

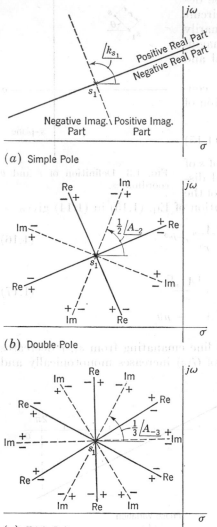

(*a*) Simple Pole

(*b*) Double Pole

(*c*) Triple Pole

FIG. 1.5. Regions of positive and negative real and imaginary parts in the vicinity of a pole.

particularly in the approximate evaluation of integrals, as in problems where transients are determined by the inverse Laplace transformation,

† It should be emphasized again that Eq. (1.18) is valid only in the immediate vicinity of the pole. As soon as the second and later terms of the series of Eq. (1.13) are significant, the loci of the constant real part are no longer radial.

are the *lines of steepest ascent:* the lines along which the real part increases most rapidly toward infinity as s tends to s_1. These lines are evidently given by the expression

$$\frac{\partial}{\partial \theta}\left[\frac{\partial \operatorname{Re} G(s)}{\partial r}\right] = 0 \tag{1.19}$$

The differentiation yields the result that the lines of steepest ascent are the loci of the zero imaginary part, a result which might be expected since these loci are angularly midway between the lines of the zero real part.

Derivation of the Laurent Series. The Laurent series, shown in Eq. (1.13), describes the function at all points (except the pole) inside a circle centered at the pole and passing through the nearest singularity. Thus, the Laurent series is similar to a Taylor series, but is an expansion about a pole-type singularity. The most direct method for calculating the coefficients of the Laurent series is based on Eqs. (1.12) and (1.13). The coefficients of the Laurent series for $G(s)$ are identical with those of the Taylor series for $(s - s_1)^n G(s)$.

The basic procedure is illustrated by consideration of the function

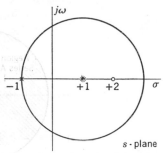

$$G(s) = \frac{s + 2}{(s - 1)^2(s + 1)} \tag{1.20}$$

FIG. 1.6. Region of validity for Laurent expansion about +1.

$G(s)$ possesses two poles: a double pole at $+1$ and a simple pole at -1. The Laurent series about the pole at $+1$ is considered first. The expansion is a valid description of $G(s)$ inside a circle of radius 2 about $+1$, as shown in Fig. 1.6. The series is developed in the following steps:

(1) $(s - 1)^2 G(s)$ is determined:

$$(s - 1)^2 G(s) = \frac{s + 2}{s + 1} \tag{1.21}$$

(2) The Taylor series for $(s + 2)/(s + 1)$ about the point $+1$ is determined from the formula for the coefficients.

$$\frac{s + 2}{s + 1} = A_{-2} + k_{+1}(s - 1) + B_0(s - 1)^2 + B_1(s - 1)^3 + \cdots \tag{1.22}$$

where $A_{-2} = \left(\frac{s + 2}{s + 1}\right)_{s=1}$

$k_{+1} = \left[\frac{d}{ds}\left(\frac{s + 2}{s + 1}\right)\right]_{s=1}$

$B_{i-2} = \frac{1}{j!}\left[\frac{d^j}{ds^j}\left(\frac{s + 2}{s + 1}\right)\right]_{s=1}$

In this particular case,

$$A_{-2} = \tfrac{3}{2} \qquad B_0 = \tfrac{1}{8}$$
$$k_{+1} = -\tfrac{1}{4} \qquad B_1 = -\tfrac{1}{16} \qquad \text{etc.} \tag{1.23}$$

Thus,

$$(s - 1)^2 G(s) = \tfrac{3}{2} - \tfrac{1}{4}(s - 1) + \tfrac{1}{8}(s - 1)^2 - \tfrac{1}{16}(s - 1)^3 + \cdots \qquad (1.24)$$

(3)　Division by $(s - 1)^2$ yields the desired Laurent series

$$G(s) = \frac{\tfrac{3}{2}}{(s - 1)^2} - \frac{\tfrac{1}{4}}{(s - 1)} + \tfrac{1}{8} - \tfrac{1}{16}(s - 1) + \cdots \qquad (1.25)$$

In an exactly similar procedure, the expansion about the simple pole at -1 can be evaluated, with the result

$$G(s) = \frac{\tfrac{1}{4}}{(s + 1)} + \tfrac{1}{2} + \tfrac{7}{16}(s + 1) + \tfrac{5}{16}(s + 1)^2 + \tfrac{13}{64}(s + 1)^3 + \cdots$$

$$(1.26)$$

Equations (1.25) and (1.26) are two representations of $G(s)$, valid within the appropriate circles of convergence except at the poles. The

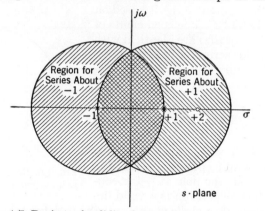

Fig. 1.7. Regions of validity for two Laurent expansions.

two regions of convergence are shown in Fig. 1.7, which indicates that in the vicinity of the origin either expansion is valid. At $s = 0$, for example, Eq. (1.25) gives

$$G(0) = \tfrac{3}{2} + \tfrac{1}{4} + \tfrac{1}{8} + \tfrac{1}{16} + \cdots \qquad (1.27)$$

The series on the right is simply a geometric series (after the first term), with a sum equal to 2, the value of $G(0)$ as determined from Eq. (1.20). Equation (1.26) also gives the zero-frequency value of 2 from the series

$$G(0) = \tfrac{1}{4} + \tfrac{1}{2} + \tfrac{7}{16} + \tfrac{5}{16} + \tfrac{13}{64} + \cdots \qquad (1.28)$$

Evaluation of the Laurent series by differentiation is a tedious process which can be avoided in most cases of engineering interest. Any series of the proper form—i.e., the form shown in Eq. (1.13)—must be the Laurent series. If $G(s)$ is a rational algebraic function and the expansion about the pole at s_1 is desired, the function $(s - s_1)^n G(s)$ is formed. Substitution of u for $s - s_1$ (replacing s by $u + s_1$) results in a rational function which is to be expanded about the origin. Simple division of the denominator into the numerator can be used to determine the coefficients in this expansion.

Derivation of Eq. (1.25), the expansion of $\dfrac{s + 2}{(s - 1)^2(s + 1)}$ about the pole at $+1$, illustrates the procedure:

(1) $(s - 1)^2 G(s)$ is formed,

$$(s - 1)^2 G(s) = \frac{s + 2}{s + 1} \tag{1.29}$$

(2) s is replaced by $u + 1$, to give the fraction

$$[(s - 1)^2 G(s)]_{s=u+1} = \frac{u + 3}{u + 2} \tag{1.30}$$

(3)   The denominator is divided into the numerator, with both polynomials written in ascending powers of u:

$$
\begin{array}{r}
\frac{3}{2} - \frac{1}{4}u + \frac{1}{8}u^2 - \frac{1}{16}u^3 + \cdots \\
2 + u\overline{)3 + u} \\
3 + \frac{3}{2}u \\
\hline
-\frac{1}{2}u \\
-\frac{1}{2}u \qquad \frac{1}{4}u^2 \\
\hline
\frac{1}{4}u^2 \\
\frac{1}{4}u^2 + \frac{1}{8}u^3 \\
\hline
-\frac{1}{8}u^3 \\
-\frac{1}{8}u^3 - \frac{1}{16}u^4 \\
\hline
\frac{1}{16}u^4
\end{array}
$$

$$\frac{u + 3}{u + 2} = \frac{3}{2} - \frac{1}{4}u + \frac{1}{8}u^2 - \frac{1}{16}u^3 + \cdots \tag{1.31}$$

(4) u is now replaced by $s - 1$ and the series divided by $(s - 1)^2$ to give

$$G(s) = \frac{\frac{3}{2}}{(s - 1)^2} - \frac{\frac{1}{4}}{(s - 1)} + \frac{1}{8} - \frac{1}{16}(s - 1) + \cdots \tag{1.32}$$

Since the form is appropriate, the expansion must be the Laurent series for $G(s)$ about the pole at $+1$.

A variety of other procedures can be used in special cases to obtain the coefficients in the Laurent series.   If $G(s)$ is not rational algebraic, it is often possible to replace transcendental terms (such as e^{-s}) by series valid in the vicinity of the pole in question.   As an example, the function considered is

$$G(s) = \frac{1 - e^{-s}}{s^4} \tag{1.33}$$

The Laurent expansion is desired about the pole at the origin.   Since both numerator and denominator go to zero as s tends to zero, the pole is not of order four [that is, $s^4 G(s)$ does not have a nonzero, finite value at $s = 0$].   The order of the pole can be determined by differentiation of the numerator, but it is simpler to investigate at once the behavior of $G(s)$ in the vicinity of the origin.   Near $s = 0$ the exponential term can be replaced by the appropriate Maclaurin series,

$$e^{-s} = 1 - s + \frac{s^2}{2!} - \frac{s^3}{3!} + \cdots \tag{1.34}$$

Substitution of Eq. (1.34) in (1.33) gives

$$G(s) = \frac{1}{s^3} - \frac{1/2!}{s^2} + \frac{1/3!}{s} - \frac{1}{4!} + \frac{1}{5!}s - \frac{1}{6!}s^2 + \cdots \tag{1.35}$$

Equation (1.35) is then the desired Laurent series and is a valid description of $G(s)$ within any circle of finite radius. The pole at the origin is of order three [since $s^3 G(s)$ approaches unity as $s \to 0$].

Other Properties. A number of other properties of functions of a complex variable are of importance in the analysis and design of passive networks and feedback systems. These characteristics and theorems are presented as needed throughout the remaining chapters. To a considerable extent, the study of network and feedback theory resolves to the application of complex-function theory to circuit problems. Laplace-transform theory is perhaps the most important example of this application, but Nyquist diagrams and the various design procedures considered in succeeding chapters are all based on the properties of functions of a complex variable.

1.2. Partial-fraction Expansions. Many problems requiring an inverse Laplace transformation or involving the synthesis of a network from a specified impedance function are most readily solved if the function is written in the form of a partial-fraction expansion. The partial-fraction expansion is a representation based on two properties considered in the last section:

(1) A function of a complex variable which has no singularities in the entire s plane (including infinity) must be a constant.

(2) In the vicinity of a pole, a function of a complex variable can be represented by a Laurent series, containing two parts: the *principal part*, which includes all terms involving $s - s_1$ raised to negative powers, and a part which is analytic in the vicinity of s_1.

The *partial-fraction expansion* of a rational algebraic function, $G(s)$, consists of the sum of all principal parts of the Laurent expansions of $G(s)$ about the various poles plus a polynomial describing the behavior of $G(s)$ as s tends to infinity.

In this section, primary interest is focused on the partial-fraction expansions of rational algebraic functions. The nature and derivation of the partial-fraction expansion can be clarified in terms of a general rational function, $G(s)$, which has finite poles at $s_1, s_2, \ldots, s_m$ of order $n_1, n_2, \ldots, n_m$, respectively. The Laurent expansion about the first pole (s_1) takes the form

$$G(s) = H_1(s) + F_1(s) \tag{1.36}$$

$H_1(s)$ is the principal part, containing n_1 terms:

$$H_1(s) = \frac{A_{-n_1}}{(s - s_1)^{n_1}} + \frac{A_{-(n_1-1)}}{(s - s_1)^{n_1-1}} + \cdots + \frac{k_{s_1}}{s - s_1} \qquad (1.37)$$

$F_1(s)$ is the remainder of the series and is analytic within at least a small region around and including s_1:

$$F_1(s) = B_0 + B_1(s - s_1) + B_2(s - s_1)^2 + \cdots \qquad (1.38)$$

In the derivation of the partial-fraction expansion, the principal part, $H_1(s)$, is subtracted from $G(s)$, leaving the function $G_1(s)$, where

$$G_1(s) = G(s) - H_1(s) \qquad (1.39)\dagger$$

The properties of $G_1(s)$ are of interest. Since $H_1(s)$ is analytic at s_2, s_3, . . . , s_m, $G_1(s)$ has all the poles present in $G(s)$ except the pole at s_1. Furthermore, in the immediate vicinity of these poles at s_2, s_3, . . . , s_m, $G_1(s)$ and $G(s)$ behave in exactly the same way: if, for example, both $G_1(s)$ and $G(s)$ were expanded in Laurent series about s_2, the principal parts of the two series would be identical.

The reduction of $G(s)$ by subtraction of a principal part is performed m times, corresponding to each of the m poles of $G(s)$, with the result

$$G_m(s) = G(s) - [H_1(s) + H_2(s) + \cdots + H_m(s)] \qquad (1.40)$$

The properties of $G_m(s)$ are now considered. $G_m(s)$ is a function with no poles in the finite part of the s plane. $G_m(s)$ is an entire function, with the only possible singularity at infinity. Accordingly, $G_m(s)$ can be represented within any circle of finite radius by the Maclaurin series

$$G_m(s) = a_0 + a_1 s + a_2 s^2 + \cdots \qquad (1.41)$$

Substitution of Eq. (1.41) in (1.40) gives

$$G(s) = H_1(s) + H_2(s) + \cdots + H_m(s) + a_0 + a_1 s + a_2 s^2 + \cdots \qquad (1.42)$$

But if $G(s)$ is the ratio of two polynomials in s,

$$G(s) \xrightarrow[s \to \infty]{} K s^p \qquad (1.43)$$

Here p, the difference between the degrees of the numerator and denominator polynomials of $G(s)$, must be finite. Consideration of Eq. (1.42) in view of (1.43) indicates that, since each $H_j(s)$ tends to zero as $s \to \infty$, all a_j's after a_p must also be zero. In other words, $G(s)$ can be written as the sum of the m principal parts and a polynomial of degree p.

$$G(s) = H_1(s) + H_2(s) + \cdots + H_m(s) + a_0 + a_1 s + \cdots + a_p s^p \qquad (1.44)$$

† $G_1(s)$ is not synonymous with $F_1(s)$, although both functions have the same Taylor expansion about s_1. $F_1(s)$ is an entire function (having a singularity at infinity only), while $G_1(s)$ has all the singularities of $G(s)$ except the pole at s_1.

Equation (1.44) represents the partial-fraction expansion of $G(s)$. This representation places in evidence the contribution of each pole, including the pole of order p at infinity.

Derivation of the partial-fraction expansion involves determination of the principal parts of the various Laurent expansions and the polynomial describing the behavior at large values of s. Details of the methods for writing the expansion are described in terms of two examples.

Example 1. The partial-fraction expansion is desired for

$$G(s) = \frac{s + 2}{(s - 1)^2(s + 1)} \tag{1.45}$$

The form of the partial-fraction expansion can be written at once:

$$G(s) = \underbrace{\frac{A_{-2}}{(s - 1)^2} + \frac{k_1}{s - 1}}_{\substack{\text{Principal part} \\ \text{for pole at } +1}} + \underbrace{\frac{k_{-1}}{s + 1}}_{\substack{\text{Principal} \\ \text{part for} \\ \text{pole at} \\ -1}} + \underbrace{p(s)}_{\substack{\text{Behavior} \\ \text{at infinity}}} \tag{1.46}$$

Evaluation of the coefficients is performed by equating $G(s)$ and the partial-fraction expansion:

$$\frac{s + 2}{(s - 1)^2(s + 1)} = \frac{A_{-2}}{(s - 1)^2} + \frac{k_1}{s - 1} + \frac{k_{-1}}{s + 1} + p(s) \tag{1.47}$$

Multiplication of both sides by $(s - 1)^2$ leaves

$$\frac{s + 2}{s + 1} = A_{-2} + k_1(s - 1) + \frac{k_{-1}(s - 1)^2}{s + 1} + (s - 1)^2 p(s) \tag{1.48}$$

If s is now made equal to $+1$, A_{-2} is determined,

$$A_{-2} = \tfrac{3}{2} \tag{1.49}$$

Differentiation of Eq. (1.48) with respect to s yields

$$\frac{1}{s + 1} - \frac{s + 2}{(s + 1)^2} = k_1 + \frac{2k_{-1}(s - 1)}{s + 1} - \frac{k_{-1}(s - 1)^2}{(s + 1)^2}$$
$$+ 2(s - 1)p(s) + (s - 1)^2 p'(s) \tag{1.50}$$

Substitution of $s = +1$ in Eq. (1.50) yields the value of k_1:

$$k_1 = -\tfrac{1}{4} \tag{1.51}$$

The operation described above is simply the evaluation of the coefficients in the principal part of the Laurent series about the pole at $+1$. The evaluation is effected by forming the function $(s - 1)^2 G(s)$, analytic in the neighborhood of $+1$, and determining the first two terms in the corresponding Taylor series.

The residue k_{-1} is found in the same manner. In this case, the pole at

-1 is simple, and no differentiation is required; k_{-1} is the value of $(s + 1)G(s)$ for $s = -1$, or

$$k_{-1} = \left[\frac{s + 2}{(s - 1)^2}\right]_{s=-1} \tag{1.52}$$

$$k_{-1} = \tfrac{1}{4} \tag{1.53}$$

All principal parts corresponding to finite poles have now been determined, and the given $G(s)$ can be written

$$\frac{s + 2}{(s - 1)^2(s + 1)} = \frac{\frac{3}{2}}{(s - 1)^2} - \frac{\frac{1}{4}}{s - 1} + \frac{\frac{1}{4}}{s + 1} + p(s) \tag{1.54}$$

$p(s)$ is evaluated from the behavior of $G(s)$ as s tends to infinity, but, for $s \to \infty$, $(s + 2)/[(s - 1)^2(s + 1)]$ tends to zero. Hence,

$$p(s) = 0 \tag{1.55}$$

The complete partial-fraction expansion for $G(s)$ is

$$\frac{s + 2}{(s - 1)^2(s + 1)} = \frac{\frac{3}{2}}{(s - 1)^2} - \frac{\frac{1}{4}}{s - 1} + \frac{\frac{1}{4}}{s + 1} \tag{1.56}$$

A rapid, partial check on the expansion is available here by considering Eq. (1.56) as s tends to zero:

$$\frac{2}{(1)(1)} = \tfrac{3}{2} + \tfrac{1}{4} + \tfrac{1}{4} \tag{1.57}$$

The expansion is correct at zero frequency.

Example 2. The second example involves the function

$$G(s) = \frac{s^4 + 4s^3 + 6s^2 + 4s + 1}{s^2 + 2s + 2} \tag{1.58}$$

The only finite poles are at $-1 \pm j1$. Since both poles are simple, the partial-fraction expansion takes the form

$$\frac{s^4 + 4s^3 + 6s^2 + 4s + 1}{s^2 + 2s + 2} = \frac{k_{-1+j1}}{s + 1 - j} + \frac{k_{-1-j1}}{s + 1 + j} + p(s) \tag{1.59}$$

The residue k_{-1+j1} is evaluated in the usual way:

$$k_{-1+j1} = \left[(s + 1 - j)\frac{s^4 + 4s^3 + 6s^2 + 4s + 1}{s^2 + 2s + 2}\right]_{s=-1+j} \tag{1.60}$$

$$k_{-1+j1} = \left[\frac{(s + 1)^4}{s + 1 + j}\right]_{s=-1+j} \tag{1.61}$$

$$k_{-1+j1} = \frac{j^4}{j2} \tag{1.62}$$

$$k_{-1+j1} = -j\tfrac{1}{2} \tag{1.63}$$

Since all coefficients are real in the numerator and denominator polynomials of $G(s)$, the residue k_{-1-j1} is the conjugate of k_{-1+j1}, or

$$k_{-1-j1} = +j\tfrac{1}{2} \tag{1.64}$$

Equation (1.59) can now be written

$$\frac{s^4 + 4s^3 + 6s^2 + 4s + 1}{s^2 + 2s + 2} = \frac{-j\tfrac{1}{2}}{s+1-j} + \frac{j\tfrac{1}{2}}{s+1+j} + p(s) \tag{1.65}$$

In this example, $p(s)$ is certainly not zero, since $G(s)$ approaches s^2 as $s \rightarrow \infty$. $p(s)$ is a polynomial of the form $a_0 + a_1 s + s^2$, and Eq. (1.65) becomes

$$\frac{s^4 + 4s^3 + 6s^2 + 4s + 1}{s^2 + 2s + 2} = \frac{-j\tfrac{1}{2}}{s+1-j} + \frac{j\tfrac{1}{2}}{s+1+j}$$
$$+ a_0 + a_1 s + s^2 \tag{1.66}$$

Evaluation of a_1 is most readily effected if s^2 is subtracted from both sides of Eq. (1.66), in order that $a_1 s$ may describe the infinite-frequency behavior of the right side.

$$\frac{s^4 + 4s^3 + 6s^2 + 4s + 1}{s^2 + 2s + 2} - s^2 = \frac{-j\tfrac{1}{2}}{s+1-j} + \frac{j\tfrac{1}{2}}{s+1+j}$$
$$+ a_0 + a_1 s \tag{1.67}$$

Collection of terms on the left side over a common denominator gives

$$\frac{2s^3 + 4s^2 + 4s + 1}{s^2 + 2s + 2} = \frac{-j\tfrac{1}{2}}{s+1-j} + \frac{j\tfrac{1}{2}}{s+1+j} + a_0 + a_1 s \tag{1.68}$$

If s tends to infinity, the left side approaches $2s^3/s^2$ or $2s$, the right side $a_1 s$; hence,

$$a_1 = 2 \tag{1.69}$$

The procedure is repeated with $2s$ subtracted from both sides of Eq. (1.68):

$$\frac{2s^3 + 4s^2 + 4s + 1}{s^2 + 2s + 2} - 2s = \frac{-j\tfrac{1}{2}}{s+1-j} + \frac{j\tfrac{1}{2}}{s+1+j} + a_0 \tag{1.70}$$

Equation (1.70) can be written

$$\frac{1}{s^2 + 2s + 2} = \frac{-j\tfrac{1}{2}}{s+1-j} + \frac{j\tfrac{1}{2}}{s+1+j} + a_0 \tag{1.71}$$

The high-frequency behavior of Eq. (1.71) indicates that a_0 is zero. Accordingly, the complete partial fraction expansion of $G(s)$ is:

$$\frac{(s+1)^4}{s^2 + 2s + 2} = \frac{-j\tfrac{1}{2}}{s+1-j} + \frac{j\tfrac{1}{2}}{s+1+j} + 2s + s^2 \tag{1.72}$$

The determination of $p(s)$ can be performed in a single step if $p(s)$ is recognized as a polynomial representing the behavior of $G(s)$ at high frequencies. If the denominator is divided into the numerator of $G(s)$, with both polynomials arranged in descending powers of s, an expansion for $G(s)$ results in the form

$$G(s) = \underbrace{a_p s^p + a_{p-1} s^{p-1} + \cdots + a_1 s + a_0}_{p(s)} + \underbrace{\frac{a_{-1}}{s} + \frac{a_{-2}}{s^2} + \cdots}_{\Sigma H_i}$$

$$(1.73)$$

The integer p is the difference between the degree of the numerator and the denominator. In this expansion, the terms with s raised to a non-negative power constitute the $p(s)$ of the partial-fraction expansion; all other terms, tending to zero as s approaches infinity, represent the expansion of the sum of the various principal parts of the Laurent series. Thus, in the example considered above, with $G(s)$ given as

$$\frac{s^4 + 4s^3 + 6s^2 + 4s + 1}{s^2 + 2s + 2}$$

$p(s)$ can be found directly:

$$
\begin{array}{r}
s^2 + 2s + \dfrac{1}{s^2} - \dfrac{2}{s^3} \\
s^2 + 2s + 2 \overline{\smash{\big)}\, s^4 + 4s^3 + 6s^2 + 4s + 1} \\
\underline{s^4 + 2s^3 + 2s^2} \\
2s^3 + 4s^2 + 4s + 1 \\
\underline{2s^3 + 4s^2 + 4s} \\
1 \\
1 + \dfrac{2}{s} + \dfrac{2}{s^2} \\
- \dfrac{2}{s} - \dfrac{2}{s^2} \\
- \dfrac{2}{s} - \dfrac{4}{s^2} - \dfrac{4}{s^3} \\
\dfrac{2}{s^2} + \dfrac{4}{s^3}
\end{array}
$$

$$(1.74)$$

$$G(s) = s^2 + 2s + \frac{1}{s^2} - \frac{2}{s^3} + \cdots$$

(The division need be carried out only until a term with a negative exponent is obtained.) Equation (1.74) indicates at once that $p(s)$ is simply $s^2 + 2s$.

Differentiation of the Denominator. The evaluation of the coefficients in the partial-fraction expansion can frequently be simplified, particularly if the pole is simple, as assumed throughout this paragraph. The function $G(s)$ is written as $p(s)/q(s)$, the ratio of two polynomials. It can then be shown that the residue of $G(s)$ in a simple pole at s_1 is

$$k_{s_1} = \frac{p(s_1)}{q'(s_1)} \qquad (1.75)$$

Here $q'(s_1)$ denotes the derivative of $q(s)$ evaluated at s_1.

The proof of Eq. (1.75) follows directly if $q(s)$ is written in terms of another polynomial, $q_1(s)$, defined by the equation

$$q(s) = (s - s_1)q_1(s) \tag{1.76}$$

k_{s_1}, the residue of $G(s)$ in the pole at s_1, is then

$$k_{s_1} = \frac{p(s_1)}{q_1(s_1)} \tag{1.77}$$

Differentiation of Eq. (1.76) yields

$$q'(s) = q_1(s) + (s - s_1)q_1'(s) \tag{1.78}$$

If s is replaced by s_1 in Eq. (1.78),

$$q'(s_1) = q_1(s_1) \tag{1.79}$$

Substitution of Eq. (1.79) in (1.77) gives the desired relation, (1.75).

If $G(s)$ is a rational algebraic function, the above method for calculating residues is in most cases no easier to apply than the basic techniques described previously. Application of Eq. (1.75) is illustrated by the function

$$G(s) = \frac{s^2 + 2s + 8}{s^3 + 7s^2 + 14s + 8} \tag{1.80}$$

$G(s)$ possesses a simple pole at -1; the corresponding residue is

$$k_{-1} = \left(\frac{s^2 + 2s + 8}{3s^2 + 14s + 14} \right)_{s=-1} \tag{1.81}$$

$$k_{-1} = \tfrac{7}{3} \tag{1.82}$$

Although the relation (1.75) is derived above on the basis of a rational algebraic function for $G(s)$, the equation is also valid if $G(s)$ is expressed as the ratio of two entire functions (*i.e.*, two functions with no singularities in the finite part of the s plane). $G(s)$ need not have only a finite number of poles, but may be a general meromorphic function—*i.e.*, a function with an infinite number of poles, but only a finite number within any finite region in the s plane.†

For example, the relation can be used to evaluate the residues of the function

$$G(s) = \frac{1}{s} \frac{1 - e^{-s}}{1 + e^{-s}} \tag{1.83}$$

The function has simple poles at the zeros of $1 + e^{-s}$, or at

$$s = \pm jn\pi \qquad n = 1, 3, 5, \ldots \tag{1.84}$$

† A meromorphic function is one with poles as the only types of singularities at finite values of s; no essential singularities are admitted except at infinity. In other words, the poles cannot have a limit point for finite s. The function $1/\sin s$ is meromorphic, with simple poles at 0, $\pm\pi$, $\pm 2\pi$, $\pm 3\pi$, ... The Mittag-Leffler theorem establishes that $1/\sin s$ can be expanded in partial fractions. *Cf.* K. Knopp, "Theory of Functions," Part II, pp. 34–57, Dover Publications, New York, 1945.

[The fact that $G(s)$ does not have a pole at the origin is clear if the exponential functions are replaced by the first few terms of the Maclaurin series.]   The residue of $G(s)$ in the pole at $+jn\pi$ is given by Eq. (1.75):

$$k_{jn\pi} = \left(\frac{1 - e^{-s}}{1 + e^{-s} - se^{-s}}\right)_{s=jn\pi} \tag{1.85}$$

Substitution of $jn\pi$ for s, with n odd, yields

$$k_{jn\pi} = \frac{2}{jn\pi} \tag{1.86}$$

As described in Sec. 1.5, the $G(s)$ in this example represents the Laplace transform of the square wave shown in Fig. 1.8, and the residue of Eq. (1.86) is proportional to the amplitude of the nth harmonic in the corresponding Fourier series.

The Remainder Theorem.   Even if rational algebraic functions only are considered, residue calculations with the formulas described above frequently present computational difficulties, particularly if the numerator and denominator polynomials of $G(s)$ are of high degree, if a large number of significant figures is required, or if complex poles are involved.   Calculation of

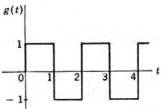

Fig. 1.8. Time function with the transform $G(s) = \dfrac{1}{s}\dfrac{1 - e^{-s}}{1 + e^{-s}}$.

residues involves evaluation of a polynomial or the derivative of a polynomial at a specified point in the s plane.   Thus, if $m(s)$ is a general polynomial, methods are needed for the determination of $m(s_1)$ and $m'(s_1)$.   In both cases, the remainder theorem provides a significant simplification in comparison with the conventional method of substituting $s = s_1$.

If s_1 is real, the remainder theorem states that $m(s_1)$ is the value of the remainder if $m(s)$ is divided by $s - s_1$.   The relation is established by considering the equation for the division

$$\frac{m(s)}{s - s_1} = n(s) + \frac{R}{s - s_1} \tag{1.87}$$

$n(s)$ is the quotient, and R the remainder.   Multiplication by $s - s_1$ in Eq. (1.87) yields

$$m(s) = (s - s_1)n(s) + R \tag{1.88}$$

If s is set equal to s_1, the theorem is established:

$$m(s_1) = R \tag{1.89}$$

If s_1 is complex, $m(s_1)$ can be determined in the same way, but division by $s - s_1$ necessitates an undesirable manipulation of complex numbers. If $m(s)$ is divided by the quadratic $(s - s_1)(s - \bar{s}_1)$, where $\bar{s}_1$ is the conjugate of s_1, the remainder is a linear function of the form $R_a s + R_b$, and the division and subsequent multiplication can be described by the equation

$$m(s) = (s - s_1)(s - \bar{s}_1)n(s) + R_a s + R_b \qquad (1.90)$$

The remainder theorem states that the value of $m(s_1)$ is simply $R_a s_1 + R_b$. Thus, the evaluation of a polynomial of any degree at a complex value of frequency s_1 can be effected by simple division followed by substitution of s_1 in a *linear* polynomial. This method avoids completely the usual, tedious procedure of writing s_1 in polar form, raising s_1 to a high power, then converting back to rectangular form, and finally adding a number of complex quantities.

If s_1 is real and the value desired is $m'(s_1)$, the appropriate relation can be derived by differentiating Eq. (1.88):

$$m'(s) = n(s) + (s - s_1)n'(s) \qquad (1.91)$$

Substitution of s_1 for s gives

$$m'(s_1) = n(s_1) \qquad (1.92)$$

Hence, $m'(s_1)$ is the remainder after the second division by $s - s_1$.

When s_1 is complex and $m'(s_1)$ is desired, Eq. (1.90) is differentiated to give

$$m'(s) = (s - \bar{s}_1)n(s) + (s - s_1)n(s) + (s - s_1)(s - \bar{s}_1)n'(s) + R_a \qquad (1.93)$$

Substitution of $s = s_1$ yields

$$m'(s_1) = (s_1 - \bar{s}_1)n(s_1) + R_a \qquad (1.94)$$

Evaluation of $m'(s_1)$ requires not only two divisions, but also the introduction of the factors $s_1 - \bar{s}_1$ and R_a. [If s_1 is a zero of $m(s)$, R_a is zero, and $m'(s_1)$ is $(s_1 - \bar{s}_1)n(s_1)$, where $s_1 - \bar{s}_1$ is just twice the imaginary part of s_1.]

The use of the remainder theorem can be illustrated by calculation of all the coefficients in the partial-fraction expansion of the function

$$G(s) = \frac{s^3 + 4s^2 + 2s + 8}{s(s + 2)^2(s^2 + s + 4)(s + 8)} \qquad (1.95)$$

If the denominator is expanded, $G(s)$ can be written as

$$G(s) = \frac{s^3 + 4s^2 + 2s + 8}{s^6 + 13s^5 + 52s^4 + 116s^3 + 176s^2 + 128s} \qquad (1.96)$$

The residues are desired in the poles at 0, -2, $-0.5 \pm j1.9365$, and -8; in addition, the coefficient of $1/(s + 2)^2$ is required. Although for illustrative purposes the remainder theorem is used exclusively to obtain the coefficients, certain of the calculations can be made more easily without use of the theorem.

(1) The residue in the pole at the origin is

$$k_0 = [sG(s)]_{s=0} \qquad (1.97)$$

Inspection of Eq. (1.96) indicates that

$$k_0 = \tfrac{8}{128} = 0.0625 \tag{1.98}$$

(2) If the numerator and denominator polynomials of $G(s)$ are denoted $p(s)$ and $q(s)$, respectively, the residue in the pole at -8 is

$$k_{-8} = \frac{p(-8)}{q'(-8)} \tag{1.99}$$

$p(-8)$ can be found from the remainder theorem if $p(s)$ is divided by $s + 8$:

$$
\begin{array}{r}
s^2 - 4s + 34 \\
s + 8\,\overline{\smash{\big)}\,s^3 + 4s^2 + 2s + 8} \\
\underline{s^3 + 8s^2} \\
-4s^2 + 2s + 8 \\
\underline{-4s^2 - 32s} \\
34s + 8 \\
\underline{34s + 272} \\
-264
\end{array}
$$

Hence,

$$p(-8) = -264 \tag{1.100}$$

Determination of $q'(-8)$ requires two divisions of $q(s)$ by $s + 8$:†

1	8	1	13	52	116	176	128	0	
			8	40	96	160	128	0	
		1	5	12	20	16	0	0	← Remainder after
			8	-24	288	-2144	17,280		first division
		1	-3	36	-268	2160	-17,280		← Remainder after
									second division

The remainder after the first division is zero (since $s + 8$ is a factor of q), and the first quotient is

$$s^5 + 5s^4 + 12s^3 + 20s^2 + 16s$$

A second division results in a remainder of $-17,280$; hence,

$$q'(-8) = -17,280 \tag{1.101}$$

On the basis of Eqs. (1.100) and (1.101), (1.99) gives

$$k_{-8} = \frac{-264}{-17,280} = 0.015278 \tag{1.102}$$

(3) A_{-2}, the coefficient of $1/(s + 2)^2$ in the partial-fraction expansion, is the value of $[(s + 2)^2 G(s)]_{s=-2}$. The simplest method for evaluating A_{-2} involves writing $G(s)$ in the form

$$G(s) = \frac{p(s)}{(s + 2)^2 h(s)} \tag{1.103}$$

† In the division of $q(s)$ by $s + 8$, as shown here, the powers of s are not written since they convey no useful information.

With this definition of the polynomial $h(s)$,

$$A_{-2} = \frac{p(-2)}{h(-2)} \tag{1.104}$$

$h(s)$ can be found by dividing $q(s)$ twice by $s + 2$:

1	2⎹1	13	52	116	176	128	0
		2	22	60	112	128	0
	1	11	30	56	64	0	0
		2	18	24	64	0
	1	9	12	32	0	0

$$h(s) = s^4 + 9s^3 + 12s^2 + 32s \tag{1.105}$$

One more division yields a remainder equal to $h(-2)$:

1	2⎹1	9	12	32	0
		2	14	−4	72
	1	7	−2	36	−72

$$h(-2) = -72 \tag{1.106}$$

$p(-2)$ is evaluated in the same fashion:

1	2⎹1	4	2	8
		2	4	−4
	1	2	−2	12

$$p(-2) = 12 \tag{1.107}$$

A_{-2} is given by Eq. (1.104):

$$A_{-2} = \frac{12}{-72} = -0.16667 \tag{1.108}$$

(4) The residue in the pole at -2 is found from the relation

$$k_{-2} = \left\{ \frac{d}{ds}\left[\frac{p(s)}{h(s)} \right] \right\}_{s=-2} \tag{1.109}$$

Differentiation yields

$$k_{-2} = \frac{p'(-2)h(-2) - p(-2)h'(-2)}{h^2(-2)} \tag{1.110}$$

$h(-2)$ and $p(-2)$ are already known. $p'(-2)$ and $h'(-2)$ can be evaluated by additional divisions by $s + 2$, with the result

$$p'(-2) = -2 \qquad h'(-2) = 60 \tag{1.111}$$

Substitution of Eqs. (1.106), (1.107), and (1.111) in (1.110) yields

$$k_{-2} = -0.11111 \tag{1.112}$$

(5)   The residue in the pole at $-0.5 + j1.9365$ is determined by dividing $s^2 + s + 4$ into $p(s)$ once and into $q(s)$ twice:

Division into $p(s)$:

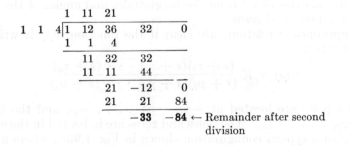

First division into $q(s)$:

Second division into $q(s)$:

Hence, from Eq. (1.94) and the discussion associated with Eq. (1.90),

$$k_{-0.5+j1.9365} = \left[\frac{-5s - 4}{2j1.9365(-33s - 84)}\right]_{s=-0.5+j1.9365} \quad (1.113)$$

Substitution of the value of the pole gives a residue of $0.027217/\!-52.24°$.

(6)   The residue in the pole at $-0.5 - j1.9365$ is the conjugate of the above value, or

$$k_{-0.5-j1.9365} = 0.027217/\!52.24° \quad (1.114)$$

Thus, the partial fraction expansion of $G(s)$ takes the form

$$\frac{s^3 + 4s^2 + 2s + 8}{s^6 + 13s^5 + 52s^4 + 116s^3 + 176s^2 + 128s} = \frac{0.0625}{s} + \frac{0.015278}{s + 8}$$

$$+ \frac{-0.16667}{(s + 2)^2} + \frac{-0.11111}{s + 2} + \frac{0.027217/\underline{-52.24°}}{s + 0.5 - j1.9365}$$

$$+ \frac{0.027217/\underline{52.24°}}{s + 0.5 + j1.9365} \quad (1.115)$$

No polynomial in s is included in the partial-fraction expansion since $G(s)$ tends to zero for large s. Actually,

$$G(s) \xrightarrow[s \to \infty]{} \frac{1}{s^3} \quad (1.116)$$

Consequently, the sum of the residues in the expansion must be zero [otherwise, the right side of Eq. (1.115) would be proportional to $1/s$ as s tends to infinity]. This sum provides a simple and convenient partial check on the calculation of the residues, since an error in any one residue would be apparent. In the case of Eq. (1.115), the sum of the residues is given by the expression

$$\Sigma k = 0.0625 + 0.015278 - 0.11111 + 2 \times 0.027217 \cos 52.24° \quad (1.117)$$

Collection of terms yields the desired value of zero.

Graphical Calculation of Residues. The coefficients in the partial-fraction expansion can also be calculated graphically after the poles and zeros are located on a sketch of the s plane. The partial-fraction coefficients can be determined from the magnitudes and angles of the vectors connecting poles and zeros.

The appropriate relations are clear if the function $G(s)$ is written in factored form:

$$G(s) = K \frac{(s + z_1)(s + z_2) \cdots (s + z_m)}{(s + p_1)(s + p_2) \cdots (s + p_n)} \quad (1.118)$$

Here the poles are located at $-p_1, -p_2, \ldots, -p_n$ and the zeros at $-z_1, -z_2, \ldots, -z_m$. The poles and zeros are indicated in the complex plane, with a typical configuration shown in Fig. 1.9(a), where a pole is indicated by an x, a zero by an o. In this figure, it is assumed that all poles and zeros are simple and that there are four distinct finite poles and one finite zero ($n = 4$, $m = 1$).

If the pole at $-p_1$ is simple, the corresponding residue, k_{-p_1}, is given by the expression

$$[(s + p_1)G(s)]_{s=-p_1}$$

Equation (1.118) indicates that the residue can be written

$$k_{-p_1} = K \left[\frac{(s + z_1)(s + z_2) \cdots (s + z_m)}{(s + p_2)(s + p_3) \cdots (s + p_n)} \right]_{s=-p_1} \quad (1.119)$$

The factor $(s + z_1)_{s=-p_1}$ can be represented by a vector from the zero at $-z_1$ to the pole at $-p_1$. Hence, k_{-p_1} is simply the constant K multiplied by the vectors from the various zeros to $-p_1$ and divided by the vectors from each *other* pole to $-p_1$. Thus, if $G(s)$ has the pole-zero configuration indicated in Fig. 1.9(a), the residue of $G(s)$ in the pole at $-p_1$ can be determined from the vectors shown in part (b) of the figure:

$$k_{-p_1} = K \frac{A}{BCD} \tag{1.120}$$

The other residues can be evaluated in the same way.

If the pole at $-p_1$ is second-order, two associated coefficients in the partial-fraction expansion must be determined. The coefficient of

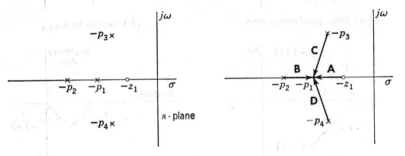

(a) Pole-zero Configuration   (b) Vectors for k_{-p_1}

Fig. 1.9. Graphical calculation of residue.

$1/(s + p_1)^2$ is evaluated in the same way as the residue of a simple pole, since this coefficient is simply

$$[(s + p_1)^2 G(s)]_{s=-p_1}$$

The vectors can also be used to calculate the residue, and in this case the advantage of a graphical procedure is pronounced. Differentiation of $(s + p_1)^2 G(s)$, with $G(s)$ written in factored form, demonstrates that the residue is given by the equation

$$k_{-p_1} = [(s + p_1)^2 G(s)]_{s=-p_1} \left[\frac{1}{s + z_1} + \frac{1}{s + z_2} + \cdots + \frac{1}{s + z_m} \right. \\ \left. - \frac{1}{s + p_2} - \frac{1}{s + p_3} - \cdots - \frac{1}{s + p_n} \right]_{s=-p_1} \tag{1.121}$$

The first term in brackets in Eq. (1.121) is the coefficient of $1/(s + p_1)^2$; the second term represents the sum of vectors and, accordingly, can be determined graphically from the measured vectors. Of course, any part of the graphical analysis can be replaced by an analytical procedure.

The polynomial, representing the infinite-frequency behavior of the partial-fraction expansion, is so readily calculated analytically that a graphical procedure seems unwarranted. Furthermore, in the majority of transfer functions of interest in feedback control, $G(s)$ tends to zero as s becomes large, and no polynomial is present in the partial-fraction expansion. Indeed, in the usual case, as s tends to infinity, $G(s)$ goes to zero at least as fast as $1/s^2$, with the result that the partial-fraction expansion has a double zero at infinity (*i.e.*, the sum of the residues is zero).

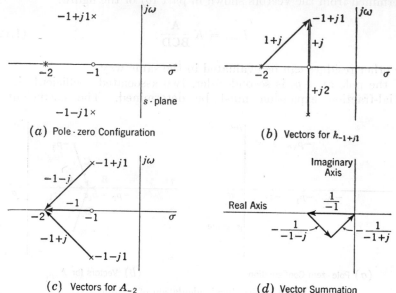

(*a*) Pole-zero Configuration   (*b*) Vectors for k_{-1+j1}

(*c*) Vectors for A_{-2} (*d*) Vector Summation

Fig. 1.10. Graphical calculation of coefficients for $G(s) = 8 \dfrac{s+1}{(s+2)^2(s^2+2s+2)}$.

One example illustrates the details of the graphical analysis. The function considered is

$$G(s) = 8 \frac{s+1}{(s+2)^2(s^2+2s+2)} \tag{1.122}$$

Figure 1.10(*a*) shows the location of the finite poles and zeros. Infinity is a third-order zero since $G(s) \xrightarrow[s \to \infty]{} 8/s^3$ (in other words, the total number of zeros and poles must be equal if infinity is included and each pole and zero is counted the number of times equal to its order). The partial-fraction expansion includes four unknown coefficients:

$$G(s) = \frac{A_{-2}}{(s+2)^2} + \frac{k_{-2}}{s+2} + \frac{k_{-1+j1}}{s+1-j} + \frac{k_{-1-j1}}{s+1+j} \tag{1.123}$$

The residue in the pole at $-1 + j1$ is calculated from the vectors shown in Fig. 1.10(*b*):

$$k_{-1+j1} = 8 \frac{+j}{(1+j)(1+j)(j2)} \tag{1.124}$$

The vector from the double pole at -2 to the pole at $-1 + j1$ is included twice. Similarly, the coefficient A_{-2} in Eq. (1.123) is determined from the vectors of Fig. 1.10(c):

$$A_{-2} = 8\frac{-1}{(-1-j)(-1+j)} \tag{1.125}$$

The residue k_{-2} can be evaluated from Eq. (1.121) and the vectors shown in part (c) of the figure:

$$k_{-2} = \left[8\frac{-1}{(-1-j)(-1+j)}\right]\left[\frac{1}{-1} - \frac{1}{-1-j} - \frac{1}{-1+j}\right] \tag{1.126}$$

The vector addition indicated by the second term is performed in Fig. 1.10(d). Simplification of the last three equations results in the partial-fraction expansion

$$\frac{8(s+1)}{(s+2)^2(s^2+2s+2)} = \frac{-4}{(s+2)^2} + \frac{0}{s+2} + \frac{-j2}{s+1-j}$$
$$+ \frac{j2}{s+1+j} \tag{1.127}$$

The graphical procedure as outlined above is primarily significant because of the assistance it offers in the rapid estimation of the various residues (and other coefficients in the partial-fraction expansion). The residues indicate directly the effects of certain poles on the system performance characteristics. For example, the amplitude of a particular component of a time function is directly related to the residue of the Laplace transform of the time function in the pole which generates this component. The ability to make a rapid estimate of the residues is also desirable if the design problem requires a study of the effects of varying certain poles or zeros. Similar graphical analyses are useful in a number of related problems (e.g., determination of the root loci, as described in Chap. 4) and are one of the basic building blocks for the successful application of all design methods based on control of the zeros and poles of the system transfer functions.

1.3. The Potential Analogy. Although the transfer function $G(s)$ is characterized by its poles and zeros and a multiplicative constant, the greatest part of the servomechanism literature is concerned with the behavior of $G(j\omega)$, the transfer function evaluated for real (sinusoidal) frequencies. Even if system design is effected primarily in terms of the poles and zeros of $G(s)$, it is ordinarily desirable that the designer be able to evaluate the performance of his system when it is driven by sinusoidal signals. Although Chaps. 3 to 8 are almost exclusively concerned with pole-zero design methods, complete system design frequently must utilize the very significant information in the gain and phase functions (in other words, in the transfer functions evaluated for $s = j\omega$).

The determination of $G(j\omega)$ from $G(s)$ can be accomplished in several ways. Clearly, $G(j\omega)$ can be evaluated analytically if s is replaced by $j\omega$. If plots of the magnitude and phase of $G(j\omega)$ as functions of ω are desired, straightforward analytical computation becomes tedious in any but the simplest cases. An alternative approach is furnished by the logarithmic plots described briefly in Sec. 6.4 and in detail in standard servomechanism texts.†   In this technique, both the logarithmic gain and the phase are determined for each multiplicative factor, and the over-all gain and phase are then evaluated by adding the components. If accurate plots are desired (*e.g.*, within 1 db of gain or a few degrees of phase), this method is rapid and simple.

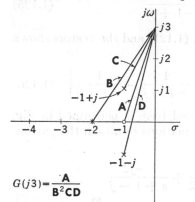

$$G(j3) = \frac{A}{B^2CD}$$

Fig. 1.11. Vectors for calculation of $G(j3)$.

It is also possible to determine $G(j\omega)$ from $G(s)$ by a graphical procedure. $G(j\omega_1)$ represents the function $G(s)$ evaluated at a specific point $s = j\omega_1$ on the $j\omega$ axis. If $G(s)$ is factored to separate the effects of individual poles and zeros, each factor is of the form $s + a$, where $-a$ is the particular critical frequency.‡   At $s = j\omega_1$, the factor can be considered as the vector from $-a$ to the point $j\omega_1$. Thus, $G(j\omega_1)$ is proportional to the product of the vectors from the zeros to $j\omega_1$ divided by the product of the vectors from the poles to $j\omega_1$. The graphical analysis, exactly analogous to that described in the last section for the evaluation of residues, is illustrated by Fig. 1.11, showing the vectors for the determination of $G(j3)$ when

$$G(s) = \frac{s + 1}{(s + 2)^2(s^2 + 2s + 2)} \qquad (1.128)$$

With a transfer function of moderate complexity, graphical evaluation of $G(j\omega)$ becomes almost as complex as straightforward, analytical computation, and the logarithmic plots constitute a more useful method of analysis. If $G(s)$ is simple, the variation of $|G(j\omega)|$ with ω can be visual-

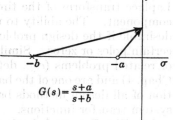

$$G(s) = \frac{s+a}{s+b}$$

Fig. 1.12. Transfer function of passive lead network.

ized merely by considering the way the magnitudes of the pertinent vectors change with ω. For example, if $G(s)$ is the transfer function of a simple, passive lead network, the appropriate vectors are shown in Fig. 1.12. As the tips of the two vectors move up the $j\omega$ axis, it is clear that $|G(j\omega)|$ increases monotonically with frequency.

In many cases, an approximate picture of the variation of $|G(j\omega)|$ with

† G. S. Brown and D. P. Campbell, "Principles of Servomechanisms," Chap. 8, John Wiley & Sons, Inc., New York, 1948; and H. Chestnut and R. W. Mayer, "Servomechanisms and Regulating System Design," Chap. 12, John Wiley & Sons, Inc., New York, 1951.

‡ The term "critical frequency" is used to denote a value of s which is either a pole or a zero.

ω can be obtained much more simply from the analogy between potential theory and network theory. In order to demonstrate the analogy, the function $G(s)$ is written in the form

$$G(s) = K \frac{(s + z_1)(s + z_2) \cdots (s + z_m)}{(s + p_1)(s + p_2) \cdots (s + p_n)} \tag{1.129}$$

The effects of the various poles and zeros can be separated if the logarithmic transfer function is considered:

$$\ln G(s) = \ln K + \ln (s + z_1) + \cdots + \ln (s + z_m) - \ln (s + p_1) \\ - \cdots - \ln (s + p_n) \tag{1.130}$$

If the real and imaginary parts are separately equated, Eq. (1.130) becomes

$$\ln |G(s)| = \ln K + \ln |s + z_1| + \cdots + \ln |s + z_m| - \ln |s + p_1| \\ - \cdots - \ln |s + p_n| \tag{1.131}$$

$$\underline{/G(s)} = \underline{/s + z_1} + \cdots + \underline{/s + z_m} - \underline{/s + p_1} - \cdots - \underline{/s + p_n} \tag{1.132}$$

Equation (1.131) states that the logarithm of the magnitude of $G(s)$ can be expressed in terms of the magnitudes of the vectors from the various zeros and poles to the particular s point of interest. This relation is, of course, the basic starting point for a description of the logarithmic gain curves.

A somewhat different interpretation of Eq. (1.131) is useful. In particular, the equation has the same form as the expression for the two-dimensional electrostatic potential if unit positive point charges are located at $-z_1, -z_2, \ldots, -z_m,$ and unit negative point charges at $-p_1, -p_2, \ldots, -p_n.$† Likewise, Eq. (1.132) demonstrates that the phase of $G(s)$ is analogous to the electrostatic stream function of potential theory; the contours of constant phase, for example, correspond to the loci of constant electric flux density. On the basis of the analogy, Table 1.1 can be constructed to indicate the more important equivalences.

Electrostatic potential theory is used above merely to illustrate the analogy, which actually is broader, relating network theory to potential theory in general. As a consequence of this analogy, the characteristics of transfer functions can be determined by considering the behavior of potential and stream functions. The electrolytic tank‡ provides a con-

---

† The statement that the system is two-dimensional implies that the charge and potential are independent of the third coordinate. In other words, the potential V is a function of σ and ω only and independent of the orthogonal coordinate. The point charges considered are then in actuality line charges, with a constant density in the z direction. They are referred to as point charges because only one point in the $\sigma\omega$ plane is involved.

The dimensions used in evaluating the electrostatic potential can be chosen such that the expression for the potential has exactly the same form as Eq. (1.131).

‡ R. E. Scott, Network Synthesis by the Use of Potential Analogues, *Proc. IRE,* Vol. 40, pp. 970–973, August, 1952; and A. R. Boothroyd, E. C. Cherry, and R.

venient method of determining the gain and phase functions or transient response corresponding to given pole-zero configurations and can be used as the basis for a trial-and-error design procedure in which the critical frequencies are adjusted until the desired performance characteristics are obtained.

A large portion of the research in network theory during the past five years has been aimed at exploiting the analogy, particularly in the

TABLE 1.1
THE POTENTIAL ANALOGY

Network function			Analogous electrostatic potential function	
Logarithmic transfer function $\ln G(s) = \alpha + j\beta$	$\ln G(s)$	$W(s)$		Complex potential, $W(s) = V + j\psi$
Real part of logarithmic transfer function	$\alpha(s)$	$V(s)$		Real, electric potential
Gain (nepers)	$\alpha(j\omega)$	$V(j\omega)$		Potential along $j\omega$ axis
Imaginary part of logarithmic transfer function	$\beta(s)$	$\psi(s)$		Stream function
Phase shift	$\beta(j\omega)$	$\psi(j\omega)$		Stream function along $j\omega$ axis
Derivative of attenuation along $j\omega$ axis	$-\dfrac{d\alpha(\omega)}{d\omega}$	$-\dfrac{dV(\omega)}{d\omega} = E_\omega(\omega)$		Electric field intensity in ω direction along $j\omega$ axis
Time delay	$-\dfrac{d\beta(\omega)}{d\omega}$	$-\dfrac{d\psi(\omega)}{d\omega} = E_\sigma(\omega)$		Electric field intensity in σ direction along $j\omega$ axis

approximation problem in which the synthesist is asked to find a network realizing a specified gain or phase characteristic along the $j\omega$ axis.[†] The conventional approach to such a problem involves determination of a rational algebraic function, $G(s)$, with suitable gain or phase. Once $G(s)$ is known, the network can be found using the procedures described in Chap. 3 or extensions of these methods. An appropriate set of poles and zeros for $G(s)$ is chosen by using the established methods of potential theory to find the charge distribution yielding a potential or stream function similar to the specified gain or phase.

In most feedback-control applications, the designer is not concerned directly with the approximation problem, but instead uses the potential analogy to obtain a physical picture of the correlation between the pole-

Makar, An Electrolytic Tank for the Measurement of Steady-state Response, Transient Response, and Allied Properties of Networks, *Proc. Inst. Elec. Engrs. (London)*, Vol. 96, pp. 163–177, May, 1949.

† S. Darlington, The Potential Analogue Method of Network Synthesis, *Bell System Tech. J.*, Vol. 30, pp. 315–365, April, 1951.

zero configuration and the gain characteristic, $|G(j\omega)|$. The clearest picture of the problem is obtained if the potential is assumed to denote the potential energy of a stretched membrane. The s plane is represented by an elastic membrane (e.g., a rubber sheet) under uniform radial tension. On the circular membrane, the σ and $j\omega$ coordinates are marked. Before the poles and zeros are introduced, the appropriate analogy must be selected. For example, if the magnitude of $G(s)$ is of interest, that analogy is selected which makes the gain correspond to the potential. Accordingly, at the poles, the membrane must be pushed upward to infinity by an infinitesimally small rod (practically, to a high value by a rod of small diameter); and at the zeros the sheet is pushed downward in the same way. All rods are of the same diameter and displaced the same distance with reference to the neutral position of the membrane. The resulting position of any point on the membrane compared to the neutral position indicates the value of $\ln |G(s)|$ at that value of s. In particular, the variation of the position of the $j\omega$ axis part of the membrane indicates $\ln |G(j\omega)|$.

The model described above is clearly unnecessarily crude and subject to very significant inaccuracy. Errors are introduced by the nonzero diameter of the rods (particularly if the poles are close to the $j\omega$ axis), the finite size of the membrane (resulting in the edge of the membrane being held at zero displacement even though the potential problem may not require this boundary condition), and the distortion of the coordinate lines by the deflection of the membrane. Such sources of error can be more easily controlled if an electrolytic tank is used rather than a rubber membrane, but the simple membrane interpretation suffices for the very qualitative applications utilized throughout this book.

The usefulness of the analogy is apparent if a specific $G(s)$ is considered:

$$G(s) = \frac{2(s + 1)}{s^2 + 2s + 2} \qquad (1.133)$$

With the transfer function as written, the zero and two poles are in a line parallel to the $j\omega$ axis. The total distortion of the $j\omega$ axis of the membrane is the sum of three components shown in Fig. 1.13(a). The total gain function is indicated in part (b) of the figure. If the zero-frequency value is used as a reference, it is clear that the gain increases as ω increases from zero toward unity. When $\omega = 1$, the point on the $j\omega$ axis opposite the pole at $-1 + j1$ is under investigation. If the zero at -1 and the pole at $-1 - j1$ were not present, the gain would reach a maximum at this ω. Because the zero at -1 is nearer $+j1$ than the pole at $-1 - j1$, the gain actually reaches a maximum slightly beyond $\omega = 1$; thereafter, the gain falls with frequency until, at a high ω, the three critical frequencies together behave as a single, simple pole.

The qualitative effects of moving the zero along the real axis are apparent. As the zero approaches the origin, the gain at zero frequency decreases rapidly, but at large values of ω the effect is negligible. Likewise, as the zero is moved away from the origin, the minimum of $\ln |G(j\omega)|$

at $\omega = 0$ becomes less pronounced and eventually is identical with the minimum produced by the two poles alone. In a similar fashion, an approximate evaluation of motion of the poles can be deduced from very qualitative reasoning.

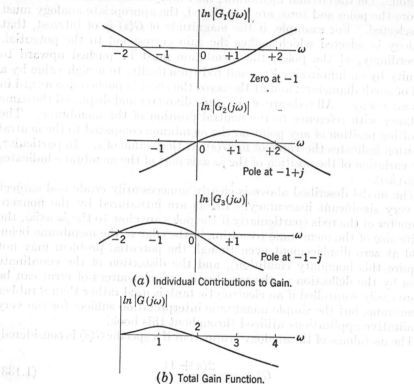

(a) Individual Contributions to Gain.

(b) Total Gain Function.

FIG. 1.13. Membrane deflection.

1.4. Laplace-transform Theory. In this section, the basic elements of Laplace-transform theory are reviewed very briefly as an introduction to the following two sections, which present certain special theorems and relations of the theory. Emphasis throughout is not on mathematical rigor or formal derivation, but instead on the methods of application in problems associated with the analysis and design of feedback systems.

The Laplace transform is formally defined by the equations

$$G(s) = \int_0^\infty g(t)e^{-st}\,dt \qquad (1.134)\dagger$$

† Strictly, the equation should be written

$$G(s) = \lim_{\substack{a \to 0 \\ T \to \infty}} \left[\int_a^T g(t)e^{-st}\,dt \right]$$

For engineering purposes, however, the form of (1.134) is adequate.

$$g(t) = \frac{1}{2\pi j} \int_{c-j\infty}^{c+j\infty} G(s)e^{ts}\, ds \qquad t > 0 \qquad (1.135)$$

Equation (1.134) is the direct Laplace transformation, giving the Laplace transform $G(s)$ in terms of the associated time function $g(t)$. Equation (1.135), with $g(t)$ described in terms of $G(s)$, is the inverse transformation; here c, the abscissa of absolute convergence, must be larger than the real parts of all singularities of $G(s)$. Equations (1.134) and (1.135), relating the time function and its Laplace transform, can be abbreviated as

$$g(t) \longleftrightarrow G(s) \qquad (1.136)$$

$g(t)$ and $G(s)$ are said to constitute a transform pair.

Introduction of the transformation permits consideration of analysis and design problems in terms of functions of the complex frequency $s = \sigma + j\omega$, rather than in terms of the time functions. The usefulness of the Laplace transform stems primarily from the fact that differentiation of the time function corresponds to multiplication of the transform by s: the differential equations in time become algebraic equations in s.

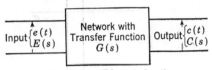

FIG. 1.14. Linear circuit.

Likewise, the analysis and synthesis problems for linear circuits are simplified if the time functions are described by the transforms and the network characteristics by an appropriate transfer function depending on s. Thus, in terms of the notation of Fig. 1.14,

Analysis problem: $C(s) = G(s)E(s)$ (1.137)

Synthesis problem: $G(s) = \dfrac{C(s)}{E(s)}$ (1.138)

Analysis involves formation of the product of $E(s)$, the transform of the input, and $G(s)$, the transfer function; synthesis requires determination of the ratio $C(s)/E(s)$.

Formal Analysis Procedures. Analysis is ordinarily effected by formation of the product $G(s)E(s)$, as indicated in Eq. (1.137). The output $c(t)$ is then the inverse transformation of $C(s)$. In the majority of cases of interest in the analysis of feedback control systems, $C(s)$ is a rational algebraic function, the ratio of two polynomials in s. The inverse transformation can be carried out by consulting published tables of Laplace-transform pairs or by consideration of Eq. (1.135). If the latter, more general method is used, a complex integral must be evaluated along the path of integration shown in Fig. 1.15(a).

Direct evaluation of the integral is difficult, but if $G(s)$ approaches zero as s tends to infinity [that is, $G(s) \to K/s^n$, where $n \geq 1$], the path of integration can be closed along a semicircle of large radius in the left-half plane [part (b) of Fig. 1.15]. If R is sufficiently large, the integrand is negligible around this semicircular contour, and the two paths of Fig. 1.15 are equivalent. The integral can then be evaluated from the theory of residues, which states that the integral of a function around a closed contour in the complex plane is $2\pi j$ multiplied by the sum of the residues in the poles within the closed contour. Thus, the value of $g(t)$ in Eq. (1.135) is given by the relation

$$g(t) = 2\pi j \sum_{\nu} k_{\nu} \tag{1.139}$$

where k_{ν} are the residues of $G(s)e^{st}$ in the poles in the left-half plane.

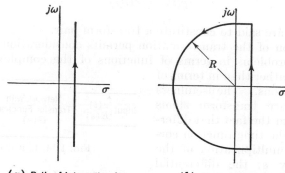

(*a*) Path of Integration for Inverse Laplace Integral   (*b*) Equivalent Path

FIG. 1.15. Paths of integration in complex plane.

A simple example illustrates the general method for evaluating the time function from the frequency function. The transform considered is

$$G(s) = \frac{s + 2}{(s + 1)(s + 3)} \tag{1.140}$$

The integrand for the inverse transformation is

$$G(s)e^{st} = \frac{(s + 2)e^{st}}{(s + 1)(s + 3)} \tag{1.141}$$

$G(s)e^{st}$ possesses two simple poles, at -1 and -3. The two residues can be written by inspection:

$$k_{-1} = \frac{e^{-t}}{2} \tag{1.142}$$

$$k_{-3} = \frac{e^{-3t}}{2} \tag{1.143}$$

Hence,

$$g(t) = \tfrac{1}{2}(e^{-t} + e^{-3t}) \tag{1.144}$$

Practical application of the Laplace transform usually utilizes a partial-fraction expansion of $G(s)$, rather than $G(s)e^{st}$. If the poles are simple, the residue of $G(s)e^{st}$ in the pole at s_1 is simply $e^{s_1 t}$ times the corresponding residue of $G(s)$. Hence, the functions $k_{s_1}e^{s_1 t}$ and $k_{s_1}/(s - s_1)$ form a Laplace-transform pair, as indicated in the first row of Table 1.2. If the poles are complex, they are most conveniently considered in conjugate pairs, as indicated in the second row of the table. If the poles are of multiple order, the relation between the residue of $G(s)$ and that of $G(s)e^{st}$ leads directly to the transform pairs of the third and fourth rows. Thus, Table 1.2, although abbreviated compared to the usual table of Laplace-transform pairs, actually contains all the information required for the inverse transformation of a rational algebraic function which has a denominator polynomial of higher degree than the numerator. $G(s)$ is written in a partial-fraction expansion, and the terms are transformed

TABLE 1.2
RATIONAL ALGEBRAIC LAPLACE TRANSFORMS

Time function	Transform
$k_{s_1}e^{s_1 t}$	$\dfrac{k_{s_1}}{s - s_1}$
$\lvert 2jk_{s_1}\rvert e^{\sigma_1 t}\sin[\omega_1 t + \underline{/2jk_{s_1}}]$	$\dfrac{k_{s_1}}{s - s_1} + \dfrac{\overline{k_{s_1}}}{s - \overline{s_1}}$ $\quad s_1 = \sigma_1 + j\omega_1$
$Ate^{s_1 t}$	$\dfrac{A}{(s - s_1)^2}$
$\dfrac{A}{(n - 1)!}\, t^{n-1}e^{s_1 t}$, n is a positive integer	$\dfrac{A}{(s - s_1)^n}$

individually. If the degree of the numerator polynomial equals or exceeds that of the denominator, the partial-fraction expansion contains a polynomial, and the corresponding time function includes impulses, as described in Sec. 1.5.

Even when the poles and zeros of $G(s)$ are known, the plotting of $g(t)$ is a tedious process if $G(s)$ contains more than a few poles. If the design of feedback systems is to be effected in terms of the poles and zeros of the pertinent transfer functions, it is very desirable that the designer be able to *estimate* rapidly the significant characteristics of the time function directly from the critical frequencies of the transform. Fortunately, the transfer functions of interest in design frequently can be reduced to the extent that only a small number of critical frequencies are significant; as a consequence of this simplicity, the general shape of the time function can be estimated without extensive calculations. The remainder of this section is devoted to a description of the time functions corresponding to several simple pole-zero configurations.

Transforms with Two Poles, No Zeros. The simplest significant pole-zero configuration for $G(s)$ includes one pole and no finite zeros. If the pole is at $-p_1$, the corresponding impulse response is a decaying exponential, $e^{-p_1 t}$, and the step-function response is $A(1 - e^{-p_1 t})$. The next case in increasing complexity is a $G(s)$ with two poles and no finite zeros. If $G(0)$ is unity,

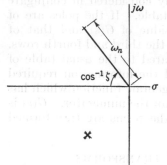

$$G_1(s) = \frac{\omega_n^2}{s^2 + 2\zeta\omega_n s + \omega_n^2} \quad (1.145)$$

The pole-zero configuration is shown in Fig. 1.16. If the poles are complex, ω_n is the radial distance from the origin to either pole, and ζ is the cosine of the angle between the radial line to the pole and the negative real axis. As ζ is increased, with ω_n constant, the poles move along the circle of radius ω_n and meet at $s = -\omega_n$ ($\zeta = 1$); they then separate and move along the real axis toward zero and infinity.

FIG. 1.16. Pole configuration for $G_1(s)$.

The corresponding step-function response [the inverse transform of $G(s)/s$] is characterized by ω_n and ζ. ω_n, the undamped natural frequency, can be considered to determine the frequency or time normalization: doubling ω_n corresponds to moving the poles radially twice as far

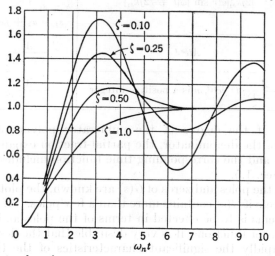

FIG. 1.17. Unit-step-function responses for system with transfer function

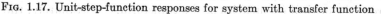

$$\frac{\omega_n^2}{s^2 + 2\zeta\omega_n s + \omega_n^2}.$$

(*From H. M. James, N. B. Nichols, and R. S. Phillips, "Theory of Servomechanisms," MIT Radiation Laboratory Series, Vol. 25, p. 143, McGraw-Hill Book Company, Inc., New York, 1947.*)

from the origin or, in terms of the time function, to halving the time for any given response. Thus, except for a normalization factor, the response is determined by ζ, as indicated by the curves of Fig. 1.17.

Although Fig. 1.17 is constructed from the actual inverse transformation of $G(s)/s$, an approximate picture of the response can be obtained from the following facts:

(1) The time constant of the envelope of the damped oscillation (if $\zeta < 1$) is the reciprocal of the real part of either pole: $i.e.$, the time constant is $1/\zeta\omega_n$. The time required for the system to settle to an essentially steady-state value after the application of a step function is between three and five time constants, the specific value depending on the quantitative definition of settling time.

(2) The overshoot also varies with ζ, as described by Fig. 1.18.

(3) At $t = 0$, the response and the first derivative are both zero, since the transform $G(s)/s$ is proportional to $1/s^3$ as s tends to infinity.

(4) The first maximum occurs for

$$t = \frac{\pi}{\omega_n \sqrt{1 - \zeta^2}} \qquad (1.146)$$

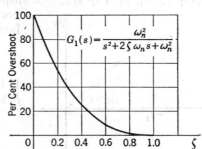

FIG. 1.18. Overshoot variation with ζ.

This value of time represents one half period of the damped oscillation.

Thus, the step-function responses of Fig. 1.17 can be sketched approximately directly from a knowledge of the pole configuration.

Since the impulse response is the derivative of the step-function response, the curves of Fig. 1.19 represent the impulse responses for a range

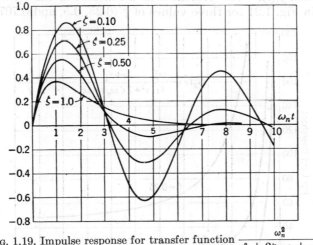

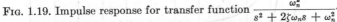

FIG. 1.19. Impulse response for transfer function $\dfrac{\omega_n^2}{s^2 + 2\zeta\omega_n s + \omega_n^2}$.

of values of ζ. The overshoot of the step-function response can be found from the corresponding impulse response: if the area under the impulse response from $t = 0$ to the time of the first zero is denoted $1 + x$, x is the desired overshoot. The maximum value of the step-function response occurs simultaneously with this first zero of the impulse response.

Two Poles and One Zero. If a single, finite zero is introduced (Fig.

1.20), the step-function response is modified, as $G(s)$ now becomes

$$G_2(s) = \frac{\omega_n^2}{z_1} \frac{s + z_1}{s^2 + 2\zeta\omega_n s + \omega_n^2} \qquad (1.147)$$

Equation (1.147) represents (1.145) with the added multiplicative factor $(s + z_1)/z_1$, or $1 + s/z_1$. Multiplication of the transform by $1 + s/z_1$ corresponds to an addition to $g(t)$ of the factor $(1/z_1)g'(t)$:

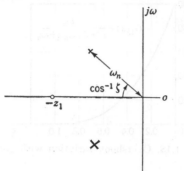

$$g_2(t) = g_1(t) + \frac{1}{z_1} g_1'(t) \qquad (1.148)$$

If the step-function response (denoted by f) is considered,

$$f_2(t) = f_1(t) + \frac{1}{z_1} f_1'(t) \qquad (1.149)$$

Since the derivative of the step-function response is the impulse response,

$$f_2(t) = f_1(t) + \frac{1}{z_1} g_1(t) \qquad (1.150)$$

FIG. 1.20. Pole-zero configuration for $G_2(s)$.

Since addition of $g_1(t)$ to $f_1(t)$ represents addition of a positive value up to the time the first maximum is reached, $f_2(t)$ exhibits a poorer relative stability than $f_1(t)$. The overshoot as a function of the zero position is sketched in Fig. 1.21 for three values of ζ (0.25, 0.5, and 0.707).

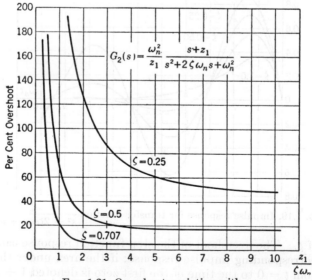

FIG. 1.21. Overshoot variation with z_1.

Three Poles. The effect of adding an additional real pole to the transform is in almost every case stabilizing, with the additional term increasing both time delay and rise time in the step-function response. Figure

1.22 illustrates the effect of an additional pole when the original ζ is 0.5. Even if the time constant associated with the real pole is one half of that resulting from the complex poles ($p_3 = 2$ in the figure), the overshoot is very small and the response simulates that of a critically damped, second-order system. The curves of Fig. 1.22 indicate that the two configurations of Fig. 1.23 can be made nearly equivalent. The lower ζ

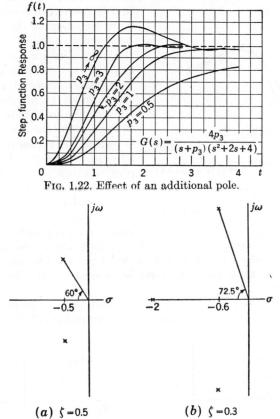

FIG. 1.22. Effect of an additional pole.

$$G(s) = \frac{4p_3}{(s+p_3)(s^2+2s+4)}$$

(a) $\zeta = 0.5$ (b) $\zeta = 0.3$

FIG. 1.23. Two pole configurations giving similar transient response.

in the three-pole case is offset by the presence of the real pole. The two curves of Fig. 1.24 show the similarity between the step-function responses associated with the configurations of Fig. 1.23.

Additional Poles. The presence of additional poles well to the left in the s plane does not alter significantly the characteristics described above. A specific numerical example illustrates the effects of such additional poles. If the two configurations of Fig. 1.25 are considered,

$$G_3(s) = \frac{4}{s^2 + 2s + 4} \tag{1.151}$$

$$G_4(s) = \frac{4p_3}{(s^2 + 2s + 4)(s + p_3)} \tag{1.152}$$

The two step-function responses assume the forms

$$f_3(t) = 1 + A_3 e^{-t} \sin(\sqrt{3}\, t + \theta_3) \tag{1.153}$$
$$f_4(t) = 1 + A_4 e^{-t} \sin(\sqrt{3}\, t + \theta_4) + B_4 e^{-p_3 t} \tag{1.154}$$

Comparison of $f_3(t)$ and $f_4(t)$ requires two investigations:

(1)   One effect of the introduction of the additional pole is the presence in $f_4(t)$ of the term $B_4 e^{-p_3 t}$. But, if p_3 is large, this term tends to be negligible for two reasons. First, the time constant of the term is $1/p_3$, or a small number; consequently, the term dies out before the step-function response attains a significant value. Second, the coefficient B_4 is small (compared to unity), since B_4 is $4p_3$ divided by the two vectors from the complex poles to $-p_3$ and the vector from the origin to $-p_3$. If $p_3 \gg 2$, the two complex vectors are of the order of magnitude of p_3, and the residue is of the order of magnitude of $4/p_3^2$ (or ω_n^2/p_3^2). If p_3 is only $5\omega_n$, the value of B_4 is roughly 0.04. Thus, not only does this term, $B_4 e^{-p_3 t}$, decay rapidly toward zero, but it never is large. The principal effect of the added term is to make an additional derivative of the step-function response zero at $t = 0$. In other words, the response is slightly slower starting.

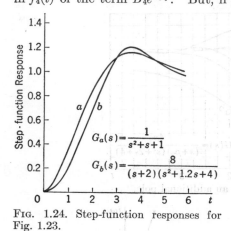

FIG. 1.24. Step-function responses for Fig. 1.23.

$$G_a(s) = \frac{1}{s^2 + s + 1}$$

$$G_b(s) = \frac{8}{(s+2)(s^2 + 1.2s + 4)}$$

(2)   The second effect of the additional pole is evidenced by the change in the amplitude and phase of the damped-oscillation term in $f(t)$.

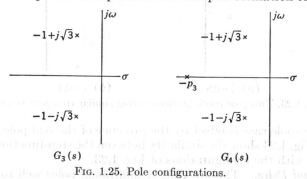

FIG. 1.25. Pole configurations.

Comparison of A_4 with A_3 and θ_4 with θ_3 is simplified if a graphical interpretation is used. For either system, $A e^{j\theta}$ is $2jk_{-1+j\sqrt{3}}$, where $k_{-1+j\sqrt{3}}$ is the residue of $G(s)/s$ in the pole at $-1 + j\sqrt{3}$. Multiplication of $G(s)$ by $p_3/(s + p_3)$ modifies both the magnitude and angle of $k_{-1+j\sqrt{3}}$, since the residue is multiplied by $p_3/(p_3 - 1 + j\sqrt{3})$. For any specific p_3, these changes can be rapidly calculated graphically.

Thus, the introduction of real, large-magnitude poles in $G(s)$ changes only slightly the form of the step-function response. The criterion commonly adopted in design is that any real poles which are to contribute negligibly to the step-function response should be placed at least six times as far from the $j\omega$ axis as those poles governing the response. Clearly, it is largely irrelevant whether such poles far from the $j\omega$ axis are actually real; complex poles are also negligible as long as the magnitude of the real part is much larger than that of the significant poles.

Dipoles. An analogous line of reasoning indicates that addition of a dipole (a pole and a zero close together) modifies the step-function response only slightly. Figure 1.26 shows the pole-zero configuration for the transfer function

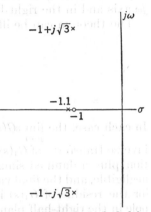

$$G(s) = \frac{4.4(s+1)}{(s^2 + 2s + 4)(s + 1.1)} \qquad (1.155)$$

The corresponding step-function response includes a term of the form $Ae^{-1.1t}$, but a graphical evaluation of the residue indicates that A is small (0.133) because of the presence of the zero at -1. Likewise, the damped-oscillation term is changed only slightly by the inclusion of the term $1.1(s + 1)/(s + 1.1)$ in the transform.

Fig. 1.26. Dipole included in pole-zero configuration.

As a result of the feasibility of neglecting poles far from the $j\omega$ axis, dipoles, etc., the majority of pole-zero configurations encountered in the design of feedback control systems resolve to two or three poles and one or two finite zeros. In terms of the classical Nyquist-diagram approach to design, a smooth tangency of the frequency locus and the circle representing the selected, maximum closed-loop gain ordinarily implies a design with transfer functions which can be effectively characterized by a very few critical frequencies. The possibility of such simplification means that the significant characteristics of the transient response can be rapidly estimated from the pole-zero configuration without recourse to the exact inverse transformation.

1.5. Special Relations in Laplace-transform Theory. In the last section, the basic relations of Laplace-transform theory are summarized, with particular emphasis placed on the information deducible from a knowledge of the pole and zero positions. The pole-zero configuration of $G(s)$ indicates directly both the frequency-domain and the time-domain characteristics of the system described by $G(s)$. The form of the Laplace integrals [Eqs. (1.134) and (1.135)] giving the relation between $g(t)$ and $G(s)$ leads to a number of special properties of the Laplace transform, properties which are important if full advantage is to be gained from use of the transform as a design and analysis tool. This section and the following contain a summary of those special relations of most importance in the study of feedback systems. In general, only a brief discussion is possible here, with emphasis directed toward the applications described in later chapters; the reader is referred to standard texts† for derivations and additional examples.

Final-value Theorem. The final-value theorem gives the final value of the time function in terms of the behavior of the Laplace transform as s tends to zero. Specifically,

$$\lim_{t \to \infty} g(t) = \lim_{s \to 0} sG(s) \qquad (1.156)\star$$

Equation (1.156) is valid only if the function $sG(s)$ is analytic on the $j\omega$ axis and in the right-half plane.‡

The theorem can be illustrated with two examples:

$$G_1(s) = \frac{s + 2}{s(s^2 + 2s + 5)} \qquad (1.157)$$

$$G_2(s) = \frac{-2}{s(s - 5)} \qquad (1.158)$$

In each case, the $\lim_{s \to 0} sG(s)$ has the value $\frac{2}{5}$. The final value of $g_1(t)$, the inverse transform of $G_1(s)$, is actually $\frac{2}{5}$, since $g_1(t)$ consists of a step function plus a damped sinusoid. As $t \to \infty$, the damped sinusoid becomes negligible, and the final value of $g_1(t)$ is simply the step-function amplitude [or the residue of $G_1(s)$ in the pole at the origin]. Because $G_2(s)$ has a pole in the right-half plane (at $+5$), the theorem is inapplicable; the function $g_2(t)$ actually increases without bound as t increases:

$$g_2(t) = \frac{2}{5} - \frac{2}{5}e^{5t} \qquad (1.159)$$

There appears to be no final-value theorem which by its very result indicates the inapplicability of the theorem. In other words, it would be very desirable to have a final-value theorem such that the required manipulation of $G(s)$ gave a result which was the correct final value when the theorem was applicable, and which gave an unbounded result when the time function increased without bound or oscillated with constant amplitude as t became large.§ If $G(s)$ is rational algebraic, Routh's test can be used to determine whether Eq. (1.156) can be applied; in other cases, however, it is not always clear whether the value given by Eq. (1.156) is correct or not. For example, in the system of Fig. 1.27, a closed-loop system with an ideal time delay, the over-all transfer function

---

† Among the many texts which have been written primarily for engineers are M. F. Gardner and J. L. Barnes, "Transients in Linear Systems," John Wiley & Sons, Inc., New York, 1942; and B. Van der Pol and H. Bremmer, "Operational Calculus Based on the Two-sided Laplace Integral," Cambridge University Press, Cambridge, England, 1950.

‡ Actually, validity of the equation also requires that $g(t)$ and $g'(t)$ be functions for which a Laplace transform exists.

§ If such a final-value theorem existed, it could of course be used for stability analysis is

$$\frac{C}{R}(s) = \frac{[K/s(s+1)]e^{-Ts}}{1 + [K/s(s+1)]e^{-Ts}} \qquad (1.160)$$

Routh's test cannot be used since the expression placing in evidence the poles of $\frac{C}{R}(s)$ takes the form

$$s(s+1) + Ke^{-Ts}$$

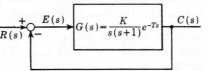

The transform of the response of the system to a unit step function is

$$C(s) = \frac{Ke^{-Ts}}{s[s(s+1) + Ke^{-Ts}]} \qquad (1.161)$$

FIG. 1.27. Closed-loop system with time delay.

If the system is stable, the final value of the response is

$$\lim_{s \to 0} \frac{Ke^{-Ts}}{s(s+1) + Ke^{-Ts}} = 1 \qquad (1.162)$$

Analytical or graphical approximations must be used, however, to establish the stability of the over-all transfer function before the final-value theorem can be used.

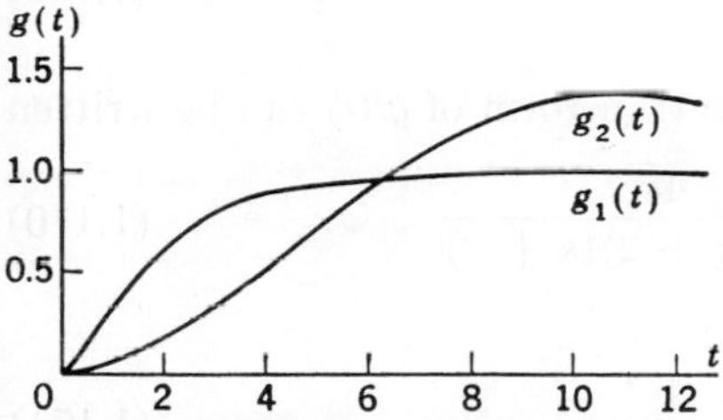

Because Eq. (1.156) indicates that the final value of $g(t)$ is established by the zero-frequency value of $sG(s)$, the statement is often made that the nature of $g(t)$ for large values of t is determined by the behavior of $G(s)$ in the vicinity of the origin in the s plane. Such a correlation must be used with considerable caution. A very simple example illustrates the difficulty. The two time functions shown in Fig. 1.28 correspond to the transforms

FIG. 1.28. $g_1(t)$ and $g_2(t)$.

$$G_1(s) = \frac{1}{s(s+1)^2} \qquad (1.163)$$

$$G_2(s) = \frac{0.09}{s(s^2 + 0.18s + 0.09)} \qquad (1.164)$$

$sG_1(s)$ and $sG_2(s)$ possess the Maclaurin expansions

$$sG_1(s) = 1 - 2s + 3s^2 - \cdots \qquad (1.165)$$
$$sG_2(s) = 1 - 2s - 7.11s^2 + \cdots \qquad (1.166)$$

Clearly, in the immediate vicinity of the origin, the two transforms behave identically; on the other hand, the similarity between the two time functions, even for moderately large t, is certainly not impressive. The invalidity of this attempted correlation between large t and small s

is considered again in Sec. 1.7, when the limitations on the use of the generalized error coefficients are discussed.

Initial-value Theorem.   The initial-value theorem states that

$$\lim_{t\to 0+} g(t) = \lim_{s\to\infty} sG(s) \qquad (1.167)^\star$$

In addition to the conditions that $g(t)$ and $g'(t)$ must have Laplace transforms, the theorem requires only that the $\lim_{s\to\infty} sG(s)$ exist: *i.e.*, the limit must be finite, or if $G(s)$ is a rational algebraic function, the number of finite poles of $G(s)$ must exceed the number of finite zeros by at least unity.

If $G(s)$ is rational algebraic, this theorem, plus recognition of the fact that the transform of $g'(t)$ is $sG(s) - g(0+)$, permits determination of not only the initial value, but more generally the initial part of the time function.   As an example, the function considered is

$$G(s) = \frac{4}{(s^2 + 2s + 2)(s + 2)} \qquad (1.168)$$

Equation (1.167) indicates at once that

$$\lim_{t\to 0+} g(t) = 0 \qquad (1.169)$$

As a result of this zero initial value, the transform of $g'(t)$ can be written

$$\mathcal{L}[g'(t)] = \frac{4s}{(s^2 + 2s + 2)(s + 2)} \qquad (1.170)$$

Hence, $g'(0)$ is also zero, and

$$\mathcal{L}[g''(t)] = \frac{4s^2}{(s^2 + 2s + 2)(s + 2)} \qquad (1.171)$$

Application of the initial-value theorem then gives

$$g''(0+) = 4 \qquad (1.172)$$

Hence, for small values of t, $g(t)$ can be written as

$$g(t) = 2t^2 + \text{(higher powers of } t) \qquad (1.173)$$

In general, if $G(s)$ behaves as K/s^n as s becomes large, $g(t)$ behaves, for sufficiently small values of t, as $[K/(n-1)!]t^{n-1}$.

The above correlation between small t and large s can be extended to demonstrate the relations between the behavior of $g(t)$ for small t and $G(j\omega)$ for large ω.   If $g(t)$ behaves as $[K/(n-1)!]t^{n-1}$ for small t,

$$G(j\omega) \xrightarrow[\omega\to\infty]{} \frac{K}{(j\omega)^n} + \frac{A}{(j\omega)^{n+1}} \qquad (1.174)$$

where A is a constant.   The first term suffices to establish the behavior of $|G(j\omega)|$ and $\underline{/G(j\omega)}$ as $\omega \to \infty$, since the magnitude decreases as $1/\omega^n$ and

the angle approaches $-n\pi/2$ rad; if the behavior of the real and imaginary parts of G is of interest, both terms are required:
If n is odd:

$$\text{Re } G(j\omega) \xrightarrow[\omega \to \infty]{} \frac{\text{constant}}{\omega^{n+1}}$$

$$\text{Im } G(j\omega) \xrightarrow[\omega \to \infty]{} \frac{\text{constant}}{\omega^n} \tag{1.175}$$

If n is even:

$$\text{Re } G(j\omega) \xrightarrow[\omega \to \infty]{} \frac{\text{constant}}{\omega^n}$$

$$\text{Im } G(j\omega) \xrightarrow[\omega \to \infty]{} \frac{\text{constant}}{\omega^{n+1}} \tag{1.176}$$

The high-frequency behavior of either the real or imaginary part alone is not sufficient to establish uniquely the value of n. For example, if the real part behaves as $1/\omega^4$, n may be either 3 or 4; if the imaginary part behaves as $1/\omega^3$, n may be 2 or 3.

Time Delay. Delay of the time function by T sec corresponds to multiplication of the transform by e^{-Ts}. In the direct Laplace transform, the statement is often made that the value of the time function for negative time is immaterial, since the integration is over the range of values of t from zero to infinity. When the delayed function is considered, however, the value of the original function from $-T$ to zero is of interest, and the theorem requires that the time function be considered zero for negative values of time.

Determination of the transform of the square wave shown in Fig. 1.29(a) illustrates the use of time delay. The square wave is considered as the sum of step functions, alternately positive and negative, as shown in part (b) of the figure. Since the transform of a unit step function starting at $t = nT$ is $(1/s)e^{-nTs}$, the transform of the complete square wave is

$$E_1(s) = \frac{1}{s} - \frac{2}{s}e^{-\frac{1}{2}s} + \frac{2}{s}e^{-s} - \frac{2}{s}e^{-\frac{3}{2}s} + \cdots \tag{1.177}$$

The series for $E_1(s)$ can be written in closed form if Eq. (1.177) is first rewritten as

$$E_1(s) = -\frac{1}{s} + \frac{2}{s}(1 - e^{-\frac{1}{2}s} + e^{-s} - e^{-\frac{3}{2}s} + \cdots) \tag{1.178}$$

The parenthetical expression is a geometric series with the sum

$$\frac{1}{(1 + e^{-\frac{1}{2}s})}$$

Hence,

$$E_1(s) = \frac{1 - e^{-\frac{1}{2}s}}{s(1 + e^{-\frac{1}{2}s})} \tag{1.179}$$

Transient and Steady-state Components. If the transform of a periodic signal, such as a square wave, can be written in closed form, it is possible to evaluate simply the response of a network to such a signal. The procedure is most readily explained in terms of the simple example illustrated in Fig. 1.30. The response is to be determined when a square wave

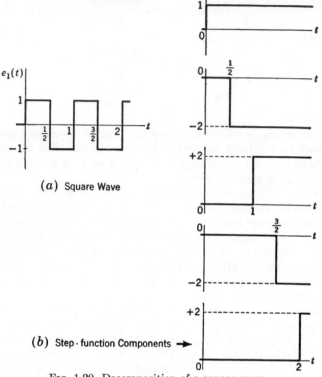

(*a*) Square Wave

(*b*) Step - function Components →

FIG. 1.29. Decomposition of a square wave.

with a period of 1 sec and a peak amplitude of unity is applied to the network with the transfer function

$$G(s) = \frac{1}{s + \frac{1}{3}} \qquad (1.180)$$

The product of the transfer function from Eq. (1.180) and the input transform, $\dfrac{1 - e^{-\frac{1}{2}s}}{s(1 + e^{-\frac{1}{2}s})}$ from Eq. (1.179), is $E_2(s)$, the transform of the output.

$$E_2(s) = \frac{1}{s + \frac{1}{3}} \frac{1 - e^{-\frac{1}{2}s}}{s(1 + e^{-\frac{1}{2}s})} \qquad (1.181)$$

Consideration of Eq. (1.181) indicates that there are two components of the output: transient and steady-state. The transient component contains natural frequencies which are the poles of the network transfer function, while the steady-state component is characterized by the frequencies of the excitation (the poles of the transform of the input signal). In the specific case of Eq. (1.181), the only pole generating a transient term is that at $-\frac{1}{3}$; the steady-state terms result from the poles of $E_2(s)$ at the zeros of $1 + e^{-\frac{1}{3}s}$, or at

$$s = \pm j2n\pi \qquad n = 1, 3, 5, \ldots \qquad (1.182)$$

If the inverse Laplace transformation is made in the usual manner, $E_2(s)$ is expanded in partial fractions and the inverse transform is determined term by term. In this example, $E_2(s)$ possesses an infinite number of poles, and the expression for the output, $e_2(t)$, contains a term of the form $Ae^{-\frac{1}{3}t}$ plus an infinite number of sinusoidal terms. In other words, the partial-fraction expansion leads to an output time function written as a

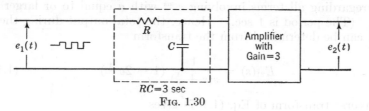

$$RC = 3 \text{ sec}$$
Fig. 1.30

transient term plus a Fourier series for the periodic or steady-state component. Such a form is not convenient if the waveform of $e_2(t)$ is desired.

A simple evaluation of $e_2(t)$ involves the following steps:

(1)   The transient component is determined for all t.
(2)   The *total* output during the first period is evaluated.
(3)   The steady-state component during the first period is found in closed form by subtracting the transient during the first period from the total output.
(4)   The total output during *any* period is the steady-state component plus the transient term evaluated during this period.

These four steps permit the determination of the total output without a period-by-period evaluation in which the solution in any period is found from the initial conditions determined by the final conditions for the preceding period. When applied to the example of Eq. (1.181), these four steps take the following form:

(1)   The transient component results from the pole at $-\frac{1}{3}$. $k_{-\frac{1}{3}}$, the residue of $E_2(s)$ in this pole, is found in the usual way, with the transcendental factor considered in its entirety. Thus,

$$k_{-\frac{1}{3}} = \left[\frac{1 - e^{-\frac{1}{3}s}}{s(1 + e^{-\frac{1}{3}s})} \right]_{s=-\frac{1}{3}} \qquad (1.183)$$

Substitution of the value of s gives a $k_{-\frac{1}{3}}$ of 0.25. Thus, the transient component, a single term in this example, is

$$e_{2t}(t) = 0.25e^{-\frac{1}{3}t} \qquad (1.184)$$

The subscript t is used to denote the transient component.

(2)   Evaluation of the total output during the first period is initiated by writing $E_2(s)$ in the form

$$E_2(s) = \frac{1}{s(s + \frac{1}{3})} (1 - e^{-\frac{1}{2}s})(1 - e^{-\frac{1}{2}s} + e^{-s} - e^{-\frac{3}{2}s} + \cdots) \qquad (1.185)$$

If the two transcendental functions are multiplied,

$$E_2(s) = \frac{1}{s(s + \frac{1}{3})} (1 - 2e^{-\frac{1}{2}s} + 2e^{-s} - 2e^{-\frac{3}{2}s} + \cdots) \qquad (1.186)$$

Since a term of the form e^{-as} represents a delay of a sec, a transform giving the correct output during the first period can be found from Eq. (1.186) by disregarding all terms involving e^{-as} with a equal to or larger than unity.   (The period is 1 sec.)   Hence, the total output during the first period can be determined from the transform

$$E_{21}(s) = \frac{1}{s(s + \frac{1}{3})} (1 - 2e^{-\frac{1}{2}s}) \qquad (1.187)\dagger$$

The inverse transform of Eq. (1.187) gives

$$e_{21}(t) = 3(1 - e^{-\frac{1}{3}t}) - 6[1 - e^{-\frac{1}{3}(t-\frac{1}{2})}]u_{-1}(t - \tfrac{1}{2}) \qquad (1.188)$$

Here $u_{-1}(t - \frac{1}{2})$, the notation for a step function starting at $t = \frac{1}{2}$, is included to make the second term zero for t less than $\frac{1}{2}$.   An alternate way of writing Eq. (1.188) is

$$e_{21}(t) = \begin{cases} 3(1 - e^{-\frac{1}{3}t}) & 0 < t \le \frac{1}{2} \\ -3 + 4.09e^{-\frac{1}{3}t} & \frac{1}{2} \le t \le 1 \end{cases} \qquad (1.189)$$

(3)   The steady-state component of the output during the first period can be found by subtracting $e_{2t}(t)$ from $e_{21}(t)$, as indicated in Fig. 1.31.‡ The analytical expression for the steady-state component during the first period is found from Eqs. (1.184) and (1.189):

$$e_{2ss}(t) = \begin{cases} 3 - 3.25e^{-\frac{1}{3}t} & 0 < t \le \frac{1}{2} \\ -3 + 3.84e^{-\frac{1}{3}t} & \frac{1}{2} \le t \le 1 \end{cases} \qquad (1.190)$$

(4)   The total output during the second cycle (as an example) is determined graphically as shown in Fig. 1.32, or can be found analytically by adding steady-state and transient components:

$$e_{22}(t) = \begin{cases} 0.25e^{-\frac{1}{3}t} + 3 - 3.25e^{-\frac{1}{3}(t-1)} & 1 \le t \le 1.5 \\ 0.25e^{-\frac{1}{3}t} - 3 + 3.84e^{-\frac{1}{3}(t-1)} & 1.5 \le t \le 2 \end{cases} \qquad (1.191)$$

† It should be emphasized that the inverse transform of $E_{21}(s)$ is equal to the correct total output during the interval $0 < t \le 1$, but has no significance for $t > 1$, even though $e_{21}(t)$ may be nonzero for $t > 1$.
‡ The curves of Fig. 1.31 are very nearly straight lines.   Actually, the curves represent the first part of exponentials.   The similarity to straight lines arises because the half period (0.5 sec) is much less than the time constant (3 sec).

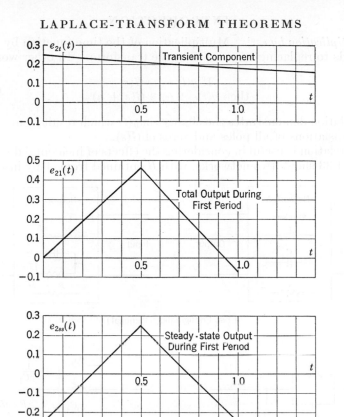

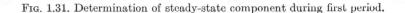

FIG. 1.31. Determination of steady-state component during first period.

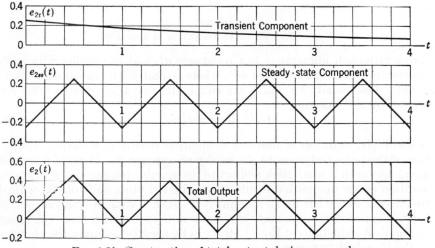

FIG. 1.32. Construction of total output during any cycle.

Multiplication by e^{-at}. Multiplication of the time function by e^{-at} corresponds to replacing s by $s + a$ in the transform. In other words,

$$\text{If } g(t) \longleftrightarrow G(s)$$
$$\text{then } g(t)e^{-at} \longleftrightarrow G(s + a) \qquad (1.192)^\star$$

This relation demonstrates the changes in $g(t)$ which result from identical, real translations of all poles and zeros of $G(s)$.

The relation is useful in considering the effects of incidental dissipation. Figure 1.33 shows two networks, with B obtained from A by inserting in

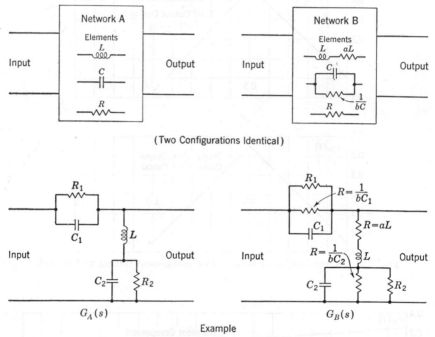

FIG. 1.33. Addition of dissipation in a network.

series with each inductance L a resistance aL and in parallel with each capacitance C a conductance bC, where a and b are constants. It is readily shown that if a and b are equal, the two transfer functions are related by the equation

$$G_A(s + a) = G_B(s) \qquad (1.193)$$

Accordingly, addition of uniform dissipation results in a simple translation of the poles and zeros to the left by an amount a. If a and b are not equal, but each is small with respect to the angular frequencies of interest, addition of the dissipation results approximately in a shift of the critical frequencies to the left by an amount $(a + b)/2$. With an analysis of this type, it is possible to estimate the errors in $G(s)$ resulting from the losses in practical inductances; Eq. (1.192) can be used to estimate the changes in the transient response.

Equation (1.192) is also useful in the analysis of modulated systems. An amplitude-modulated wave can be described by the relation

$$e_m(t) = A[1 + e(t)] \cos \omega_0 t \qquad (1.194)$$

Here $e_m(t)$ is the modulated signal, A is a constant amplitude, ω_0 is the carrier frequency, and $e(t)$ represents the modulating signal. The transform of $e_m(t)$ in terms of $e(t)$ can be found by application of Eq. (1.192)

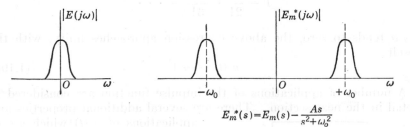

$$E_m^*(s) = E_m(s) - \frac{As}{s^2 + \omega_0^2}$$

FIG. 1.34. Spectrum in amplitude modulation.

after $\cos \omega_0 t$ is replaced by the sum of two exponentials. Thus,

$$E_m(s) = A \left[\frac{s}{s^2 + \omega_0^2} + \frac{E(s - j\omega_0)}{2} + \frac{E(s + j\omega_0)}{2} \right] \qquad (1.195)$$

If $E(j\omega)$, the spectrum of $e(t)$, is zero for $\omega \geq \omega_0$ (that is, the energy of the modulating signal is exclusively in a frequency band below the carrier), the relation between $E_m(j\omega)$ and $E(j\omega)$ is that shown in Fig. 1.34. Amplitude modulation simply translates the spectrum in both directions by an amount ω_0 and introduces the carrier component. In suppressed-carrier amplitude modulation, the $As/(s^2 + \omega_0^2)$ term above is absent.

Impulse Functions. The impulse functions are basic tools for the analysis and synthesis of linear systems. The unit impulse function $u_0(t)$ can be defined in a number of ways; perhaps the simplest definition in terms of conventional Laplace-transform theory is indicated by Fig. 1.35, showing

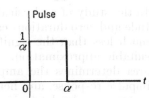

FIG. 1.35. Pulse for definition of unit impulse.

a pulse of width α and amplitude $1/\alpha$. The unit impulse is defined as the function resulting from considering the limit as α tends to zero. Thus,

$$u_0(t) = \lim_{\alpha \to 0} \frac{1}{\alpha} [u_{-1}(t) - u_{-1}(t - \alpha)] \qquad (1.196)$$

Here $u_{-1}(t)$ is used to denote a step function with the jump at $t = 0$. The unit impulse, as defined above, is characterized by the fact that the area under the pulse is unity, regardless of the value of α.

The transform of the pulse of width α is $\dfrac{1}{\alpha} \left(\dfrac{1}{s} - \dfrac{1}{s} e^{-\alpha s} \right)$. The behavior of this transform for small values of α can be determined from a Maclaurin expansion of $1 - e^{-\alpha s}$ about $\alpha = 0$:

$$1 - e^{-\alpha s} = 1 - \left(1 - \alpha s + \frac{\alpha^2 s^2}{2!} - \cdots\right) \qquad (1.197)$$

Substitution of Eq. (1.197) into the transform gives

$$1 - \frac{\alpha s}{2!} + \frac{\alpha^2 s^2}{3!} - \cdots$$

As α tends to zero, the above expression approaches unity, with the result

$$u_0(t) \longleftrightarrow 1 \qquad (1.198)$$

A number of applications of the impulse function are considered in detail in the next section. There are several additional properties and applications of $u_0(t)$ which are of considerable importance in the design of feedback control systems.

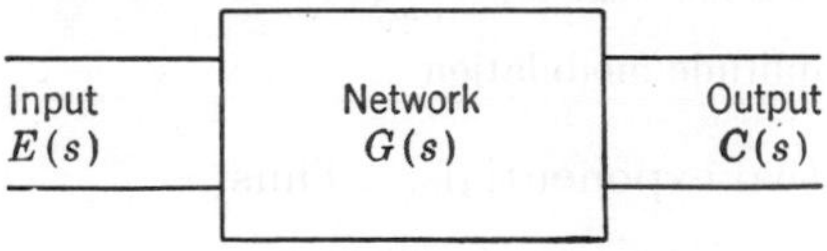

FIG. 1.36. Two-terminal-pair network.

(1) The fact that the transform of $u_0(t)$ is unity means that the inverse transform of the transfer function of a physical system is the impulse response. With the notation of Fig. 1.36,

$$C(s) = G(s)E(s) \qquad (1.199)$$

If $e(t)$ is a unit impulse, $E(s) = 1$, and

$$C(s) = G(s) \qquad (1.200)$$

In the study of a physical system, an impulse (a signal of infinite amplitude and zero duration) cannot be generated, but a pulse with a duration much less than the significant time constants of the system provides a suitable approximation. The waveform of the pulse is immaterial; the area determines the amplitude of the equivalent impulse. Thus, the impulse response, and hence the transfer function, of certain mechanical systems can be determined experimentally by striking the system with a short-duration pulse of force. For example, the MIT Instrumentation Laboratory has determined the flight-control characteristics of aircraft by firing a bullet from the plane and utilizing the reactive force as the system excitation.

(2) If impulses are introduced, the difficulties occasionally experienced with initial conditions are avoided. For example, the unit impulse can be considered as the derivative of a step function. This viewpoint modifies the usual differentiation theorem of Laplace-transform theory, stating that if $g(t)$ and $G(s)$ comprise a transform pair,

$$\mathcal{L}[g'(t)] = sG(s) - g(0+) \qquad (1.201)$$

The term $-g(0+)$ is omitted if impulse functions are considered. Thus, if $g(t)$ is a unit step function, $G(s)$ is $1/s$ and $sG(s)$ is unity; hence, $g'(t)$ is the unit impulse at $t = 0$. Likewise, any jump discontinuity in $g(t)$ results in an impulse in $g'(t)$.

(3) The unit impulse function is identical with the Dirac delta function or the Green's function for a point source or sink. The function is zero everywhere except at $t = 0$, and

$$\int_{-\infty}^{\infty} u_0(t)\, dt = 1 \qquad (1.202)$$

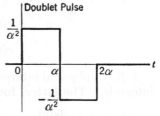

FIG. 1.37. Pulse for definition of unit doublet impulse.

Higher-order impulses can be defined in a similar manner.† For example, $u_1(t)$, the unit doublet impulse, is defined from Fig. 1.37 when the limit is considered as α tends to zero. The transform pair resulting is

$$u_1(t) \longleftrightarrow s \qquad (1.203)$$

$u_1(t)$ is the derivative of $u_0(t)$. Similarly, if $u_j(t)$ denotes the impulse of order $j + 1$,

$$u_j(t) \longleftrightarrow s^j \qquad (1.204)‡$$

1.6. Transform Multiplication. The Laplace transform of the output of a linear system is the product of the system transfer function and the transform of the input time function. The system of Fig. 1.38, for example, is described by the equation

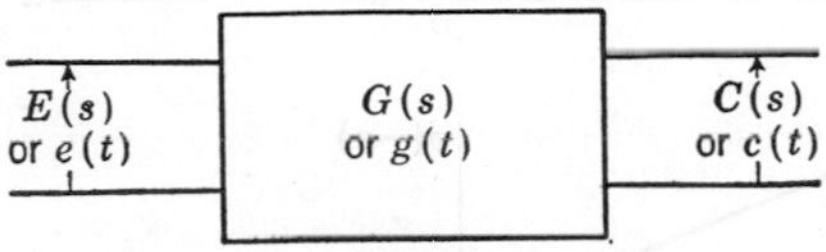

$$C(s) = G(s)E(s) \qquad (1.205)$$

$E(s)$ or $e(t)$ | $G(s)$ or $g(t)$ | $C(s)$ or $c(t)$

FIG. 1.38. Transfer system.

In the analysis problem, with $e(t)$ and $G(s)$ known, the output $c(t)$ is customarily determined by evaluation of $E(s)$, formation of the product $G(s)E(s)$, and inverse transformation of $C(s)$.

In a number of important problems, this use of the frequency domain for the evaluation of system response breaks down completely. In many cases, failure occurs because $e(t)$, the driving function, does not possess a rational algebraic Laplace transform; $e(t)$ may be known only graphically or experimentally or the transform of $e(t)$ may be such a complex expression that evaluation of $c(t)$ from $C(s)$ becomes impossible. In such situations, it is desirable to be able to perform the transform multiplication indicated by (1.205) by working with the two time functions $g(t)$ and $e(t)$, the inverse transforms of $G(s)$ and $E(s)$, respectively. The multiplication in the frequency domain is equivalent to convolution in the time domain; in other words, in terms of the time functions, Eq. (1.205) takes either of two equivalent forms:

† B. Friedman, Techniques of Applied Mathematics—Theory of Distributions, *NYU Research Rept. EM-47*, pp. 100–102, October, 1952.

‡ The notation used throughout this book is described by Eq. (1.204). Thus, the unit step function, with the transform $1/s$, is denoted $u_{-1}(t)$. The subscript associated with u equals the power of s involved in the transform.

$$c(t) = \int_{-\infty}^{\infty} g(x)e(t - x)\,dx \tag{1.206}$$

$$c(t) = \int_{-\infty}^{\infty} e(x)g(t - x)\,dx \tag{1.207}$$

Since in the usual Laplace-transform theory, $g(t)$ and $e(t)$ are both assumed zero for $t < 0$, Eqs. (1.206) and (1.207) can be written

$$c(t) = \int_{0}^{t} g(x)e(t - x)\,dx \tag{1.208}$$

$$c(t) = \int_{0}^{t} e(x)g(t - x)\,dx \tag{1.209}$$

A direct physical interpretation can be placed on these two convolution integrals. The latter, for example, states that $c(t)$, the output at any

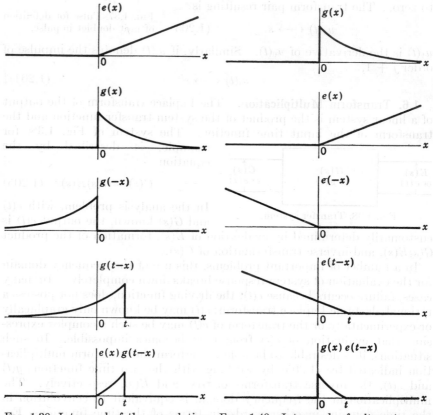

FIG. 1.39. Integrand of the convolution integral.   FIG. 1.40. Integrand of alternate convolution integral.

time t, can be determined by the graphical procedure indicated by the specific example of Fig. 1.39. The input, $e(x)$, and the impulse response, $g(x)$, are plotted as functions of x. The impulse response is now reflected about the $x = 0$ axis to form $g(-x)$. This reflected wave is advanced in time by t sec and then multiplied by $e(x)$. The area under the product represents the value of $c(t)$. Thus, $g(x)$, the system impulse response, can be considered as a weighting function; the output at any instant depends on the input at the same time and at all earlier times; the importance of the various parts of the past input is determined by this weighting function.

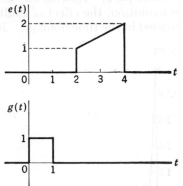

The interpretation of $g(t)$ as a weighting function is also evident from Eq. (1.208). In this case, the input signal is reflected and translated (Fig. 1.40). The output at any time t depends on the input α sec earlier multiplied by the value of the impulse response $g(\alpha)$, where α is allowed to vary from zero to t. The significance of the weighting function is considered further with the aid of three examples.

Example 1. In the first example, the output of a network is desired when the input and the unit-impulse response are as shown in Fig. 1.41. Since the trans-

Fig. 1.41. Time functions in Example 1.

form of the output is the product of the transfer function and the transform of the input,

$$c(t) = g(t) * e(t) \tag{1.210}$$

Here the symbol $*$ is used to indicate convolution.

Direct application of Eq. (1.209) yields the desired output waveform. The system impulse response is reflected about the $x = 0$ axis and advanced t sec. Finally, the product $e(x)g(t - x)$ is integrated from 0 to t. Clearly, in this specific example, the output is zero until $t = 2$, since the product is everywhere zero until the two pulses overlap. As t increases from 2 to 3, both pulses are present during an increasingly longer interval. During this time, the output, increasing quadratically with t, starts at zero and increases monotonically to a value (when $t = 3$) of $\frac{5}{4}$. The complete location of the parabolic segment can be established from any single additional point or characteristic: *e.g.*, from the fact that the derivative of the output is unity at $t = 2$.

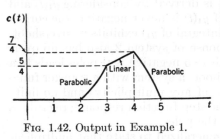

Fig. 1.42. Output in Example 1.

In the interval $3 \leq t \leq 4$, the $g(t - x)$ pulse lies entirely within the $e(x)$ pulse, and the output increases linearly with time. The curve of the output is determined from the two end points, evaluated by inspection:

$$\begin{aligned} t &= 3 & c(t) &= \tfrac{5}{4} \\ t &= 4 & c(t) &= \tfrac{7}{4} \end{aligned} \tag{1.211}$$

During the interval $4 \leq t \leq 5$, the output decreases to zero along a parabolic curve, with a derivative of -2 at $t = 5$. Thus, the complete output, shown in Fig. 1.42, can be determined with essentially no calculations. Alternatively, of course, the values of the functions could be substituted in Eq. (1.209) and the integral evaluated.

Example 2. Effect of an Added Pole or Zero. In the second example of convolution, the effect of multiplying a transform by $a/(s + a)$ is investigated in the time domain. In other words, what is the relation between $g_2(t)$ and $g_1(t)$ if

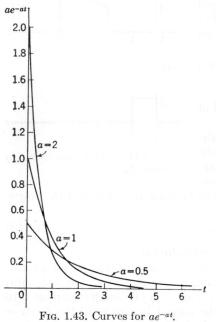

$$G_2(s) = \frac{a}{s + a} G_1(s) \quad (1.212)$$

If $g_1(t)$ is known, what characteristics of $g_2(t)$ can be readily deduced by describing $g_2(t)$ as the convolution of $g_1(t)$ and ae^{-at}, the inverse transform of $a/(s + a)$? The function ae^{-at} is sketched in Fig. 1.43 for a variety of values of a. Consideration of the form of ae^{-at} leads directly to the following conclusions:

(1) If $g_1(t)$ is never negative, $g_2(t)$ likewise never goes negative if a is a positive real number. This statement can be substantiated by considering reflection and translation of the function ae^{-at}. The product of $g_1(x)$ and $ae^{-a(t-x)}$ is positive or zero for all x; accordingly, $g_2(t)$ can never be negative. An

FIG. 1.43. Curves for ae^{-at}.

important corollary of this argument is derived by considering $g_1(t)$ and $g_2(t)$ as system impulse responses. If $g_1(t)$ is never negative, the corresponding step-function response (the integral of g_1) exhibits no overshoot. Consequently, the step-function response of system 2 also has no overshoot. Since a transfer function with two negative real poles leads to a step-function response without overshoot, a system with a transfer function having only negative real poles (of any multiplicity) and no finite zeros can never exhibit overshoot in the step-function response, regardless of the number or specific location of the poles.

(2) The above comments can be generalized to state that multiplication of $G_1(s)$ by $a/(s + a)$ is always a stabilizing change in the sense that the overshoot of the step-function response always decreases. This statement is substantiated by consideration of Fig. 1.43. Regardless of the value of a, the area under the curve ae^{-at} is unity, with the result that the final values of the step-function responses of systems 1 and 2 are equal. With a very large value of a, the exponential ae^{-at} approaches a spike or short pulse of unit area, and $f_2(t)$ is identical with $f_1(t)$, where $f(t)$ is used to denote the step-function response. As a tends to zero, ae^{-at}

approaches a step function of amplitude a, and $f_2(t)$ becomes a times the integral of $f_1(t)$.

Thus, the interpretation of transform multiplication as convolution of the time functions is useful in the approximate evaluation of changes in the transform function. The ideas of the simple example considered above can be extended in a number of directions. For example, multiplication of $G_1(s)$ by the function $Ts + 1$ corresponds to convolution of $g_1(t)$ with $Tu_1(t) + u_0(t)$, where $u_1(t)$ and $u_0(t)$ are unit doublet and simple impulses, respectively. The resulting function is $Tg_1'(t) + g_1(t)$, with $g_1'(t)$ denoting the derivative of $g_1(t)$. Thus, knowledge of $g_1(t)$ permits rapid evaluation of the inverse transform of $(Ts + 1)G_1(s)$.

The same line of reasoning indicates the changes in the time function if $G_1(s)$ is multiplied by $(s + a)/(s + b)$, or $1 + (a - b)/(s + b)$. If $g_1(t)$ is the inverse transform of $G_1(s)$, $g_2(t)$, the inverse transform of $[(s + a)/(s + b)]G_1(s)$, can be written

$$g_2(t) = g_1(t) + (a - b)e^{-bt} * g_1(t) \tag{1.213}$$

$g_2(t)$ is formed by adding to $g_1(t)$ a time function formed by the convolution of $(a - b)e^{-bt}$ with $g_1(t)$. Since the result of this convolution (before combination with g_1) is a waveform exhibiting greater relative stability than the original $g_1(t)$, the general effect of adding the convolution product is ordinarily stabilizing if $a > b$. In contrast, if $b > a$, Eq. (1.213) indicates a subtraction, and the effect is usually destabilizing, since the amount subtracted increases with time and is less at the time of peak overshoot than in the steady state.

Example 3. The Superposition Integral. In the third example of

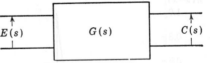

FIG. 1.44. Transducer.

convolution, the system of Fig. 1.44 is considered, with

$$C(s) = G(s)E(s) \tag{1.214}$$

$$c(t) = \int_0^t e(x)g(t - x)\,dx \tag{1.215}$$

Equation (1.215), a form of the superposition integral, can be applied even if the transform of $e(t)$ cannot be conveniently evaluated. The procedure can be illustrated with the time function of Fig. 1.45(a), a function characteristic of a number of fire-control problems. $e(t)$ can be written

$$e(t) = \begin{cases} 0 & t < 0 \\ \arctan(10 - t) & t > 0 \end{cases} \tag{1.216}$$

For simplicity, the system considered is a single-section RC low-pass filter as shown in Fig. 1.45(b):

$$G(s) = \frac{1}{s + 1} \tag{1.217}$$

The output $c(t)$ is to be evaluated for the first 10 sec after $t = 0$: *i.e.*, the output is desired from the time the input is applied until the input function again reaches zero.

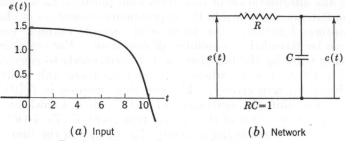

(a) Input   (b) Network

FIG. 1.45. Input and network for Example 3.

Use of the Laplace transform in the evaluation of $c(t)$ requires the

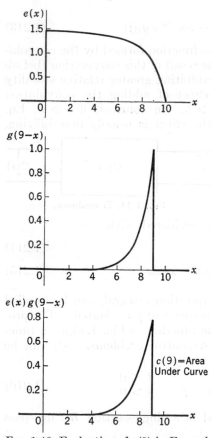

FIG. 1.46. Evaluation of $c(9)$ in Example 3.

inverse transformation of $E(s)G(s)$. In this example, $E(s)$ is a complicated combination of exponentials, sine integrals, and cosine integrals of s. A more reasonable problem results if $e(t)$ is approximated over the interval from 0 to 10 sec by a combination of polynomials or exponential functions. The primary disadvantage of such a procedure arises because of the difficulty of evaluating the effects of the approximation error on the output waveform. The convolution (or superposition) integral provides an approach which is markedly simpler.

If the appropriate values of $e(t)$ and $g(t)$ are substituted, Eq. (1.215) becomes

$$c(t) = \int_0^t \arctan(10 - x)e^{-(t-x)} \, dx$$
$$(1.218)$$

For any given value of t, the integral can be evaluated graphically, either with a planimeter or with any of the customary methods for the approximate numerical evaluation of integrals. Figure 1.46 shows the steps required for $t = 9$. The function $e^{-(9-x)}$ corresponds to the weighting: *i.e.*, the value of $e(t)$ at $t = 9$ is most important in determining the output at $t = 9$; $e(8)$ is less important by the factor e^{-1}, $e(7)$ by e^{-2}, etc. Clearly, the output at any time depends primarily on the input during the previous 3 sec, since the weighting function decreases by 95 per cent over the course of 3 sec.

This graphical interpretation of convolution is also termed superposition because it is equivalent to considering the input function as a sequence of very short pulses. In the example of Fig. 1.46, the same value of $c(9)$ is obtained if the input function is replaced by a series of pulses, each pulse of sufficiently short duration that the impulse response (or weighting function) does not change significantly during the pulse. Each pulse can then be replaced by an impulse, where the impulse amplitude is equal to the pulse area and the impulse occurs at the center of the pulse. The output is then the sum of the outputs resulting from the various impulses: that is, $c(9)$ is one point on the sum of a number of impulse responses.

The superposition integral as given in elementary electrical-engineering texts ordinarily is phrased in terms of the step-function response rather than the impulse response. The input and output transforms are related by the equation

$$C(s) = G(s)E(s) \tag{1.219}$$

If the right side of Eq. (1.219) is multiplied and divided by s,

$$C(s) = \frac{G(s)}{s} sE(s) \tag{1.220}$$

The corresponding convolution integral is

$$c(t) = \int_0^t e'(x)g^{(-1)}(t - x)\,dx \tag{1.221}$$

Here $e'(x)$ is the derivative of the input and $g^{(-1)}(t - x)$ is the integral of the impulse response (*i.e.*, the step-function response) after reflection and translation. Equation (1.221) corresponds to approximation of $e(t)$ by a series of step functions, where the amplitude of each step depends on the change (or first derivative) of the input, and evaluation of the output is the summation of the responses to the component step functions.

Impulses Used to Simplify Analysis. The primary disadvantage of analysis based on the convolution integral derives from the fact that the determination of the output at each value of time requires a separate integration. Sufficient information to permit plotting of the total output of a network can be obtained only by a number of integrations of the product of two time functions. If the transform equation is used, however, the entire output is determined in one operation: evaluation of the inverse transform of the output, or

$$C(s) = G(s)E(s)$$

where $G(s)$ is the transfer function and $E(s)$ is the input transform.

If either the impulse response $g(t)$ or the input $e(t)$ can be expressed as the sum of impulses, evaluation of the convolution integral is simplified. For example, if $g(t)$ and $e(t)$ are the functions shown in Fig. 1.47, convolution requires the reflection and translation of the train of four impulses.

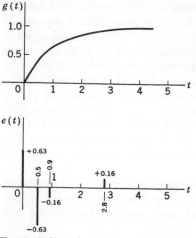

As an impulse is moved across the time function $g(t)$, the integral of the product of the impulse and $g(t)$ is simply the value of $g(t)$ at the time of the impulse multiplied by the impulse area. In other words, if $u_0(t - t_1)$ is a unit impulse occurring at $t = t_1$,

$$\int_{-\infty}^{\infty} u_0(t - t_1)g(t)\, dt = g(t_1) \quad (1.222)$$

This equation follows directly from the fact that, since the integrand is zero for all t except $t = t_1$, $g(t)$ can be replaced by the constant value $g(t_1)$. When $g(t_1)$ is taken outside the integral, the equation results.

Consequently, the convolution of a time function $g(t)$ with an impulse occurring at $t = t_1$ and of area α is the time function $\alpha g(t - t_1)u_{-1}(t - t_1)$: that is, the original time function multiplied by α and delayed by t_1.

Fig. 1.47. Impulse response and input.

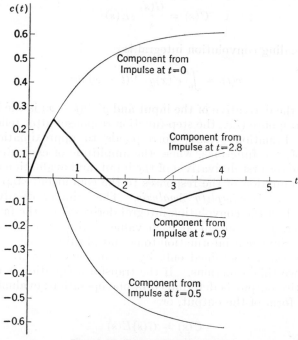

Fig. 1.48. Output for Fig. 1.47.

The convolution of the two functions of Fig. 1.47 results in the output shown in Fig. 1.48, an output made up of the four components representing the four convolutions of an impulse with $g(t)$.

If both time functions are sequences of impulses, the convolution product is also an impulse train. In the special case for which both sequences have the same sampling period (time between successive samples), the output can be determined by simple multiplication. Figure 1.49 illustrates the problem, with $e(t)$ and $g(t)$ impulse trains with a period of 0.2 sec. The convolution of $e(t)$ and $g(t)$ can be effected by reflecting and translating $g(t)$. The output at $t = 0$ is simply an impulse of area equal to the product of the areas of the initial impulses of $e(t)$ and $g(t)$. In terms of the signals of Fig. 1.49,

$$c(0) = 6u_0(t) \qquad (1.223)$$

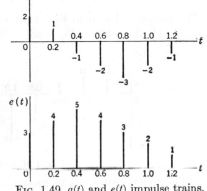

The area of the output impulse at $t = 0.2$ is the product of the first pulse of $e(t)$ times the second pulse of $g(t)$ added to the cross product in the opposite direction. Thus,

$$c(0.2) = (3 + 8)u_0(t - 0.2) \qquad (1.224)$$

Similarly, the output pulse at $t = 0.2n$ depends on the $n + 1$ cross products between the $e(t)$ and the $g(t)$ impulses.

FIG. 1.49. $g(t)$ and $e(t)$ impulse trains.

In terms of the Laplace transforms, $G(s)$ and $E(s)$ can be written

$$G(s) = 2 + e^{-0.2s} - e^{-0.4s} - 2e^{-0.6s} - 3e^{-0.8s} - 2e^{-s} - e^{-1.2s}$$
$$E(s) = 3 + 4e^{-0.2s} + 5e^{-0.4s} + 4e^{-0.6s} + 3e^{-0.8s} + 2e^{-s} + e^{-1.2s} \qquad (1.225)$$

Multiplication term by term gives the series for the output,

$$C(s) = 6 + 11e^{-0.2s} + 11e^{-0.4s} + 3e^{-0.6s} - 12e^{-0.8s} - 25e^{-s} - 33e^{-1.2s}$$
$$- 33e^{-1.4s} - 27e^{-1.6s} - 18e^{-1.8s} - 10e^{-2s} - 4e^{-2.2s} - e^{-2.4s} \qquad (1.226)$$

Thus, the output train can be determined simply by considering the successive amplitudes of the impulses of both $g(t)$ and $e(t)$ as the coefficients of polynomials and by then multiplying the polynomials for $g(t)$ and $e(t)$.† For the signals of Fig. 1.49, the total output is found from the multiplication

---

† The polynomial concept rests on a firmer theoretical basis than indicated here. As described in some detail in Chap. 9, the z transform of a train of impulses, $g(t)$, is defined as $G(s)$ with e^{Ts} replaced by z. Hence, the function of Eq. (1.225) becomes

$$G(z) = 2 + \frac{1}{z} - \frac{1}{z^2} - \frac{2}{z^3} - \frac{3}{z^4} - \frac{2}{z^5} - \frac{1}{z^6}$$

$G(z)$ is a polynomial in the variable $1/z$ and with coefficients equal to the impulse areas. Chapter 9 includes a more detailed description of the characteristics and permissible manipulations of z transforms.

```
  2   1  -1  -2   -3   -2   -1
  3   4   5   4    3    2    1
 ─────────────────────────────
  6   3  -3  -6   -9   -6   -3
      8   4  -4   -8  -12   -8   -4
         10   5   -5  -10  -15  -10   -5
              8    4   -4   -8  -12   -8   -4
                   6    3   -3   -6   -9   -6   -3
                        4    2   -2   -4   -6   -4   -2
                             2    1   -1   -2   -3   -2   -1
 ────────────────────────────────────────────────────────
  6  11  11   3  -12  -25  -33  -33  -27  -18  -10   -4   -1
```

The output, shown in Fig. 1.50, consists of the train of impulses of areas 6, 11, 11, 3, −12, −25, −33, −33, −27, −18, −10, −4, and −1.

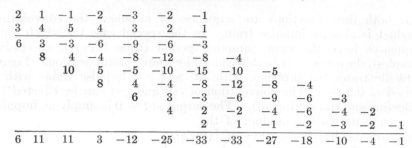

Fig. 1.50. Output for Fig. 1.49.

The usual problems of analysis involve continuous functions of time, and the determination of the output of a network directly from the input time function and the impulse response is not possible. In a wide variety of cases, an approximate plot of the convolution product

$$c(t) = g(t) * e(t)$$

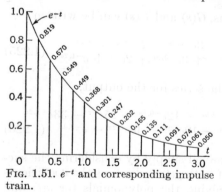

Fig. 1.51. e^{-t} and corresponding impulse train.

can be obtained by approximating either $g(t)$ or $e(t)$ (or both) by a train of regularly spaced impulses.† If both $g(t)$ and $e(t)$ are replaced by impulses, multiplication as described above gives the samples of the output at the sampling instants.

The conventional method of approximation is to replace the continuous

† The approximation of continuous functions by trains of impulses in order to simplify the evaluation of the convolution was developed by F. W. Bubb in several Air Force Technical Reports. Of particular interest in connection with the discussion of this section are the two reports: A New Linear Operational Calculus, *Air Force Tech. Rept.* 6581, May, 1951; and Synthesis of Physical Systems, *Air Force Tech. Rept.* 6724, January, 1952, both from Wright-Patterson Air Force Base, Dayton, Ohio. The commonest application of this technique is in the programming of digital computers: the entire operation of the computer is based on this sampling technique. The discussion of this section is directed toward indicating the manner in which manual calculations of transient response can be simplified if computer methods are incorporated.

time function by a train of impulses, with each impulse having an area equal to the function at the sampling time. Figure 1.51 shows the exponential function e^{-t} and the corresponding impulse train if the sampling period is 0.2 sec.

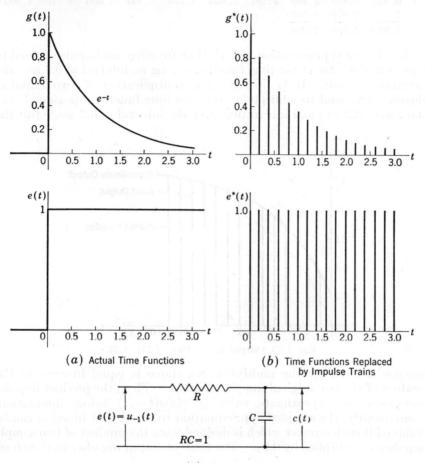

(a) Actual Time Functions

(b) Time Functions Replaced by Impulse Trains

(c) Network

FIG. 1.52. Example for convolution of two time functions.

The convolution of the two time functions shown in Fig. 1.52(a) can be used to illustrate this approximate procedure. The two functions are

$$e(t) = u_{-1}(t) \qquad g(t) = e^{-t} \tag{1.227}$$

The output $c(t)$, the convolution product of $e(t)$ and $g(t)$, is the step-function response of the network of Fig. 1.52(c). The output is determined in the following steps:

(1) Each time function is replaced by a train of impulses [part (b) of Fig. 1.52, where the starred notation is used to indicate the approximation].

(2)   The two pulse trains are convolved by the multiplication

1	0.819	0.670	0.549	0.449	0.368	0.301	0.247	0.202	0.165	0.135
1	1	1	1	1	1	1	1	1	1	1
1	0.819	1.819	2.489	3.487	3.855	4.156	4.403	4.605	4.770	4.905
1	0.670	0.549								
1.819	2.489	3.038								

(3)   In the approximation of each time function, an impulse is used to represent the *value* of the time function during an interval of 0.2 sec (the sampling period). It is desired that multiplication of two impulses should correspond to multiplying the two time functions (assumed constant over 0.2 sec) and integrating over the interval of 0.2 sec. But the

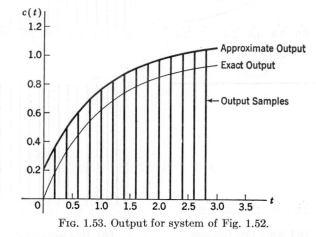

Fig. 1.53. Output for system of Fig. 1.52.

impulse derived by the multiplication above is equal in area to the product of the two original sample impulses. Thus, the product impulse represents the approximate value of $g(x)e(t - x)$ before integration. Consequently, the sampled approximation to the output function can be obtained if each number which is derived from the product of two sample impulses is multiplied by 0.2†. The train of output impulses is, therefore,

0.2   0.363   0.498   0.608   0.697   0.771   0.831   0.881   0.921   0.954
     0.981   1.003   1.021   1.036   1.048   1.058

Figure 1.53, showing the accurate and approximate outputs, indicates that the approximation in this case is not especially good. This example was selected only to illustrate the procedure and with no particular attempt to show the method to good advantage. Another example, shown below in Fig. 1.55, results in an approximation of more satisfactory accuracy. The principal error in this example occurs because the first

† Alternatively, the impulse area in the two approximating functions [Fig. 1.52(b)] might be multiplied by 0.2, in order that the area of each impulse might represent the appropriate area of the continuous function. This would be a more logical procedure than that discussed in the text, but represents slightly more work.

product (1)(1) is given a weight equal to that of later samples, even though it is more logical to consider the samples as representing the function over an interval of 0.1 sec on either side of the sample. This interpretation would require reduction of the first sample product by $\frac{1}{2}$, hence would decrease all output samples by 0.1. The approximate and accurate outputs are then very nearly identical.

The error in the above analysis results from the approximation of a time function by a train of impulses. A slight modification can be made in the procedure to improve the approximation without discarding the simplicity of the method. The problem considered is illustrated by Fig. 1.54. Here the network is characterized by the transfer function

$$G(s) = \frac{s}{s+1} \qquad (1.228)$$

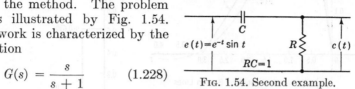

FIG. 1.54. Second example.

The output is desired when the input is a damped sinusoid,

$$e(t) = e^{-t} \sin t \qquad (1.229)$$

The output is determined in the following steps:

(1) The input is approximated by a set of *straight lines*, as indicated in Fig. 1.55(a). For reasons discussed below, the break times† of the broken-line approximation are selected to be harmonically related, with as large a fundamental interval as possible. In other words, it must be possible to describe the various break times as nT_0, where n need have only integer values. Furthermore, T_0 should be as large as possible, consistent with the desired accuracy of approximation. For example, in Fig. 1.55(a), the breaks occur at 0, 0.5, 1, and 3 sec. These values have the common fundamental period of 0.5. In general, it is always possible to satisfy this relation among the break times by changing slightly the straight-line approximation.

(2) The straight-line approximation $e^*(t)$ is differentiated twice to obtain impulses at $t = 0, 0.5, 1,$ and 3, as shown in Fig. 1.55(b).

(3) These impulses comprise an approximation to $e''(t)$. The set of impulses can be considered as the nonzero components of a train of impulses occurring every 0.5 sec, 0.25 sec, or any other submultiple of the fundamental interval.

(4) One of these submultiples is now selected as the sampling interval. The particular value chosen depends on the accuracy desired and the nature of $g(t)$. If $g(t)$ is a rapidly varying function, a short interval is required. In this example, the sampling period is chosen as 0.25 sec.

(5) The output $c(t)$ is the convolution of $e''(t)$ with the second integral of $g(t)$. In other words, in terms of the Laplace transforms,

$$C(s) = s^2 E(s) \frac{G(s)}{s^2} \qquad (1.230)$$

† The term "break times" denotes the values of t at which the straight-line approximation changes slope.

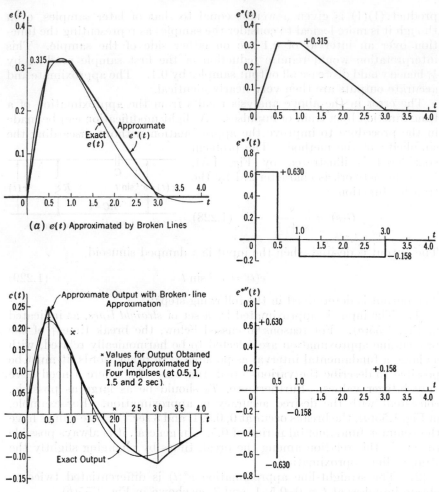

(a) $e(t)$ Approximated by Broken Lines

(c) Actual and Approximate Outputs

(b) Two Differentiations of $e^*(t)$

FIG. 1.55. Broken-line approximation for convolution.

The inverse transform of $G(s)/s^2$ is determined; in particular, the value every 0.25 sec is required. In this example, the time function is $1 - e^{-t}$, and the samples are

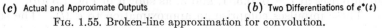

0   0.221   0.393   0.528   0.632   0.714   0.777   0.826   0.865
                                    0.895   0.918   0.936   0.950   0.961   0.970   0.982

(6)   The train of impulses, $e^{*\prime\prime}(t)$, is convolved with $1 - e^{-t}$ by multiplication of the sequence of impulse amplitudes and the sequence of samples above. The multiplication is shown in Calculation 1.1.

(7)   A smooth curve is drawn through the points given by the above sequence of amplitudes at time intervals separated by 0.25 sec. The approximate output curve is shown in Fig. 1.55(c).

CALCULATION 1.1

0	0.221	0.393	0.528	0.632	0.714	0.777	0.826	0.865	0.895	0.918	0.936	0.950	0.961
0.630	0	−0.630	0	−0.158	0	0	0	0	0	0	0	0.158	0
	0.139	0.248	0.333	0.398	0.450	0.490	0.520	0.545	0.564	0.578	0.590	0.599	0.605
		0	−0.139	−0.248	−0.333	−0.398	−0.450	−0.490	−0.520	−0.545	−0.564	−0.578	−0.590
		0.248	0.194	0	−0.035	−0.062	−0.083	−0.100	−0.113	−0.123	−0.131	−0.137	−0.141
0	0			0.150	0.082	0.030	−0.013	−0.045	−0.069	−0.090	−0.105	0	0.035
												−0.116	−0.091

Several comments concerning this procedure are appropriate at this point:

(1) As indicated by Fig. 1.55(c), the accuracy of the approximation is improved significantly if the time function is approximated by straight lines rather than impulses. The disadvantage of this approach arises from the necessity of integrating the time function which is not approximated. If both the input and the impulse response are given graphically, a double integration must be performed. Although numerical analysis provides a variety of formulas for evaluating the integral numerically,† the method described above for evaluating the output is most accurate and simplest when the transform of one of the time functions is known and the double integration is simply equivalent to division of the transform by s^2. Under these conditions, the

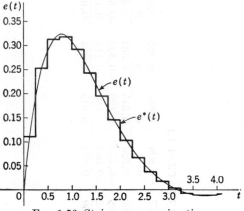

Fig. 1.56. Staircase approximation.

output determined is exactly the time function which would be obtained if the broken-line function were used as the network input.

(2) A staircase type of approximation might be used rather than the broken-line method described above. Figure 1.56 shows a staircase approximation of the damped sinusoid previously considered. The first derivative of $e^*(t)$ is then the set of impulses, and $g(t)$ need be integrated only a single time. The accuracy is in general better with the broken-line approximation if the same number of break points is used.

(3) The breaks of the broken-line approximation are chosen harmonically related in the example. If this is not done, the output has to be considered as the sum of the convolution products of the $1 - e^{-t}$ function with each of the impulses of $e^{*''}(t)$. The total output can be found by graphical addition, considerably more complicated than the simple multiplication which suffices in the example.

(4) Since the final pulse train is assumed to have a sampling period of 0.25 sec, the work involved in the above example is not greatly increased if the initial broken-line approximation is done by line segments, each 0.25 sec in duration. The only increase in difficulty arises because the second row of the product in step (6) above does not contain the numerous zeros. As indicated by Fig. 1.57, considerably better accuracy can be realized if this additional complexity is admitted.

† For example, cf. F. E. Nixon, "Principles of Automatic Controls," Chap. 12, Prentice-Hall, Inc., New York, 1953; F. W. Bubb, "A New Linear Operational Calculus," *Air Force Tech. Rept.* 6581, WADC, pp. 9–13, May, 1951; and I. J. Schoenberg, Contributions to the Problem of Approximation of Equidistant Data by Analytical Functions, *Quart. Appl. Math.*, April and June, 1946.

(5) Clearly, if the output is desired during only a finite time interval starting at zero, it is necessary to sample the impulse response only during the same interval.

The method described above permits rapid approximate calculation of the convolution product: *e.g.*, the determination of the output of a network from the input time function and the impulse response or transfer function. The method is particularly useful when

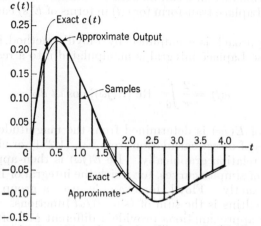

FIG. 1.57. Approximate output when broken lines used with duration 0.25 sec.

the transforms are of high degree or when the input time function is specified graphically or given analytically in a form with no simple transform. Because the method develops the time function progressively toward larger values of time, the calculations can be stopped whenever sufficient information about the output is available.

Closed-loop Transient Response from Open-loop Characteristics. The possibility of evaluating the convolution integral rapidly when the time functions are represented by impulses provides a useful approach to a number of problems which were previously troublesome because of the necessity of working in the frequency domain and then taking inverse Laplace transforms. For

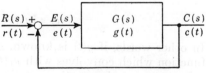
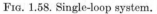

FIG. 1.58. Single-loop system.

example, one of the classical problems of servomechanism analysis is the determination of the closed-loop transient response from the open-loop characteristics. In the notation of Fig. 1.58, the problem as usually stated requires the evaluation of $e(t)$ or $c(t)$ when $r(t)$ is a unit impulse or step function and the forward transfer function $G(s)$ is known.

The problem is phrased analytically as follows: $G(s)$ is known; if $r(t)$ is a unit impulse, $R(s) = 1$, and $E(s)$, the transform of the actuating signal, can be written

$$E(s) = \frac{1}{1 + G(s)} \qquad (1.231)$$

Even if $G(s)$ is known in factored form, determination of the exact inverse transform of $E(s)$ requires factoring of the denominator polynomial of $E(s)$, evaluation of the various residues, and summation of the components of $e(t)$. The tedious labor imposed by this direct approach can be avoided in two ways: (1) A number of authors have plotted extensive charts relating the characteristics of $e(t)$ with the behavior of $G(j\omega)$, and these computational results can be used to estimate the time function; or (2) the inverse Laplace transform for $e(t)$ in terms of $E(s)$ can be evaluated approximately.

The latter approach is exemplified by Floyd's method.† As the first step, the inverse Laplace integral is manipulated into a real integral,

$$e(t) = \frac{2}{\pi} \int_0^{\infty} \text{Re} \, [E(j\omega)] \cos \omega t \, d\omega \qquad (1.232)$$

The real part of $E(j\omega)$ is determined from the magnitude and phase of $G(j\omega)$ by means of direct calculation from Eq. (1.231) or charts prepared to present the relation graphically. Re $E(j\omega)$ is then approximated by a combination of simpler curves, for which the integral of Eq. (1.232) can be evaluated exactly. Floyd, for example, uses a group of trapezoids, and the $e(t)$ resulting is the sum of $(\sin \omega t)/\omega t$ functions.

The impulse approximations provide a different and often much simpler approach to the problem of calculating closed-loop transient response. If the closing of the loop, as represented by Eq. (1.231), is studied in the time domain, the relation between $e(t)$ and $g(t)$ can be established. The dependence of $e(t)$ on $G(s)$ can then be investigated from the time functions. In particular, Eq. (1.231) can be written

$$E(s)[1 + G(s)] = 1 \qquad (1.233)$$

In terms of the time functions,

$$e(t) * [u_0(t) + g(t)] = u_0(t) \qquad (1.234)$$

In other words, if $g(t)$ is known, $e(t)$ can be determined by finding the function which convolves with $u_0(t) + g(t)$ to give simply $u_0(t)$.

In terms of the continuous time functions, the determination of an appropriate $e(t)$ from a given $g(t)$ is difficult. The problem is illustrated in Fig. 1.59(a), drawn for

$$g(t) = 2(1 - e^{-2t}) \qquad G(s) = \frac{4}{s(s + 2)} \qquad (1.235)$$

The convolution corresponds first to reflection of $u_0(x) + g(x)$ about the $x = 0$ axis. This reflected function is now translated to the right by an amount t and then multiplied by $e(x)$; the product is integrated from zero to infinity (or zero to t) to obtain the value of the convolution at time t.

† G. S. Brown and D. P. Campbell, "Principles of Servomechanisms," Chap. 11, John Wiley & Sons, Inc., New York, 1948.

Thus, an $e(t)$ must be found such that the integration yields zero at all times except $t = 0$.

Clearly, if the only impulse in $u_0(t) + g(t)$ is that of $u_0(t)$ [in other words, $G(s) \to 0$ as $s \to \infty$], $e(t)$ must contain a unit impulse at $t = 0$. The remainder of the $e(t)$ function is bounded. As the reflected function is moved to the right, Fig. 1.59(b) demonstrates that the product of $u_0(t - x) + g(t - x)$ and $e(x)$ contains the following components:

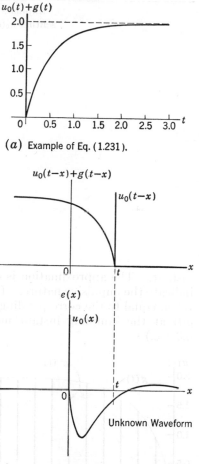

$u_0(t)+g(t)$

(a) Example of Eq. (1.231).

$u_0(t-x)+g(t-x)$

$u_0(t-x)$

$e(x)$

$u_0(x)$

Unknown Waveform

(b) Two Terms in Integrand of Convolution Integral Shown for a Single Value of t

Fig. 1.59. Nature of functions.

(1) The impulse in $e(x)$ at $x = 0$ multiplied by the value of $u_0(t - x) + g(t - x)$ at $x = 0$.

(2) The impulse $u_0(t - x)$, located at $x = t$, multiplied by $e(t)$.

(3) The product of $g(t - x)$ and $e(x) - u_0(x)$ over the time range $0 \le x \le t$.

Integration of these three components yields the following three terms, respectively:

(1) $u_0(t) + g(t)$, since the integral under an impulse is simply the area of the impulse.

(2) $e(t)$.

(3) The integral of $g(t - x)[e(x) - u_0(x)]$ from zero to t.

The sum of these three components must be zero. The last component is the one causing trouble, because the appropriate value of $e(t)$ depends on the value of $e(t)$ and $g(t)$ for smaller values of t. This difficulty can be avoided if the time function $g(t)$ is approximated by a train of regularly spaced impulses, as described with the following example:

(1) For the single-loop system of Fig. 1.58, the forward system is described by the equations

$$G(s) = \frac{4}{s(s + 2)} \tag{1.236}$$

$$g(t) = 2(1 - e^{-2t}) \tag{1.237}$$

The corresponding impulse response $e(t)$ is to be determined.

(2) $g(t)$ is approximated by a train of impulses as shown in Fig. 1.60, where the impulse area is chosen equal to the value of $g(t)$ at the sampling

CALCULATION 1.2

Impulses representing $e(t) \to 1$ -0.902

1   0.902   1.398   1.669   1.818   1.900   1.945   1.970   1.984   1.991 |1

   0.271   0.419   0.500   0.545   0.570   0.584   0.591   0.595   0.597   1   0.902

Impulses repre-
senting $u_0(t) + g(t)$

-0.902
-0.902
-0.902

instant. The approximation is denoted $g^*(t)$, with the asterisk used to indicate the impulsive nature. (Alternatively, the impulse area might be taken equal to the corresponding area under the $g(t)$ wave—*i.e.*, equal to $g(t)$ at the sampling instant multiplied by the sampling period, here 0.3 sec.)

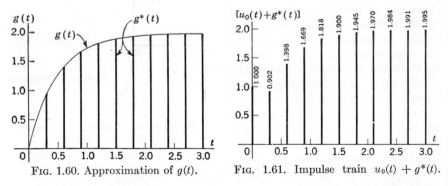

Fig. 1.60. Approximation of $g(t)$.   Fig. 1.61. Impulse train $u_0(t) + g^*(t)$.

(3) The function $u_0(t) + g^*(t)$ is shown in Fig. 1.61. The approximate $e^*(t)$ is the function which when convolved with $u_0(t) + g^*(t)$ gives a unit impulse at $t = 0$. Hence, $e^*(t)$ must be a train of impulses, occurring every 0.3 sec. Consideration of the convolution process indicates that the amplitudes of the impulses of $e^*(t)$ can be determined one by one, as the reflected train is translated to represent the advance of time. If the impulses of Fig. 1.61 actually constitute $u_0(t) + g(t)$, the impulse

CALCULATION 1.2 (*Continued*)

−1.154	−0.988	−0.626	−0.247	+0.021	+0.161	+0.196	+0.161
1.398	1.669	1.818	1.900	1.945	1.970	1.984	1.991
−1.398	−1.669	−1.818	−1.900	−1.945	−1.970	−1.984	−1.991
−0.244	−0.368	−0.451	−0.492	−0.514	−0.526	−0.532	−0.536
−1.154	−1.301	−1.367	−1.408	−1.431	−1.444	−1.452	−1.455
−1.154	−0.313	−0.473	−0.577	−0.629	−0.656	−0.674	−0.680
	−0.988	−0.894	−0.831	−0.802	−0.788	−0.778	−0.775
	−0.988	−0.268	−0.414	−0.494	−0.538	−0.562	−0.576
		−0.626	−0.417	−0.308	−0.250	−0.216	−0.199
		−0.626	−0.170	−0.262	−0.313	−0.341	−0.357
			−0.247	−0.046	+0.063	+0.125	+0.158
			−0.247	−0.067	−0.104	−0.124	−0.135
				+0.021	+0.167	+0.249	+0.293
				+0.021	+0.006	+0.009	+0.011
					+0.161	+0.240	+0.282
					+0.161	+0.044	+0.068
						+0.196	+0.214
						+0.196	+0.053
							+0.161
							+0.161

train for $e(t)$ can be found from the polynomial representation of the transform $1 + G(s)$. Under these conditions, if the area of the impulse in $e(t)$ at $t = 0.3n$ is denoted E_n, the amplitudes E_n can be found from the relation

$$[E_0 \quad E_1 \quad E_2 \quad E_3 \quad E_4 \quad . \ . \ .][1 \quad 0.902 \quad 1.398 \quad 1.669 \quad . \ . \ .]$$
$$= [1 \quad 0 \quad 0 \quad 0 \quad . \ . \ .] \quad (1.238)$$

Here, the first term in brackets represents the impulses of $e(t)$; the second term, the impulses of $u_0(t) + g(t)$; and the right side, the convolution product. Thus, the first term can be found by dividing the second term into the right side by long division, considering the successive amplitudes as the coefficients of polynomials.

(4) The analysis of the last paragraph is based on the assumption that the impulse train of Fig. 1.61 represents $u_0(t) + g(t)$. In actuality, however, only the first impulse (at $t = 0$) is a true impulse; all others represent samples of the continuous $g(t)$. In the sequence $\{E_n\}$, likewise, E_0 represents a true impulse, but all other E_n are samples of a continuous function. Whenever a sample from the first term of Eq. (1.238) is multiplied by a sample in the second term, the product must in addition be multiplied by the sampling period 0.3.

(5) The sequence $\{E_n\}$ is now obtained by division, as indicated in Calculation 1.2.

The row of numbers under the divisor (*i.e.*, the row beginning 0.271 0.419 . . .) in Calculation 1.2 is written to facilitate inclusion of the factor of 0.3 discussed above. Each term of this row represents the number just above multiplied by 0.3. Whenever a *sample* amplitude in $e(t)$ (that is, -0.902, -1.154, etc., but not the first term, 1) is multiplied by a sample in $[u_0(t) + g^*(t)]$, this second row is used.

(6) The resulting $e^*(t)$ is shown in Fig. 1.62. As indicated in the figure, the continuous $e(t)$ is obtained by passing a smooth curve through the sample values.

Although the above description of the procedure is lengthy, if the discussion is omitted, the essential steps are only three in number:

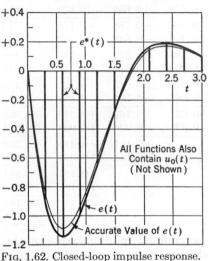

FIG. 1.62. Closed-loop impulse response. [Actuating signal with $r(t) = u_0(t)$.]

(1) The time function $g(t)$ must be evaluated; in particular, the values of $g(t)$ at the sampling instants are needed.

(2) The polynomial representing these samples plus $u_0(t)$ is divided into unity.

(3) A smooth curve is drawn through the sample amplitudes determined for $e(t)$.

If $g(t)$ can be obtained without undue labor, the method is considerably simpler than conventional techniques for finding $e(t)$. The division, even with the accuracy and the number of samples used in the example above, is not tedious, particularly if a desk calculator is used. The number of samples required depends on the nature of $g(t)$; if $g(t)$ contains a large-amplitude, lightly-damped sinusoid, the number of samples may be excessive, but in this case the conventional methods for determining $e(t)$ also present computational difficulties.

1.7. Specifications. The mathematical techniques described in the preceding sections of this chapter are the basic tools for the design of feedback systems. Although the wide variety of design problems makes it difficult to formulate generalities, in most cases design can be broken into three parts:

(1) Insofar as possible, the specifications are interpreted analytically (*i.e.*, in terms of constraints on the mathematical functions describing system characteristics).

(2) A number of systems are determined, each meeting the analytical specifications derived in (1).

(3) One system is selected on the basis of specifications which are not readily phrased analytically: *e.g.*, such practical constraints on design as the spread of element values, the number of elements, the difficulties associated with physical construction of the system, etc. This part of the design ordinarily includes experimental verification and adjustment of the design, with the test performed on a computer, on a model, or on the actual equipment.

The extent to which the design leaves the realm of analysis and approaches pure synthesis is measured by the relative magnitudes of steps (1) and (3) above. Ideally, synthesis implies a straightforward, logical development from specifications to final system; design by analysis, in contrast, denotes an empirical adjustment of the system to obtain satisfactory performance characteristics. Historically, the feedback art has seen a steady progression toward more nearly complete synthesis procedures, although even today it is indeed an unusual problem which can be treated as synthesis alone.

The extent to which the designer is able to apply synthesis techniques is dependent directly on his ability to utilize the analytical tools available. These mathematical methods can be used most advantageously only if the designer is able to interpret the specifications in mathematical terms. It is the purpose of this section to outline briefly the nature of such interpretations and the physical significance of the mathematical terms available.

The discussion is handicapped at the outset by the impossibility of settling on a typical set of specifications. In the practical design of feedback systems, the specifications range from such qualitative statements as "the system should be as nearly perfect as possible" to definite, quantitative descriptions of system performance. By the very nature

of the problem, however, it is clear that the specifications in general describe the system in both the time and frequency domains, whether the system be a feedback amplifier to transmit pulses or a feedback control system. In the following discussion, attention is focused on feedback control systems, but the comments are also applicable to more general feedback systems. Furthermore, only performance specifications are included; no consideration is given to

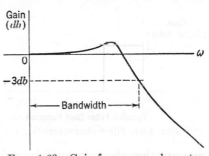

Fig. 1.63. Gain-frequency characteristic. (Linear frequency scale.)

specifications concerning the nature of certain components which must be used for economic or availability reasons (such as the motor in a servomechanism). Constraints of this nature are considered in subsequent chapters.

Frequency-domain Specifications. The bandwidth is the characteristic of the frequency response which is most often specified. Ordinarily the bandwidth is defined as indicated in Fig. 1.63, although the 3-db figure may be changed in certain special applications. The bandwidth is significant because it indicates the rise time or speed of response (as described below), it measures in part the ability of the system to reproduce the input signal, and it approximately describes the filtering characteristics of the system. This filtering action is illustrated by Fig. 1.64, showing a common form for the frequency spectra of the signal and of noise superimposed on the signal. If the noise spectrum extends to frequencies well above the highest significant frequency in the signal spectrum, the bandwidth is a measure of the noise-rejection characteristics of the system. The concepts of Chaps. 7 and 8 are useful in a more quantitative analysis of the filtering properties of the feedback system.

In many design problems, not only the bandwidth is specified, but also the characteristics of the cutoff: *e.g.*, the rate of cutoff just beyond the cutoff frequency or at very high frequencies. Figure 1.65 shows two frequency characteristics which are quite different, although both exhibit the same bandwidth. The characteristic of part (*b*) is desirable when the noise entering with the input signal possesses large amounts of energy at frequencies just beyond the end of the signal spectrum. In many problems, the feedback system is simply one of a number of tandem components, and the other elements afford sufficient attenuation at frequencies well beyond cutoff. In such cases, the curve of Fig. 1.65(*b*) may be desirable, even if the attenuation is small at high frequencies.

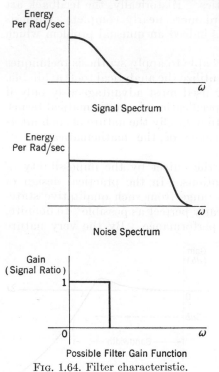

Fig. 1.64. Filter characteristic.

The above comments relate only to the nature of the gain characteristic; often the phase characteristic is even more important. The conditions for distortionless transmission are that the gain must be independent of frequency and the phase a linear function of frequency, each over the frequency band within which the signal energy lies. In the transmission of pulses, phase distortion is at least as troublesome as amplitude distortion, and the specifications frequently include the permissible deviation of the phase characteristic from linearity over a specified frequency range. In control problems, the time delay of the closed-loop system is often significant, particularly if the system is one link in an over-all closed loop. The time delay is given by the relation

$$T_d = -\frac{d\beta}{d\omega} \qquad (1.239)$$

where β is the phase shift, or angle of output with respect to input (not the phase lag). In such cases, the

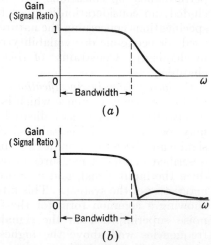

Fig. 1.65. Two filter characteristics with same bandwidth.

average value of $d\beta/d\omega$ may be specified over the frequency band of interest.

Clearly, a wide variety of other types of frequency-domain specifications may be encountered in the design of feedback systems. For example, if noise is concentrated in a narrow band of frequencies, it may be necessary to design a system blocking the transmission in this band, but passing both higher and lower frequencies.

Time-domain Specifications. Frequently, the desired characteristics of system performance are readily interpreted in terms of the nature of the transient response. Although a linear system is completely characterized by its response to any aperiodic signal, the step-function response is customarily considered. (The impulse response or ramp-function response is also a common means of description.) A typical step-func-

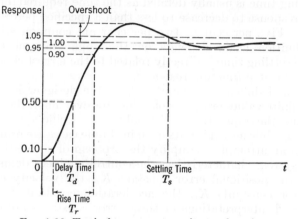

FIG. 1.66. Typical response to unit step function.

tion response for a feedback control system is shown in Fig. 1.66. The curve can be described approximately in terms of four quantities: overshoot, delay time, rise time, and settling time.

The overshoot (a percentage of the final value) is one measure of the relative stability of the system. The permissible values of overshoot depend on the application of the system and vary from 0 or 1 per cent in the case of certain measuring equipment to the 5 or 10 per cent allowable for video amplifiers (in television systems, for example) to the 25 per cent or more acceptable in certain servomechanisms.

The time delay indicates the time between the application of the step function and the appearance of a significant response. Although there is no universally accepted quantitative definition of a significant response, time delay is ordinarily defined as the time required for the response to reach half the final value.

The rise time is usually defined either as the time required for the response to go from 10 to 90 per cent of its final value (occasionally 5 to 95 per cent) or as the reciprocal of the slope of the response at the instant the response is half the final value. In pulse transmission, the rise time indicates the sharpness of the leading edge of the output pulse, or the precision with which this leading edge can be located in time. In control problems, the rise time is related to the signal distortion introduced by the system. In a system with a step-function response exhibiting less than 10 per cent overshoot, the rise time is related to the bandwidth by the approximate equation

$$T_r B = 0.30 \text{ to } 0.45 \tag{1.240}$$

Here T_r, the rise time, is measured in seconds, the bandwidth B, in cycles per second. In general, the value of the product $T_r B$ increases as the overshoot increases; values in the range 0.3 to 0.35 correspond to negligible overshoot; values in the neighborhood of 0.45 refer to systems with about 10 per cent overshoot.

The settling time is usually defined as the time required for the oscillation of the response to decrease to less than a specified percentage of the final value. Five per cent or two per cent are common criteria. The specific definition again depends on the application of the system. Clearly, the settling time is directly related to the largest significant time constant in the step-function response.

The principal difficulty encountered by the designer in attempts to establish definite values or ranges of values for overshoot, time delay, etc., arises because these quantities refer only to a specific aperiodic input, a step function, while actual inputs even in simple cases are ordinarily more general. In an attempt to simplify the problem of correlating specifications with system characteristics, the control engineer defines the *error coefficients:* the positional error constant K_p, the velocity constant (or velocity error constant) K_v, the acceleration constant K_a, etc. The definitions and interpretations of these error constants are discussed in detail in the next section.

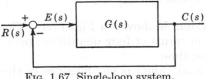

FIG. 1.67. Single-loop system.

1.8. Error Constants. The error constants, or error coefficients, are defined below and then interpreted in terms of the characteristics of system performance in both the time and frequency domains.

Classical Definition. The error constants were first used to describe the steady-state errors of a servomechanism with simple aperiodic inputs. The definition is most readily given in terms of the simple system of Fig. 1.67, although the concepts can be extended to more complex configurations. For this system, the actuating signal $E(s)$ is the error directly, and the definitions are

$$K_p = \lim_{s \to 0} G(s) \tag{1.241}$$

$$K_v = \lim_{s \to 0} sG(s) \tag{1.242}$$

$$K_a = \lim_{s \to 0} s^2 G(s) \tag{1.243}$$

As a result of these definitions, only one of the error constants possesses a finite, nonzero value for any given system. For example, if $G(s)$ possesses a simple pole at the origin, K_p is infinite, K_a is zero, and K_v is finite and nonzero. Thus, only one of the error coefficients conveys useful information.

The value of the nonzero, finite error constant describes the low-frequency behavior of the open-loop transfer function: the larger the error constant, the higher the loop gain as $\omega \to 0$. Accordingly, this error constant is a measure of the effectiveness of the feedback. As discussed in detail in Chap. 2, the feedback is used primarily to reduce the sensitivity of system characteristics to variations of system parameters and to control the output impedance. The extent to which the feedback accomplishes these two objectives is measured by the magnitude of the loop gain or, at least in part, by the error constant.

Steady-state Errors. The classical definition leads directly to the interpretation of the error constants in terms of the steady-state errors for the system of Fig. 1.67, with

$$E(s) = \frac{1}{1 + G(s)} R(s) \qquad (1.244)$$

If $E(s)$ possesses poles in the left-half plane only, the steady-state error is given by the final-value theorem,

$$e_{ss} = \lim_{s \to 0} \frac{sR(s)}{1 + G(s)} \qquad (1.245)$$

Three particular forms for $r(t)$ are of interest:

(1) $r(t)$ a unit step function: in this case,

$$e_{ss} = \lim_{s \to 0} \frac{1}{1 + G(s)} \qquad (1.246)$$

Substitution of Eq. (1.241) yields

$$e_{ss} = \frac{1}{1 + K_p} \quad \text{with } r(t) = u_{-1}(t) \quad \text{and} \quad R(s) = \frac{1}{s} \quad (1.247)$$

(2) $r(t)$ a unit ramp function $[r(t) = t, R(s) = 1/s^2]$:

$$e_{ss} = \lim_{s \to 0} \frac{1/s}{1 + G(s)} = \lim_{s \to 0} \frac{1}{sG(s)} = \frac{1}{K_v} \qquad (1.248)$$

(3) $r(t)$ a unit parabolic function $[r(t) = t^2/2, R(s) = 1/s^3]$:

$$e_{ss} = \frac{1}{K_a} \qquad (1.249)$$

Thus, K_p, K_v, and K_a are measures of the steady-state errors if the input is a unit step, a unit ramp, and a unit parabolic function, respectively.

Generalized Definitions. The primary disadvantage of the above definitions rests in the limited amount of information available from the specification of the error constants, since only one constant is significant. The generalized definitions† represent an attempt to circumvent this

† H. M. James, N. B. Nichols, and R. S. Phillips, "Theory of Servomechanisms," MIT Radiation Laboratory Series, Vol. 25, pp. 147–151, McGraw-Hill Book Company, Inc., New York, 1947.

difficulty by defining all error constants in terms of the low-frequency behavior of $E(s)/R(s)$, or $1/[1 + G(s)]$. If $1/[1 + G(s)]$ is expanded in a Maclaurin series in s, the error constants are defined in terms of the successive coefficients:

$$\frac{E}{R}(s) = \frac{1}{1 + G(s)} = \frac{1}{1 + K_p} + \frac{1}{K_v}s + \frac{1}{K_a}s^2 + \cdots \qquad (1.250)$$

With this definition, the value of any constant is not forced to be zero whenever the preceding constant is nonzero and finite. A comparison of Eq. (1.250) with (1.241) to (1.243) indicates that the definitions give the same values for all error constants up to and including the one which is nonzero and finite in the classical definition. Thus, the steady-state errors with step, ramp, or parabolic inputs are still measured by the generalized error constants. In addition, however, the generalized constants indicate several important aspects of system performance.

Errors with Low-frequency Inputs. Equations (1.244) and (1.250) state that the generalized error coefficients define the relation between the error and the reference input:

$$E(s) = \frac{1}{1 + K_p}R(s) + \frac{1}{K_v}sR(s) + \frac{1}{K_a}s^2R(s) + \cdots \qquad (1.251)$$

If the inverse transform of the series of Eq. (1.251) is taken term by term and impulses at $t = 0$ are neglected,

$$e(t) = \frac{1}{1 + K_p}r(t) + \frac{1}{K_v}r'(t) + \frac{1}{K_a}r''(t) + \cdots \qquad (1.252)$$

In problems in which the above operation is valid, the error constants yield an expression for the error in terms of the derivatives of the input.

Equation (1.252) describes the steady-state error.† When the transfer function $1/[1 + G(s)]$ is replaced by its Maclaurin series, the transient terms of $e(t)$ are discarded. At best, then, Eq. (1.252) is a valid description of the error only after sufficient time has elapsed to allow those terms in $e(t)$ which are generated by poles of $1/[1 + G(s)]$ to decay to insignificant amplitudes. Furthermore, the usefulness of Eq. (1.252) evidently depends on the rapidity of convergence of the series. As a result of considerations of this nature, care must be exercised in the use of the generalized error coefficients.‡

Application of Eq. (1.252) is most easily illustrated if the input $r(t)$ is a polynomial,

$$r(t) = \sum_{n=0}^{N} a_n t^n \qquad (1.253)$$

---

† Throughout this section, the steady-state output is defined as that representing the complex frequencies of the input. In contrast, the transient output is characterized by the poles of the transfer function. In other words, the steady-state output is the solution of the nonhomogeneous differential equation; the transient component of the output is the solution of the homogeneous differential equation.

‡ The following discussion of Eq. (1.252) is based on the M. S. thesis of T. A. Savo, "Significance of the Generalized Error Coefficients in Servomechanism Synthesis," Purdue University, Lafayette, Ind., 1953.

The following discussion is made explicit by assuming an N of 2, or

$$r(t) = a_0 + a_1 t + a_2 t^2 \tag{1.254}$$

Substitution of Eq. (1.254) in (1.252) yields

$$e(t) = \frac{1}{1 + K_p}(a_0 + a_1 t + a_2 t^2) + \frac{1}{K_v}(a_1 + 2a_2 t) + \frac{2}{K_a}a_2 \tag{1.255}$$

Exactly the same results are obtained if the ordinary inverse transform of $R(s)/[1 + G(s)]$ is taken and only the terms representing critical frequencies of $R(s)$ are considered.

Thus, if $r(t)$ is a second-degree polynomial, the steady-state error depends on the first three error coefficients: K_p, K_v, and K_a. More generally, if the polynomial is of Nth degree, the first $N + 1$ error coeffi-

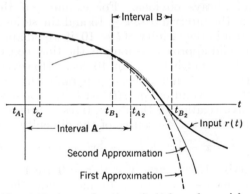

FIG. 1.68. Approximation of $r(t)$ by polynomials.

cients are used. In practice, it is possible to extend such results to more general input functions. The extension is customarily justified with the following line of reasoning, based on Fig. 1.68. The only permissible input functions are ones which can be accurately approximated by a quadratic polynomial over each of the overlapping intervals indicated. In interval A, Eq. (1.255) gives an accurate measure of the error after sufficient time has elapsed for the transient terms to decrease to insignificant magnitudes (*i.e.*, after t_α in the figure). Thus, Eq. (1.255) is an accurate description of the error† from t_α to t_{A_2}. If interval B can be made to start sufficiently long before t_{A_2} (that is, if $t_{A_2} - t_{B_1}$ is long enough to allow the transient to die out), the equation adequately describes the error from t_{A_2} to t_{B_2} if the coefficients of the polynomial of the second approximation are used. Continuation of this type of reasoning leads to the conclusion that Eq. (1.255) is valid if the input is so slowly varying that it can be approximated by a set of quadratics in overlapping intervals much longer than the significant time constants of $1/[1 + G(s)]$. Thus,

† For the unity-feedback system, the error is identical with the actuating signal. In the more general case, the error coefficients are defined in terms of the actual error function, rather than the actuating signal.

when the input contains predominantly low-frequency energy, a few of the generalized error coefficients suffice to describe system performance.

This interpretation of the significance of the generalized error constants is not always valid, however, and there is no simple method for determining the validity. The trouble arises in part from the difficulty of evaluating the significance of errors in approximating the actual input by a set of polynomials. The proper significance to be attached to these errors clearly depends not only on $r(t)$, but also on the transfer function $1/[1 + G(s)]$. For example, if when $R(s)$ is a rational algebraic function there is a time constant associated with $1/[1 + G(s)]$ which is larger than any time constant in $r(t)$, Eq. (1.252) can never be a valid description of the error, since the steady-state is never reached; the transient terms, those from the poles of $1/[1 + G(s)]$, last longer than the steady-state components from the poles of $R(s)$.

How rapidly the series (1.252) converges, or even whether it actually converges, is not always obvious. For example, if the input $r(t)$ is arctan $(10 - t)$ in the interval $0 < t \leq 15$ and the series is to be used to investigate the error in the vicinity of $t = 10$, it would appear that the use of the series is a valid approach as long as the time constants associated with $1/[1 + G(s)]$ are much less than 10 sec. However, the values of error given by the series do not agree, in general, with the accurate values calculated by the convolution of $r(t)$ with the inverse transform of $1/[1 + G(s)]$. Investigation of the derivatives of arctan $(10 - t)$ in the vicinity of $t = 10$ indicates the source of the difficulty, since

$$\arctan x = x - \tfrac{1}{3}x^3 + \tfrac{1}{5}x^5 - \tfrac{1}{7}x^7 + \cdots \qquad x^2 < 1 \qquad (1.256)$$

The odd-order derivatives of arctan x at $x = 0$ are $1, -(2!), 4!, -(6!)$, ... Since the derivatives increase in magnitude, the successive error coefficients must decrease *very* rapidly if Eq. (1.252) is to be valid. In such a situation, the difficulties are compounded by the fact that the first neglected term in Eq. (1.252) gives no significant indication of the error resulting from the use of only a finite number of terms in the series.

Thus, the generalized error coefficients indicate the steady-state error when the input is a polynomial; when $r(t)$ is the sum of exponentials, Eq. (1.252) is valid if there is a time constant of $r(t)$ much larger than any of the time constants associated with $1/[1 + G(s)]$; when $r(t)$ is a general input, the validity of Eq. (1.252) and the significance of the generalized error coefficients must be investigated in more detail.

Interpretation in Terms of Moments. The generalized error coefficients measure the moments of the impulse response of the closed-loop system function. The relation is most easily derived if Eq. (1.251) is combined with the equation

$$C(s) = \frac{G(s)}{1 + G(s)} R(s) = \left[1 - \frac{1}{1 + G(s)} \right] R(s) \qquad (1.257)$$

Hence,

$$C(s) = \frac{K_p}{1 + K_\infty} R(s) - \frac{1}{K_v} sR(s) - \frac{1}{K_a} s^2 R(s) - \cdots \qquad (1.258)$$

If $r(t)$ is a unit impulse, $c(t)$ is the impulse response, and

$$C(s) = \frac{K_p}{1 + K_p} - \frac{1}{K_v} s - \frac{1}{K_a} s^2 - \cdots \qquad (1.259)$$

(1) Thus, $K_p/(1 + K_p)$ is the area under the response to a unit impulse. If the final value of the unit-step-function response is unity, this area is also unity, or K_p is infinite.

(2) $-1/K_v$ is the zero-frequency value of the derivative of $C(s)$. But the Laplace integral states that

$$C(s) = \int_0^\infty c(t)e^{-st}\,dt \qquad (1.260)$$

Differentiation with respect to s gives

$$C'(s) = \int_0^\infty -tc(t)e^{-st}\,dt \qquad (1.261)$$

Substitution of $s = 0$ yields

$$\frac{1}{K_v} = \int_0^\infty tc(t)\,dt \qquad (1.262)$$

Thus, $1/K_v$ is the first moment of the impulse response, or the centroid of the response if the area is unity ($K_p = \infty$).

(3) Differentiation of Eq. (1.261) gives

$$C''(s) = \int_0^\infty t^2 c(t)e^{-st}\,dt \qquad (1.263)$$

But from Eq. (1.258), $-1/K_a$ is $\frac{1}{2}C''(0)$, or

$$\frac{1}{K_a} = -\frac{1}{2}\int_0^\infty t^2 c(t)\,dt \qquad (1.264)$$

The acceleration constant measures the second moment of the impulse response.

In a similar fashion, the relations between the higher-order error coefficients and moments are established.

Time Delay and Rise Time. The relations between the error coefficients and the moments have led to attempts to derive correlations between the error constants and the time delay and rise time of the step-function response.† The relation between the velocity constant and the time delay is established by inspection of Fig. 1.69(a), showing a typical impulse response and the integral (the corresponding step-function response). Unit impulse and step functions are considered, and the assumption is made that the final value of the step-function response is unity. If the time delay is defined as previously (the time for step-function response to reach 0.5), the time delay is approximately given by the equation

$$T_d = \frac{1}{K_v} \qquad (1.265)$$

Equation (1.265) is exact if the impulse response possesses symmetry about the line through the centroid, as shown in Fig. 1.69(b); in general, the required symmetry does not exist [as indicated in part (a) of the figure], and Eq. (1.265) is useful primarily in fixing the order of magnitude

† W. C. Elmore and M. Sands, "Electronics," National Nuclear Energy Series, Div. V, Vol. 1, pp. 137–138, McGraw-Hill Book Company, Inc., New York, 1949.

of the time delay for systems with small overshoot. If the overshoot is large, there is very little correlation between the time delay and K_v.

If the step-function response does not exhibit large overshoot, there is a similar relation between the second moment and the rise time. Figure 1.69(c), showing two impulse responses and the corresponding step-function responses, demonstrates that the smaller the second moment of the

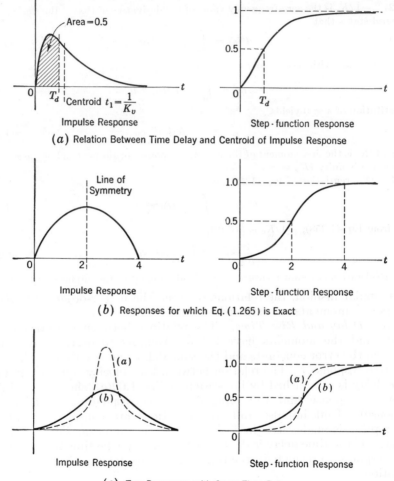

(a) Relation Between Time Delay and Centroid of Impulse Response

(b) Responses for which Eq. (1.265) is Exact

(c) Two Responses with Same Time Delay

FIG. 1.69. Relations between error constants and step-function response.

impulse response about the centroid, the smaller the rise time of the step-function response. This second moment is given by the equation

$$\sigma^2 = \int_0^\infty (t - t_1)^2 c(t)\, dt \tag{1.266}$$

where t_1 is the centroid† of $c(t)$ and σ^2 is the second moment about t_1.

† t_1 is approximately equal to the time delay if the overshoot is negligible.

Expansion of the squared term leads to

$$\sigma^2 = \int_0^\infty t^2 c(t) \, dt - 2t_1 \int_0^\infty t c(t) \, dt + t_1^2 \int_0^\infty c(t) \, dt \qquad (1.267)$$

Substitution of unity for $\int_0^\infty c(t) \, dt$ and t_1 for the first moment gives

$$\sigma^2 = \int_0^\infty t^2 c(t) \, dt - t_1^2 \qquad (1.268)$$

Equations (1.262) and (1.264) can be used to express σ^2 in terms of the error constants:

$$\sigma^2 = -\frac{2}{K_a} - \frac{1}{K_v^2} \qquad (1.269)$$

Thus, the quantity $-2/K_a - 1/K_v^2$ is a measure of the *order of magnitude* of the rise time if the overshoot of the step-function response is small. Elmore uses the specific relation for the second moment,

$$\sigma^2 = \frac{1}{2\pi} T_r^2 \qquad (1.270)$$

Hence,

$$\frac{1}{2\pi} T_r^2 = -\frac{2}{K_a} - \frac{1}{K_v^2} \qquad (1.271)$$

1.9. Conclusions. The last two sections summarize very briefly the nature of the performance specifications most commonly encountered by the designer of feedback systems. These specifications must be interpreted in mathematical terms in order to state the problem in a form amenable to design and synthesis procedures. Certain common mathematical terms are described briefly.

Once the problem is formulated analytically, the selection of a particular design procedure is guided by the particular nature of the problem. Regardless of the design method, even if design is effected entirely in the frequency domain in terms of the classical Nyquist diagram, the success of the designer depends in large measure on his circumspection. He must be able to correlate the information obtainable from the variety of analysis techniques available. The complex-function theory and Laplace-transform theory, reviewed very briefly in the first six sections of this chapter, form the foundation for the various analyses and design procedures described in the following chapters.

CHAPTER 2

SIGNAL-FLOW DIAGRAMS AND FEEDBACK THEORY

There are two concepts which are basic in the analysis of feedback systems. The first, and more fundamental, is the circuit concept, the visualization of a combination of physical components as a topological configuration of basic elements which obey simple natural laws. The second is the block-diagram approach to the analysis of complex systems. After the system is visualized as a circuit, the various independent sections are analyzed individually. A set of transfer functions is developed, each function representing the transfer characteristics of one section. The block diagram portrays the interconnection of these various sections to form the over-all system, this interconnection of component blocks in itself constituting a circuit.

The success of the block-diagram approach to analysis, and ultimately to design, is dependent upon the engineer's ability to determine which grouping of physical components results in noninteractive blocks. The very nature of the block diagram assumes that the transfer function of the tandem combination of two blocks is the product of the individual transfer functions. Clearly, the over-all system can be represented by a single block with no danger of any interaction. The primary advantage of the block-diagram approach lies, however, in the ease with which the contributions of various components to over-all system performance can be evaluated. The full realization of this advantage usually demands that the component blocks be as simple as possible without interacting.

Closely related to this demand on the designer for the decisions as to what elements to put in each block is the requirement imposed on the engineer to analyze successfully the various block transfer functions. The determination of these transfer functions is ordinarily effected in either of two ways: directly from the integrodifferential equations describing system behavior, or from circuit analysis. In the former case, the equations are written on the basis of physical laws (Ohm's law in electrical systems, Newton's laws in mechanical systems, etc.). The Laplace transforms of the set of simultaneous equations are taken, and the resulting simultaneous algebraic equations are solved for the transfer function.†
If the circuit approach is used throughout, the circuit diagram is drawn

---

† It suffices at this point in the discussion to assume that the system consists only of linear lumped-parameter elements (R, L, and C in electrical systems, M, B, and K in mechanical systems, etc.). As a result of this assumption, the description of system behavior involves only linear integrodifferential equations with constant coefficients, not partial differential equations or nonlinear differential equations.

for the elements in the block under investigation and the circuit transfer function is evaluated directly in terms of the complex frequency s by any of the numerous methods familiar to electrical engineers (*e.g.*, the writing of loop or node equations).

There are several fundamental limitations and disadvantages of the block-diagram approach to the analysis and design of feedback systems:

(1) In a complex system, it is extremely difficult to determine, from the simultaneous equations describing system behavior, which group of elements can be isolated in a block. The interaction of one set of elements on another is not at all apparent, with the result that the block diagram drawn for the system frequently contains too few blocks, each with an unnecessarily complicated transfer function.

(2) Once the block diagram is drawn, the designer loses contact completely with the flow of signals within the block. A single block represents, in general, a moderately complicated configuration of physical elements, with the entire configuration described by a single transfer function. The subsidiary transfer functions, relating the block input signal to other signals within the circuit represented by the block, can be determined only by a return to the simultaneous equations describing system behavior.

(3) This loss of contact with the physical system is a distinct disadvantage if the effect of a single parameter on over-all system performance is to be studied in detail. For example, the effects of variations in a system parameter on the over-all system function are frequently desired in analysis.

(4) Since the signals between blocks represent only a specialized few of the many signals actually present in the system, the effects of disturbances entering the system at points other than the input must be analyzed by modifying the block diagram of the system to such a form that the disturbance enters between blocks or through an artificial block to a point already present in the block diagram.

The above disadvantages certainly do not mean that the block-diagram approach to analysis is not a useful tool of the engineer. On the contrary, it is an invaluable aid in the analysis of the stability and dynamic performance of feedback systems. The difficulties do indicate, however, that, for a wide variety of feedback analysis problems, an alternate representation of the system is desirable, a representation which pictures the system in more detail than a block diagram, but which retains the visual representation of the flow of signals through the system. The signal-flow diagrams, originated by S. J. Mason,† provide this representation of system performance. This chapter begins with a description of signal-flow diagrams and then illustrates the application of the diagrams in the derivation of certain basic relations of general feedback theory.

2.1. The Signal-flow Diagram. The conventional analysis of a physical system is initiated by writing the set of simultaneous equations describing system behavior. The first step in writing these equations is the selection of the variables. The discussion is made specific by the consideration of a system with only one driving signal, x_0, and with n dependent variables, $x_1, x_2, \ldots, x_n$. The simultaneous equations take the general form

† S. J. Mason, Feedback Theory—Some Properties of Signal Flow Graphs, *Proc. IRE*, Vol. 41, No. 9, pp. 1144–1156, September, 1953.

$$a_0x_0 + a_1x_1 + a_2x_2 + \cdots + a_nx_n = 0$$
$$b_0x_0 + b_1x_1 + b_2x_2 + \cdots + b_nx_n = 0$$
$$\cdots\cdots\cdots\cdots\cdots\cdots\cdots\cdots\cdots\cdots\cdots \tag{2.1}$$
$$n_0x_0 + n_1x_1 + n_2x_2 + \cdots + n_nx_n = 0$$

If n independent equations are written, they can be solved for the n dependent variables from the known driving function x_0. In the general linear lumped-parameter system, the coefficients a_j, b_j, $\ldots$, n_j, are integrodifferential operators. The equations are made algebraic by Laplace transformations, with the initial conditions modifying the terms, a_0x_0, b_0x_0, $\ldots$, n_0x_0.

The set of equations with n equal to 3 is sufficiently simple to permit detailed discussion:

$$a_0x_0 + a_1x_1 + a_2x_2 + a_3x_3 = 0$$
$$b_0x_0 + b_1x_1 + b_2x_2 + b_3x_3 = 0 \tag{2.2}$$
$$c_0x_0 + c_1x_1 + c_2x_2 + c_3x_3 = 0$$

The equations can be rewritten in the form

$$x_1 = t_{01}x_0 + t_{11}x_1 + t_{21}x_2 + t_{31}x_3$$
$$x_2 = t_{02}x_0 + t_{12}x_1 + t_{22}x_2 + t_{32}x_3 \tag{2.3}$$
$$x_3 = t_{03}x_0 + t_{13}x_1 + t_{23}x_2 + t_{33}x_3$$

On one side of each of Eqs. (2.3), a dependent variable appears alone. The n equations now take the form of expressions for the n dependent variables, in turn, in terms of the other variables. The t_{jk} factor represents the contribution of x_j to the value of x_k with the equations in the form shown. The factors t_{jk} are directly related to the a_j, b_j, and c_j of Eqs. (2.2),

$$t_{j1} = \begin{cases} a_j & j \neq 1 \\ a_1 - 1 & j = 1 \end{cases} \tag{2.4}$$

$$t_{j2} = \begin{cases} b_j & j \neq 2 \\ b_2 - 1 & j = 2 \end{cases} \tag{2.5}$$

$$t_{j3} = \begin{cases} c_j & j \neq 3 \\ c_3 - 1 & j = 3 \end{cases} \tag{2.6}$$

In almost any physical system, certain of the t_{jk} factors are zero and the equations are less complicated than indicated in (2.3).

Equations (2.2) can be represented in the somewhat simpler form

$$x_1 = -\frac{a_0}{a_1}x_0 - \frac{a_2}{a_1}x_2 - \frac{a_3}{a_1}x_3$$

$$x_2 = -\frac{b_0}{b_2}x_0 - \frac{b_1}{b_2}x_1 - \frac{b_3}{b_2}x_3 \tag{2.7}$$

$$x_3 = -\frac{c_0}{c_3}x_0 - \frac{c_1}{c_3}x_1 - \frac{c_2}{c_3}x_2$$

The apparent simplicity of this form is deceptive, however, for, as soon as an equation is divided by one of the coefficients, the stability question must be considered. Thus, the above equations (2.7) are valid only if none of the coefficients a_1, b_2, and c_3 takes on the value zero for the circuit parameters lying within their operating ranges. If the Laplace transforms of the equations are considered and a_1, b_2, and c_3 are functions of the complex frequency s, the zeros of a_1, b_2, and c_3 must be restricted to the left half of the s plane if the various coefficients of Eqs. (2.7) are to represent stable transfer functions. It is more convenient to postpone these questions of stability to a later point in the analysis of a feedback system, rather than introducing the problems at the very outset.

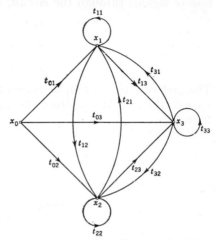

FIG. 2.1. Signal-flow diagram for Eqs. (2.3).

Rules for the Signal-flow Diagram. The form of the describing equations (2.3) leads directly to the representation of system behavior in terms of the signal-flow diagram. The three equations can be represented topologically as shown in Fig. 2.1. The variables are represented as nodes; the transmittances t_{jk}, as directed branches. The diagram is drawn on the basis of four rules:

Rule 1. Signals travel along branches only in the direction of the arrows.

Rule 2. A signal traveling along any branch is multiplied by the transmittance of that branch.

Rule 3. The value of the variable represented by any node is the sum of all signals entering the node.

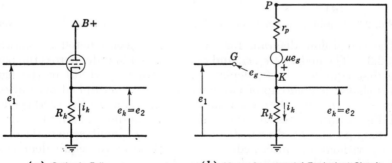

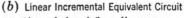

(a) Cathode Follower   **(b)** Linear Incremental Equivalent Circuit

FIG. 2.2. Circuit to illustrate construction of signal-flow diagram.

Rule 4. The value of the variable represented by any node is transmitted on all branches leaving that node.

Example of a Signal-flow Diagram. A very simple example illustrates the construction of the signal-flow diagram from a physical system. For the cathode-follower circuit of Fig. 2.2(a), the linear incremental equivalent circuit is shown in Fig. 2.2(b), with the grid, plate, and cathode terminals marked G, P, and K, respectively. The set of equations describing system performance can take a wide variety of forms, but, if an effort is made to write the equations in an order corresponding to the flow of signals through the circuit, a set similar to the following results:

$$e_g = e_1 - e_k \tag{2.8}$$

$$e_k = \frac{\mu R_k}{r_p + R_k} e_g \tag{2.9}$$

$$e_2 = e_k \tag{2.10}$$

The first equation, (2.8), describes the manner in which e_1 causes e_g; the second, the e_k resulting from this e_g; and the third, the output resulting from e_k.

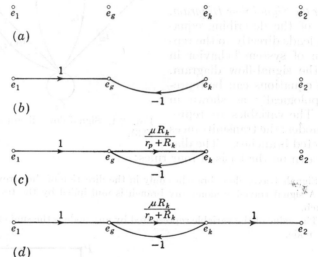

FIG. 2.3. Step-by-step construction of signal-flow diagram for cathode follower.

The signal-flow diagram for the circuit is constructed as shown in Fig. 2.3. The nodes e_1, e_g, e_k, and e_2 are located in order across the paper. The first equation, (2.8), depicted as shown in part (b) of the figure, states that e_g is made up of two components, e_1 multiplied by unity and e_k by -1. In Fig. 2.3(c), the branch corresponding to Eq. (2.9) is added, and Fig. 2.3(d) represents the complete signal-flow diagram. Clearly, the diagram can be drawn directly from the circuit schematic of Fig. 2.2(a), without the intermediate construction of the equivalent circuit and writing of the simultaneous equations.

One feature of the signal-flow diagram is worthy of special note. A partial check on the accuracy of the final diagram is available from an inspection of the dimensions of the various transmittances. In the diagram of Fig. 2.3(d), all nodes represent voltages, with the result that each transmission must be dimensionless. If the system performance of the cathode follower is described in terms of the variables e_1, e_g, i_k, and e_2, the signal-flow diagram is shown in Fig. 2.4. The transmittance from

e_1 to e_g is dimensionless, that from e_g to i_k has the dimension of mhos, and those from i_k to e_g and e_2 have the dimension of ohms.

The signal-flow diagram is governed by the four rules listed previously. There are two additional rules which are introduced merely for standardization and for convenience in the analysis described in the following

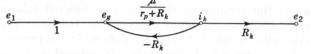

FIG. 2.4. Alternate diagram for cathode follower.

sections.   The diagram is always drawn in such a way that no branch enters the input node and none leaves the output.   If the input represents the drive, the former condition is always satisfied.   The latter condition can always be met by introduction of an additional variable.   For example, if the equations as originally written are in a form leading to the partial diagram shown in Fig. 2.5(a), where e_2 is the output variable, one additional equation is written,

$$e_{\text{out}} = e_2 \qquad (2.11)$$

The output is now considered to be e_{out}, and the partial signal-flow diagram is shown in Fig. 2.5(b). No branch leaves the output node.

What is gained by the introduction of the signal-flow diagram?   The advantageous features of an analysis with signal-flow diagrams are described in detail in succeeding sections, but certain features of the diagram are evident from an example as simple as the cathode-follower circuit described above:

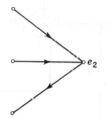

(a) Output Section of Original Diagram

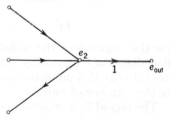

(b) Output Section of Modified Diagram

FIG. 2.5. Realization of diagram in which no branch leaves output node.

(1)   The signal-flow diagram pictures the passage of signals through the network.

(2)   The feedback paths are placed in evidence by the closed loops of the signal-flow diagram. For example, the diagram of Fig. 2.3(d) indicates that in the cathode follower there is one feedback loop, present because e_k depends on e_g, which in turn depends on e_k.   In more complicated systems, there may be a large number of complex, intermeshed feedback loops.

(3)   The signal-flow diagram presents exactly the same information as the corresponding set of simultaneous equations.   In a great many cases, however, the form of the diagram suggests a procedure for solving the equations, a sequence for the successive elimination of the dependent variables.   This use of signal-flow diagrams is described in detail in Sec. 2.3 and is only poorly illustrated by the cathode-follower example, in which it is clear from either the equations or the signal-flow diagram that, if e_2/e_1 is the desired transmission, e_g should be eliminated first by substituting Eq. (2.8) in (2.9).

A Second Example. Construction of the signal-flow diagram for the circuit of Fig. 2.6 illustrates the procedure in a more comprehensive example and also indicates certain problems not brought to light by the analysis of the simple cathode-follower circuit. The construction is guided by the desire to maintain a correspondence between the diagram and actual signal flow. This desire is best satisfied if the successive steps in building up the signal-flow diagram are directed toward working through the circuit from the input signal to the output. The variables required to describe system behavior are defined in the process of tracing the path of signals through the network. In general, as many variables are defined as are required to permit the writing of the system equations

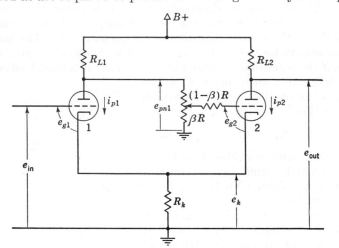

Fig. 2.6. Circuit diagram for second example.

(or the drawing of the signal-flow diagram) by inspection. The signal-flow diagram is so readily simplified, as outlined in Sec. 2.3, that it is not desirable at this point to expend any significant effort toward a reduction of the number of variables.

The signal-flow diagram is drawn in the steps listed below, lettered to correspond to the appropriate part of Fig. 2.7. The variables are defined in the circuit diagram of Fig. 2.6. Only incremental quantities are considered, and the two tubes are described by the linear incremental equivalent circuits.

(1) The signal-flow diagram must contain the input and output nodes e_{in} and e_{out}.

(2) The input voltage causes a grid-to-cathode voltage on tube 1, with

$$e_{g1} = e_{\text{in}} - e_k \qquad (2.12)$$

The signal-flow diagram contains the variables e_{g1} and e_k. The primary variable e_{g1} occurs in the principal signal path from input to output and is placed on the direct line from e_1 to e_2; the secondary variable e_k is added below this primary transmission path. There is a certain arbitrariness in this construction, based as it is on the assumption that the primary

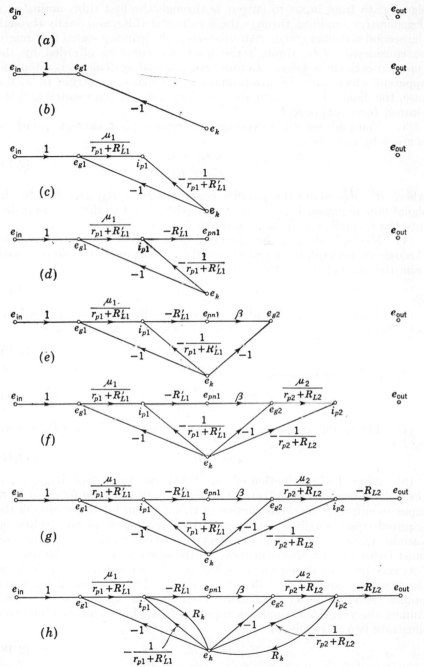

FIG. 2.7. Development of the signal-flow diagram for circuit of Fig. 2.6.

signal path from input to output is through the first tube, acting as a degenerative amplifier, through the β-voltage divider, and finally through the second amplifier stage.   Alternatively, the primary signal flow might be considered to be through the intertube coupling afforded by the common cathode resistor.   In more complicated systems, it is often less apparent which variables are primary and which secondary.   In such a case, the diagram is redrawn after all equations are represented and the clearest form is apparent.

(3)   The grid-to-cathode voltage generates a plate current i_{p1}, which is given by the relation

$$i_{p1} = \frac{\mu_1 e_{g1} - e_k}{r_{p1} + R'_{L1}} \tag{2.13}$$

where R'_{L1} represents the parallel combination of R_{L1} and R.   In the signal-flow diagram, Eq. (2.13) is represented by two directed branches into the i_{p1} node, one from e_{g1} and one from e_k.

(4)   If emphasis remains directed on the flow of signals passing through the network toward the output, i_{p1} causes an incremental voltage from the plate of tube 1 to ground,

$$e_{pn1} = -R'_{L1} i_{p1} \tag{2.14}$$

(5)   A fraction β of this plate-to-ground voltage is fed to the grid of tube 2 and combined with e_k to generate a grid-to-cathode voltage,

$$e_{g2} = \beta e_{pn1} - e_k \tag{2.15}$$

(6) e_{g2} in turn causes i_{p2}:

$$i_{p2} = \frac{\mu_2 e_{g2} - e_k}{r_{p2} + R_{L2}} \tag{2.16}$$

(7)   The output voltage is the negative of the drop through R_{L2} caused by i_{p2},

$$e_{\text{out}} = -R_{L2} i_{p2} \tag{2.17}$$

(8)   After the introduction of Eq. (2.17), the signal-flow diagram has the form shown in Fig. 2.7(g).   The signal path has been followed from input to output.   The construction of this diagram (or the writing of the required equations) has necessitated the introduction of one additional variable e_k, for which no equation has as yet been written.   An equation must be written for this e_k in terms of the other variables if the relation between the seven dependent variables is to be expressed in a set of seven simultaneous equations.   (In other words, there must be at least one branch entering every dependent node in the signal-flow diagram.) Among the variety of equations apparent from the circuit, the following illustrate two possibilities:

$$e_k = (i_{p1} + i_{p2}) R_k \tag{2.18}$$
$$e_k = \mu_1 e_{g1} - i_{p1}(r_{p1} + R'_{L1}) \tag{2.19}$$

The selection of the equation for e_k depends upon the requirement that the n equations (for n dependent variables) must be independent: *i.e.*, no equation can be a linear combination of other equations of the set. Equation (2.18) satisfies this requirement of independence, while (2.19) does not. In general, there is no simple way to determine what equation to write for e_k to assure the independence of the set. This is not a difficulty characteristic of the signal-flow diagrams, but, rather, one which arises regardless of the method of analysis. Actually, the signal-flow-diagram method exhibits the advantage characteristic of most formalized methods for writing the simultaneous equations: the advantage that the probability of two dependent equations occurring is reduced by the systematic procedure. As a guide in the selection of the equations, there is one necessary, although not sufficient, condition which can be used. Any circuit parameter which affects the gain must appear at least once in the set of equations. In the example considered above, it is clear that the gain of the system depends upon the value of R_k. If Eq. (2.19) is used for e_k, R_k does not appear in the signal-flow diagram. The presence of R_k in Eq. (2.18) does not guarantee that the use of the equation results in an independent set, but, if the set is not independent, the attempts to determine e_{out}/e_{in} by reduction of the signal-flow diagram (cf. Sec. 2.3) demonstrate that the equations must be rewritten. Therefore, Eq. (2.18) is used to complete the diagram, as shown in Fig. 2.7(h).

Nature of the Signal-flow Diagram. At this point, several comments are relevant in connection with the above example. First, it is clear that the signal-flow diagram can be drawn without the necessity of writing Eqs. (2.12) to (2.18). They are included above merely to clarify the manner in which the signal-flow diagram is constructed.

Second, both examples described in this section involve signal-flow diagrams in which all transmittances are constants. Clearly, these are both special cases, in the sense that in general the transmittances are functions of the complex frequency s. The node variables are then the Laplace transforms of the corresponding time functions.

Third, there is considerable flexibility in the selection of the variables and equations. For example, the system of Fig. 2.6 can be described without the use of the two plate currents as variables, but with the equations entirely in terms of the voltages throughout the circuit. In this way, the number of equations (and, hence, the number of nodes in the signal-flow diagram) can be reduced. The amount of the circuit to be lumped together and represented by one transmittance depends primarily on the facility the engineer has in analyzing circuits.

Fourth, the nodes in the signal-flow diagram might be arranged in markedly different order. For example, if the analyst feels that the primary transmission from input to output is furnished by the coupling through the cathode resistor, the signal-flow diagram can be drawn with the primary signal flow from e_{in} to e_{g1} to e_k to e_{out}. Although the order in which the equations are written is largely arbitrary, full utilization of the picture the signal-flow diagram presents of the paths of signals through the network requires that as much correlation as possible be retained between the diagram and actual operation of the circuit. The only time at which this correlation should be abandoned is when the specifications require an investigation of the effect of one particular parameter on the over-all transmission. In this special case, it is desirable, as indicated in Sec. 2.4, to draw the diagram in such a way that the parameter under study appears in only one branch.

The examples of this section illustrate the basic characteristics of the signal-flow diagram. Here, at the beginning of the chapter, it is appropriate to emphasize the very distinct differences between signal-flow diagrams and block diagrams. The signal-flow diagram is a detailed picture of system behavior; the block diagram indicates the mode of interconnection of the various sections of the system. The signal-flow diagram is useful in analyzing complicated systems, in establishing basic relations of feedback theory, and in investigating the role taken by one particular parameter in the over-all feedback system; the block diagram

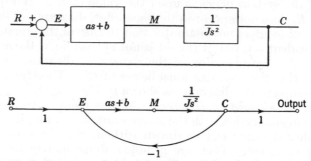

FIG. 2.8. Block diagram and signal-flow diagram for simple servomechanism.

is useful in the analysis and design of the characteristics of sections of the over-all system. Once the design reaches the point where the desired block diagram of the system is known, the transfer functions of the various blocks must be realized individually. If a transfer function is to be realized by a passive network, the techniques of Chap. 3 are employed. If an active network employing feedback is desired, the various possible networks can be analyzed with signal-flow diagrams and one network can be selected on the basis of the effectiveness of the utilization of the feedback. Manipulation of the signal-flow diagrams according to the rules outlined and illustrated in Sec. 2.3 also provides a flexible method for determining a wide variety of feedback configurations equivalent to a given system.† Thus, although there is no general, clearly defined synthesis procedure for the realization of a given transfer function by means of a feedback network, the signal-flow diagrams facilitate the synthesis.

In a simple system, the signal-flow diagram and block diagram may present the same information. The single-loop servomechanism with a purely inertial load and proportional-plus-derivative tandem compensation illustrates this identity of the two diagrams. Figure 2.8 presents

† The manipulation of block diagrams is described in two papers by T. M. Stout, A Block-diagram Approach to Network Analysis, *Trans. AIEE, Applications and Industry*, Vol. 71, pp. 225–260, 1952, and Block-diagram Solutions for Vacuum-tube Circuits, *Trans. AIEE, Communications and Electronics*, Vol. 72, pp. 561–567, 1953.

both diagrams for such a system. The example of Sec. 2.9, on the other hand, illustrates the very significant difference between the two methods of analysis. In a complex system, step-by-step reduction of the complexity of the signal-flow diagram can be used to derive an appropriate block diagram.

2.2. System Order. The most important system characteristic placed in evidence by the signal-flow diagram is the *order* of the system, for this order determines the system complexity, which, in turn, establishes the degree of difficulty associated with the determination of the over-all gain and stability. The order of the system is essentially a measure of the number of independent feedback loops.

The signal-flow diagram gives a pictorial representation of the feedback loops. For example, the diagram (Fig. 2.3) for the cathode follower

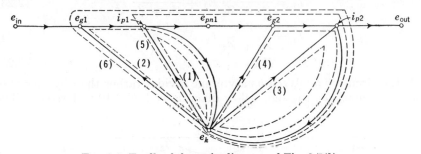

FIG. 2.9. Feedback loops in diagram of Fig. 2.7(h).

demonstrates that one closed (or feedback) loop exists in the system, the loop from e_g to e_k and back to e_g. This feedback loop represents the cathode degeneration in the physical circuit. The more complicated signal-flow diagram of Fig. 2.7(h) indicates six feedback loops, as shown in Fig. 2.9:

(1) e_k to i_{p1} to e_k
(2) e_k to e_{g1} to i_{p1} to e_k
(3) e_k to i_{p2} to e_k
(4) e_k to e_{g2} to i_{p2} to e_k
(5) e_k to i_{p1} to e_{pn1} to e_{g2} to i_{p2} to e_k
(6) e_k to e_{g1} to i_{p1} to e_{pn1} to e_{g2} to i_{p2} to e_k

Loops (1) and (2) represent the effect of the cathode degeneration in tube 1 alone; loops (3) and (4), that of tube 2 alone; and loops (5) and (6), the effects of the intertube coupling furnished by the common cathode resistor.

It is noteworthy in Fig. 2.9 that, as a result of the manner in which the signal-flow diagram is constructed, each physical feedback is represented by two closed paths in the diagram. The number of feedback loops is, thus, a result of the manner in which the equations are written, rather than an accurate indication of the complexity of the system. This vagueness in the definition of feedback runs throughout the literature on the subject. The absence of precise correlation between the feedback loops obvious physically and those presented by the mathematical description of the system is even more startlingly demonstrated by an analysis of the simple ladder network of Fig. 2.10. The loop equations for this circuit are

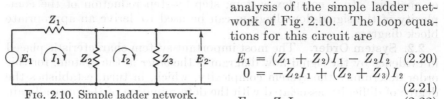

FIG. 2.10. Simple ladder network.

$$E_1 = (Z_1 + Z_2)I_1 - Z_2I_2 \quad (2.20)$$
$$0 = -Z_2I_1 + (Z_2 + Z_3)I_2 \quad (2.21)$$
$$E_2 = Z_3I_2 \quad (2.22)$$

A signal-flow diagram can be drawn (Fig. 2.11) if the equations are written in the form

$$I_1 = \frac{1}{Z_1 + Z_2}E_1 + \frac{Z_2}{Z_1 + Z_2}I_2 \quad (2.23)$$

$$I_2 = \frac{Z_2}{Z_2 + Z_3}I_1 \quad (2.24)$$

$$E_2 = Z_3I_2 \quad (2.25)$$

If the circuit is analyzed as a voltage divider rather than by means of the loop equations, the signal-flow diagram of Fig. 2.12 is derived. The

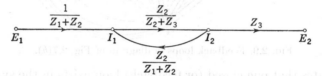

FIG. 2.11. Signal-flow diagram for circuit of Fig. 2.10 if loop equations used.

apparent feedback of Fig. 2.11 is completely absent in 2.12. The ambiguity here arises from the fact that, even though feedback may have a very definite physical interpretation, any precise mathematical definition reduces feedback to an analytical tool. Physical reasoning indicates that the circuit of Fig. 2.10 does not include feedback: in the ordinary sense, no energy is fed back through a return transmission. Mathematically, the circuit does include feedback if the loop equations are used for analysis. Thus, the number of feedback loops in the signal-flow diagram measures the complexity of the particular set of equations used to describe system behavior.

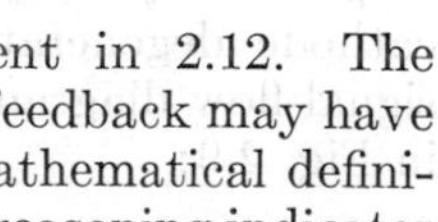

$$\overset{Z_2Z_3}{\underset{Z_1Z_2+Z_1Z_3+Z_2Z_3}{\xrightarrow{\hspace{2cm}}}}$$
$$E_1 \qquad\qquad E_2$$

FIG. 2.12. Signal-flow diagram for circuit of Fig. 2.10 if voltage-divider equation used.

That the number of feedback loops is not an appropriate measure of system complexity is further indicated by Fig. 2.13. The two diagrams represent the same system and an equivalent set of equations, yet part (a) exhibits two feedback loops, part (b) only one. The *order* (or essential complexity) of the system obviously depends on the number of independent feedback loops, where the term "independent" means that the loops cannot be combined by simple addition.

The concept of order of a diagram or system is made more precise by the definition of *essential nodes* as those nodes which must be removed from a signal-flow diagram to eliminate all feedback paths. Here, a node removal is interpreted as an equating of the value of the node variable to zero or, equivalently, a simple deletion of all branches leaving the node. *The order of the signal-flow diagram is the minimum number of essential nodes.*

Figure 2.14(a) shows a signal-flow diagram of order one. Since both feedback loops ($e_1e_2e_1$ and $e_1e_2e_3e_1$) pass through e_1 and e_2, removal of either e_1 or e_2 eliminates all loops. Part (b) of the figure shows the diagram if the node e_1 is removed. Either e_1 or e_2 can be considered the

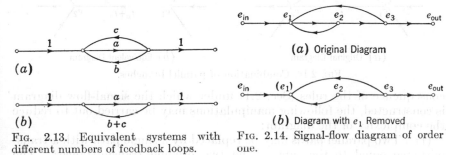

(a)

(b)

Fig. 2.13. Equivalent systems with different numbers of feedback loops.

(a) Original Diagram

(b) Diagram with e_1 Removed

Fig. 2.14. Signal-flow diagram of order one.

single essential node of the complete diagram. e_3 is not an essential node, because removal of e_3 leaves the $e_1e_2e_1$ loop unbroken.

The diagram of Figs. 2.7(h) and 2.9 is a more elegant example of a system of order one. The essential node in this case can only be e_k. Elimination of any other node leaves feedback loops in the diagram. The discussion of the next section demonstrates that the diagram of Fig. 2.7(h) is basically no more complicated than that of Fig. 2.14 if the analysis is directed toward determination of the gain and stability of the over-all system.

A diagram of order two is shown in Fig. 2.15. All three loops ($e_1e_2e_1$, $e_3e_4e_3$, and $e_1e_2e_3e_4e_1$) can be eliminated only by removal of either e_1 or e_2

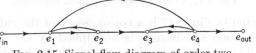

Fig. 2.15. Signal-flow diagram of order two.

and either e_3 or e_4. In a complex diagram with order greater than two, evaluation of the order is generally a difficult task, requiring a trial-and-error analysis to determine which nodes form the essential set. Fortunately, it is not too important to be able to ascertain whether a system is of order four or five, for example. If the order determined is inaccurately high, the analysis is still valid, although more complicated in certain aspects. In the great majority of systems encountered in practice, the order is less than or equal to two.

2.3. Reduction of the Signal-flow Diagram. The fundamental problem in system analysis is the determination of the over-all system gain. If the system is analyzed from the set of simultaneous equations, the equations can be solved either with matrix algebra or by a one-by-one elimination of variables. In either case, the analyst rapidly loses any correlation between the equations and the physical system. If the analysis is carried through in terms of the signal-flow diagrams, this correlation can be retained.

Basic Reduction Rules. System analysis with signal-flow diagrams involves a step-by-step reduction of the complexity of the diagram. As a

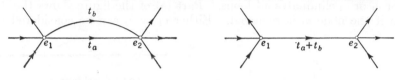

(*a*) Original Diagram   (*b*) Equivalent Diagram

Fig. 2.16. Combination of parallel branches.

consequence of the rules (Sec. 2.1) under which the signal-flow diagram is constructed, the following manipulations may be carried out to reduce the complexity of the diagram:

(1) Two parallel paths may be replaced by a single path with a transmittance equal to the sum of the two original transmittances. The equivalence is illustrated in Fig. 2.16. The validity of the equivalence is the direct result of the rule which states that the value of any node variable is the sum of the incoming signals.

(2) Two tandem paths are equivalent to a single path with a transmittance equal to the product of the two original transmittances. The

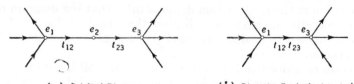

(*a*) Original Diagram   (*b*) Diagram Equivalent to (*a*)

Fig. 2.17. Combination of tandem branches.

relation illustrated in Fig. 2.17 is a consequence of the rule stating that a signal traveling along any branch is multiplied by the transmittance of that branch. The reduction in this case involves the creation of a new signal-flow diagram with the variable e_2 no longer included.

(3) The termination of a branch can be shifted one node if suitable changes are made in the signal-flow diagram. In Fig. 2.18(*a*), the branch with transmittance t_{42} is to be shifted to enter node e_3 rather than e_2. The change is effected in three steps, represented by parts (*b*), (*c*), and (*d*) of the figure. The first step involves the definition of the new node e_2' on which the branches with transmittances t_{32} and t_{12} terminate. The variable e_2' is defined by the equation

$$e_2' = e_2 - t_{42}e_4 \tag{2.26}$$

The node variable e_2 is unchanged by this transformation. In the second step [Fig. 2.18(*c*)], the branch from e_2 to e_5 is moved back to start from

e_2'. Equation (2.26) indicates, however, that e_2' does not contain all the information present in e_2. In order to leave e_5 unchanged, a branch must be added in Fig. 2.18(c) from e_4 directly to e_5. e_5 represents any node receiving a branch from e_2. Thus, if there is a branch from e_2 to e_4 in the original diagram, the added branch of Fig. 2.18(c) takes the form of a self-loop at node e_4. The final step, involving the elimination of e_2 from the diagram, results in Fig. 2.18(d). Thus, moving the terminal end of the branch t_{42} is a simple operation requiring only redefinition of the node variable e_2 if the only path leaving e_2 in the original diagram is the one to e_3.†

(4)   The starting end of a branch can be moved one node, as outlined

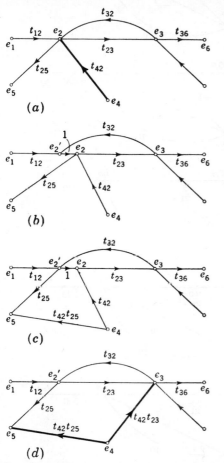

(a)

(b)

(c)

(d)

FIG. 2.18. Changes required if terminal end of a branch moved one node.

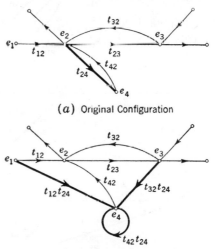

(a) Original Configuration

(b) Equivalent Diagram

FIG. 2.19. Changes required if starting end of a branch moved one node.

in Fig. 2.19.   Part (a) of the figure shows the original signal-flow diagram, in which the origin of the t_{24} branch is to be moved to e_3.   The change can be determined either by manipulation of the signal-flow diagram or by consideration of the equations.   If the latter method is used,

† Alternatively, the translation can be accomplished by adding a branch from e_4 to e_6 and replacing the node variable e_3 by a new variable e_3' equal to $e_3 + (t_{42}/t_{32})e_4$. In this case, the terminal end of the original t_{42} branch is moved along the t_{32} path, and the final transmittance from e_4 to e_3 is t_{42}/t_{32}. This alternative procedure is not ordinarily used, however, because it involves dividing by the transmittance t_{32}. As indicated in Sec. 2.1, such a division means that the transmittances in the modified diagram may not be stable.

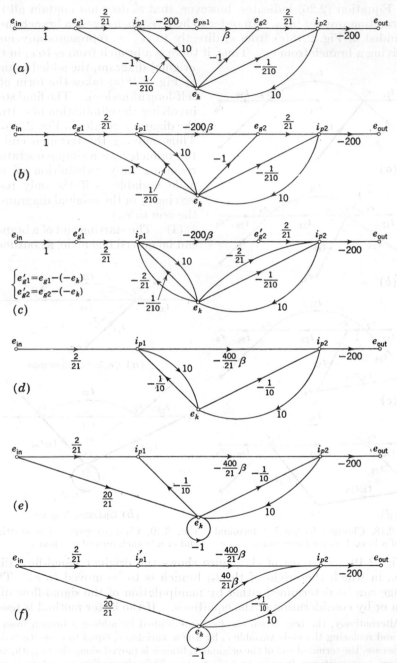

FIG. 2.20. Step-by-step reduction to an essential diagram. (Resist-

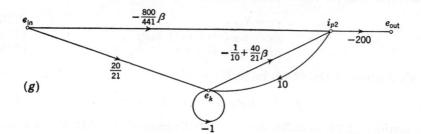

(g)

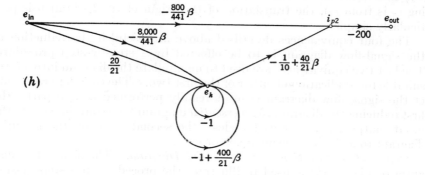

(h)

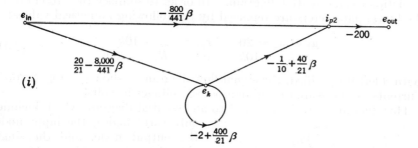

(i)

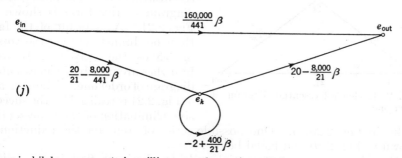

(j)

ances in kilohms, currents in milliamps, voltages in volts.)

the equations for the original diagram are

$$e_4 = t_{24}e_2 \tag{2.27}$$
$$e_2 = t_{42}e_4 + t_{12}e_1 + t_{32}e_3 \tag{2.28}$$
$$e_3 = t_{23}e_2 + \cdot \cdot \cdot \tag{2.29}$$

Substitution of Eq. (2.28) in (2.27) yields

$$e_4 = t_{42}t_{24}e_4 + t_{12}t_{24}e_1 + t_{32}t_{24}e_3 \tag{2.30}$$

Equations (2.28) to (2.30) describe the diagram of Fig. 2.19(b). Clearly, if t_{42} and t_{12} are zero in the original diagram (i.e., if the only branch entering e_2 is from e_3), the translation of the origin of the t_{24} branch is particularly simple.

The four equivalences described above are useful if the reduction of the signal-flow diagram is to be effected by a step-by-step procedure. The last two equivalences are used to manipulate the diagram into a form suitable for application of either of the first two. The complete reduction of the signal-flow diagram is most readily performed in two parts, the first reducing the diagram to an *essential* diagram (one containing only the input, output, and essential nodes), the second reducing the essential diagram to a single transmittance or gain.

Step-by-step Reduction to an Essential Diagram. The signal-flow diagram of Fig. 2.7(h) is used to illustrate the procedure in a step-by-step reduction to an essential diagram. In order to simplify the presentation, the literal parameters are replaced by the following numerical values:

$$\mu_1 = \mu_2 = 20 \qquad r_{p1} = r_{p2} = 10k$$
$$R_k = 10k \qquad R'_{L1} = R_{L2} = 200k \tag{2.31}$$

With β left unspecified, the signal-flow diagram is shown in Fig. 2.20(a). Currents are measured in milliamperes, voltages in volts.

This diagram is to be reduced to an essential diagram which includes only three nodes: the input node, the output node, and the single essential node e_k. The most general diagram of this form is shown in Fig. 2.21. As a result of the fact that no branch enters the input or leaves the output, only four branches are possible in an essential diagram of order one. The diagram of Fig. 2.21 is realized by the successive elimination of the nonessential

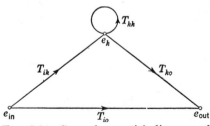

FIG. 2.21. General essential diagram of order one.

nodes in Fig. 2.20(a). One possible series of steps for the reduction is shown in Fig. 2.20 and listed below:

(1)   The obvious nonessential node to eliminate first is e_{pn1}. The equivalent diagram is shown in Fig. 2.20(b), where the tandem combination of the transmittances -200 and β is replaced by a single transmittance -200β.

(2)   The removal of e_{g1} can be effected if the termination of the branch from e_k to e_{g1} is moved one node forward, from e_{g1} to i_{p1}. This translation can be carried out if the transmittance -1 is multiplied by that from e_{g1} to i_{p1}. The node which was e_{g1} is then e_{g1} minus the contribution which entered along the -1 path, but i_{p1} and all other nodes are unchanged. Figure 2.20(c) illustrates the modification and the same change in the -1 branch from e_k to e_{g2}.

(3)   The nodes e'_{g1} and e'_{g2} can now be removed in the same manner in which e_{pn1} was originally deleted. In addition, the two parallel branches from e_k to i_{p1} and the two from e_k to i_{p2} can be combined into single branches. The two simplifications are shown in part (d) of the figure.

(4)   The variables i_{p1} and i_{p2} must be eliminated before an essential diagram is obtained. If i_{p1} is to be removed first, the origin of the branch from i_{p1} with transmittance 10 is moved from i_{p1} to e_{in}. The signal-flow diagram takes the form shown in Fig. 2.20(e). The extra self-loop at node e_k must be added, as indicated in Fig. 2.19. The transmittance of the self-loop is equal to that in Fig. 2.20(d) from e_k to i_{p1} and back to e_k.

(5)   The termination of the branch from e_k to i_{p1} is moved to i_{p2}, and a new variable i'_{p1} is defined,

$$i'_{p1} = i_{p1} - (-\tfrac{1}{10})e_k \tag{2.32}$$

Figure 2.20(f) results.

(6)   The node i'_{p1} is removed, and the two parallel branches from e_k to i_{p2} are combined. Figure 2.20(g) demonstrates that the elimination of i_{p1} is now completed, and i_{p2} is the only remaining node which does not appear in the essential diagram.

(7) i_{p2} is eliminated in exactly the same way as i_{p1}; the steps are shown in parts (h), (i), and (j) of the figure. The result is the essential diagram, Fig. 2.20(j).

The seven steps above illustrate the techniques for the step-by-step reduction of a signal-flow diagram to an essential diagram. Ordinarily, a number of branches can be combined at once, especially if the original diagram has been drawn without any particular efforts to minimize the number of variables used to describe the circuit. The reduction is continued by moving the terminating and originating ends of branches, corresponding to appropriate changes of variables, in order to realize a diagram in which nodes can be eliminated by inspection. Clearly, a number of the steps listed in the example above can be combined; in fact, this combination can be carried to the point where the reduction can be entirely effected in one step, as described in the following paragraph.

Single-step Reduction to Essential Diagram. The original signal-flow diagram can be reduced to an essential diagram in the following manner. The reduction is illustrated by the previous example, with the signal-flow diagram shown in Fig. 2.22(a). The essential diagram contains the input and output nodes and essential nodes equal in number to the order of the diagram. In this case, the essential diagram takes the form shown in Fig. 2.22(b), with the nodes e_{in} and e_{out} and the single essential node e_k.

In an essential diagram of order one, there are only four possible transmittances, T_{io}, T_{ik}, T_{ko}, and T_{kk}.†

The determination of the essential diagram resolves to an evaluation of these four transmittances. But the four transmittances can be found by inspection of the original signal-flow diagram. As an example, T_{io}

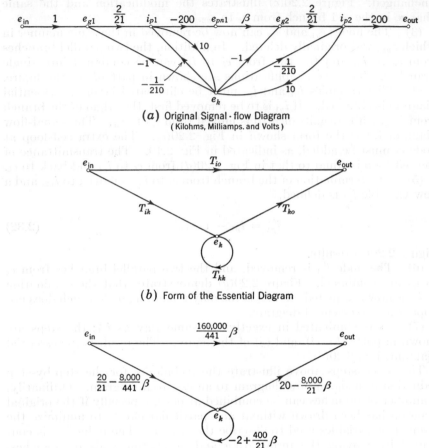

(*a*) Original Signal - flow Diagram
(Kilohms, Milliamps. and Volts)

(*b*) Form of the Essential Diagram

(*c*) Essential Diagram

Fig. 2.22. Single-step reduction to essential diagram.

measures the total transmission from input to output without passing through the node e_k. Figure 2.22(*a*) indicates that there is only one path, the horizontal path, from input to output; any downward digression immediately leads to e_k. Hence,

$$T_{io} = (1)(\tfrac{2}{21})(-200)(\beta)(\tfrac{2}{21})(-200) \tag{2.33}$$

$$T_{io} = \frac{160,000}{441}\beta \tag{2.34}$$

† Capital letters are used in this example to denote transmittances in the essential diagram.

T_{ik}, the total transmittance from the input to e_k without departing from e_k, is somewhat more complicated because of the existence of two parallel paths. From e_{in} there is only one possible path, to e_{g1}. Again, from e_{g1} there is no alternative but the path to i_{p1}. From i_{p1}, however, there are two parallel paths to e_k: one direct path through a branch with a transmittance 10; the other, through e_{pn1}, e_{g2}, and i_{p2}. The total T_{ik} is the sum of these two transmittances:

$$T_{ik} = (1)(\tfrac{2}{21})[(10) + (-200)(\beta)(\tfrac{2}{21})(10)] \qquad (2.35)$$
$$T_{ik} = \tfrac{20}{21} - \tfrac{8000}{441}\beta \qquad (2.36)$$

T_{ko}, measuring the total transmission from the essential node to the output without entering the node e_k, is the sum of four separate transmittances, representing the four possible paths of departure from e_k:

$$T_{ko} = \underbrace{(-1)(\tfrac{2}{21})(-200)(\beta)(\tfrac{2}{21})(-200)}_{\text{Departure toward } e_{g1}} + \underbrace{(-\tfrac{1}{210})(-200)(\beta)(\tfrac{2}{21})(-200)}_{\text{Departure toward } i_{p1}}$$
$$+ \underbrace{(-1)(\tfrac{2}{21})(-200)}_{\text{Departure toward } e_{g2}} + \underbrace{(-\tfrac{1}{210})(-200)}_{\text{Departure toward } i_{p2}} \qquad (2.37)$$

T_{kk}, also, can be calculated by considering each of the four paths leaving e_k:

$$T_{kk} = \underbrace{(-1)(\tfrac{2}{21})[(10) + (-200)(\beta)(\tfrac{2}{21})(10)]}_{\text{Departure toward } e_{g1}}$$
$$+ \underbrace{(-\tfrac{1}{210})[(10) + (-200)(\beta)(\tfrac{2}{21})(10)]}_{\text{Departure toward } i_{p1}} + \underbrace{(-1)(\tfrac{2}{21})(10)}_{\text{Departure toward } e_{g2}}$$
$$+ \underbrace{(-\tfrac{1}{210})(10)}_{\text{Departure toward } i_{p2}} \qquad (2.38)$$

Actually a number of terms in each of the last two equations can be combined, but as a general procedure it is convenient to consider individually the paths leaving the node. The two equations (2.37) and (2.38) can be simplified to yield, with (2.34) and (2.36), the essential transmittances shown in Fig. 2.22(c). The values are, of course, identical with those derived in the step-by-step reduction process.

This methodical procedure for evaluation of the essential transmittances can also be incorporated into the step-by-step reduction process. The elimination of any single node (except an essential node) can be accomplished by drawing the signal-flow diagram without the undesired node. All possible transmittances are shown in this diagram and are evaluated one by one from the original diagram. For example, the extended analysis required in connection with Fig. 2.20(e) to eliminate i_{p1} can be carried out very simply with this approach.

Exactly the same techniques are used to determine essential diagrams of higher order. The most general forms for essential diagrams of order two and three are shown in Fig. 2.23. Once the order of the signal-flow diagram is determined, the essential diagram can be found by evaluation of the required essential transmittances.

Characteristics of the Reduction. Regardless of the method used, reduction of the signal-flow diagram to an essential diagram has one very important characteristic: the essential transmittances are the sums and products of transmittances of the original diagram. There is no division involved. Thus, if all transmittances in the original diagram are stable (*i.e.*, without poles in the right-half plane), as is ordinarily the case if the diagram describing circuit behavior is written by inspection of the circuit,

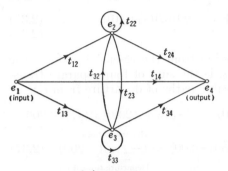

(*a*) Order Two

all essential transmittances are also stable. For the purposes of stability analysis, the simpler essential diagram can be used in preference to the more complex multiloop signal-flow diagram drawn from the circuit.

In terms of that manipulation of the equations which corresponds to reduction of the signal-flow diagram, the reduction to an essential diagram corresponds to elimination of variables in the original equations by direct substitution. No dividing of coefficients is necessary. In a stability analysis, the essential diagram is a picture of the essential complexity of the feedback system.

Reduction of the Essential Diagram. The essential diagram represents an intermediate stage in the determination of the over-all system function. The reduction of the essential diagram to a single transmittance relating input and output requires the removal of a self-loop, a loop starting and ending on the same node, as shown in

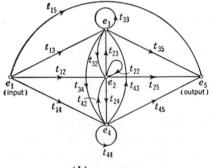

(*b*) Order Three

FIG. 2.23. Essential diagrams.

the most basic form in Fig. 2.24(*a*). Such a self-loop, with loop transmittance t_{22}, can be removed if all inputs to the node are divided by $1 - t_{22}$. This relationship is established from the equations describing the system of Fig. 2.24(*a*):

$$e_2 = e_1 + t_{22}e_2 \qquad (2.39)$$
$$e_3 = e_2 \qquad (2.40)$$

Equation (2.39) can be written

$$e_2 = \frac{1}{1 - t_{22}} e_1 \qquad (2.41)$$

The corresponding signal-flow diagram is shown in Fig. 2.24(*b*). The equivalence of the two parts of Fig. 2.24 can also be deduced from physical reasoning. If it is assumed, with reference to part (a) of the figure, that e_3 is unity, e_2 must also be unity. But the value of e_2 is the sum of the entering signals. Since the signal arriving on the t_{22} path has a value t_{22}, the signal entering from e_1 must have the value $1 - t_{22}$. Hence, e_1 is $1 - t_{22}$, and

$$\frac{e_2}{e_1} = \frac{1}{1 - t_{22}} \tag{2.42}$$

The reduction of the essential diagram of order one depends upon a single application of this principle. Figure 2.25(a) represents the essential diagram; part (b) of the figure, the simplified diagram if the self-loop at node e_k is removed; and part (c), the equivalent single transmittance. Once the loop is removed, the diagram possesses no essential nodes and the over-all transmittance is found from the addition of the transmittances of the parallel paths:

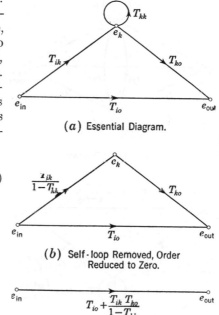

$$T = T_{io} + \frac{T_{ik} T_{ko}}{1 - T_{kk}} \tag{2.43}$$

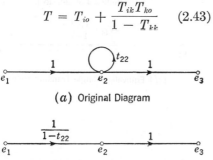

(a) Essential Diagram.

(b) Self-loop Removed, Order Reduced to Zero.

(c) Equivalent Transmittance.

FIG. 2.25. Reduction of essential diagram of order one.

(a) Original Diagram

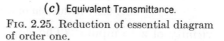

(b) Equivalent Diagram

FIG. 2.24. Removal of a self-loop.

The reduction of the essential diagram of order two is a two-step procedure. The general form of the diagram is shown in Fig. 2.26(a). The self-loop at node e_2 is first removed by dividing the transmittances of all other paths entering e_2 by $1 - t_{22}$. The resulting diagram, Fig. 2.26(b), is of order one with one nonessential node, e_2, and can be reduced to an essential diagram in the usual way. The self-loop at e_3 is then removed to reduce the order to zero and yield the over-all transmittance. The reduction of essential diagrams of even higher orders is effected by repeated application of the above procedure.

The example considered in detail previously is used to illustrate this reduction. The essential diagram for the circuit of Fig. 2.6 is shown in Fig. 2.22(c). Substitution of the values of the essential transmittances in Eq. (2.43) results in the over-all gain,

$$T = \frac{e_{\text{out}}}{e_{\text{in}}} = \frac{160,000}{441}\beta + \frac{(\frac{20}{21} - \frac{8000}{441}\beta)(20 - \frac{8000}{21}\beta)}{3 - \frac{400}{21}\beta} \qquad (2.44)$$

One application of the circuit is as a limiter,† in which case β is adjusted to make the theoretical gain of the linear circuit infinite. The appropriate value of β is $\frac{63}{400}$. The resulting input-output characteristic takes the form shown in Fig. 2.27, with a very sharp break in the curve in the

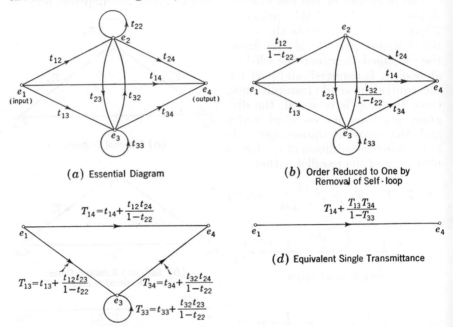

(a) Essential Diagram

(b) Order Reduced to One by Removal of Self-loop

(c) Essential Diagram of Order One

(d) Equivalent Single Transmittance

FIG. 2.26. Reduction of essential diagram of order two.

vicinity of zero input. (The slope at the origin is infinite if the system is linear.)

Comments on the Reduction Process. The signal-flow diagrams provide a guide to a logical sequence of operations in the solution of a set of simultaneous linear equations describing system behavior. The diagrams permit simple determination of the variables (the nonessential nodes) which can be eliminated at the outset of the analysis without extensive labor. Throughout the reduction, the engineer is aware of the part of the system with which he is working and the correspondence

† In much the same way the circuit can be used as an integrator (for example, in feedback control systems) if frequency-dependent negative feedback is added (no feedback at zero frequency, and feedback added as the frequency increases in order to reduce the gain). *Cf.* G. E. Valley, Jr., and H. Wallman, "Vacuum Tube Amplifiers," MIT Radiation Laboratory Series, Vol. 18, pp. 482–483, McGraw-Hill Book Company, Inc., New York, 1948.

between his mathematical manipulations and the physical circuit. If the original signal-flow diagram is drawn to correspond as closely as possible with the actual flow of signals, the analyst retains a picture of circuit operation.

For example, if the circuit is essentially the tandem combination of two simpler circuits, the signal-flow diagram may place this equivalence in evidence in cases in which the set of simultaneous equations does not. If a complicated diagram can be manipulated into a form in which a line cutting through the diagram can be drawn such that all branches crossing this line are directed from left to right, the system can be considered as the tandem combination of two simple systems: one to the left of the line, the other to the right. This situation, portrayed in Fig. 2.28, is termed

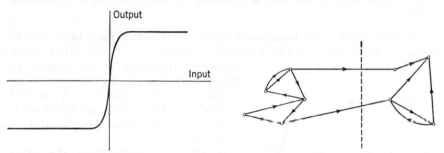

FIG. 2.27. Output-input characteristic of cathode-coupled limiter.

FIG. 2.28. Diagram in form for partitioning.

by Mason *partitioning* of the signal-flow diagram. In terms of the simultaneous equations, the signal-flow diagram in the form amenable to partitioning is equivalent to the equations in such a form that the determinant can be factored into the product of determinants of lower order.†

In every case, the advantages associated with working in terms of the signal-flow diagrams are basically the advantages accruing from the pictorial representation of the equations. Nothing can be done with the signal-flow diagrams that cannot be done with the equations. Arguments for the use of the diagrams must be based on the greater ease with which analysis is carried out. Although such an argument can be convincingly presented in terms of the ideas presented in this and preceding sections of this chapter, the advantages of signal-flow diagrams are most pronounced when some of the more specialized aspects of feedback theory are considered. For example, the next section indicates the manner in which an analysis based on signal-flow diagrams simplifies the concept of return difference, a concept which tends to be elusive when described in terms of the simultaneous equations and the corresponding determinants.

2.4. Return Difference. Although feedback may appear unintentionally in systems far more numerous than those in which it is purpose-

† E. A. Guillemin, "The Mathematics of Circuit Analysis," pp. 11–12, John Wiley & Sons, Inc., New York, 1949.

fully introduced, the situations of primary interest to the designer of feedback systems are those in which he is using feedback for a definite purpose. Usually this definite purpose falls into one of the following categories:

(1) Simplification of the practical realization of a specified transfer function (*e.g.*, the low-frequency selective amplifiers using RC networks in the feedback path to realize the characteristics of a tuned RLC network).

(2) Reduction of the sensitivity of the system characteristics to changes in one or more parameters.

(3) Control over the impedance seen looking into the system at various points.

(4) Simultaneous control over a number of different transmittances, corresponding to multiple inputs to the single system.

(5) Control over the stability, or instability, of the system, as in an oscillator circuit.

In the first application mentioned above, feedback is used primarily to overcome limitations of the physical components. In all other cases,

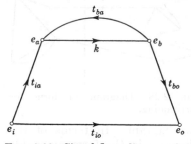

FIG. 2.29. Signal-flow diagram for definition of return difference with reference to k.

however, feedback is introduced to effect a specific change in the characteristics of the system. A unified analysis of these four applications is based upon a mathematical description of the feedback.

In all these applications, the effect of feedback can be measured by a quantity termed the *return difference*. The return difference referred to a particular parameter k is most readily defined in terms of the signal-flow diagram. The diagram is drawn in such a way that k appears in only one branch and as the transmittance of that branch. One suitable form for the diagram is shown in Fig. 2.29. In general, a leakage transmission exists from input to output, a transmission resulting in a system gain (t_{io}) even if k is made zero. There is a branch (with transmittance t_{ia}) from the input to the origin of the k branch, a branch (with transmittance t_{bo}) from the terminal of the k branch to the system output, and a feedback branch (with transmittance t_{ba}) around the k branch.

A given signal-flow diagram, containing k as a multiplier in only one branch, can always be manipulated into this form, for, since no branch enters e_i or leaves e_o, the only other possible branches are those from e_i to e_b (with transmittance t_{ib}) and e_a to e_o (with transmittance t_{ao}). The former can be avoided by definition of a new e_b' equal to $e_b - t_{ib}e_i$ and elimination of the e_b node to realize a diagram in terms of the variables e_i, e_a, e_b', and e_o. Likewise, a branch with transmittance t_{ao} can be circumvented by introducing a new node variable e_a' part way along the k branch. e_a' is defined as $e_a \times (1)$, and the diagram is then reduced to one with only the nodes e_i, e_a', e_b, and e_o.

The return difference with reference to k is defined in the following way:

the system is broken at the beginning of the branch with transmittance k.
Figure 2.30 shows the break, with the points α and α' on either side.
From α', a *unit* signal is transmitted, and the signal returning to α is
determined.   (In this determination, the system input, e_i of Fig. 2.30,
is set equal to zero.)   The difference between the transmitted and
returned signal is the return difference.   In terms of the transmittances
of the diagram of Fig. 2.30, the return difference with reference to k,
denoted as F_k, is given by the relation

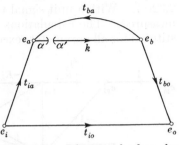

$$F_k = 1 - kt_{ba} \qquad (2.45)$$

With the transmitted signal equal to
unity, the returned signal is kt_{ba}.   If the
signal-flow diagram is always manipulated into the form of Fig. 2.29, the return
difference might equally well be defined
directly from Eq. (2.45).   In general, the
effort required to convert the diagram to
this form is unwarranted; the return
difference can be calculated directly from

FIG. 2.30. Diagram broken for
calculation of F_k.

the original signal-flow diagram drawn from the study of the physical system.
The return difference with reference to a given element is a quantitative measure of the feedback around the element.   In the single-loop
system shown in Fig. 2.31, for example, the return difference with reference to K is just $1 - \beta K$.   As a quantitative measure of the feedback,
the return difference not only indicates the effect of the feedback in
controlling system impedances and sensitivity, but also serves as the
basis for stability analysis.   In the single-loop case, for example, the

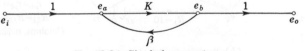

FIG. 2.31. Single-loop system.

location of the zeros of the return difference determines the stability of the
system if both K and β are stable transfer functions.
The cathode-coupled limiter analyzed in detail in the previous section
can be used to illustrate the calculation of the return difference.   The
return difference with reference to the cathode resistance R_k is desired.
In the signal-flow diagram, shown in Fig. 2.7(h), the parameter R_k
appears as a multiplying factor in the transmittances of two branches,
one from i_{p1} to e_k, the other from i_{p2} to e_k.† The two branches represent
the two components in the equation

$$e_k = R_k(i_{p1} + i_{p2}) \qquad (2.46)$$

The diagram can be modified to one in which R_k appears only once if the
current i_k is defined as the sum of the plate currents.   Equation (2.46)

† If the reference element appears in the denominator of a transmittance, the
signal-flow diagram (or the equations describing system behavior) must be rewritten.

is then equivalent to the two equations

$$i_k = i_{p1} + i_{p2} \tag{2.47}$$
$$e_k = R_k i_k \tag{2.48}$$

The signal-flow diagram is shown in Fig. 2.32(a).

F_{R_k}, the return difference with reference to R_k, is calculated by setting e_{in} equal to zero and breaking the diagram at α and α', shown in Fig. 2.32(b). With a unit signal transmitted from α', the signal reaching α is measured. The calculations are simplified if numerical values are substituted for all parameters except β and R_k. The values used are identical

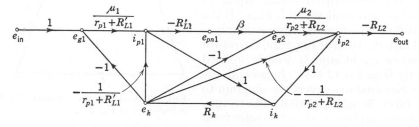

(a) Signal-flow Diagram of Fig. 2.7 (h) with R_k Alone

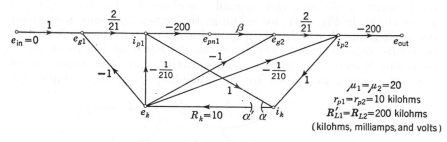

(b) Diagram for Calculation of F_{R_k}

Fig. 2.32. Calculation of F_{R_k} for cathode-coupled limiter.

with those of Eq. (2.31) and are given in the figure. The signal leaving α' flows to e_k, at which point there are four parallel paths. e_k is transmitted along each of the four. If one path is considered at a time,

$$F_{R_k} = 1 - R_k\{(-1)(\tfrac{2}{21})[(1) + (-200)(\beta)(\tfrac{2}{21})(1)]$$
$$+ (-\tfrac{1}{210})[(1) + (-200)(\beta)(\tfrac{2}{21})(1)]$$
$$+ (-1)(\tfrac{2}{21})(1) + (-\tfrac{1}{210})(1)\} \tag{2.49}$$

The signal returning is actually equal to the essential transmittance T_{kk}, evaluated in the preceding section. Simplification of Eq. (2.49) yields

$$F_{R_k} = 1 - R_k(-\tfrac{2}{10} + \tfrac{40}{21}\beta) \tag{2.50}$$

This example is sufficiently simple that Eq. (2.49), for the return difference, can be written by inspection of the signal-flow diagram. In more complex cases, the returned signal can be evaluated by redrawing the signal-flow diagram with α' as the input node and α as the output and by applying the usual reduction techniques to obtain the over-all transmittance from α' to α. Use of the signal-flow diagram results in the outline of a direct procedure for the calculation of the return difference.

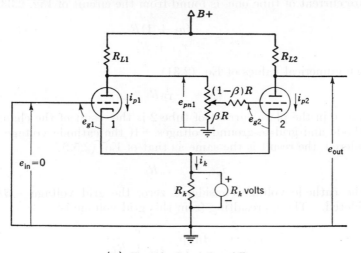

(a) Circuit for Calculation of F_{R_k}

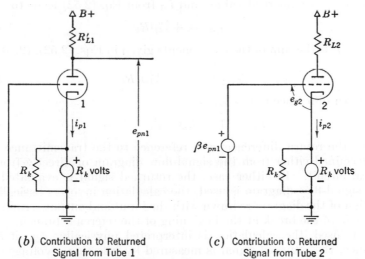

(b) Contribution to Returned   (c) Contribution to Returned
Signal from Tube 1   Signal from Tube 2

FIG. 2.33. Determination of F_{R_k} from circuit directly.

The return difference can also be interpreted in terms of the physical circuit. In the above example, F_{R_k} has the following significance: the loop is broken at α and α', with the result that all feedback loops are opened. Changes in i_k no longer affect the cathode voltage e_k. The transmission of a unit signal from α' corresponds to raising e_k by R_k volts. The returned signal is the change in i_k resulting from this e_k. In the circuit, the measurement is equivalent to placing across R_k a generator of R_k volts and measuring the resulting change in i_k. The test circuit is shown in Fig. 2.33(a). Since there is no cathode degeneration, the two tubes do not interact and can be analyzed separately. i_{p1}, the change in the plate current of tube one, is found from the circuit of Fig. 2.33(b):

$$i_{p1} = -\frac{(\mu_1 + 1)R_k}{r_{p1} + R'_{L1}} \tag{2.51}$$

With the numerical values of Eq. (2.31),

$$i_{p1} = -\tfrac{1}{10}R_k \tag{2.52}$$

The change in the plate current of tube 2 is the result of the changes in the cathode and grid-to-ground voltages. If the cathode voltage alone is considered, the result is the same as that of Eq. (2.52),

$$i_{p2_1} = -\tfrac{1}{10}R_k \tag{2.53}$$

With the cathode voltage considered zero, the grid voltage $-\beta R'_{L1}i_{p1}$ is considered. The i_{p2} resulting from this grid voltage is

$$i_{p2_2} = -\beta R'_{L1}i_{p1}\frac{\mu_2}{r_{p2} + R_{L2}} \tag{2.54}$$

Substitution of numerical values and i_{p1} from Eq. (2.52) leads to

$$i_{p2_2} = +\tfrac{40}{21}\beta R_k \tag{2.55}$$

The total i_k is the sum of the components given in Eqs. (2.52), (2.53), and (2.55),

$$i_k = (-\tfrac{2}{10} + \tfrac{40}{21}\beta)R_k \tag{2.56}$$

The return difference is $1 - i_k$, or

$$F_{R_k} = 1 - R_k(-\tfrac{2}{10} + \tfrac{40}{21}\beta) \tag{2.57}$$

Thus, the return difference with reference to the transmittance k can be determined either from the signal-flow diagram or directly from the physical circuit. In either case, the returned signal is evaluated first. If the signal-flow diagram is used, the calculation involves basically the reduction of the diagram redrawn with the input and output terminals on either side of the break at the beginning of the reference branch. If the circuit is used, the calculation is interpreted physically: $e.g.$, if k is a resistance, the returned signal is measured by inserting a voltage across the resistor and measuring the resulting change of current through the parallel combination of resistor and generator. If k is a tube transconductance g_m, the returned signal is evaluated by assuming that the current generator $(g_m e_g)$ in the equivalent circuit has a value of g_m amp and determining the change in e_g resulting from this current. If k is the tube amplification factor μ, a similar procedure is used except that the voltage generator (μe_g) in the series equivalent circuit is assumed to be μ volts. In the determination of the return difference with reference to either

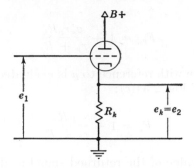

(a) Cathode-follower Circuit

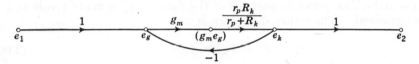

(b) Signal-flow Diagram for Calculation of F_{g_m}

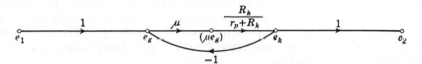

(c) Diagram for Calculation of F_μ

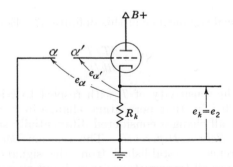

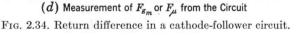

(d) Measurement of F_{g_m} or F_μ from the Circuit

Fig. 2.34. Return difference in a cathode-follower circuit.

g_m or μ, the procedure is equivalent to breaking the circuit at the grid terminal of the tube, applying a unit grid-to-cathode signal, and measuring the voltage across the break.

The calculation of the return difference with reference to g_m or μ is clarified by consideration of the cathode-follower circuit of Fig. 2.34(*a*). One form of the signal-flow diagram is shown in part (*b*) of the figure. The return difference with reference to g_m is evaluated by inspection of the diagram:

$$F_{g_m} = 1 + \frac{g_m r_p R_k}{r_p + R_k} \tag{2.58}$$

The return difference with reference to μ is evaluated in a similar fashion from the diagram of Fig. 2.34(c):

$$F_\mu = 1 + \frac{\mu R_k}{r_p + R_k} \tag{2.59}$$

In either case, the value of the returned signal is also apparent directly from the circuit. The system input signals are replaced by the internal impedances (in this case, e_1 is set equal to zero), and the circuit is broken at α and α', as shown in part (d) of the figure. e'_α is made 1 volt and e_α is measured. The return difference is

$$F_\mu = F_{g_m} = 1 - e_\alpha \tag{2.60}$$

2.5. Sensitivity. The return difference is a direct measure of the effects of feedback on system sensitivity (*i.e.*, the degree of dependence of the system gain on the value of a particular element). Before the relation between return difference and sensitivity can be stated explicitly, it is necessary to have a quantitative measure of sensitivity. The sensitivity of an over-all gain or transmittance T with respect to a given parameter k is defined by the equation

$$S_k^T = \frac{d \ln T}{d \ln k} \tag{2.61}$$

What is the physical significance of this definition? Equation (2.61) can be written

$$S_k^T = \frac{dT/T}{dk/k} \tag{2.62}$$

In other words, the sensitivity of T with respect to k is the percentage change in T divided by that percentage change in k which causes the change in T, with all changes considered differentially small.†

Sensitivity and Return Difference. The relation between sensitivity and return difference is established from the signal-flow diagram of Fig. 2.35. The over-all transmittance from input to output is

$$T = \frac{e_o}{e_i} = t_{io} + \frac{t_{ia} k t_{bo}}{1 - k t_{ba}} \tag{2.63}$$

---

† The definition given by Bode is the reciprocal of that of Eq. (2.61), as he defines the sensitivity as the percentage change in k divided by the resulting percentage change in T. Since feedback is ordinarily used to reduce the effects of the variation of a system parameter such as tube gain or operating voltage, the ideal system in Bode's notation is one with infinite sensitivity; in Mason's definition [Eq. (2.61)], which is used throughout this chapter, the ideal system has zero sensitivity.

Equation (2.62) states that the sensitivity can be expressed by the equation

$$S_k^T = \frac{k}{T} \frac{dT}{dk} \qquad (2.64)$$

The derivative dT/dk can be evaluated from Eq. (2.63):

$$\frac{dT}{dk} = \frac{t_{ia}t_{bo}}{(1 - kt_{ba})^2} \qquad (2.65)$$

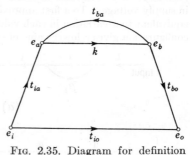

Substitution of Eqs. (2.63) and (2.65) in (2.64) yields

$$S_k^T = \frac{kt_{ia}t_{bo}}{T(1 - kt_{ba})^2} \qquad (2.66)$$

The return difference with reference to k is simply $1 - kt_{ba}$. Hence, Eq. (2.66) can be written in terms of F_k, t_{io}, and T:

FIG. 2.35. Diagram for definition of sensitivity.

$$S_k^T = \frac{1}{F_k}\left(1 - \frac{t_{io}}{T}\right) \qquad (2.67)\star$$

The applications of Eq. (2.67) are illustrated by a number of simple examples:

(1) In the single-loop system (Fig. 2.36) if the sensitivity desired is with respect to the forward transmission, the leakage transmittance (t_{io}) is zero because with K

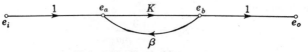

FIG. 2.36. Single-loop system.

equal to zero there is no transmission from input to output. The sensitivity is in this case the reciprocal of the return difference:

$$S_K^T = \frac{1}{F_K} = \frac{1}{1 - \beta K} \qquad (2.68)$$

(2) In the same single-loop system, if the sensitivity of interest is with respect to the feedback transmittance β, the leakage transmittance is K, and Eq. (2.67) yields

$$S_\beta^T = \frac{1}{1 - \beta K}\left(1 - \frac{K}{K/(1 - \beta K)}\right) \qquad (2.69)$$

Simplification of the equation gives

$$S_\beta^T = \frac{\beta K}{1 - \beta K} \qquad (2.70)$$

Comparison of Eqs. (2.68) and (2.70) demonstrates the well-known fact that a value of K large with respect to unity results in a system insensitive to changes in K but with the closed-loop gain essentially equal to $1/\beta$ and the sensitivity of T with respect to β approximately -1.

(3) Another example is furnished by an investigation of the comparative merits of the two configurations shown in Fig. 2.37. The two diagrams represent alternative designs for a feedback amplifier. Three amplifier stages are available, each with a gain of a, and the over-all gain to be realized is specified (less than a^3). Negative feedback is to be introduced to reduce the sensitivity of the over-all gain to variations in supply voltage. To a first approximation, this voltage variation can be considered equivalent to a variation in each value of a. The question to be answered is: Which configuration gives a lower value of sensitivity of the over-all gain with respect to a?

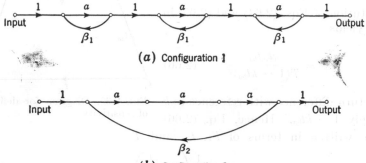

(a) Configuration 1

(b) Configuration 2

FIG. 2.37. Two configurations for three-stage amplifier with negative feedback.

For the first configuration [part (a) of the figure], the over-all gain T_1 is

$$\left[\frac{a}{(1 - \beta_1 a)}\right]^3$$

The sensitivity of T_1 with respect to a is three times the sensitivity of an individual stage with feedback, or

$$S_a^{T_1} = \frac{3}{1 - \beta_1 a} \tag{2.71}$$

For the second configuration, with a single over-all feedback path, the over-all gain T_2 is $a^3/(1 - \beta_2 a^3)$. The sensitivity of T_2 with respect to a is three times the sensitivity with respect to a^3. Hence,

$$S_a^{T_2} = \frac{3}{1 - \beta_2 a^3} \tag{2.72}$$

The two sensitivities of Eqs. (2.71) and (2.72) are to be compared on the basis of the equality of T_1 and T_2. This equality establishes the relation between β_1 and β_2,

$$(1 - \beta_1 a)^3 = 1 - \beta_2 a^3 \tag{2.73}$$

Substitution of Eq. (2.73) into (2.72) yields

$$S_a^{T_2} = \frac{3}{(1 - \beta_1 a)^3} \tag{2.74}$$

Comparison of Eqs. (2.74) and (2.71) indicates that the sensitivity of the second system is always less than that of the first if negative feedback is being used ($1 - \beta_1 a$ greater than unity). Thus, the single over-all feedback path results in a system with less sensitivity to changes in a.

Null Return Difference. The sensitivity can be related to the return difference in a somewhat different manner if the *null return difference* is defined. The null return difference is the return difference evaluated under the condition that the input is adjusted to give zero output. In terms of the signal-flow diagram of Fig. 2.38, for example, the null return difference is determined as follows: the diagram is broken at α and α', and a unit signal is transmitted from α'. The signal reaching e_b is k. This is transmitted back to e_a and also on to the output node e_o. At e_o, the signal kt_{bo} arrives along the branch from e_b. If the input is adjusted to make the output zero, the signal $-kt_{bo}$ must be arriving at e_o along the branch from e_i. Hence, e_i is $-kt_{bo}/t_{io}$. This input is also transmitted

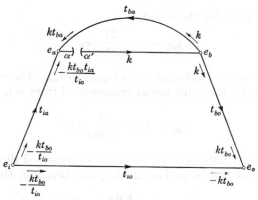

Fig. 2.38. Diagram for definition of null return difference.

along the branch from e_i to e_a, and the returned signal is the sum of the two signals arriving at e_a. F'_k, the null return difference with reference to k, is given by the relation

$$F'_k = 1 - \left(kt_{ba} - \frac{kt_{bo}t_{ia}}{t_{io}} \right) \qquad (2.75)$$

The return difference is measured with the input zero; the null return difference is measured with the input adjusted to make the output zero. Both return differences depend on the particular variables chosen as the input and output. The dependence on the choice of an output variable is obviously necessary if the return difference is to be a measure of the effect of the feedback on the characteristics of the over-all transmission. In terms of the signal-flow diagram of Fig. 2.38, this dependence corresponds to the changes in the various transmittances of the diagram if a change is made in that variable which is considered the output in the original signal-flow diagram.

The null return difference can be evaluated directly from the original signal-flow diagram in much the same manner as the return difference. The determination of the null return difference with respect to R_k in the cathode-coupled limiter previously analyzed serves as an example. The signal-flow diagram of the basic system is shown in Fig. 2.32. If the output is zero, i_{p2} must also be zero, with the result that the branch from i_{p2} to i_k can be omitted. In addition, the fact that i_{p2} is zero serves to fix the relation between e_{g2} and e_k, because i_{p2} consists of two contributions, one from e_k and the other from e_{g2}. In particular,

$$\tfrac{2}{21}e_{g2} = \tfrac{1}{210}e_k \tag{2.76}$$
$$e_{g2} = \tfrac{1}{20}e_k \tag{2.77}$$

If the process of working backward through the diagram is continued, it is found that Eq. (2.77) implies that

$$e_{pn1} = \frac{21}{20\beta}\,e_k \tag{2.78}$$

Likewise, i_{p1} is given by the equation

$$i_{p1} = -\frac{21}{4000\beta}\,e_k \tag{2.79}$$

The returned signal (arriving at α) is equal to i_{p1}. Consequently, since e_k is equal to R_k (with a unit signal transmitted from α'),

$$F'_{R_k} = 1 + \frac{21}{4000\beta}\,R_k \tag{2.80}$$

This null return difference can also be determined directly from the circuit diagram as shown in Fig. 2.39. The break in the circuit again

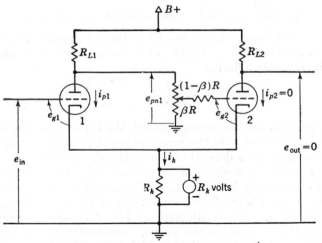

FIG. 2.39. Circuit for determination of F'_{R_k}.

corresponds to placing a voltage generator across R_k and measuring i_k. In this case, however, the input is not zero, but rather is adjusted to make the output, or i_{p2}, equal to zero. Tube 2 enters the evaluation of F'_{R_k} only in that the tube circuit specifies the required input voltage. With R_k volts applied to the cathode of tube 2, R_k/μ_2 volts must be the applied grid-to-cathode potential if i_{p2} is to be zero, since the grid-to-cathode voltage is μ_2 times as effective as the plate voltage in causing a change in the plate current. The grid-to-ground voltage must be $R_k(1 + 1/\mu_2)$, where the first term offsets the effect of the cathode potential on the grid-to-cathode voltage and the second term counteracts the decrease in plate current caused by the drop in plate-to-cathode potential when the cathode voltage is applied. The plate-to-ground voltage of tube 1 is $(1 + 1/\mu_2)R_k/\beta$ volts, and i_{p1} is

$$-\frac{(1 + 1/\mu_2)R_k}{\beta R'_{L1}}$$

With i_{p2} equal to zero, the returned signal is simply i_{p1}, and the null return difference is given by

$$F'_{R_k} = 1 + \frac{(1 + 1/\mu_2)R_k}{\beta R'_{L1}} \tag{2.81}$$

Substitution of the values for R'_{L1} (200) and μ_2 (20) gives

$$F'_{R_k} = 1 + \frac{21}{4000\beta} R_k \tag{2.82}$$

Sensitivity in Terms of Null Return Difference. The relation between the sensitivity and the null return difference is derived from the basic signal-flow diagram of Fig. 2.38. For this system,

$$S_k^T = \frac{1}{F_k}\left(1 - \frac{t_{io}}{T}\right) \tag{2.83}$$

From Eq. (2.75),

$$F'_k = F_k + \frac{t_{ia}kt_{bo}}{t_{io}} \tag{2.84}$$

The expression $t_{ia}kt_{bo}$ is expressed in terms of T, t_{io}, and F_k by Eq. (2.63). Substitution in Eq. (2.84) yields

$$F'_k = F_k + \frac{T - t_{io}}{t_{io}} F_k \tag{2.85}$$

Division by F_k gives an expression relating the over-all gain, the leakage transmittance, and the two return differences,

$$\frac{F'_k}{F_k} = \frac{T}{t_{io}} \tag{2.86}$$

Substitution of Eq. (2.86) in (2.83) leads to an expression for the sensitivity in terms of the two return differences,

$$S_k^T = \frac{1}{F_k} - \frac{1}{F'_k} \tag{2.87}\star$$

Equation (2.87) provides a direct basis for evaluation of the sensitivity of the gain of the cathode-coupled limiter with respect to changes in cathode resistance R_k. F_k and F'_k, the return difference and null return difference, are given by Eqs. (2.57) and (2.80), respectively. The resulting sensitivity is expressed by the equation

$$S^T_{R_k} = \cfrac{1}{1 - R_k\left(-\cfrac{2}{10} + \cfrac{40}{21}\beta\right)} - \cfrac{1}{1 + \cfrac{21}{4000\beta}R_k} \tag{2.88}$$

If the sensitivity is evaluated for an operating R_k of 10,

$$S^T_{R_k} = \cfrac{1}{3 - \cfrac{400}{21}\beta} - \cfrac{1}{1 + \cfrac{21}{400\beta}} \tag{2.89}$$

The concept of the null return difference is particularly useful in the calculation of sensitivity if the leakage transmission is not zero. If this transmission is zero, the null return difference does not exist, since no adjustment of the input results in zero output. If the leakage transmission is zero, however, the sensitivity is simply the reciprocal of the return difference.

Significance of Sensitivity. The concept of the sensitivity as a measure of the quality of the system requires further interpretation. The sensi-

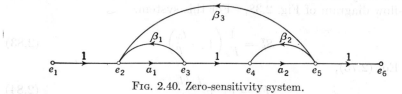

Fig. 2.40. Zero-sensitivity system.

tivity of a system gain with respect to a particular parameter is measured by the first logarithmic derivative of the gain with respect to the logarithm of the parameter. Involving only the first derivative, the sensitivity is a measure of system characteristics only for very small changes in the parameter. Specifically, the fact that the sensitivity is small in no way guarantees that higher derivatives are also small.

For example, a pedagogical problem of some practical interest relates to the design of zero-sensitivity systems. The signal-flow diagram of Fig. 2.40 is one example of such a system. The gain of the system is given by the relation

$$T = \frac{e_6}{e_1} = \frac{a_1 a_2}{(1 - a_1\beta_1)(1 - a_2\beta_2) - a_1 a_2\beta_3} \tag{2.90}$$

The sensitivity of T with respect to a_1 (or a_2) is determined from the return difference, since there is no leakage transmission:

$$S^T_{a_1} = \cfrac{1}{1 - a_1\left(\beta_1 + \cfrac{a_2\beta_3}{1 - a_2\beta_2}\right)} \tag{2.91}$$

$$S_{a_2}^T = \frac{1}{1 - a_2\left(\beta_2 + \dfrac{a_1\beta_3}{1 - a_1\beta_1}\right)} \qquad (2.92)$$

If $a_1\beta_1$ and $a_2\beta_2$ are unity, both sensitivities are zero and the over-all transmission is $-1/\beta_3$. The inner loops alone are unstable, and the over-all gain depends only on the negative feedback.

The derivation of other zero-sensitivity systems can be carried out by manipulation of signal-flow diagrams. Such configurations, however, serve primarily as a guide to the designer and should not be considered a complete synthesis procedure. Even if the practical difficulties associated with the realization of a configuration of the form of Fig. 2.40 are neglected, the system is not necessarily ideal. Although each of the sensitivities is zero for the design conditions, a small drift in $a_1\beta_1$ or $a_2\beta_2$ away from unity can lead to very sizable sensitivities. A sensitivity of zero merely indicates that the curve of gain versus the value of the variable parameter has zero slope at the operating point; there is no indication about the behavior off the operating point, and any of the three curves of Fig. 2.41 may describe the system.

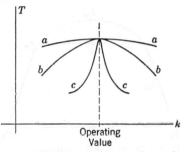

FIG. 2.41. Three curves for gain versus k, each curve for a zero-sensitivity system.

One additional factor complicates the application of the concept of sensitivity. In the general system, the sensitivity is a complicated function of the complex frequency s. A given percentage change in the parameter k generates different percentage changes in gain T, depending on the frequency. In a feedback system, the variation in sensitivity with frequency results in a variation in the nature of the transient response. At the present time, very little is known of the significance of the functional dependence of sensitivity on frequency.

2.6. Impedances. Feedback is commonly introduced to permit control of the impedances seen looking into the system at various points. For example, negative feedback is used in the output stages of the audio amplifier of certain communication receivers to realize a low output impedance, in order that load changes, represented by addition or subtraction of speakers or headphones in parallel with the output, do not cause large variations in output volume. If a variation in load impedance is not to change the output voltage, the output impedance must be much less than the load impedance. Another example to illustrate the use of feedback to control output impedance is furnished by a servomechanism driving a radar antenna. Gusts of wind must not cause large oscillations of the antenna position. The mechanical impedance seen looking into the system from the output must be high if impedance is defined as the ratio of force to velocity. In general, the effect of disturbing signals in a closed-loop system can be evaluated either in terms of the transmittance from the point of disturbance introduction to the output or by a consideration of the impedance seen looking into the system at this point of disturbance introduction.

Impedances in a feedback system are usually calculated most conveniently from the basic theorem presented by Bode.[†] The theorem can be stated by means of the equation

$$\frac{Z}{(Z)_{k=0}} = \frac{F'_k \text{ (with terminals shorted)}}{F_k \text{ (with terminals open)}} \qquad (2.93)\star$$

Here, Z is the impedance seen looking into a pair of terminals of the system, with each source replaced by its internal impedance; $(Z)_{k=0}$ is

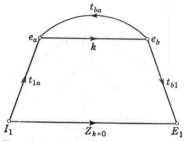

the same impedance when a specified element of the system is made zero; and F'_k and F_k are the null return difference and the return difference with reference to k. These return differences are evaluated for a system in which the input is the current into one of the terminals at which the impedance is being measured and out of the other terminal, and the output is the voltage between the two terminals. Hence F'_k is the return difference with reference to k with the ter-

FIG. 2.42. Signal-flow diagram for determination of impedance.

minals shorted, and F_k is the return difference with reference to k with the terminals open.

The validity of the theorem can be established directly from the signal-flow diagram of Fig. 2.42 and the partial circuit shown in Fig. 2.43. The impedance Z looking into two terminals of the circuit is to be evaluated, with all signal sources replaced by the appropriate internal impedances. The signal-flow diagram of Fig. 2.42 is constructed with $I_1(s)$ the current flowing into the circuit and $E_1(s)$ the resultant voltage between the two terminals. The impedance Z can be determined by finding the ratio E_1/I_1 from standard network analysis, by construction and subsequent reduction of the signal-flow diagram,

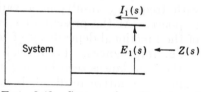

FIG. 2.43. System for diagram of Fig. 2.42.

or by application of the theorem of Eq. (2.93).

The proof of Eq. (2.93) follows if the various terms are identified with combinations of the transmittances of the signal-flow diagram of Fig. 2.42. Z is the over-all gain of the diagram and $(Z)_{k=0}$ is the gain with k equal to zero, or the leakage transmittance. F'_k, measured with the terminals shorted, is the return difference with reference to k and with the output E_1 equal to zero. Thus, F'_k is the null return difference with

† H. W. Bode, "Network Analysis and Feedback Amplifier Design," p. 68, D. Van Nostrand Company, Inc., New York, 1945.

reference to k for the diagram of Fig. 2.42. F_k is the return difference with the terminals open (*i.e.*, with I_1 equal to zero). Thus, Eq. (2.93) is nothing more than a restatement of Eq. (2.86) in terms of the signal-flow diagram for the calculation of impedances. Several examples illustrate the application of this theorem in the analysis of feedback systems.

Single-loop Feedback Amplifier. Application of the theorem to the analysis of the single-loop feedback amplifier drawn in Fig. 2.44 leads to two well-known relations of feedback theory.[†] The impedance seen from point A to ground is evaluated first, with the gain of the forward amplifier used as the reference element for the evaluation of the return

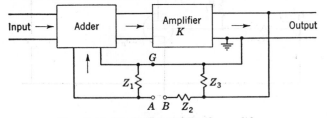

FIG. 2.44. Single-loop feedback amplifier.

differences. With the forward gain zero, $(Z_{AG})_{K=0}$ is merely the parallel combination of Z_1 and $Z_2 + Z_3$,

$$(Z_{AG})_{K=0} = \frac{Z_1(Z_2 + Z_3)}{Z_1 + Z_2 + Z_3} \tag{2.94}$$

The null return difference (evaluated with the terminals A and G shorted) is unity because the feedback is removed by the short circuit. The return difference with the terminals open (normal operation) is $1 - \beta K$, where K is the open-loop gain and β is the feedback gain. The impedance looking into the feedback circuit at terminals A and G is found from Eq. (2.93):

$$Z_{AG} = \frac{Z_1(Z_2 + Z_3)}{Z_1 + Z_2 + Z_3} \frac{1}{1 - \beta K} \tag{2.95}$$

If the feedback path is broken from A to B and the impedance measured looking into these two terminals, the value with K equal to zero is $Z_1 + Z_2 + Z_3$. The null return difference (evaluated with the terminals A and B shorted) is the normal value, $1 - \beta K$, and the return difference with the same terminals open (the feedback removed) is unity. Hence,

$$Z_{AB} = (Z_1 + Z_2 + Z_3)(1 - \beta K) \tag{2.96}$$

Equations (2.95) and (2.96) state that the impedance measured across the feedback path is divided by the return difference $1 - \beta K$, while that measured in any series line is multiplied by the return difference.

Input and Output Impedances of an Electronic Circuit. Analysis of the circuit of Fig. 2.45(*a*) illustrates the calculation of both input and output impedances. The corresponding signal-flow diagram can be drawn directly

[†] H. W. Bode, *op. cit.*, pp. 69–70.

from the circuit or from the linear incremental equivalent circuit of Fig. 2.45(b). It is desirable to draw the signal-flow diagram in a sufficiently general form that one diagram can be used for the evaluation of gain, input impedance, and output impedance. For the measurement of gain, e_1 is the input, e_2 is the output, and i_2 is zero. Output impedance can be measured

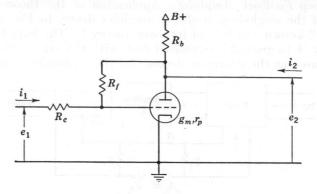

(a) Circuit Diagram.

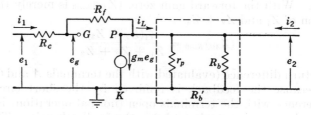

(b) Linear Equivalent Circuit

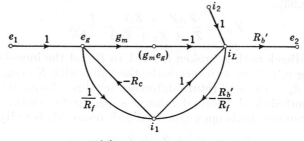

(c) Signal-flow Diagram.

Fig. 2.45. Determination of input admittance and output impedance.

with e_1 equal to zero, i_2 considered the input, and e_2 used as the output. If the input admittance, rather than the impedance, is calculated, e_1 is the input and i_1 the output. Thus, all three quantities can be determined from a diagram in which e_1 and i_2 appear as independent node variables and i_1 and e_2 as dependent variables. The signal-flow diagram is presented in Fig. 2.45(c). Here, R_b' represents the parallel combination of the actual plate load resistance and the dynamic plate resistance of the tube.

The input admittance is determined first. In terms of the admittance functions, Eq. (2.93) can be written

$$\frac{Y}{(Y)_{k=0}} = \frac{F'_k \text{ (with terminals open)}}{F_k \text{ (with terminals shorted)}} \tag{2.97}$$

Since, for the calculation of admittance, the signal-flow diagram uses the voltage between terminals as the input and the current as the output, F'_k, the null return difference, is evaluated with the terminals open (with the voltage adjusted to make the current zero). For the same reason, F_k is measured with the terminals shorted (i.e., with the input—E—equal to zero). Equation (2.97) can also be derived from (2.93) by replacing Z by $1/Y$. The term F'_k (with terminals open) in Eq. (2.97) is the same as the term F_k (with terminals open) in Eq. (2.93). In both cases, the term is the return difference with reference to k and evaluated with the terminals, between which the impedance or admittance is to be measured, left open. The prime appears in Eq. (2.97) and not in (2.93) because of the change in those variables which are considered as the input and output.

In order to use Eq. (2.97) for the calculation of the input admittance, the branch with transmittance g_m is taken as the reference element and the return differences are calculated under the assumptions that e_1 is the input, i_1 is the output, and i_2 is zero. The admittance with the tube dead $(g_m = 0)$ is read from the signal-flow diagram:

$$(Y_1)_{g_m=0} = \left(\frac{i_1}{e_1}\right)_{g_m=0} = \frac{1/R_f}{1 - (-R_c/R_f - R'_b/R_f)} = \frac{1}{R_c + R_f + R'_b} \tag{2.98}$$

This value for the admittance is also apparent from the circuit. Setting g_m equal to zero corresponds to replacing the tube by the passive resistance r_p. The input admittance, consequently, is that of the circuit shown in Fig. 2.46 and given by Eq. (2.98).

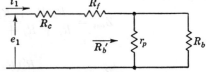

The return differences are now evaluated. F_{g_m}, the return difference with reference to g_m and evaluated

FIG. 2.46. Circuit of Fig. 2.45 with tube dead.

with e_1 equal to zero, is written from the signal-flow diagram:

$$F_{g_m} = 1 - \frac{g_m(-1)(-R'_b/R_f)(-R_c)}{1 - [(1)(-R'_b/R_f) + (-R_c)(1/R_f)]} \tag{2.99a}$$

$$F_{g_m} = 1 + \frac{g_m R'_b R_c}{R_c + R_f + R'_b} \tag{2.99b}$$

F'_{g_m} is the return difference evaluated with e_1 adjusted to make i_1 equal to zero. If i_1 is zero, e_g and e_2 are equal (otherwise, the current through R_f would not be zero). If a unit test signal is transmitted through the g_m branch, the output, with i_1 equal to zero, is simply $-g_m R'_b$. Consequently, the returned signal is $-g_m R_b'$, and

$$F_{g_m}' = 1 + g_m R_b' \qquad (2.100)$$

The input admittance is derived by substitution of Eqs. (2.98), (2.99), and (2.100) in (2.97):

$$Y_1 = \frac{i_1}{e_1} = \frac{1}{R_c + R_f + R_b'} \frac{1 + g_m R_b'}{1 + \dfrac{g_m R_b' R_c}{R_c + R_f + R_b'}} \qquad (2.101)$$

The input impedance is $1/Y_1$, or

$$Z_1 = \frac{R_c + R_f + R_b' + g_m R_b' R_c}{1 + g_m R_b'} \qquad (2.102)$$

The same value for the admittance can be obtained by an evaluation of the transmission from e_1 to i_1 in the diagram of Fig. 2.45(c).

Calculation of the output impedance of the circuit requires that e_1 be made zero, i_2 be considered the drive for the network, and e_2 the output. The significant quantities are determined from the signal-flow diagram of Fig. 2.45(c).

$$(Z_{\text{out}})_{g_m=0} = \frac{R_b'}{1 + \dfrac{R_b'/R_f}{1 + R_c/R_f}} = \frac{R_b'(R_c + R_f)}{R_c + R_f + R_b'} \qquad (2.103)$$

$$F_{g_m}' = 1 \quad (\text{return difference with } e_2 = 0) \qquad (2.104)$$

$$F_{g_m} = 1 + \frac{R_c g_m R_b'}{R_c + R_f + R_b'} \quad (\text{return difference with } i_2 = 0) \qquad (2.105)$$

The output impedance is again found by application of the theorem of Eq. (2.93):

$$Z_{\text{out}} = \frac{R_b'(R_c + R_f)}{R_c + R_f + R_b'} \frac{1}{1 + \dfrac{R_c g_m R_b'}{R_c + R_f + R_b'}} \qquad (2.106a)$$

$$Z_{\text{out}} = \frac{R_b'(R_c + R_f)}{R_c + R_f + R_b' + R_c g_m R_b'} \qquad (2.106b)$$

The output impedance can also be calculated from the more fundamental theorem,

$$Z_{\text{out}} = \frac{e_{2oc}}{-i_{2sc}} \qquad (2.107)\dagger$$

The open-circuit output voltage is found from the signal-flow diagram, redrawn in Fig. 2.47(a) with i_2 set equal to zero. With only the single essential node i_1, the essential diagram is drawn in part (b) of the figure.

† The minus sign appears because i_2 is defined in Fig. 2.45(a) as the current flowing into the network.

The open-circuit voltage is

$$e_{2_{oc}} = e_1 \left[-g_m R_b' \right.$$
$$\left. + \frac{1 + g_m R_b'}{R_f} (1 + g_m R_c) R_b' \frac{1}{1 + (R_c + R_b' + R_c g_m R_b')/R_f} \right] \quad (2.108)$$

Collection of terms over a common denominator yields

$$e_{2_{oc}} = e_1 \frac{R_b'(1 - g_m R_f)}{R_c + R_f + R_b' + R_c g_m R_b'} \quad (2.109)$$

The short-circuit current is $-i_2$ with e_2 equal to zero and can be found by

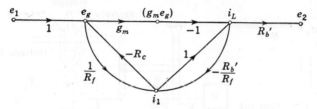

$$i_1$$

(a) Signal-flow Diagram for Gain Calculation

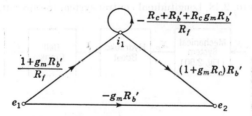

(b) Essential Diagram

FIG. 2.47. Open-circuit voltage and short-circuit current.

evaluating $e_{2_{oc}}/R_b'$ as R_b' tends to zero.   The limit is

$$-i_{2_{sc}} = e_1 \left(-g_m + \frac{1 + g_m R_c}{R_c + R_f} \right) \quad (2.110)$$

$$-i_{2_{sc}} = e_1 \frac{1 - g_m R_f}{R_c + R_f} \quad (2.111)$$

The output impedance is given by the ratio of Eqs. (2.109) and (2.111),

$$Z_{\text{out}} = \frac{e_{2_{oc}}}{-i_{2_{sc}}} = \frac{R_b'(R_c + R_f)}{R_c + R_f + R_b' + R_c g_m R_b'} \quad (2.112)$$

Clearly, the use of the feedback theorem [Eq. (2.93)] has not particularly simplified the calculation of output impedance in this example.   The primary advantage of the theorem here is that impedances are expressed in terms of return differences, which are also useful in the analysis of sensitivity, stability, over-all gain, etc., and in terms of the impedance with the feedback loop broken.

Impedance of a Feedback Control System.   Figure 2.48 shows the basic components of a power-boost system for control of the elevator of an aircraft.   A pilot force applied to the stick results in the motion x_b, which is transmitted through a push rod to a hydraulic power-boost system.   The damper B, mass M, and spring K represent the mechanical load on the

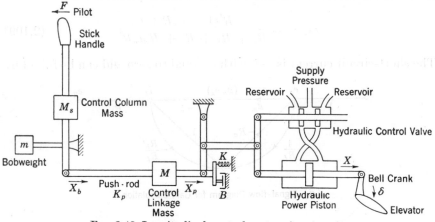

FIG. 2.48. Longitudinal control system for aircraft.

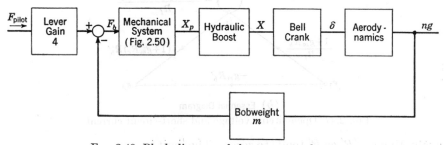

FIG. 2.49. Block diagram of elevator-control system.

push rod, while M_s represents the mass of the stick and associated equipment referred to the input of the push rod.   The closed-loop hydraulic system drives the elevator through a bell crank.   The elevator motion, in turn, causes a normal acceleration ng of the aircraft; this normal acceleration is measured by the bob weight, and the loop is closed by the mechanical comparison of the bob-weight force and pilot force.   The block diagram of the system is shown in Fig. 2.49.

One impedance is of particular interest in design: the impedance seen by the pilot looking into the system.†   With the system open-loop, the

† Mechanical impedance is defined here as the ratio force/velocity.   It is also possible to define impedance as velocity/force, force/displacement, etc.   The particular definition used is rather immaterial, as long as it is precise and usage is consistent.

impedance seen by the pilot is proportional to the input impedance of the mechanical network shown in Fig. 2.50:

$$Z_b = \frac{F_b}{sX_b} = (M_s + m)s + \frac{K_p}{s} \frac{Ms^2 + Bs + K}{Ms^2 + Bs + K + K_p} \quad (2.113)$$

The impedance seen by the pilot is $Z_b/16$, as a result of the $4:1$ ratio of the stick lever arms. If the bell-crank gain or a similar element in the forward loop is used as the reference element, the two return differences can be determined. The return difference "with the terminals shorted" is, in this case, the return difference measured with the pilot force zero and is $1 - T_L$, where T_L is the loop gain. The return difference "with the terminals open," in contrast, is the return difference measured with zero

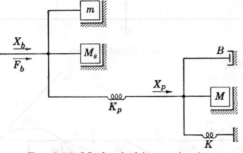

Fig. 2.50. Mechanical input circuit.

stick velocity (*i.e.*, the fixed-stick return difference). If the stick is fixed, the bob weight cannot move and the over-all feedback loop is broken; the return difference is unity. Thus, the impedance seen by the pilot is the open-loop impedance multiplied by the return difference with reference to the bell-crank gain. In terms of the system transfer functions,

$$Z_{\text{pilot}} = \frac{1}{16} Z_b \left[1 - \left(\frac{X_p}{F_b}\right)\left(\frac{X}{X_p}\right)\left(\frac{\delta}{X}\right)\left(\frac{ng}{\delta}\right)\left(\frac{F_b}{ng}\right) \right] \quad (2.114)†$$

Here, $F_b/(ng)$, measured with the pilot force zero, is the result of the bob-weight action.

Output Impedance of the Cathode-coupled Limiter. Determination of the output impedance of the cathode-coupled limiter [Fig. 2.51(a)] affords another example of the application of the theorem of Eq. (2.93) and also illustrates the manner in which the signal-flow diagram must be modified for the determination of the output impedance. The element

† An equation of this form always is confusing because of the desire to cancel factors in the product of the parenthetical expressions. The product

$$\left(\frac{X_p}{F_b}\right)\left(\frac{X}{X_p}\right)\left(\frac{\delta}{X}\right)\left(\frac{ng}{\delta}\right)\left(\frac{F_b}{ng}\right)$$

is the open-loop gain and is of course evaluated *with the loop broken.*

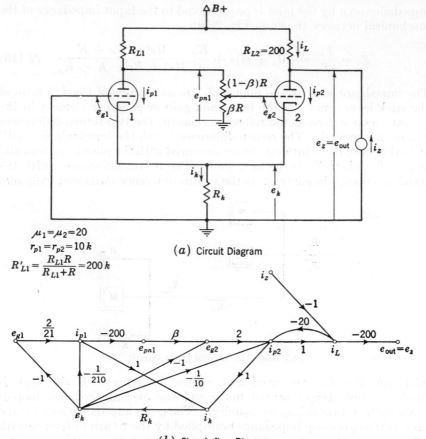

$\mu_1 = \mu_2 = 20$
$r_{p1} = r_{p2} = 10\,k$

(a) Circuit Diagram

$$R'_{L1} = \frac{R_{L1}R}{R_{L1}+R} = 200\,k$$

(b) Signal-flow Diagram

(Currents in ma., Resistance in kilohms, and Voltage in volts)

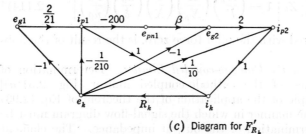

(c) Diagram for F'_{R_k}

Fig. 2.51. Output impedance of cathode-coupled limiter.

selected as the reference is the cathode resistance R_k, in order that the return differences previously evaluated, may be used. The signal-flow diagram, shown in Fig. 2.32(a) for the calculation of the transmission through the network, is redrawn in Fig. 2.51(b) to permit consideration of i_z as the input and e_z as the output. Here i_z is the current flowing through the output lead toward the plate of tube 2, and e_Z is equal to the output voltage e_{out}. The addition of the driving signal i_Z is represented by the changes shown in the signal-flow diagram. The variable i_L is defined as the current flowing through R_{L2}. The relations between i_L, i_{p2}, i_Z, and e_Z are established by inspection of the circuit:

$$i_{p2} = \frac{\mu e_{g2} - e_k - i_L R_{L2}}{r_{p2}} \tag{2.115}$$

$$i_L = i_{p2} - i_Z \tag{2.116}$$

$$e_Z = -R_{L2}i_L \tag{2.117}$$

The evaluation of the output impedance involves determination of the three quantities $(Z)_{R_k=0}$, F'_{R_k}, and F_{R_k}:

(1) $(Z)_{R_k=0}$, the output impedance if R_k is set equal to zero, is the transmission, in the signal-flow diagram of Fig. 2.51(b), from i_Z to e_Z with the branch R_k removed. This transmission can be evaluated by inspection:

$$(Z)_{R_k=0} = \frac{(-1)(-200)}{1 - (-20)(1)} \tag{2.118}$$

$$(Z)_{R_k=0} = \tfrac{200}{21} \tag{2.119}†$$

Alternately, $(Z)_{R_k=0}$ can be determined by inspection of the circuit of Fig. 2.51(a). The output impedance with the cathode grounded is the parallel combination of r_{p2} and R_{L2}, or

$$(Z)_{R_k=0} = \frac{10 \times 200}{10 + 200} = \tfrac{200}{21} \tag{2.120}$$

(2) F_{R_k} is the return difference with i_Z equal to zero, or just the normal return difference as evaluated in Sec. 2.4. Hence, from Eq. (2.50),

$$F_{R_k} = 1 - R_k(-\tfrac{2}{10} + \tfrac{40}{21}\beta) \tag{2.121}$$

(3) F'_{R_k} is the return difference with reference to R_k and with i_Z adjusted to make e_Z equal to zero. Inspection of the signal-flow diagram indicates that if e_Z is zero, i_L is also. The signal-flow diagram reduces to that of Fig. 2.51(c), the same diagram as that used in Sec. 2.4 to calculate the normal return difference with reference to R_k except that R_{L2} is set equal to zero in order that e_{out} may be zero. If Eq. (2.49) is modified to represent a change in R_{L2} from 200 to zero, the null return difference results:

$$F'_{R_k} = 1 - R_k \{(-1)(\tfrac{2}{21})[(1) + (-200)(\beta)(2)(1)]$$
$$+ (-\tfrac{1}{210})[(1) + (-200)(\beta)(2)(1)] + (-1)(2)(1)$$
$$+ (-\tfrac{1}{10})(1)\} \tag{2.122}$$
$$F'_{R_k} = 1 - R_k(-2.2 + 40\beta) \tag{2.123}$$

† All resistances are measured in kilohms throughout this example.

The output impedance is found by substituting Eqs. (2.120), (2.121), and (2.123) in Eq. (2.93):

$$Z = \tfrac{200}{21}\frac{1 - R_k(-2.2 + 40\beta)}{1 - R_k(-0.2 + \tfrac{40}{21}\beta)} \tag{2.124}$$

The value of R_k equal to 10 gives

$$Z = 200\,\frac{23 - 400\beta}{63 - 400\beta} \tag{2.125}$$

As β is increased from zero toward the value $\tfrac{63}{400}$, at which the gain becomes infinite, the output impedance decreases to zero (with a β of $\tfrac{23}{400}$) and then goes negative for values of β in the range from $\tfrac{23}{400}$ to $\tfrac{63}{400}$.

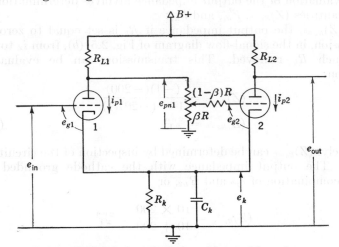

FIG. 2.52. Circuit for calculation of internal impedance.

An Internal Impedance Calculation. The last example of this section illustrates the calculation of an impedance faced by an element within the network. The circuit of Fig. 2.52 is similar to that of the cathode-coupled limiter, but with the cathode capacitor added. The element values are the same as used previously, and C_k is assumed 0.1 μf. The step-function response of the network is to be determined.

Before extensive calculations are initiated, it is useful to consider what can be learned about the nature of the response by inspection of the circuit. The initial and final values of the response can each be determined without consideration of the capacitor, because initially the capacitor acts as a short circuit and in the steady-state it behaves as an open circuit. Thus, the initial value of the output is determined as the gain of a two-stage direct-coupled amplifier without feedback. If the input e_in is a unit step function,

$$e_\text{out}(0) = (-\tfrac{400}{21})^2\beta \tag{2.126}$$

(The gain of each amplifier stage is $-\tfrac{400}{21}$, and the gain of the coupling network is β.)

The final value includes the feedback through the cathode resistor R_k. The same circuit, without C_k, is analyzed in Sec. 2.3, where the gain is given by Eq. (2.44), repeated below:

$$T = (-\tfrac{400}{21})^2\beta + \frac{\tfrac{20}{21}(1 - \tfrac{400}{21}\beta)^2}{3 - \tfrac{400}{21}\beta} \tag{2.127}$$

The right side of Eq. (2.127) is the final value of the response to a unit step function. If the specific value of $\tfrac{21}{400}$ is chosen for β, the initial and final values are both $\tfrac{400}{21}$, and the system responds instantaneously (except, of course, for the effect of the neglected distributed capacitances throughout the circuit). Any other value of β less than $\tfrac{63}{400}$ results in the final value exceeding the initial value. If, for example, β is chosen as $\tfrac{42}{400}$, the initial value is $\tfrac{800}{21}$; the final value, $\tfrac{820}{21}$.

What is the nature of the transition of the response from its initial to final value? With the cathode capacitor the single energy-storage element in the circuit, the transition must be described by a simple exponential curve (Fig. 2.53). Since the initial and final values of the single exponential are known, the description of the response is completed by the evaluation of the time constant, which is the product of C_k and the resistance faced by the capacitor. The resistance looking into terminals a and b in Fig. 2.54(a) is determined with the aid of the theorem of Eq. (2.93).

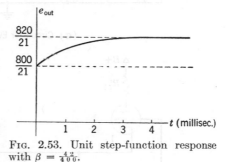

FIG. 2.53. Unit step-function response with $\beta = \tfrac{42}{400}$.

The reference element is rather arbitrarily selected as μ_2. The only basis governing this selection is a desire to simplify as much as possible the calculation of the impedance with the reference element dead and the two return differences. On the basis of this desire for simplicity, a reference element should be chosen which is a branch of as many of the feedback loops as possible. With the choice of μ_2, the impedance between a and b with μ_2 equal to zero is the output impedance of the cathode follower, represented by tube 1 and with a cathode resistor consisting of the parallel combination of R_k and $r_{p2} + R_{L2}$. The partial circuit for the determination of $(R_{ab})_{\mu_2=0}$ is shown in Fig. 2.54(b). The impedance can be calculated in the conventional manner:

$$(R_{ab})_{\mu_2=0} = \tfrac{210}{43} \text{ kilohms} \tag{2.128}$$

The return difference with reference to μ_2 is to be evaluated with i_{in} [as shown in Fig. 2.54(a)] adjusted to make e_k equal zero and again with i_{in} equal to zero. The former value is unity, for with e_k equal to zero all feedback is eliminated. A signal transmitted in tube 2 never reaches tube 1. The second return difference is that of the basic signal-flow diagram for the circuit without the cathode capacitor and can be found

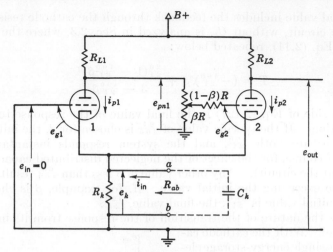

(a) Circuit for Evaluation of R_{ab}

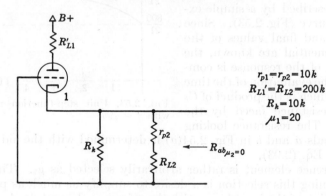

(b) Circuit for Evaluation of $R_{ab\mu_2=0}$

$$r_{p1}=r_{p2}=10k$$
$$R_{L1}'=R_{L2}=200k$$
$$R_k=10k$$
$$\mu_1=20$$

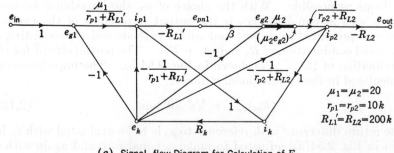

(c) Signal-flow Diagram for Calculation of F_{μ_2}

$$\mu_1=\mu_2=20$$
$$r_{p1}=r_{p2}=10k$$
$$R_{L1}'=R_{L2}=200k$$

FIG. 2.54. Determination of R_{ab}.

from Fig. 2.54(a). The signal-flow diagram of Fig. 2.54(c) assists in the evaluation,

$$F_{\mu_2} = \frac{63 - 400\beta}{43} \tag{2.129}$$

The impedance faced by C_k is now given by Eq. (2.93),

$$R_{ab} = \frac{210}{43} \frac{1}{(63 - 400\beta)/43} \qquad \text{kilohms} \tag{2.130}$$

If β is $\frac{42}{400}$,

$$R_{ab} = 10 \text{ kilohms} \tag{2.131}$$

With this particular value of β, the impedance is exactly equal to R_k. As β is varied from zero to the value $(\frac{63}{400})$ giving instability, the impedance increases monotonically, reaching infinity at the point of instability. The time constant governing the step-function response of the circuit of Fig. 2.52 is $R_{ab}C_k$, or 1 msec if β is $\frac{42}{400}$. The corresponding response is shown in Fig. 2.53.†

2.7. Theorems Relating to Return Difference. There are two additional theorems‡ relating to utilization of the concept of return difference. In this section, the two theorems are presented, proved on the basis of analysis by signal-flow diagrams, and illustrated with simple examples. The theorems are both primarily useful in simplifying the analysis outlined in the preceding sections; neither presents any new concept.

Theorem 1. The first theorem is particularly useful in the evaluation of the return difference with reference to one element if the return difference with reference to a different element is known. The theorem is most readily stated in terms of the single equation

$$\frac{F_x}{F_y} = \frac{(F_x)_{y=0}}{(F_y)_{x=0}} \tag{2.132}$$

The ratio of the return differences with two different reference transmittances x and y is equal to the ratio of the same return differences when each return difference is computed with the other reference transmittance zero.

The proof of Eq. (2.132) is based on the signal-flow diagram of Fig. 2.55, which represents the general diagram around two reference elements x and y. The generality of the diagram is established as follows:

† The resistance across ab in this particular example is more readily calculated from the fact that this resistance is the final value of e_k divided by the initial value of the capacitor current. The final value of e_k is determined from the essential diagram [Fig. 2.22(c)] and is $-\frac{20}{21}$ with β equal to $\frac{42}{400}$. The initial capacitor current $(-\frac{2}{21})$ is the sum of the two initial plate currents, each calculated from the initial ($t = 0$) operation of the circuit as a two-stage amplifier without feedback [in other words, from the direct transmittances from e_{in} to i_{p1} and i_{p2} in Fig. 2.22(a)].

‡ A large number of other theorems on feedback are derived by Bode, but are omitted here. *Cf.* H. W. Bode, "Network Analysis and Feedback Amplifier Design," Chaps. V and VI, D. Van Nostrand Company, Inc., New York, 1945.

the calculation of the return difference with reference to x, the transmittance of a branch from e_a to e_b, involves only the feedback paths from e_b back to e_a. All such paths fall into one of two categories: paths of one type pass through y, while those of the other type do not. Since both types are included in Fig. 2.55, this figure suffices for the study of the general system.

In terms of the transmittances of Fig. 2.55, the four return differences of Eq. (2.132) are

$$F_x = 1 - x\left(t_{ba} + \frac{t_{bc}yt_{da}}{1 - yt_{dc}}\right) \tag{2.133}$$

$$F_y = 1 - y\left(t_{dc} + \frac{t_{da}xt_{bc}}{1 - xt_{ba}}\right) \tag{2.134}$$

$$(F_x)_{y=0} = 1 - xt_{ba} \tag{2.135}$$
$$(F_y)_{x=0} = 1 - yt_{dc} \tag{2.136}$$

Substitution of the four relations above in Eq. (2.132) substantiates the equality and, hence, the theorem.

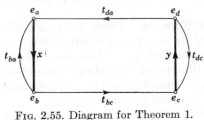

FIG. 2.55. Diagram for Theorem 1.

The theorem is illustrated with the cathode-coupled limiter analyzed in detail throughout the preceding sections. The signal-flow diagram is shown in Fig. 2.54(c), with the two reference elements μ_2 and R_k indicated. The return difference with reference to R_k is calculated in Sec. 2.4 and given by Eq. (2.50). With β equal to $\frac{42}{400}$ and R_k equal to 10,

$$F_{R_k} = 1 \tag{2.137}$$

F_{R_k} evaluated with μ_2 equal to zero can be found from Fig. 2.54(c):

$$(F_{R_k})_{\mu_2=0} = 1 - 10[(-\tfrac{1}{210})(1) + (-1)(\tfrac{2}{21})(1) + (-\tfrac{1}{210})(1)] \tag{2.138}$$
$$(F_{R_k})_{\mu_2=0} = \tfrac{43}{21} \tag{2.139}$$

F_{μ_2} with R_k equal to zero is unity because opening the R_k branch removes all feedback. Substitution of these three values in Eq. (2.132) gives F_{μ_2}, the normal return difference with reference to μ_2:

$$F_{\mu_2} = 1\frac{1}{\frac{43}{21}} = \frac{21}{43} \tag{2.140}$$

The result of this derivation agrees with the value of Eq. (2.129), derived in the last example of the last section. Clearly, the theorem represents a simplification of the problem of finding a desired return difference only if a return difference with another reference is already known.

Theorem 2. The second theorem of this section relates the gain of part of the circuit to a specific return difference. The theorem is again stated most conveniently in terms of an equation,

$$\frac{T_g}{T_{go}} = \frac{1}{F_{g_m}} \tag{2.141}$$

T_g is the transmission from any point in the system to the grid of a specific tube; T_{go} is the same transmission with the tube dead (g_m set equal to zero, but r_p still present); and F_{g_m} is the return difference with reference to the g_m of the tube.†

The proof of the theorem follows from the general signal-flow diagram of Fig. 2.56. In terms of the transmittances of this diagram,

$$T_g = \frac{t_{ig}}{1 - g_m t_{gg}} \tag{2.142}$$

$$T_{go} = t_{ig} \tag{2.143}$$

$$F_{g_m} = 1 - g_m t_{gg} \tag{2.144}$$

These three equations obviously satisfy Eq. (2.141).

A simple application of this theorem is in the analysis of the single-loop multistage feedback amplifier. The theorem states in this case that as a result of the feedback the signal at the grid of any tube is reduced by division by F, the return difference with reference to any g_m. (All re-

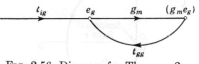

FIG. 2.56. Diagram for Theorem 2.

turn differences with reference to tandem elements are identical and equal to $1 - T_L$, where T_L is the open-loop gain.)

2.8. Stability. The investigation of the stability of multiloop systems is readily carried out using the Nyquist-diagram approach. The principles underlying the Nyquist-diagram method of stability analysis are reviewed very briefly in the beginning of this section. The last part of the section includes a description of the application of the diagrams in the study of multiloop systems.

The Nyquist Diagram. The basic principles of the Nyquist diagram‡ are most readily discussed in terms of the linear single-loop system shown in block-diagram form in Fig. 2.57. $G(s)$ is the open-loop transfer function (or the negative of the open-loop transfer function if the conventional terminology of feedback-amplifier

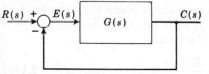

FIG. 2.57. Single-loop system.

theory is used). The over-all system function is

$$\frac{C}{R}(s) = \frac{G(s)}{1 + G(s)} \tag{2.145}$$

Clearly, the stability of the system depends on the location of the poles of C/R, or the zeros of $1 + G(s)$, the return difference with reference to any

---

† Here g_m can be replaced by μ throughout if the series form of the linear incremental equivalent circuit of the tube is preferred. In addition, Bode shows that the reference condition need not be a g_m (or μ) of zero, but may be any general value. *Cf.* H. W. Bode, *op. cit.*, p. 77.

‡ W. R. Ahrendt and J. F. Taplin, "Automatic Feedback Control," pp. 91–100, McGraw-Hill Book Company, Inc., New York, 1951. The presentation by Ahrendt and Taplin is in considerably more detail than is possible in this section.

tandem element. The system is stable if all zeros of $1 + G(s)$, all -1 points of $G(s)$, are located in the left half of the s plane.

The Nyquist diagram is a graphical method for the determination of stability. The diagram is essentially a mapping into the $G(s)$ plane of a contour enclosing the major portion of the right half of the s plane. Figure 2.58 shows the Nyquist plot in a typical, simple case. The path in the s plane is up the $j\omega$ axis from $-jR$ to $+jR$, with semicircular detours to avoid any poles of $G(s)$ on the axis. At $+jR$, the path turns $90°$ to the right and returns to $-jR$ along a large semicircle of radius R.

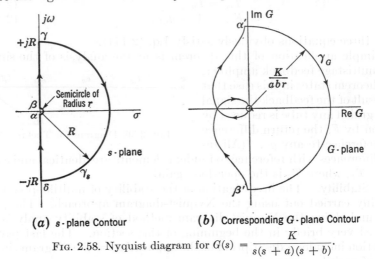

(a) s-plane Contour   (b) Corresponding G-plane Contour

FIG. 2.58. Nyquist diagram for $G(s) = \dfrac{K}{s(s + a)(s + b)}$.

The corresponding motion in the $G(s)$ plane is shown in Fig. 2.58(b).†
Since the interior of the right half of the s plane is always to the right of the contour γ_s, the corresponding region in the G plane is to the right of γ_G. When γ_s turns $90°$ to the right (e.g., at point α), γ_G does also (at α'). The contour γ_G shown is for a $G(s)$ of the form

$$G(s) = \frac{K}{s(s + a)(s + b)} \qquad (2.146)$$

For very small values of s, $G(s)$ is large, behaving as K/abs. A $+180°$ change in the phase of s results in a $-180°$ change in the phase of $G(s)$, with the result that, as γ_s moves counterclockwise from α to β, γ_G moves clockwise from α' to β'. When s is large, $G(s)$ behaves as K/s^3. The γ-to-δ section of γ_s corresponds to a $540°$ counterclockwise motion of γ_G on a circle of radius K/R^3 about the origin.

† It is assumed throughout this section that $G(s)$ is a rational algebraic function of s. The more general problem, involving a $G(s)$ with branch points or essential singularities, has been treated at some length by a number of authors. For example, cf. L. S. Dzung, The Stability Criterion, "Automatic and Manual Control," Proceedings of the Cranfield Conference 1951, edited by A. Tustin, pp. 12–23, Butterworths Scientific Publications, London, 1952. This paper contains a list of additional references.

For a mapping of this type, each point in the s plane corresponds to a single point in the G plane, but the correspondence is not 1:1 in the reverse direction. A point in the G plane may correspond to a number of s-plane points. (For example, infinity in the G plane corresponds to the s-plane points 0, $-a$, and $-b$.) If the values of s at which $G(s)$ is equal to A and B are denoted the A *points* and B *points*, respectively, the Nyquist diagram permits the determination of the difference between the number of B points and the number of A points in the right half of the s plane. A and B may take on any values.

Demonstration of this application of the Nyquist diagram can be effected with the aid of Fig. 2.59. The points A and B are marked in the G plane, and the corresponding sets of points in the s plane are denoted

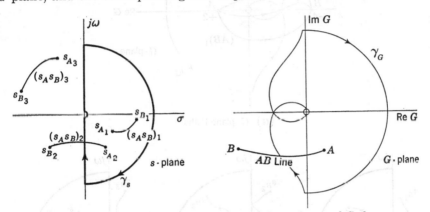

FIG. 2.59. Corresponding line segments in the s plane and G plane.

s_{A_1}, s_{A_2}, . . . , s_{A_n} and s_{B_1}, s_{B_2}, . . . , s_{B_n}. (With the function of Eq. 2.146, n is 3, since the equation for s in terms of G is a cubic.) If a line is drawn in the G plane from A to B, there are n corresponding lines in the s plane, from s_{A_1} to s_{B_1}, s_{A_2} to s_{B_2}, . . . , s_{A_n} to s_{B_n}. The number of times the AB line in the G plane crosses γ_G must equal the total number of crossings of all the $s_A s_B$ lines and γ_s, and the direction of the crossings must be identical. If, as γ_G is traversed in the direction of the arrow, the AB line crosses the contour from right to left once, there must be one right-to-left crossing of γ_s by one of the $s_A s_B$ lines. The right-to-left crossing in the s plane corresponds to a line from the right-half into the left-half plane; consequently, in the right half of the s plane the number of A points exceeds the number of B points by exactly unity.

Figure 2.60 illustrates the application of the Nyquist criterion in a simple example. The two values of $G(s)$ of interest are $+2$ and -4. The point $+2$ is labeled A, and -4 is denoted B in the G plane. The path from $+2$ to -4 can be drawn in a variety of ways, as indicated by the three curves $(AB)_1$, $(AB)_2$, and $(AB)_3$. Only one of these paths is necessary, but all three are shown in order to demonstrate that they yield identical results. The nature, but not the specific location, of the corresponding paths in the s plane can now be determined. If it is assumed that three s-plane points correspond to each point in the G plane, the three paths $(s_A s_B)_1$ can be drawn first. (The exact number of s-plane points for each G-plane point is immaterial, as long as it is large enough to permit construction of s-plane paths of all significant types.) Since $(AB)_1$ crosses γ_G only once, there is only one s-plane path which crosses

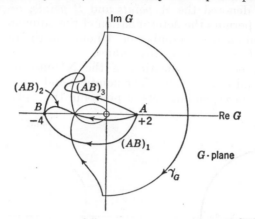

(*a*) *G*-plane Paths

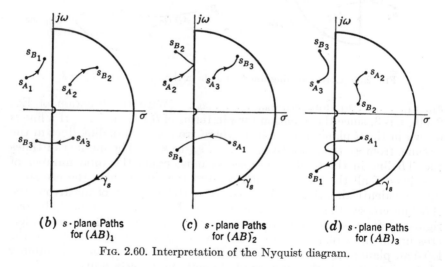

| (*b*) *s*-plane Paths for $(AB)_1$ | (*c*) *s*-plane Paths for $(AB)_2$ | (*d*) *s*-plane Paths for $(AB)_3$ |

FIG. 2.60. Interpretation of the Nyquist diagram.

γ_s. Each of the other two paths may lie entirely in the right-half plane or entirely in the left-half plane. As a test point travels along γ_G in the direction of the arrow, the crossing of $(AB)_1$ is from right to left. Consequently, if γ_s is followed in the direction of the arrow, the s-plane crossing must also be from right to left. A possible configuration of the three paths is shown in Fig. 2.60(*b*).†

† Actually, additional information concerning the nature of the s-plane paths is available as a result of the fact that conjugate complex values of s result in conjugate

The three s-plane paths corresponding to either $(AB)_2$ or $(AB)_3$ are drawn in the same way. In either case, the s-plane paths make it apparent that the number of A points in the right half of the s plane exceeds the number of B points by unity. The choice of a particular AB path is immaterial, because the net number of crossings is in every case the item of interest.

Conventional application of the Nyquist diagram to the analysis of feedback control systems involves the choice of A and B as -1 and infinity, respectively, in order to obtain a measure of the excess of -1 points over poles of $G(s)$ in the right-half plane. Alternatively, if the diagram is drawn for the return difference $1 + G(s)$ rather than the open-loop transfer function $G(s)$, the appropriate values of A and B are zero and infinity. In the analysis of the common single-loop system, $G(s)$ is stable (without poles in the right-half plane) and the Nyquist diagram indicates directly the number of -1 points in the right-half plane [$i.e.$, the number of zeros of the return difference $1 + G(s)$, or poles of the closed-loop system function $G(s)/1 + G(s)$]. If the forward path, itself, contains closed loops, $G(s)$ may be unstable, and the determination of the stability of the over-all system requires an investigation of the internal structure of the block represented by $G(s)$.

Stability of Multiloop Systems. If the forward path of a feedback amplifier contains closed loops, the Nyquist diagram for a single return difference does not suffice to establish the stability of the system. The analysis of a multiloop system in general involves the plotting of a number of Nyquist diagrams. Such an analysis can be systematized in the following four steps:

(1) The signal-flow diagram for the system is considered. It is assumed that this diagram is not reduced beyond an essential diagram, and, consequently, the diagram is in a form sufficiently basic that each transmittance is stable. In the diagram, the dependent node variables are numbered 1, 2, . . . , n, with node n representing the output. (The independent nodes, representing the drives or inputs, need not be considered because the stability of a linear system is independent of external signals.) The numbering is most conveniently effected by considering first all nonessential nodes except the output; the next N nodes are the essential nodes; and the last node is the output.

(2) The $n - 1$ return differences F_1, F_2, . . . , F_{n-1} are evaluated. F_j is the return difference of node j† with all higher-numbered nodes removed (by setting the node variables equal to zero). As a result of the method of numbering, the first

---

complex values of G, but this information need not be used in the stability investigation, once γ_G is determined. If the sequence of right-to-left and left-to-right crossings of γ_G is considered, the Nyquist plot of $G(s)$ can also be used in certain cases to prove instability even if the number of right-half-plane poles of $G(s)$ is unknown.

† In the previous sections, the term *return difference* is always used with reference to a particular transmittance. The return difference of a node e_j is equivalent to the return difference with reference to the unit transmittance of a branch from e_{j1}, a node which all the input branches to e_j enter, to e_{j2}, a node from which all the output branches from e_j depart. The nature of the branch with unit transmittance is shown in Fig. 2.61.

$n - N - 1$ return differences are all calculated with the removal of all essential nodes. All feedback paths are absent, and these $n - N - 1$ return differences are unity.

(3) The next N return differences (from F_{n-N} to F_{n-1}, inclusive) are, in general, different from unity and functions of the complex frequency s. The Nyquist diagram is used to determine the excess of zeros over poles for each of the N return differences.

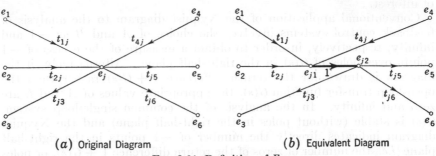

(a) Original Diagram (b) Equivalent Diagram

FIG. 2.61. Definition of F_j.

(4) The numerator of the over-all system function is a stable transmittance, and the denominator is the product of the N return differences. The number of right-half-plane zeros of this denominator is measured by the sum of the N excesses measured in step (3). If the system is stable, this sum is zero.

The procedure is illustrated by a system of order two, shown in Fig. 2.62. The dependent node variables are denoted e_1 and e_2 (the non-essential nodes), e_3 and e_4 (the two essential nodes), and e_5 (the output node). The $n - 1$ return differences are F_1, F_2, F_3, and F_4. These can be determined directly from the figure. With the two essential nodes e_3

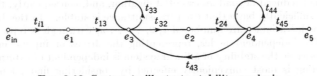

FIG. 2.62. System to illustrate stability analysis.

and e_4 removed, all feedback loops are broken, and

$$F_1 = 1 \tag{2.147}$$
$$F_2 = 1 \tag{2.148}$$

With node e_4 removed, the only loop transmission is through the self-loop at e_3. Consequently,

$$F_3 = 1 - t_{33} \tag{2.149}$$

F_4 is evaluated with all nodes except e_5 present:

$$F_4 = 1 - \left(t_{44} + \frac{t_{43}t_{32}t_{24}}{1 - t_{33}} \right) \tag{2.150}$$

The denominator of the over-all gain T is given by the product of the four return differences. In this case,

$$T = \frac{t_{i1}t_{13}t_{32}t_{24}t_{45}}{F_1F_2F_3F_4} \qquad (2.151)$$

The system is stable only if the product $F_1F_2F_3F_4$ has no zeros in the right half of the s plane. The Nyquist plots of F_3 and F_4 determine the excess of right-half-plane zeros over poles for F_3 and F_4, respectively. If each transmittance (in particular, t_{33}) in the original diagram is stable, F_3 is also stable, and the diagram of F_3 determines the number of right-half-plane zeros. These zeros are simply the right-half-plane poles of F_4, since t_{44}, t_{43}, t_{32}, and t_{24} are stable. Hence, the number of right-half-plane poles of F_4 is known, and the Nyquist plot gives the number of right-half-plane zeros. For example, if the plot for F_3 indicates j right-half-plane zeros and the plot for F_4 indicates that F_4 has k more zeros than poles in the right-half plane, the factor $F_1F_2F_3F_4$ has $j + k$ right-half-plane zeros. Unless $j + k$ equals zero, the system is unstable.

The general method for establishing the validity of the above procedure for stability analysis is indicated in the remainder of this section. The stability analysis is based on the proposition that the total excess of right-half-plane zeros over poles for $F_1F_2F_3 \cdots F_{n-1}$ is equal to the number of right-half-plane poles of the over-all system function if all transmittances in the original diagram are stable. The proposition can be substantiated by the following seven steps:[†]

(1) The equations describing system behavior are written in the following manner:

$$\sum_{j=1}^{n} t_{jk}x_j = \begin{cases} x_k & k = 1, 2, \ldots, n-1 \\ T_n x_n & k = n \end{cases} \qquad (2.152)$$

The node x_n is the input; $T_n x_n$ is the output; and T_n is the over-all gain or transmittance. In the case with n equal to 3, the equations become

$$t_{11}x_1 + t_{21}x_2 + t_{31}x_3 = x_1 \qquad (2.153)$$
$$t_{12}x_1 + t_{22}x_2 + t_{32}x_3 = x_2 \qquad (2.154)$$
$$t_{13}x_1 + t_{23}x_2 + t_{33}x_3 = T_3 x_3 \qquad (2.155)$$

This form, with the subscript n denoting both input and output, can be used as a result of the fact no branch enters the input and none leaves the output. Hence, t_{jn} is the transmittance of a branch from x_j to the output; t_{nj} describes a branch from the input to x_j; and t_{nn} is the transmittance of the branch from the input directly to the output.

(2) The determinant P_n is defined as

$$P_n = \begin{vmatrix} 1 - t_{11} & -t_{21} & -t_{31} & \cdots & -t_{n1} \\ -t_{12} & 1 - t_{22} & -t_{32} & \cdots & -t_{n2} \\ \cdots & \cdots & \cdots & \cdots & \cdots \\ -t_{1n} & -t_{2n} & -t_{3n} & \cdots & 1 - t_{nn} \end{vmatrix} \qquad (2.156)$$

[†] S. J. Mason, "Notes on Subject 6.633—Electronic Circuit Theory," pp. 149–150, Massachusetts Institute of Technology, Cambridge, Mass., 1948.

(3) P_i is defined as the determinant consisting of the first i rows and i columns of P_n:

$$P_i = \begin{vmatrix} 1 - t_{11} & -t_{21} & -t_{31} & \ldots & -t_{i1} \\ -t_{12} & 1 - t_{22} & -t_{32} & \ldots & -t_{i2} \\ \ldots & \ldots & \ldots & \ldots & \ldots \\ -t_{1i} & -t_{2i} & -t_{3i} & \ldots & 1 - t_{ii} \end{vmatrix} \qquad (2.157)$$

(4)   The over-all gain is expressed in terms of the determinants by the relation

$$T_n = 1 - \frac{P_n}{P_{n-1}} \qquad (2.158)$$

Equation (2.158) can be established from the fact that the determinant P of Eqs. (2.152) must be zero if T_n is to be independent of x_n. The only difference between P and P_n is that in P the element of row n, column n, is $T_n - t_{nn}$, while in P_n the same element is $1 - t_{nn}$. The cofactor of this element in each case is P_{n-1}. Hence,

$$P = P_n - P_{n-1} + T_n P_{n-1} \qquad (2.159)$$

Substitution of $P = 0$ in Eq. (2.159) gives (2.158). Equation (2.158) demonstrates that, when each t_{jk} is a stable transmittance (with the result that P_n has no right-half-plane poles), T_n *is a stable transmittance if P_{n-1} has no right-half-plane zeros.*

(5)   The transmittance T_i is defined as the total transmittance from node x_i back to itself with all higher-number nodes removed. In exactly the same manner as Eq. (2.158) was derived, the relation for T_i in terms of the determinants is established:

$$T_i = 1 - \frac{P_i}{P_{i-1}} \qquad (2.160)$$

(6)   The return difference F_i is defined as $1 - T_i$. F_i is then the return difference of node x_i with all higher-number nodes removed. Equation (2.160) indicates that F_i can be written in terms of the determinants.

$$F_i = \frac{P_i}{P_{i-1}} \qquad (2.161)$$

(7)   From Eq. (2.161), the relation for P_{n-1} in terms of the return differences is apparent:

$$P_{n-1} = F_1 F_2 F_3 \cdots F_{n-1} \qquad (2.162)$$

Hence, the stability of the system depends entirely on the zeros of the product $F_1 F_2 F_3 \cdots F_{n-1}$.

Thus, the concept of return difference is closely related to the stability analysis of a multiloop system. The order of the diagram is again a measure of the inherent system complexity, in that the order is the number of Nyquist plots required in an investigation of stability.

EXAMPLE 151

2.9. Example. Analysis of the circuit† of Fig. 2.63 illustrates several of the concepts presented in the preceding sections. The system shown is a velocity servomechanism, with the generated voltage of the tachometer T proportional to the output velocity of the system. The difference between the input and the tachometer output drives tube 1, the first stage of electronic amplification. Both positive and negative feedback are used in this stage: at all frequencies positive feedback through tube 2,

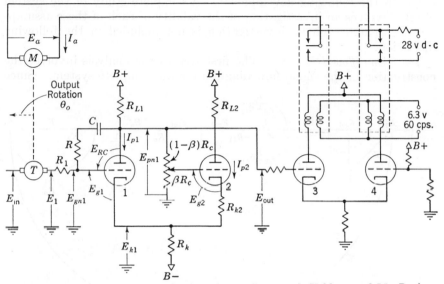

FIG. 2.63. Velocity servomechanism. (*From Greenwood, Holdam, and MacRae.*)

and at all nonzero frequencies negative feedback through the RC circuit. The negative feedback tends to make the gain of the amplifier fall off with frequency in order to avoid saturating the amplifier with commutator ripple, noise, or sudden changes of the input voltage. The armature voltage of the motor is controlled by a pair of relays driven by tubes 3 and 4.

The analysis of this section is directed toward answering the following questions:

(1) What is the quantitative variation of the d-c gain of the circuit of tube 1 with changes in the value of β?

(2) What is the transfer function of the circuit of tube 1 and the time constant associated with the capacitor C when the system is operated open-loop?

(3) What is the input impedance of the closed-loop system?

(4) What is the output impedance of the closed-loop system?

(5) What is the sensitivity of the system gain with respect to K_a, the gain of the power amplifier?

† The circuit is taken from the book by I. A. Greenwood, Jr., J. V. Holdam, Jr., and D. MacRae, Jr., "Electronic Instruments," MIT Radiation Laboratory Series, Vol. 21, p. 488, McGraw-Hill Book Company, Inc., New York, 1948. In the circuit diagram given there, actual values of the parameters are used. The operation of the power amplifier and motor is described in Sec. 12.20 of the same book.

Clearly, a large number of other characteristics might be of interest, but the above suffice to illustrate the general method of analysis. A more complete study of the system would involve a determination of the sensitivity of the over-all gain with respect to the gain of one stage of amplification, the stability of the system as a function of β, etc.

Appreciable simplification results if various assumptions are made early in the analysis. These assumptions are mentioned at the appropriate points in the following development. A complete study of the system clearly involves an investigation of the validity of each of these assumptions, although such an investigation is not included in the following discussion.

The Signal-flow Diagram. The first step in the analysis involves the construction of the signal-flow diagram for the complete system. Since

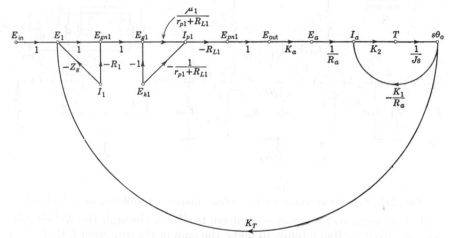

FIG. 2.64. Partial signal-flow diagram.

it is evident that the amplifier circuit including tubes 1 and 2 is independent of the remainder of the circuit, this amplifier might be considered alone. In other words, a block diagram can be constructed at once for the system, and the individual blocks analyzed separately. In a configuration as simple as this, however, it is as convenient to consider the system as a whole.

The signal-flow diagram is drawn by working through the system from input to output and following, as much as possible, the actual primary signal path. The input E_{in} causes a voltage E_1, which in turn causes a grid-to-cathode voltage on tube 1. The resulting plate current I_{p1} flowing through R_{L1} generates a voltage E_{pn1}, which drives tubes 3 and 4. The armature voltage of the motor results in an armature current, hence a torque driving the load at the output velocity. This output velocity is measured by the tachometer, and the output is compared with E_{in}. The operation of the system is described in terms of the variables of Fig. 2.63. The part of the signal-flow diagram for the primary signal path is shown in Fig. 2.64.

EXAMPLE   153

The following assumptions are implied by the diagram of Fig. 2.64:

(1)   Either R_c is much greater than R_{L1}, or R_{L1} represents the parallel combination of R_c and the plate-load resistor of tube 1.

(2)   The magnitude of I_1 is much less than that of I_{p1}, with the result that the current through R_{L1} is approximately equal to I_{p1}. With this assumption, I_{p1} is given by the equation

$$I_{p1} = \frac{\mu_1 E_{g1} - E_{k1}}{r_{p1} + R_{L1}} \qquad (2.163)$$

If this condition is not satisfied, the signal-flow diagram is slightly more complicated, but the analysis procedure is unchanged.

(3)   Smooth control of the motor is achieved by the amplifier-relay system. Consequently, the armature voltage E_a can be considered proportional to E_{pn1}, the output of the first stage of amplification. This smooth control can be very closely approximated in practice.

(4)   The armature inductance of the motor is negligible, and the armature current is proportional to the difference of the armature voltage and the induced voltage $K_{18}\theta_o$.

(5)   The load consists of inertia only, with the output acceleration proportional to the developed torque.

None of these conditions are difficult to approximate in practice unless the bandwidth required by the specifications is unusually wide or the speed of response particularly high.

Construction of the partial signal-flow diagram shown in Fig. 2.64 involves the introduction of the two secondary dependent variables I_1 and E_{k1}. The complete signal-flow diagram must include branches describing the determination of these two variables (in other words, branches entering the two nodes and representing an equation for each of the two quantities). I_1 is described in terms of the impedance of the RC series combination and the voltage E_{RC} across this combination. E_{RC}, in turn, is simply $E_{gn1} - E_{pn1}$. The relation for E_{k1} is slightly more complicated. Clearly,

$$E_{k1} = R_k I_{p1} + R_k I_{p2} \qquad (2.164)$$

I_{p1} is already present in the diagram as a primary variable, but an equation is required for I_{p2}. I_{p2} depends upon E_{g2} in the manner

$$I_{p2} = \frac{\mu_2 E_{g2}}{r_{p2} + R_{k2} + R_{L2}} - \frac{E_{k1}}{r_{p2} + R_{k2} + R_{L2}} \qquad (2.165)$$

E_{g2} can be expressed in terms of E_{pn1}, E_{k1}, and I_{p2}:

$$E_{g2} = \beta E_{pn1} - E_{k1} - R_{k2} I_{p2} \qquad (2.166)$$

In this case, derivation of an expression for E_{k1} involves the introduction of two additional variables, I_{p2} and E_{g2}. This complexity is not surprising, however. because the gain of the amplifier must depend on the values of β, R_{k2}, r_{p2}, μ_2, and R_{L2}, none of which are included in the original diagram of Fig. 2.64. The feedback path through tube 2 must be described by the set of equations derived to determine E_{k1}.

On the basis of the above discussion, the signal-flow diagram is completed in Fig. 2.65. The diagram places in evidence a large number of feedback loops, but only three of these are of primary importance: the over-all loop closed through the tachometer, the amplifier positive-feedback loop closed through tube 2, and the amplifier negative-feedback loop through the RC circuit. The signal-flow diagram presents clearly the procedure for constructing the block diagram, since the signal-flow diagram can be partitioned into an amplifier section, a motor section, and the primary-feedback section.

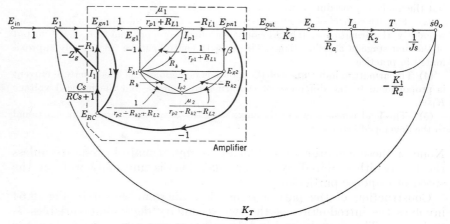

FIG. 2.65. Complete signal-flow diagram.

Zero-frequency Characteristics of the Amplifier. In the signal-flow diagram pictured in Fig. 2.65, the dashed lines enclose the section which describes the operation of the amplifier (tubes 1 and 2 and the associated circuits). If the velocity servo is to exhibit zero steady-state error when a step function is applied to the input, the zero-frequency value of the open-loop gain must be infinite. Since the output variable is the velocity, there is no integration in the motor;† the integration must be introduced in the amplifier. Consequently, it is desirable to consider initially the zero-frequency behavior of the amplifier. At zero frequency, the capacitor C presents an open circuit, and the only feedback loop within the amplifier is the positive feedback through tube 2. In terms of the signal-flow diagram, substitution of a value of zero for s simplifies the diagram by removing from consideration the five branches shown in heavy lines in Fig. 2.65. The simplification results from the zero value of the transmittance from E_{RC} to I_1.

The zero-frequency gain of the first stage of amplification is determined from the diagram of Fig. 2.66. The diagram, of order two, can be reduced to a single transmittance in the manner described in Sec. 2.3. The result is the expression for the gain, E_{out}/E_{gn1}, which is denoted A:

† The branch with transmittance $1/Js$ does not represent integration because of the minor loop closed through the feedback branch with transmittance $-K_1/R_a$.

EXAMPLE 155

$$A = -$$

$$\frac{\mu_1 R_{L1}[r_{p2}+R_{k2}+R_{L2}+\mu_2 R_{k2}+(1+\mu_2)R_k]}{(r_{p1}+R_{L1})(1+\mu_2)R_k+[(\mu_1+1)R_k+r_{p1}+R_{L1}](r_{p2}+R_{k2}+R_{L2}+\mu_2 R_{k2})-(\mu_1+1)\mu_2\beta R_k R_{L1}} \quad (2.167)$$

Complete analysis now requires substitution of appropriate values for the circuit parameters and evaluation of Eq. (2.167). Instead of this rather tedious procedure, an approximation is considered. In particular, it is assumed that the numerator of A is equal to $\mu_1 R_{L1}\mu_2 R_k$ and the denominator is of the form $R^2 - \mu_1\mu_2\beta R_k R_{L1}$, where R^2 is a constant defined as everything before the minus sign in the denominator of the right side of

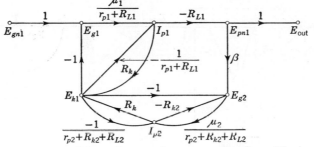

Fig. 2.66. Diagram for zero-frequency gain of amplifier.

Eq. (2.167). These are valid approximations if

$$\mu_1 \gg 1 \quad (2.168)$$

$$\mu_2 \gg \frac{r_{p2} + R_{k2} + R_{L2} + \mu_2 R_{k2} + R_k}{R_k} \quad (2.169)$$

Under these two conditions, which are not difficult to satisfy approximately in an actual circuit, A can be written

$$A = \frac{-\mu_1\mu_2 R_k R_{L1}}{R^2 - \beta\mu_1\mu_2 R_k R_{L1}} \quad (2.170)$$

Division by R^2 yields

$$A = \frac{-\mu_1\mu_2 \dfrac{R_k R_{L1}}{R^2}}{1 - \beta \dfrac{\mu_1\mu_2 R_k R_{L1}}{R^2}} \quad (2.171)$$

Without the two approximations made above, a similar expression for A can be derived, but the numerator includes an additional multiplicative factor slightly different from unity.

For the purposes of this example, it is sufficient to assume that the circuit parameters are such that $\mu_1\mu_2 R_k R_{L1}/R^2$ is known. The value 29 is used in the following. If the problem is strictly one of analysis, substitution of parameter values gives this constant; on the other hand, if design is the ultimate objective, the parameters are chosen to give an appropriate value for this constant. With the value 29, Eq. (2.171) becomes

$$A = \frac{-29}{1 - 29\beta} \tag{2.172}$$

A value of β equal to $\frac{1}{29}$ yields an infinite gain at zero frequency. Practically, a value of β somewhat smaller may be used to realize a high gain and, at the same time, a system which is open-loop stable even if the parameter values change slightly during operation.

Transfer Function of the Amplifier. Once Eq. (2.172) is determined, the signal-flow diagram for the over-all system can be redrawn, with the

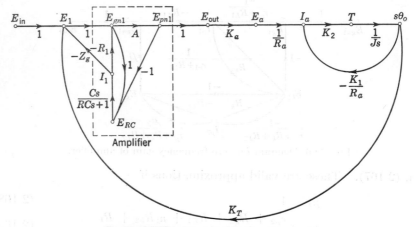

FIG. 2.67. Simplified signal-flow diagram.

elements shown in Fig. 2.66 being replaced by the single transmittance $-29/(1 - 29\beta)$. The simplified diagram is shown in Fig. 2.67. The transfer function of the amplifier, alone, is determined from the section of the figure within the dashed lines. (Here, Z_g can be omitted if the internal impedance of the tachometer is either negligible or is not considered part of the amplifier. Z_g can be inserted later by replacing R_1 by $R_1 + Z_g$.)

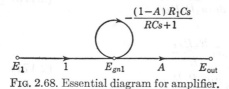

FIG. 2.68. Essential diagram for amplifier.

The diagram of the amplifier is of order one, with the single essential node I_1 or E_{gn1} or E_{RC}. If E_{gn1} is chosen, the essential diagram is that of Fig. 2.68. The over-all transmittance is

$$\frac{E_{out}}{E_1} = \frac{A(RCs + 1)}{1 + Cs[R + (1 - A)R_1]} \tag{2.173}$$

The circuit is the conventional Miller integrator, with the forward gain A including the effect of the positive feedback.

The value of β equal to $\frac{1}{29}$ yields an infinite value of A and the transfer function

EXAMPLE 157

$$\frac{E_{\text{out}}}{E_1} = -\frac{RCs + 1}{R_1 Cs} \tag{2.174}$$

With the magnitude of A finite and much greater than $(R + R_1)/R_1$, the transfer function is

$$\frac{E_{\text{out}}}{E_1} = A\frac{RCs + 1}{-AR_1Cs + 1} \tag{2.175}$$

A is, of course, negative. With A infinite, the circuit gives ideal integral compensation, and with A finite, the conventional passive integral compensation. The time constant associated with the charging of C when the system is operating with the primary-feedback path open is the coefficient of s in the denominator of Eq. (2.173), or approximately $-AR_1C$ if the magnitude of A is large.

Input Impedance. The input impedance of the closed-loop system can be evaluated directly from the signal-flow diagram of Fig. 2.67. Actually, since the input admittance is just the transmittance from E_{in} to I_1, this admittance is more readily determined than the impedance. The transmittance I_1/E_1 can be found either by reduction of the diagram or by utilization of Eq. (2.97),

$$Y = Y_o\frac{F'}{F} \tag{2.176}$$

The latter method is used here, since the return difference F is desired in a later part of the example.

The reference element selected is the motor gain K_a. The admittance Y_o, measured with K_a equal to zero, is found from the diagram of Fig. 2.67, or can be written by recognizing that the impedance Z_o, equal to $1/Y_o$, is the direct impedance $R_1 + Z_g$ plus the RC-circuit impedance modified by the Miller effect.

$$Z_o = R_1 + Z_g + \frac{R}{1 - A} + \frac{1}{(1 - A)Cs} \tag{2.177}$$

$$Y_o = \frac{(1 - A)Cs}{RCs + 1 + (1 - A)Cs(R_1 + Z_g)} \tag{2.178}$$

The quantity F' of Eq. (2.176) is the return difference with reference to K_a and measured with the input E_{in} adjusted to make I_1 equal to zero. But if I_1 is zero, E_{gn1} is also. Consequently, the returned signal is zero and

$$F' = 1 \tag{2.179}$$

F is the return difference with reference to K_a and evaluated with the input E_{in} equal to zero. This return difference is determined from the over-all signal-flow diagram, Fig. 2.67. The returned signal is equal to the transmittance from E_{out} to E_1 multiplied by the transmittance from E_1 to E_{out}, with both transmittances measured with the primary loop opened at E_{out}.

$$F = 1 - \frac{K_a K_2 K_T}{R_a J s + K_1 K_2} \cdot \frac{A}{1 + (R_1 + Z_g)\dfrac{(1 - A)Cs}{RCs + 1}} \qquad (2.180)$$

Substitution of Eqs. (2.178) to (2.180) in (2.176) gives

$$Y = \frac{1}{\dfrac{1}{Y_o} - \dfrac{K_a K_2 K_T}{R_a J s + K_1 K_2} \dfrac{A(RCs + 1)}{(1 - A)Cs}} \qquad (2.181)$$

$$Z = R_1 + Z_g + \frac{RCs + 1}{(1 - A)Cs}\left[1 - \frac{K_a K_2 K_T A}{R_a J s + K_1 K_2}\right] \qquad (2.182)$$

The input impedance is the sum of two components, $R_1 + Z_g$, the impedance of the elements outside the loop, and the RC-circuit impedance corrected for the Miller effect and then multiplied by the return difference of the over-all system.

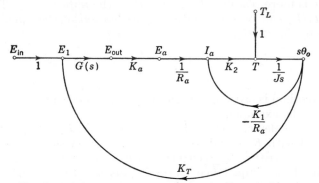

Fig. 2.69. Diagram for calculation of output impedance.

Output Impedance. The output impedance is determined from the diagram of Fig. 2.69. In this figure, the transfer function $G(s)$ is E_{out}/E_1, given by Eq. (2.173). Again, the admittance (angular velocity/torque) is more readily calculated than the impedance. A load-torque disturbance is inserted as shown and the output velocity determined. The transfer function, $s\theta_o/T_L$, is

$$\frac{s\theta_o}{T_L} = \frac{\dfrac{1}{Js}}{1 + \dfrac{1}{Js}\left[\dfrac{K_1 K_2}{R_a} - \dfrac{K_a K_2 K_T G(s)}{R_a}\right]} \qquad (2.183)$$

A more conventional form is

$$\frac{s\theta_o}{T_L} = \frac{\dfrac{R_a}{R_a J s + K_1 K_2}}{1 - \dfrac{K_a K_2 K_T G(s)}{R_a J s + K_1 K_2}} \qquad (2.184)$$

The numerator represents the transmittance with the over-all feedback loop broken ($K_T = 0$). This term is divided by the return difference to obtain the output admittance of the closed-loop system.

Sensitivity with Respect to Power-amplifier Gain. The sensitivity of the over-all transmittance with respect to the gain of the power amplifier (tubes 3 and 4 and the relay system) is simply the reciprocal of the return difference with reference to K_a and with the input zero. With this return difference given by Eq. (2.180), the sensitivity can be written directly,

$$S_{K_a}^T = \cfrac{1}{1 - \cfrac{K_a K_2 K_T}{R_a J s + K_1 K_2} \cfrac{A}{1 + (R_1 + Z_g)\cfrac{(1 - A)Cs}{RCs + 1}}} \qquad (2.185)$$

Substitution of $G(s)$ for the expression $\dfrac{A(RCs + 1)}{1 + Cs[R + (R_1 + Z_g)(1 - A)]}$ gives

$$S_{K_a}^T = \cfrac{1}{1 - \cfrac{K_a K_2 K_T G(s)}{R_a J s + K_1 K_2}} \qquad (2.186)$$

Other Characteristics of the System. As indicated in the first part of this section, once the signal-flow diagram of the over-all system is drawn,

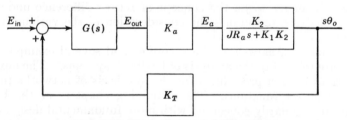

Fig. 2.70. Block diagram of the system.

determination of the various gain functions, sensitivities, and impedances is routine. Likewise, the stability of the system can be analyzed in a straightforward fashion. The signal-flow diagram also serves as a logical basis for the construction of the block diagram. For example, the block diagram for the system considered in this example can be drawn directly from Fig. 2.65. The result is shown in Fig. 2.70, with $G(s)$ used again to denote the transfer function of the amplifier.

2.10. Concluding Remarks. The preceding sections of this chapter describe the use of signal-flow diagrams as an aid in the analysis of complex feedback systems. From these sections, there emerge certain fundamental concepts which underly the study of feedback:

(1) The signal-flow diagram
(2) The order of the system
(3) The return difference

The *signal-flow diagram* simplifies the derivation of specific rules and techniques for the analysis of feedback systems. By presenting a continual picture of the flow of signals through the system, the signal-flow diagram places physical significance on the fundamental relations of feedback theory and permits a physical evaluation and a heuristic proof of basic feedback theorems. The signal-flow diagram is the natural first step in the construction of the block diagram of the system. Once the signal-flow diagram is drawn and preliminary analysis of the detailed system behavior is accomplished, the independent groups of components can be considered as the elements of a block diagram or analyzed with the use of signal-flow diagrams. Throughout the remaining chapters of this book, block diagrams are used extensively, primarily because of the greater familiarity most engineers have with this method.

The *order of the system*, or of the signal-flow diagram, is a measure of the inherent complexity of the system. The order indicates the degree of difficulty associated with an evaluation of the gain, output impedances, or sensitivities, and the number of Nyquist plots required in a stability analysis.

The *return difference* is a quantitative measure of the feedback. The return difference with reference to a particular element is directly related to the sensitivity of the gain to changes in the element value. The concept of return difference simplifies the calculation of impedances at various points through the system. Finally, the concept of return difference allows the systemization of the stability analysis of multiloop systems. In many ways, the concept of return difference underlies all feedback analysis and unifies the consideration of the various effects of feedback.

These concepts, as well as the theorems and several examples of this chapter, are related to the analysis of feedback systems. The next chapter describes certain procedures for the synthesis of networks to realize specified transfer functions. The remaining chapters of the book, in contrast, are primarily concerned with more fundamental design of feedback systems; principal attention is concentrated on the determination of suitable transfer functions or characteristics for the component blocks in the system block diagram. Thus, in a sense, this chapter and the following are the groundwork upon which later chapters are constructed. As a result of the analysis techniques and synthesis procedures presented in these two chapters, emphasis can be directed in later chapters toward the broader aspects of system design.

CHAPTER 3

SYNTHESIS OF *RC* NETWORKS

For many years the design of feedback control systems has been characterized in at least one sense by a stereotyped approach. Techniques for the design of electric and mechanical networks to yield specified frequency characteristics would seem to be an essential tool of the designer, yet there has been little or no discussion in the feedback-control literature of techniques for network synthesis. The general procedure in design has consistently been to work with the fundamental lead or integral networks, with as many of these building blocks inserted in the system as required to obtain satisfactory performance.

The development of the root locus method of design, the presentation of synthesis procedures based on the complex-frequency behavior of the

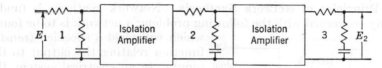

FIG. 3.1. Three integral networks with isolation amplifiers.

system, the extension of the basic design principles to mechanical systems, and many other similar developments have emphasized the necessity for the engineer to have available techniques for the synthesis of networks with prescribed frequency characteristics. This emphasis has been increased by the development of systems in which isolation amplifiers are not readily introduced. In other words, the use of three integral networks is straightforward if isolation amplifiers are available as shown in Fig. 3.1. For such a configuration, the over-all voltage ratio is simply proportional to the product of the voltage ratios of the three integral networks:

$$\frac{E_2}{E_1} = K \frac{T_{n1}s + 1}{T_{d1}s + 1} \frac{T_{n2}s + 1}{T_{d2}s + 1} \frac{T_{n3}s + 1}{T_{d3}s + 1} \tag{3.1}$$

Here $T_{d1} > T_{n1}$, $T_{d2} > T_{n2}$, and $T_{d3} > T_{n3}$. If isolation amplifiers cannot be used (in a mechanical system, for example), the realization of a voltage ratio of the form of Eq. (3.1) is less straightforward. The simple tandem connection of the individual networks (Fig. 3.2) does not yield the desired transfer function as a result of the loading effects of the second section on the first, etc. Methods drawn from the field of network synthesis indicate techniques for the determination of both network configuration and parameter values to yield a transfer function of the form of Eq. (3.1).

It is impossible in a text of this size to present in detail any comprehensive summary of the field of network synthesis.† Fortunately, however, only a small part of network synthesis is of direct applicability in the design of feedback control systems. In this chapter, an attempt is

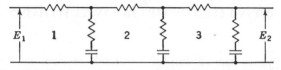

FIG. 3.2. Tandem connection of three integral networks.

made to present the basic principles of network synthesis and a detailed discussion of certain aspects of the synthesis of *RC* networks, of particular importance because a large percentage of networks in control systems are forced to consist of only resistors and capacitors because of the low frequency range of interest. Certain specialized techniques for the synthesis of networks containing inductances (as well as resistances and capacitances) are discussed in detail in Sec. 6.7 in connection with the synthesis of electric and mechanical compensation networks for carrier systems.

3.1. Principles of Network Synthesis. Network synthesis is fundamentally concerned with the following problem: a network is to be found which will yield a specified transfer function relating the output to the input. In an electrical system, the specified transfer function may be a voltage ratio, current ratio, transfer impedance, or transfer admittance.

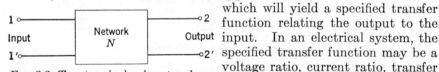

FIG. 3.3. Two-terminal-pair network.

Frequently the problem is also characterized by specification of the output impedance of the signal source and the load impedance. In other words, the signal source (possibly a cathode follower, a pentode or triode amplifier, or an error-measuring potentiometer) and the device into which the network is to work (*e.g.*, the grid of an amplifier stage) are known.

The networks of interest in the design of feedback control systems are ordinarily two-terminal-pair networks. Customarily a network of the form shown in Fig. 3.3 is desired, a network with a pair of input terminals 1-1' and a distinct pair of output terminals 2-2'. If the network is to be unbalanced, a common ground ordinarily connects 1' and 2'. In addition, in certain special cases a two-terminal network may be required, a network in which the output is taken from those terminals at which the input is applied, or, from another viewpoint, a network to realize a desired driving-point impedance or admittance. In the following sec-

† General references on network synthesis are: H. W. Bode, "Network Analysis and Feedback Amplifier Design," D. Van Nostrand Company, Inc., New York, 1945; E. A. Guillemin, "Communication Networks," Vol. II, John Wiley & Sons, Inc., New York, 1935; and E. A. Guillemin, A Summary of Modern Methods of Network Synthesis, *Advances in Electronics*, Vol. 3, 1951.

tions emphasis is placed on the synthesis of two-terminal-pair networks, although several synthesis techniques to realize prescribed driving-point functions are developed as interim steps in the general discussion.

A two-terminal-pair network can be characterized completely in a number of different ways. In contrast to the one-terminal-pair network, for which only one impedance or admittance function of the complex frequency s is required for complete characterization, the complete description of two-terminal-pair networks requires in general three functions of frequency.† Either of two sets of three functions are most commonly used in modern network synthesis. The first set includes the open-circuit driving-point and transfer impedances $z_{11}(s)$, $z_{22}(s)$, and $z_{12}(s)$, Figure 3.3 indicates the network, N, with terminal pairs 1-1′ and 2-2′. z_{11}, the open-circuit driving-point impedance at the input terminals, is the impedance seen looking into terminals 1-1′ with terminals 2-2′ left open-circuited. z_{22}, likewise, is the impedance seen looking in 2-2′ with 1-1′ open. z_{12}, the open-circuit transfer impedance, is the output voltage $E_{2-2'}$ divided by the input current I_1, with the 2-2′ terminals open circuited. Since the network N is assumed to contain only passive, linear elements (R, L, and C), z_{12} and z_{21} are identical, or the open-circuit transfer impedance can be measured in either direction. Of some value in analysis are the physical representations based upon considering z_{11} as the voltage across 1-1′ if 1 amp of current is forced in terminal 1 and out 1′ with 2 and 2′ left open. Likewise, z_{12} is the voltage across the open terminals 2-2′ with 1 amp in terminal 1.

A second set of functions which completely describes the behavior of N as a transducer consists of the three short-circuit admittances of the network, $y_{11}(s)$, $y_{22}(s)$, and $y_{12}(s)$. $y_{11}(s)$, the short-circuit admittance at the input, is the admittance seen looking in 1-1′ with a short circuit connecting 2 and 2′. Alternatively, y_{11} is the current in 1 if 1 volt is impressed across 1-1′ with 2-2′ shorted. Likewise, y_{22} is the admittance looking into 2-2′ with 1-1′ shorted. y_{12}, the short-circuit transfer admittance, is the current in the shorting bar from 2 to 2′ divided by the voltage impressed on 1-1′. These definitions of the short-circuit admittances as well as those of the open-circuit impedances are illustrated by the sketches of Fig. 3.4.

Either set of functions (the y's or the z's) serves to describe completely the behavior of the network as a transmission device regardless of the loading impedances on either end. The two sets of characterizing parameters are related by Eqs. (3.2) to (3.9):‡

$$z_{11} = \frac{y_{22}}{\Delta_y} \qquad (3.2) \qquad z_{12} = -\frac{y_{12}}{\Delta_y} \qquad (3.4)$$

$$z_{22} = \frac{y_{11}}{\Delta_y} \qquad (3.3) \qquad \Delta_y = y_{11}y_{22} - y_{12}^2 \qquad (3.5)$$

† E. A. Guillemin, "Communication Networks," Vol. II, p. 139, John Wiley & Sons, Inc., New York, 1935.

‡ E. A. Guillemin, *op. cit.*, p. 137.

$$y_{11} = \frac{z_{22}}{\Delta_z} \qquad (3.6) \qquad\qquad y_{12} = -\frac{z_{12}}{\Delta_z} \qquad (3.8)$$

$$y_{22} = \frac{z_{11}}{\Delta_z} \qquad (3.7) \qquad\qquad \Delta_z = z_{11}z_{22} - z_{12}^2 \qquad (3.9)$$

Most logical procedures for the synthesis of networks for prescribed transfer functions involve the following steps:

(1)   The nature of the specified transfer function is determined—*i.e.*, whether the function is to be realized as a voltage ratio, a current ratio, a transfer impedance, or a transfer admittance, and the loading desired on the network.

(2)   The above type of transfer function is expressed in terms of the z's or y's.

(3)   Equating of the expression of (2) with the specified transfer function permits determination of the required z's or y's as function of s.

(4)   A network is synthesized from these z's or y's.

A simple example illustrates this general procedure.   The function $s/(s+1)$ is to be realized as the voltage ratio of a network working into

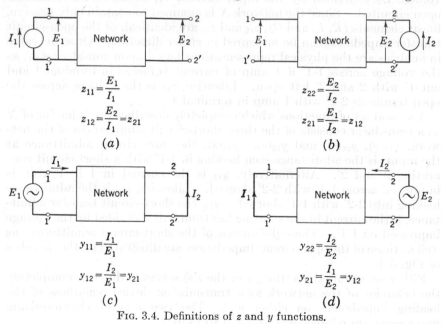

$$z_{11} = \frac{E_1}{I_1}$$

$$z_{12} = \frac{E_2}{I_1} = z_{21}$$

(a)

$$z_{22} = \frac{E_2}{I_2}$$

$$z_{21} = \frac{E_1}{I_2} = z_{12}$$

(b)

$$y_{11} = \frac{I_1}{E_1}$$

$$y_{12} = \frac{I_2}{E_1} = y_{21}$$

(c)

$$y_{22} = \frac{I_2}{E_2}$$

$$y_{21} = \frac{I_1}{E_2} = y_{12}$$

(d)

FIG. 3.4. Definitions of z and y functions.

an open-circuit and from an ideal voltage source.   It is shown in Sec. 3.2 that under these loading conditions

$$\frac{E_2}{E_1} = \frac{y_{12}}{y_{22}} \qquad (3.10)$$

The required y's can be determined by equating the expression of Eq. (3.10) to the desired transfer function:

$$\frac{y_{12}}{y_{22}} = \frac{s}{s+1} \qquad (3.11)$$

It is clear that the desired voltage ratio will be realized if a network can be found with

$$y_{12} = s \tag{3.12}$$
$$y_{22} = s + 1 \tag{3.13}$$

[The value of $y_{11}(s)$ does not enter into the determination of the voltage ratio.] The network of Fig. 3.5 is one possible configuration with the desired y_{12} and y_{22}, and the synthesis problem is solved. The solution for this simple example could, of course, have been written without any knowledge of network synthesis, but it is included here to illustrate the general procedure.

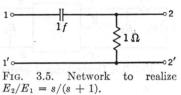

FIG. 3.5. Network to realize $E_2/E_1 = s/(s + 1)$.

It might be noted at this point that the above example can be used to illustrate one of the intriguing aspects of network synthesis, the existence of a great number of solutions to any problem. Clearly, Eqs. (3.12) and (3.13) are not the only identifications which can be made for y_{12} and y_{22} to yield the desired ratio shown in Eq. (3.11). An equally valid set of functions can be obtained by dividing both numerator and denominator of the specified transfer function by any polynomial in s. For example, if numerator and denominator are both divided by s, the identifications are

$$y_{12} = 1 \tag{3.14}$$
$$y_{22} = 1 + \frac{1}{s} \tag{3.15}$$

The resultant network is shown in Fig. 3.6. With relative ease one can derive a large number of other networks, all of which yield the same voltage ratio.

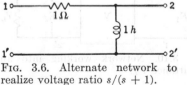

FIG. 3.6. Alternate network to realize voltage ratio $s/(s + 1)$.

Thus, actual synthesis of the network is always preceded by identification of suitable values for either the short-circuit driving-point and transfer admittances or the open-circuit driving-point and transfer impedances. Success in this task depends upon relationships between the various types of transfer functions that arise in practice and the z and y functions. The remainder of this section is devoted to the development of these relationships, with the results summarized in Table 3.1. For the purposes of this development the various transfer-function types are conveniently subdivided into classes on the basis of the nature of the signal source.

Signal Source an Ideal Voltage Source. The network is driven by the voltage E_1, which is independent of the impedance looking into the network. This situation is closely approximated in practice by a cathode-follower signal source and by many error-measuring devices used in feedback control systems. The assumption involved here, illustrated by Fig. 3.7, is that $|Z_s| \ll |Z|$ at all frequencies of interest, with the result that E_1 is essentially equal to E_s and the circuit of Fig. 3.7 can be replaced by that of Fig. 3.8.

This drive condition can be associated with an open circuit on the load end of the network, in which case the specified transfer function is the voltage ratio E_2/E_1 (Fig. 3.9). For this circuit, the input current is

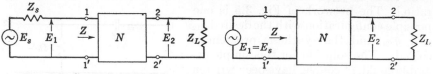

FIG. 3.7. General signal source.   FIG. 3.8. Signal source an ideal voltage generator.

simply E_1/z_{11}; the output voltage E_2 is the input current multiplied by z_{12}. Hence,

$$\frac{E_2}{E_1} = \frac{z_{12}}{z_{11}} \tag{3.16}$$

If the voltage ratio is desired in terms of the y's rather than the z functions, z_{12} and z_{11} of Eq. (3.16) can be replaced by the equivalent expressions in terms of the y's as given in Eqs. (3.2) and (3.4). Then

$$\frac{E_2}{E_1} = -\frac{y_{12}}{y_{22}} \tag{3.17}†$$

The result in Eq. (3.17) can be derived directly by application of Norton's theorem, since $-y_{12}E_1$ is the short-circuit current at the 2-2′ terminals

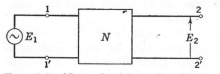

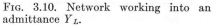

FIG. 3.9. Network driven by ideal voltage source and working into open circuit.   FIG. 3.10. Network working into an admittance Y_L.

and $1/y_{22}$ is the impedance seen looking back into the network with the voltage source replaced by its internal impedance of zero.

A second transfer function, which may be specified if the network is driven by an ideal voltage source, is the voltage ratio with the network loaded at the output by an admittance (as shown in Fig. 3.10). E_2/E_1 is readily calculated by application of Thévenin's theorem. The open-circuit voltage is given by Eq. (3.17); the Thévenin equivalent impedance looking back into the 2-2′ terminals is $1/y_{22}$. The output voltage is simply the voltage-divider ratio times the open-circuit voltage:

† The minus sign, arising because I_2 is defined as flowing into the network, is of no concern and, as in the remainder of this chapter, can be discarded in the synthesis.

$$\frac{E_2}{E_1} = \frac{y_{12}}{y_{22}} \frac{y_{22}}{(y_{22} + Y_L)} \tag{3.18}$$

$$\frac{E_2}{E_1} = \frac{y_{12}}{y_{22} + Y_L} \tag{3.19}$$

Signal Source an Ideal Current Source. A second group of transfer functions of practical interest is characterized by an infinite-impedance signal source, as portrayed in Fig. 3.11. This situation is closely approximated when the network is driven by a pentode and the dynamic plate resistance r_p is much larger than the input impedance of the network. With a general impedance $Z_L(s)$ as a load on the network, the significant transfer function is the transfer impedance $Z_{12}(s)$, defined as

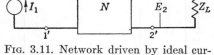

FIG. 3.11. Network driven by ideal current source.

$$Z_{12}(s) = \frac{E_2}{I_1} \tag{3.20}$$

On the basis of the definition of $z_{12}(s)$, the open-circuit voltage of the network is $z_{12}I_1$. Since the Thévenin equivalent impedance looking back into the 2-2′ terminals is z_{22}, the transfer impedance is simply

$$Z_{12}(s) = \frac{z_{12}Z_L}{z_{22} + Z_L} \tag{3.21}$$

Signal Source With Nonzero, Finite Internal Impedance. This situation, portrayed in Fig. 3.12, exists whenever the network is driven by a triode amplifier or any source with an output impedance of the same order of magnitude as the input impedance of the network. The expression for the voltage ratio E_2/E_s can be derived again by the use of Thévenin's or Norton's theorem. The short-circuit current is determined first. If the 2-2′ terminals are shorted, the input voltage E_1 is

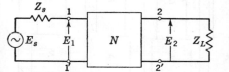

FIG. 3.12. Network with general drive and load.

$$E_1 = \frac{1}{1 + y_{11}Z_s} E_s \tag{3.22}$$

The short-circuit current at the 2-2′ terminals is found from the definition of y_{12}.

$$I_{2sc} = \frac{y_{12}}{1 + y_{11}Z_s} E_s \tag{3.23}$$

The Thévenin equivalent impedance is the impedance looking into the 2-2′ terminals with the network loaded at the 1-1′ end by an impedance

TABLE 3.1
RELATIONS BETWEEN TRANSFER FUNCTIONS AND DESCRIBING FUNCTIONS

Source impedance	Load impedance	System schematic	Transfer function in terms of z_{11}, z_{22}, z_{12}	Transfer function in terms of y_{11}, y_{22}, y_{12}
0	∞	E_1 — N — E_2	$\dfrac{E_2}{E_1} = \dfrac{z_{12}}{z_{11}}$	$\dfrac{E_2}{E_1} = \dfrac{y_{12}}{y_{22}}$
	Z_L	E_1 — N — Z_L — E_2	$\dfrac{E_2}{E_1} = \dfrac{z_{12}Z_L}{\Delta_z + z_{11}Z_L}$	$\dfrac{E_2}{E_1} = \dfrac{y_{12}}{y_{22} + Y_L}$
∞	∞	I_1 — N — E_2	$\dfrac{E_2}{I_1} = z_{12}$	$\dfrac{E_2}{I_1} = \dfrac{y_{12}}{\Delta_y}$
	Z_L	I_1 — N — Z_L — E_2	$\dfrac{E_2}{I_1} = \dfrac{z_{12}Z_L}{z_{22} + Z_L}$	$\dfrac{E_2}{E_s} = \dfrac{y_{12}}{\Delta_y + y_{11}Y_L}$
Z_s	∞	Z_s, E_s — N — E_2	$\dfrac{E_2}{E_s} = \dfrac{z_{12}}{z_{11} + Z_s}$	$\dfrac{E_2}{E_s} = \dfrac{y_{12}}{y_{22} + \Delta_y Z_s}$
	Z_L	Z_s, E_s — N — Z_L — E_2	$\dfrac{E_2}{E_s} = \dfrac{z_{12}Z_L}{\Delta_z + z_{22}Z_s + z_{11}Z_L + Z_sZ_L}$	$\dfrac{E_2}{E_s} = \dfrac{y_{12}Y_s}{\Delta_y + y_{11}Y_L + y_{22}Y_s + Y_LY_s}$

Z_s. This can be determined from the equivalent circuit of Fig. 3.13. Straightforward circuit analysis yields the result

$$Z_{Th} = \frac{1 + y_{11}Z_s}{y_{22} + \Delta_y Z_s} \tag{3.24}$$

where

$$\Delta_y = y_{11}y_{22} - y_{12}^2 \tag{3.25}$$

The transfer voltage ratio is given from Eqs. (3.23) and (3.24) as

$$\frac{E_2}{E_s} = \frac{y_{12}Z_L}{1 + y_{11}Z_s + y_{22}Z_L + \Delta_y Z_s Z_L} \tag{3.26}$$

In the special case when the network is open-circuited, Z_L becomes infinite and

$$\frac{E_2}{E_s} = \frac{y_{12}}{y_{22} + \Delta_y Z_s} \tag{3.27}$$

The above relationships between the transfer functions and the network functions (the z's and y's) are the foundations of logical synthesis

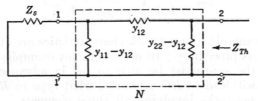

FIG. 3.13. Evaluation of Thévenin equivalent impedance.

procedures. Although all these equations are readily derived on the basis of Thévenin's theorem, they are repeated and summarized in Table 3.1 for later reference.

3.2. Characteristics of *RC* Networks. The vast majority of synthesis problems in the design of feedback control systems demand realization of the prescribed transfer functions by networks consisting entirely of resistors and capacitors. Inductors are avoided because of the excessive

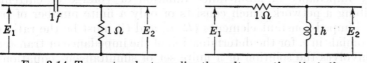

FIG. 3.14. Two networks to realize the voltage ratio $s/(s+1)$.

weight and size required by the low frequencies of interest. If the synthesis of a suitable compensation network is to be approached logically, the designer must have at least a surface familiarity with the general characteristics of the transfer functions of networks of the type with which he is working.

This need is pointed out by the very simple example of network synthesis given in Sec. 3.1. There it was indicated that either of the two networks shown in Fig. 3.14 is appropriate for the realization of the voltage ratio

$$\frac{E_2}{E_1} = \frac{s}{s+1} \qquad (3.28)$$

Both networks result from an identification of y_{12} and y_{22} which is based on the formula

$$\frac{E_2}{E_1} = \frac{y_{12}}{y_{22}} \qquad (3.29)$$

The identifications for the two networks were carried out in two slightly different ways. For the *RC* network, the direct identification was made:

$$\frac{y_{12}}{y_{22}} = \frac{s}{s+1} \qquad \begin{matrix} y_{12} = s \\ y_{22} = s+1 \end{matrix} \qquad (3.30)$$

Synthesis of the *RL* network was accomplished by first dividing both numerator and denominator polynomials by s:

$$\frac{y_{12}}{y_{22}} = \frac{1}{1+\dfrac{1}{s}} \qquad \begin{matrix} y_{12} = 1 \\ y_{22} = 1 + \dfrac{1}{s} \end{matrix} \qquad (3.31)$$

In this trivial example, the network characteristics are evident throughout the synthesis procedure. In more complex examples, however, it is essential that the synthesist be able to tell in advance what type of identifications will lead to *RC* networks, what type to *RL* networks, or what type to networks involving all three elements. This ability to foresee the nature of the end result of the synthesis is achieved by a knowledge of the characteristics of the z's or y's of *RC*, *RL*, and *RLC* networks. In other words, what conditions must be imposed on z_{11}, z_{22}, and z_{12} (or the y's) if these functions are to be realizable by an *RC* network? These conditions, termed generally the realizability conditions, are described in this section for *RC* networks. Because of lack of space, the conditions are stated below essentially without proof, although an attempt is made to indicate the logical nature of the requirements.

Any impedance or admittance function or voltage or current ratio describing a network which consists of only a finite number of passive, linear lumped-constant elements (R, L, and C) must be the ratio of two polynomials in s, for the determination of the impedance or transfer function involves the solution of a finite set of simultaneous equations (*e.g.*, the loop or node equations). In these equations, each coefficient is of the form R, Ls, Cs, or the reciprocals. The solution of the equations, whether this solution is effected by the use of determinants or by algebraic manipulation, must then involve only addition, subtraction, multiplication, and division of these three basic elements. The net result, when simplified, must be a rational algebraic function, the ratio of two polynomials in s. Furthermore, all coefficients of both numerator and denominator polynomials must be real. Consequently, if $G(s)$ is the transfer function, impedance, or admittance of interest and $p(s)$ and

$q(s)$ are polynomials in s, $G(s)$ can be written

$$G(s) = \frac{p(s)}{q(s)} \qquad (3.32)$$

Once the nature of $G(s)$ as the ratio of two polynomials is established, it is clear that the characteristics of $G(s)$ can be directly described in terms of the locations of the zeros of $p(s)$ and $q(s)$, or the zeros and poles of $G(s)$. Specification of these poles and zeros completely determines $G(s)$ except for a constant multiplier, which is usually of only secondary interest in the network-synthesis problem. What, then, are the characteristics of the poles and zeros of a $G(s)$ associated with an *RC* network? The answer to this question depends on the nature of $G(s)$: that is, whether G is a driving-point impedance, a voltage ratio, etc.

RC Driving-point Impedance. The case of $G(s)$ as the driving-point impedance of an *RC* network leads to the most stringent conditions on the poles and zeros. In this case, the critical frequencies must satisfy the following conditions:†

(1) All poles and zeros are simple and lie on the negative real axis in the *s* plane.
(2) The poles and zeros alternate along the axis.
(3) The lowest critical frequency (that nearest the origin) is a pole.
(4) The highest critical frequency (that farthermost from the origin) is a zero.

Fig. 3.15 presents a suitable pole-zero configuration, with the associated impedance function taking the analytic form

$$Z(s) = K \frac{(s + z_1)(s + z_2)(s + z_3)}{(s + p_1)(s + p_2)(s + p_3)}$$
$$(3.33)$$

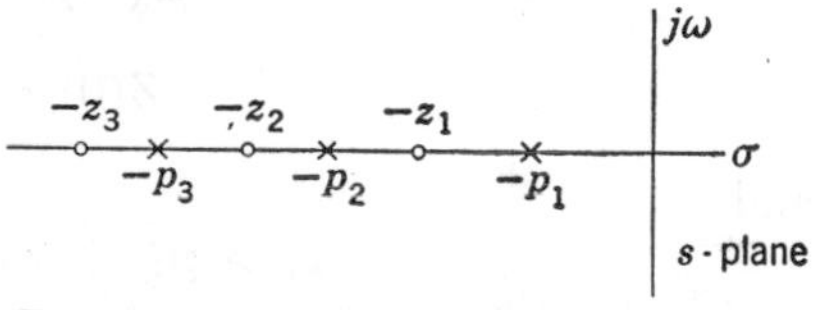

FIG. 3.15. Suitable pole-zero configuration for *RC* driving-point impedance. (Poles denoted by x, zeros by o.)

The parameters $(z_1, z_2, z_3, p_1, p_2, p_3)$ are all real, positive numbers.

Either or both of two special cases is permissible. The lowest critical frequency, the pole at $-p_1$ in Fig. 3.15, may be located at the origin in which case

$$Z(s) = K \frac{(s + z_1)(s + z_2)(s + z_3)}{s(s + p_1)(s + p_2)} \qquad (3.34)$$

Similarly, the highest critical frequency, the zero at $-z_3$, may be located at infinity, with

$$Z(s) = K \frac{(s + z_1)(s + z_2)}{(s + p_1)(s + p_2)(s + p_3)} \qquad (3.35)$$

The preceding two paragraphs are sufficient to define completely the conditions under which a given rational algebraic function of s can be

† E. A. Guillemin, "Communication Networks," Vol. II, pp. 211–212, John Wiley & Sons, Inc., New York, 1935.

realized as the driving-point impedance of an *RC* network. It is desirable, however, to investigate somewhat more completely the characteristics of functions meeting these realizability conditions. Since all poles and zeros of the impedance function are located on the negative real axis, the characteristics of $Z(s)$ are completely portrayed by a plot of the impedance as a function of the real variable σ. For the function with the pole-zero configuration shown in Fig. 3.15, such a plot takes the form of

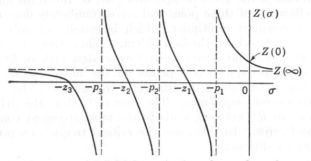

Fig. 3.16. Behavior of *RC* driving-point impedance along the real axis.

Fig. 3.16. A sketch of this nature places in evidence two characteristics of $Z(s)$ which are of fundamental importance in network synthesis:

(1) $Z(\infty) \leq Z(0)$. This fact can be established generally from Eq. (3.33), for

$$Z(\infty) = K \tag{3.36}$$

$$Z(0) = K \frac{z_1}{p_1} \frac{z_2}{p_2} \frac{z_3}{p_3} \tag{3.37}$$

and

$$z_1 > p_1 \qquad z_2 > p_2 \qquad z_3 > p_3 \tag{3.38}$$

$Z(\infty)$ is equal to $Z(0)$ only in the special case when $Z(s)$ is a constant.

(2) $dZ(\sigma)/d\sigma$ is negative for all values of σ. This characteristic is most readily shown from the partial-fraction expansion of $Z(s)$. For the function of Eq. (3.33), this partial-fraction expansion is of the form

$$Z(s) = \frac{k_1}{s + p_1} + \frac{k_2}{s + p_2} + \frac{k_3}{s + p_3} + k \tag{3.39}$$

Each of the residues k_1, k_2, and k_3, as well as the constant k, is positive, since in the evaluation of each residue there are an even number of negative multiplicative factors. The value of $Z(\sigma)$ is written directly from this partial-fraction expansion:

$$Z(\sigma) = \frac{k_1}{\sigma + p_1} + \frac{k_2}{\sigma + p_2} + \frac{k_3}{\sigma + p_3} + k \tag{3.40}$$

The derivative of $Z(\sigma)$ with respect to σ can now be written by inspection:

$$\frac{dZ(\sigma)}{d\sigma} = -\frac{k_1}{(\sigma + p_1)^2} - \frac{k_2}{(\sigma + p_2)^2} - \frac{k_3}{(\sigma + p_3)^2} \tag{3.41}$$

Since k_1, k_2, and k_3 are real, positive numbers, this derivative is negative for all values of the real variable σ.

In the preceding discussion the necessary and sufficient conditions for the realization of a $Z(s)$ function as the driving-point impedance of an *RC* network were expressed in terms of the poles and zeros of $Z(s)$. These conditions could have been stated equally well in terms of the poles and residues of $Z(s)$:

(1)   All poles of $Z(s)$ are simple and lie on the negative real axis.
(2)   All residues are real and positive.
(3) $Z(s)$ may have a pole at the origin but not at infinity.

The above discussion is concerned exclusively with the characteristics of driving-point impedance functions.   Alternatively, the development could be based on driving-point admittance functions.   If attention is switched from impedance to admittance functions, the roles of poles and zeros are simply interchanged.   The poles and zeros still alternate along the axis, but, for a $Y(s)$ function, the lowest critical frequency is a zero, the highest a pole.   Furthermore, $dY(\sigma)/d\sigma$ is positive for all σ, for

$$\frac{dY(\sigma)}{d\sigma} = \frac{d}{d\sigma}\left[\frac{1}{Z(\sigma)}\right] \tag{3.42}$$

$$\frac{dY(\sigma)}{d\sigma} = -\frac{1}{Z^2(\sigma)}\frac{dZ(\sigma)}{d\sigma} \tag{3.43}$$

If a partial-fraction expansion of $Y(s)$ is made, all residues are negative. It should be noted here, however, that division of the admittance function $Y(s)$ by s results in a rational algebraic function possessing all the characteristics of an *RC* impedance function.

The realizability conditions and characteristics of the driving-point impedance and admittance functions of *RC* networks are summarized in Table 3.2.

Transfer Functions.   The discussion of transfer functions in Sec. 3.1 indicated that the transmission characteristics of linear bilateral networks could be completely described in terms of either of two sets of three functions, either z_{11}, z_{22}, and z_{12} or y_{11}, y_{22}, and y_{12}.   The conditions for the realizability of a given set of z functions, for example, in an *RC* network are simply stated.   First, both z_{11} and z_{22} must satisfy the conditions for an *RC* driving-point impedance, as shown in Table 3.2.   In addition, z_{12} must satisfy the following conditions:

(1) $z_{12}(s)$ must have only simple poles, and at each pole the residue condition must be satisfied,

$$k_{11}k_{22} - k_{12}^2 \geq 0 \tag{3.44}$$

Here k_{11} is the residue of z_{11} at the pole in question, k_{22} the residue of z_{22} at the same pole, and k_{12} the corresponding residue of z_{12}.
(2)   At infinity,

$$z_{11}z_{22} - z_{12}^2 \geq 0 \tag{3.45}\dagger$$

† It should be noted that, in contrast to the situation with driving-point impedances,

What is the significance of these two conditions? Clearly, satisfaction of condition (1) demands that all poles of z_{12} be simple, lie on the negative real axis, and be also poles of both z_{11} and z_{22}. (Otherwise, k_{11} or k_{22} is zero at one of the poles of z_{12}.) Since z_{12} is the ratio of two polynomials

TABLE 3.2

REALIZABILITY CONDITIONS FOR *RC* DRIVING-POINT FUNCTIONS

	Driving-point-impedance functions, $Z(s)$	Driving-point-admittance functions, $Y(s)$
Necessary and sufficient conditions on the rational functions $Z(s)$ or $Y(s)$ for realization as an *RC* network in terms of poles and zeros	1. All poles and zeros simple and on the negative real axis in the s plane 2. Poles and zeros alternate along axis 3. Lowest critical frequency a *pole* 4. Highest critical frequency a *zero*	1. All poles and zeros simple and on the negative real axis in the s plane 2. Poles and zeros alternate along axis 3. Lowest critical frequency a *zero* 4. Highest critical frequency a *pole*
Conditions in terms of poles and residues	1. All poles of $Z(s)$ simple and on negative real axis 2. All residues of $Z(s)$ real and positive 3. $Z(s)$ may have pole at origin, none at infinity	1. All poles of $\dfrac{Y(s)}{s}$ simple and on negative real axis 2. All residues of $\dfrac{Y(s)}{s}$ real and positive 3. $\dfrac{Y(s)}{s}$ may have pole at origin, none at infinity
Form of sketch of $Z(\sigma)$ or $Y(\sigma)$	$Z(\sigma)$, $Z(0)$, $Z(\infty)$, σ	$Y(\sigma)$, $Y(\infty)$, $Y(0)$, σ
Important characteristics	1. $\dfrac{d[Z(\sigma)]}{d\sigma}$ negative 2. $Z(\infty) < Z(0)$	1. $\dfrac{dY(\sigma)}{d\sigma}$ positive 2. $Y(\infty) > Y(0)$

with real coefficients, all residues are real. The residue condition indicates that these residues can be either positive or negative, but they are restricted in size. Essentially, this condition places a constraint on the magnitude of the multiplying factor which can be realized for $z_{12}(s)$.

This constraint is illustrated by a simple example for which the open-circuit impedances are specified as

there are no conditions imposed directly on the location of the zeros of $z_{12}(s)$, other than the elementary restriction that these zeros must occur in conjugate complex pairs if the numerator polynomial of z_{12} possesses only real coefficients.

$$z_{11} = \frac{(s+2)(s+5)}{(s+1)(s+4)} \tag{3.46}$$

$$z_{22} = 4\frac{(s+3)(s+6)}{(s+1)(s+4)} \tag{3.47}$$

$$z_{12} = K\frac{s^2+1}{(s+1)(s+4)} \tag{3.48}$$

The constant K is to be chosen as large as possible consistent with the realizability conditions.   The first step in the evaluation of this maximum K involves partial-fraction expansions of all three functions:

$$z_{11}(s) = 1 + \frac{\frac{4}{3}}{s+1} + \frac{\frac{2}{3}}{s+4} \tag{3.49}$$

$$z_{22} = 4 + \frac{\frac{40}{3}}{s+1} + \frac{\frac{8}{3}}{s+4} \tag{3.50}$$

$$z_{12} = K + \frac{\frac{2}{3}K}{s+1} + \frac{-\frac{17}{3}K}{s+4} \tag{3.51}$$

There are two poles of z_{12}, at -1 and -4.   For the pole at -1, the residue condition yields

$$\tfrac{4}{3} \times \tfrac{40}{3} - (\tfrac{2}{3}K)^2 \geq 0 \tag{3.52}$$

$$K \leq \sqrt{40} \tag{3.53}$$

For the pole at -4,

$$\tfrac{2}{3} \times \tfrac{8}{3} - (\tfrac{17}{3}K)^2 \geq 0 \tag{3.54}$$

$$K \leq \tfrac{4}{17} \tag{3.55}$$

At infinity, condition (2) above yields

$$1 \times 4 - K^2 \geq 0 \tag{3.56}$$

$$K \leq 2 \tag{3.57}$$

The maximum value of K, if all three conditions are to be satisfied, is $\tfrac{4}{17}$. In other words, regardless of the synthesis procedure used, a network can never be found which yields the specified z_{11}, z_{22}, and z_{12} with a value of K larger than $\tfrac{4}{17}$.   This condition is particularly important in synthesis, because it is often essential that the synthesis procedure be initiated with three functions which meet all realizability conditions.   If the synthesis is started with a nonrealizable set of functions, considerable labor may merely lead to a network with negative element values.

Although the conditions on y_{11}, y_{22}, and y_{12} for realizability by an *RC* network can be presented in a similar manner, the discussion is simpler if the functions considered are y_{11}/s, y_{22}/s, and y_{12}/s, for these three functions must satisfy exactly the same conditions as the set of impedance functions.   Again the extra freedom allowed in transfer functions but not in driving-point functions is expressed by a relaxation of restrictions on the location of the zeros.

Once the conditions for realization in *RC* networks are established for the z and y functions, Table 3.1 can be used to determine appropriate conditions on the various transfer functions (open-circuit voltage ratio, etc.).   Two examples serve to illustrate the general procedure used in the derivation of the results shown in Table 3.3.

(1)   Source with zero impedance working into an open circuit:

$$\frac{E_2}{E_1} = \frac{z_{12}}{z_{11}} \tag{3.58}$$

The conditions for the realizability of a given rational function as the voltage ratio of an *RC* network are desired. z_{12} and z_{11} are written as the ratio of polynomials in s:

$$z_{11}(s) = \frac{p(s)}{(s + a)(s + b)q(s)} \tag{3.59}$$

$$z_{12}(s) = \frac{m(s)}{q(s)} \tag{3.60}$$

The poles of z_{12} are the zeros of the polynomial $q(s)$.   All these poles must be present in $z_{11}(s)$; in addition, z_{11} may have other poles, represented above by the factors $s + a$ and $s + b$. $p(s)$ has all zeros on the negative real axis; $m(s)$ may have zeros anywhere.   Substitution of Eqs. (3.59) and (3.60) into (3.58) yields

$$\frac{E_2}{E_1} = \frac{m(s)(s + a)(s + b)}{p(s)} \tag{3.61}$$

The important characteristics of E_2/E_1 are the permissible locations of the poles and zeros and the behavior at both zero and infinite frequency. Equation (3.61) contains the required information about the finite, non-zero critical frequencies.   All finite poles of E_2/E_1 are at the zeros of $p(s)$ and hence must be simple and lie on the negative real axis, but the zeros of E_2/E_1 may lie anywhere in the plane as a result of the nature of $m(s)$.   The infinite-frequency behavior of E_2/E_1 is most readily investigated by consideration of Eq. (3.58).   Neither z_{12} nor z_{11} can have a pole at infinity.   If z_{11} has a simple zero at infinity, z_{12} must have at least a simple zero, or the infinite-frequency realizability condition on z_{11}, z_{22}, and z_{12} cannot be fulfilled.   Consequently, E_2/E_1 cannot have a pole at infinity, but it can have either a constant value or a zero.   In other words, the degree of the denominator polynomial of E_2/E_1 must be at least as high as the degree of the numerator.

As the last step, the zero-frequency behavior is considered.   The following pairs of possibilities exist for the zero-frequency behavior of z_{11} and z_{12}:

z_{11}	z_{12}	$E_2/E_1 = z_{12}/z_{11}$
Constant	Constant	Constant
Constant	Zero of any order	Zero of any order
Simple pole	Constant	Simple zero
Simple pole	Simple pole	Constant
Simple pole	Zero of any order	Zero of any order

TABLE 5.3
REALIZABILITY CONDITIONS FOR RC TRANSFER FUNCTIONS

Source impedance	Load impedance	System schematic	Transfer function in terms of z's or y's	Realizability conditions
0	∞		$\dfrac{E_2}{E_1} = \dfrac{z_{12}}{z_{11}} = \dfrac{y_{12}}{y_{22}}$	No poles at ∞ or 0 Poles simple, on negative real axis
	$Z_L = 1$		$\dfrac{E_2}{E_1} = \dfrac{y_{12}}{1 + y_{22}} = \dfrac{z_{12}}{z_{11} + \Delta_z}$	No poles at ∞ or 0 Poles simple, on negative real axis
	∞		$\dfrac{E_2}{I_1} = z_{12} = \dfrac{y_{12}}{\Delta_y}$	No pole at ∞ Poles simple, on negative real axis
∞	$Z_L = 1$		$\dfrac{E_2}{I_1} = \dfrac{z_{12}}{1 + z_{22}} = \dfrac{y_{12}}{y_{11} + \Delta_y}$	No poles at 0 or ∞ Poles simple, on negative real axis
	∞		$\dfrac{E_2}{E_s} = \dfrac{z_{12}}{1 + z_{11}} = \dfrac{y_{12}}{y_{22} + \Delta_y}$	No poles at 0 or ∞ Poles simple, on negative real axis
$Z_s = 1$	$Z_L = 1$		$\dfrac{E_2}{E_s} = \dfrac{z_{12}}{1 + z_{11} + z_{22} + \Delta_z} = \dfrac{y_{12}}{1 + y_{11} + y_{22} + \Delta_y}$	No poles at 0 or ∞ Poles simple, on negative real axis
General conditions			z_{11}, z_{22}, z_{12} y_{11}, y_{22}, y_{12}	z_{11} and z_{22}: *RC* driving-point impedances z_{12}: Poles simple, on negative real axis, residue condition satisfied y/s functions same as z

Consequently, E_2/E_1 can have either a constant value or a zero of any order.   No pole is permitted at the origin.

(2)   Source with zero impedance working into a 1-ohm load:

$$\frac{E_2}{E_1} = \frac{y_{12}}{1 + y_{22}} \qquad (3.62)$$

With loading on the network, it is simpler to consider an over-all network which includes the load and the network N.   Inclusion of the terminating resistor to yield the over-all network N', rather than N, does not change the RC character of the network.   The short-circuit admittance functions of N' are simply related to those of N, as indicated by consideration of Fig. 3.17.   In particular, y_{11} and y_{12} are identical for the two networks, for the determination of both admittance functions is effected by shorting the load terminals.   In terms of the y functions, the only difference between the two networks is that y'_{22} contains an additional 1-mho conductance:

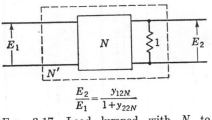

$$\frac{E_2}{E_1} = \frac{y_{12N}}{1+y_{22N}}$$

Fig. 3.17.   Load lumped with N to form N'.

$$y'_{22} = 1 + y_{22} \qquad (3.63)$$

Consequently, y'_{22}, in addition to satisfying all RC-realizability conditions, must have a zero-frequency value greater than unity to ensure the realizability of y_{22}.

The voltage ratio of interest is the open-circuit ratio for the network N', or

$$\frac{E_2}{E_1} = \frac{y'_{12}}{y'_{22}} \qquad (3.64)$$

The general characteristics of this transfer function were derived in Example (1) just above. E_2/E_1 possesses only simple poles on the negative real axis and no pole at infinity.   The additional constraint imposed above on y'_{22} does not affect E_2/E_1 because y'_{12} can have either a constant value or a zero of any order at the origin.   The only result of this additional constraint is evident when, from a specified voltage ratio, suitable values of y'_{12} and y'_{22} are chosen as the first step in the synthesis procedure. At that point, y'_{22} must be chosen to possess a nonzero value at zero frequency.

3.3. Synthesis of RC Driving-point Impedances.   Although the primary concern of the designer of feedback control systems is with the realization of specified transfer functions, most of the techniques for the synthesis of transfer functions are based at least in part on the synthesis of driving-point impedance or admittance functions.   There are four fundamental methods by which networks for RC impedance functions can be synthesized.[†]   Each method yields a canonic network, one with

† E. A. Guillemin, "Communication Networks," Vol. II, pp. 212–215, John Wiley & Sons, Inc., New York, 1935.

the minimum number of elements required to realize the specified impedance function. Each method depends on the technique of writing the
function in such a form that a suitable network configuration and element
values can be determined by inspection.

Partial-fraction Expansion of Z(s). The first canonic form (termed the
first Foster form) entails a partial-fraction expansion of the impedance
function $Z(s)$. This expansion is of the form

$$Z(s) = a_\infty + \frac{a_0}{s} + \frac{a_1}{s + p_1} + \cdots + \frac{a_n}{s + p_n} \tag{3.65}$$

If $Z(s)$ satisfies the conditions for realizability as an *RC* network, all the
a's $(a_\infty, a_0, a_1, \ldots, a_n)$ are zero or real, positive numbers and all p_j are,
likewise, real and positive. The corresponding network can be written
by inspection and is drawn in Fig. 3.18.

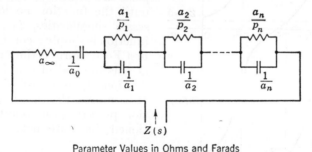

Parameter Values in Ohms and Farads

Fɪɢ. 3.18. First Foster form for *RC* driving-point impedance.

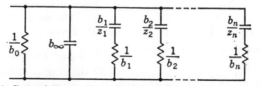

Fɪɢ. 3.19. Second Foster form for *RC* driving-point impedance.

Partial-fraction Expansion of Y(s)/s. The second Foster form is based
on a partial-fraction expansion of $Y(s)/s$. For an *RC* function, this
expansion takes a form similar to that of a driving-point impedance.

$$\frac{Y(s)}{s} = b_\infty + \frac{b_0}{s} + \frac{b_1}{s + z_1} + \cdots + \frac{b_n}{s + z_n} \tag{3.66}$$

Multiplication by s yields

$$Y(s) = b_\infty s + b_0 + \frac{b_1 s}{s + z_1} + \cdots + \frac{b_n s}{s + z_n} \tag{3.67}$$

Again here, all b's are zero or real and positive; all z's are real and positive.
The network is simply the parallel connection (Fig. 3.19) of $n + 2$ individual networks, each representing one term in the above expansion.

It is appropriate at this time to pause a moment and consider briefly an alternate way of viewing the synthesis procedures represented by these first two canonic forms. The synthesis problem is one of finding a network from a given $Z(s)$. One possible approach is to attempt to decrease the complexity of $Z(s)$ step by step until there is nothing left. Each step in the reduction must meet two requirements: the removed quantity must be recognizable as a simple impedance and the remainder must be an *RC* impedance function.

These remarks are clarified by a consideration of the development of the first Foster form. To reduce the complexity of the given impedance function $Z(s)$, a pole is removed. It was pointed out in Sec. 1.2 that a simple pole can be completely removed by subtraction of a term of the form $k/(s+p)$. Here $-p$ is the pole, k the associated residue. The poles are removed, one at a time, until the function no longer possesses singularities, *i.e.*, until the function is simply a constant. The first Foster form is the embodiment of this method of step-by-step reduction of the complexity of $Z(s)$. It is noteworthy that in this reduction process both conditions mentioned above are met:

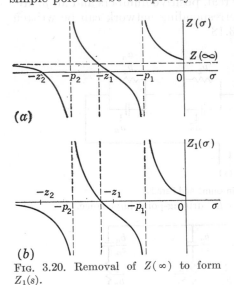

(1) The removed part, of the form of $k/(s+p)$, is recognizable as the impedance of a simple *RC* network.

(2) The remainder is still realizable as an *RC* network.

FIG. 3.20. Removal of $Z(\infty)$ to form $Z_1(s)$.

The first two canonic forms for an *RC* driving-point impedance function represent a reduction of the function complexity by the successive removal of poles. The second two forms, the two Cauer forms, effect this reduction by removal of poles, but in a somewhat different manner, as demonstrated in the discussion below.

Continued-fraction Expansion about Infinity. The first Cauer form is based on a continued-fraction expansion of the impedance function. The nature of a typical $Z(\sigma)$ along the real σ axis is shown in Fig. 3.20(a). (The following discussion is made explicit by assuming that $Z(s)$ is a nonzero constant at infinity. The possibility does exist that $Z(\infty)$ may be zero.) As indicated in the last item of Table 3.2, $Z(\infty) < Z(0)$. Consequently, a constant equal to $Z(\infty)$ can be subtracted from $Z(s)$, leaving a remainder function $Z_1(s)$ which still meets all *RC*-realizability conditions. The net effect of the removal of this constant is shown by Fig. 3.20(b). The poles are left unchanged, the zeros are shifted, a zero is introduced at infinity, and the zero-frequency value is decreased, but still positive. In terms of the network, the removal of this resistance represents the insertion of a series resistance. In terms of the functional form of $Z(s)$, the denominator has been left unchanged, since the poles are unaffected, but the degree of the numerator is reduced by one.

The procedure can be illustrated by a simple example. The function considered is

$$Z(s) = \frac{(s+2)(s+4)}{(s+1)(s+3)} \tag{3.68}$$

After removal of the infinite-frequency value of unity, the remainder function is

$$Z_1(s) = \frac{(s+2)(s+4)}{(s+1)(s+3)} - 1 \tag{3.69}$$

$$Z_1(s) = \frac{2s+5}{s^2+4s+3} \tag{3.70}$$

The network representation of this first step in reduction is shown in Fig. 3.21. The function $Z_1(s)$ remains to be synthesized.

Up to this point, the procedure has been identical with that leading to the first Foster form. If the Foster form were being used, the next step would be the removal of one of the two poles at -1 and -3. In the first Cauer

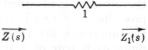

FIG. 3.21. Network representation of removal of $Z(\infty)$.

form, however, attention remains focused on the behavior of the function at infinite frequency, where $Z_1(s)$ possesses a zero. Zeros cannot be removed directly, but, if the function is inverted

$$\left[Y_1(s) = \frac{1}{Z_1(s)} \right]$$

$Y_1(s)$ has a pole at infinity, which can be removed without destroying the RC character of the remainder. For the example used in the preceding paragraph, the form of $Y_1(\sigma)$ is shown in Fig. 3.22. Removal of the pole at infinity leaves the other pole of $Y_1(s)$ unaltered, but moves the zeros. Analytically, this reduction step takes the form

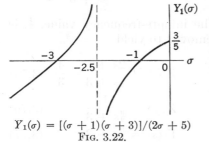

$$Y_1(\sigma) = [(\sigma+1)(\sigma+3)]/(2\sigma+5)$$
FIG. 3.22.

$$Y_1(s) = \frac{s^2+4s+3}{2s+5} \tag{3.71}$$

As $s \to \infty$, $Y_1(s) \to \frac{1}{2}s$. Removal of $s/2$ yields

$$Y_2(s) = \frac{s^2+4s+3}{2s+5} - \frac{1}{2}s \tag{3.72}$$

$$Y_2(s) = \frac{\frac{3}{2}s+3}{2s+5} \tag{3.73}$$

The complexity of the analytical form of the admittance function has been decreased by a reduction of one in the degree of the numerator. The resulting form of $Y_2(\sigma)$ is shown in Fig. 3.23. The network representation of this step is the addition of a shunt capacitor of value $\frac{1}{2}$, as shown in Fig. 3.24.

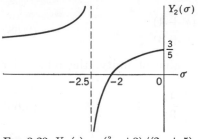

FIG. 3.23. $Y_2(\sigma) = (\frac{3}{2}\sigma + 3)/(2\sigma + 5)$.

Continuation of the synthesis involves reciprocation of $Y_2(s)$ to obtain $Z_2(s)$, since $Y_2(\infty) > Y_2(0)$ and $Y_2(\infty)$ cannot be removed without destroy-

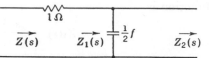

FIG. 3.24. Network after development to $Y_2(s) = 1/Z_2(s)$.

ing the *RC* character of the remainder. Once $Z_2(s)$ is considered, the situation is identical with that existing at the outset of the synthesis procedure. $Z_2(\infty)$ is removed to create an impedance zero at infinity; the function is inverted, and the admittance pole at infinity is removed. Since each pair of reductions of this sort reduces the degree of both numerator and denominator polynomials by one, continued iteration of these reduction steps eventually results in a complete dissolution of the function.

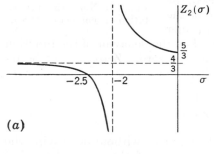

(a)

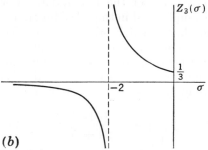

(b)

FIG. 3.25. Removal of $Z_2(\infty)$ to create $Z_3(s)$.

The example started above is readily completed. $Z_2(s)$ has the form shown in Fig. 3.25.

$$Z_2(s) = \frac{2s + 5}{\frac{3}{2}s + 3} \qquad (3.74)$$

The infinite-frequency value, $\frac{4}{3}$, is removed to yield

$$Z_3(s) = \frac{2s + 5}{\frac{3}{2}s + 3} - \frac{4}{3} \qquad (3.75)$$

$$Z_3(s) = \frac{1}{\frac{3}{2}s + 3} \qquad (3.76)$$

$$Y_3(s) = \frac{3}{2}s + 3 \qquad (3.77)$$

At this point the remainder of the network can be recognized, and the complete network is as shown in Fig. 3.26.

Several comments concerning the synthesis procedure are appropriate.

(1) If the original $Z(s)$ function possesses a zero at infinity, the first step is reciprocation and removal of the admittance pole at infinity.

The network then starts with a shunt capacitance rather than the series resistance of the example above.

(2) The successive subtraction and reciprocation are represented analytically as a continued-fraction expansion. In the above example, the synthesis procedure essentially resolves to the problem of finding an expansion of $Z(s)$ in the following form:

$$Z(s) = 1 + \cfrac{1}{\frac{1}{2}s + \cfrac{1}{\frac{4}{3} + \cfrac{1}{\frac{3}{2}s + \cfrac{1}{\frac{1}{3}}}}}$$

(3.78)

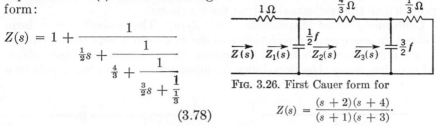

FIG. 3.26. First Cauer form for

$$Z(s) = \frac{(s+2)(s+4)}{(s+1)(s+3)}.$$

(3) The process of making this continued-fraction expansion can be mechanized as successive long division and reciprocation. For example, removal of the constant value of $Z(s)$ at infinity amounts to simply a single division of the denominator polynomial of $Z(s)$ into the numerator. In the numerical example,

$$Z(s) = \frac{s^2 + 6s + 8}{s^2 + 4s + 3}$$

(3.79)

$$s^2 + 4s + 3 \overline{\smash{\big)}\ \begin{aligned}&1\\[-2pt] &s^2 + 6s + 8\end{aligned}}$$
$$\underline{s^2 + 4s + 3}$$
$$2s + 5$$

$$Z(s) = 1 + \frac{2s + 5}{s^2 + 4s + 3}$$

(3.80)

The complete synthesis procedure can be carried out as a purely routine procedure in the form shown below:

$$
\begin{array}{r}
1 \\
s^2 + 4s + 3\,\overline{\smash{\big)}\,s^2 + 6s + 8} \\
s^2 + 4s + 3 \qquad \tfrac{1}{2}s \\
\overline{2s + 5\,\big)\,s^2 + 4s + 3} \\
s^2 + \tfrac{5}{2}s \qquad \tfrac{4}{3} \\
\overline{\tfrac{3}{2}s + 3\,\big)\,2s + 5} \\
2s + 4 \qquad \tfrac{3}{2}s \\
\overline{1\,\big)\,\tfrac{3}{2}s + 3} \\
\tfrac{3}{2}s \qquad \tfrac{1}{3} \\
\overline{3\,\big)\,1} \\
1
\end{array}
$$

$$Z(s) = 1 + \cfrac{1}{\frac{1}{2}s + \cfrac{1}{\frac{4}{3} + \cfrac{1}{\frac{3}{2}s + \cfrac{1}{\frac{1}{3}}}}}$$

(3.81)

The network elements arising from this continued-fraction expansion are the successive quotients in the division and reciprocation process.

The synthesis procedure has been discussed in considerable detail because it is the basis for many of the techniques for the realization of transfer functions. An understanding of the significance of the various steps in the synthesis is essential if the procedure is to be intelligently extended to the realization of transfer functions.

Continued-fraction Expansion about Zero. The second Cauer form follows the same general techniques as the first form except that attention is now focused on the behavior of the functions at the origin in the *s* plane. At zero frequency, the impedance function has either a simple pole or a

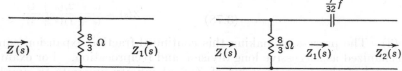

FIG. 3.27. Removal of $Y(0)$ to create $Z_1(s)$ with pole at origin.

FIG. 3.28. Network after first complete cycle in development of second Cauer form.

constant value, and $Z(0) > Z(\infty)$. Consequently, a pole at the origin can be removed from the impedance function or $Y(0)$ removed from the admittance function without destroying the *RC* character of the remainder. Synthesis of the same numerical example used as an illustration of the first Cauer form serves to demonstrate the procedure.

In this example,

$$Z(s) = \frac{(s + 2)(s + 4)}{(s + 1)(s + 3)} \tag{3.82}$$

$Z(s)$ does not possess a pole at the origin. Since $Z(0) > Z(\infty)$, removal of $Z(0)$ would leave $Z(\infty)$ negative, the remainder not realizable. Consequently, $Y(s)$ is considered, and the zero-frequency value is removed as a shunt conductance.

$$Y_1(s) = Y(s) - Y(0) \tag{3.83}$$

$$Y_1(s) = \frac{(s + 1)(s + 3)}{(s + 2)(s + 4)} - \frac{3}{8} \tag{3.84}$$

$$Y_1(s) = \frac{\frac{5}{8}s^2 + \frac{7}{4}s}{s^2 + 6s + 8} \tag{3.85}$$

The remainder impedance function is

$$Z_1(s) = \frac{s^2 + 6s + 8}{\frac{5}{8}s^2 + \frac{7}{4}s} \tag{3.86}$$

Fig. 3.27 shows the present status in the development of the network.

The zero-frequency pole of the impedance function is removed. Since $Z_1(s)$ has a residue of $\frac{32}{7}$ in the pole at the origin, the remainder impedance, $Z_2(s)$, is

$$Z_2(s) = \frac{s^2 + 6s + 8}{\frac{5}{8}s^2 + \frac{7}{4}s} - \frac{\frac{32}{7}}{s} \tag{3.87}$$

$$Z_2(s) = \frac{s + \frac{22}{7}}{\frac{5}{8}s + \frac{7}{4}} \tag{3.88}$$

The network as determined to this point is drawn in Fig. 3.28.

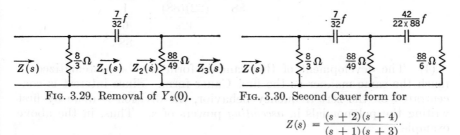

FIG. 3.29. Removal of $Y_2(0)$.   FIG. 3.30. Second Cauer form for

$$Z(s) = \frac{(s+2)(s+4)}{(s+1)(s+3)}.$$

The process is repeated with the removal of $Y_2(0)$, the value of the admittance function at the origin:

$$Y_3(s) = Y_2(s) - Y_2(0) \tag{3.89}$$

$$Y_3(s) = \frac{\frac{5}{8}s + \frac{7}{4}}{s + \frac{22}{7}} - \frac{49}{88} \tag{3.90}$$

$$Y_3(s) = \frac{\frac{6}{88}s}{s + \frac{22}{7}} \tag{3.91}$$

At this stage, the network takes the form of Fig. 3.29. The remainder of the network can be written by inspection:

$$Z_3(s) = \frac{88}{6} + \frac{(22)(88)}{42s} \tag{3.92}$$

The final network is that of Fig. 3.30.

Again, several comments are in order:

(1)   The effect of each step in the synthesis procedure can be demonstrated effectively by a series of sketches of the various impedance and admittance functions versus the real variable σ. Sketches of this type are shown for the above example in Fig. 3.31.†

(2)   If $Z(s)$ possesses a pole at the origin at the outset, the procedure is initiated by removal of this pole; the network starts with a series capacitance.

† Throughout this chapter there are a number of figures of the nature of 3.31, figures which portray the reduction in the complexity of an impedance function by plots of the various functions along the negative real axis. Since these sketches are only to guide the designer through the synthesis and are not used for numerical evaluation of network parameters, there is no attempt to plot accurately to scale.

(3)   The successive subtraction and reciprocation again can be represented as a continued fraction expansion of the impedance function.   In the above example,

$$Z(s) = \cfrac{1}{\cfrac{3}{8} + \cfrac{1}{\cfrac{32}{7s} + \cfrac{1}{\cfrac{49}{88} + \cfrac{1}{\cfrac{(22)(88)}{42s} + \cfrac{1}{\cfrac{6}{88}}}}}} \qquad (3.93)$$

(4)   The development of this canonic form can be systematized in much the same manner as the first Cauer form.   Since interest is concentrated on the zero-frequency behavior, the division is done by first writing the polynomials in *ascending* powers of *s*.   Thus, in the above example

$$Z(s) = \frac{8 + 6s + s^2}{3 + 4s + s^2} \qquad (3.94)$$

Since the first step is reciprocation, the process is started by dividing the numerator of Eq. (3.94) into the denominator.   The complete division and reciprocation process takes the form shown below:

$$8 + 6s + s^2 \overline{\smash{\big)}3 + 4s + s^2} \quad \frac{3}{8}$$

(3.95)

The elements of the continued fraction expansion [Eq. (3.93)] are the successive quotients of the division and reciprocation process.

The four canonic forms described above for the realization of *RC* driving-point impedance functions are simply methods for logical step-by-step reduction of the function complexity.   Clearly, at any time in the development, the designer may switch from one canonic form to another.   If more than the minimum number of elements are allowed, the procedures can be modified to yield a great variety of different networks.   For example, only part of a pole need be removed at any stage in the design.   The synthesis of *RC* driving-point impedances demonstrates the flexibility available to the network synthesist, the multitude of solutions available for a synthesis problem.

What are the practical applications of methods for the synthesis of driving-point impedances? In the design of feedback control systems, there are two principal applications. First, and more important, the techniques described above serve as a basis for the realization of transfer functions. This application is emphasized in the remaining sections of this chapter. Second, driving-point impedances are of importance in their own right as a means for realizing given gain functions. The commonest example of this is the use of a driving-point impedance in conjunction with a pentode amplifier stage. This application is illustrated by the circuit of Fig. 3.32. (Here only the incremental circuit is shown; bias supplies, etc., are omitted.) If the dynamic plate resistance r_p of the pentode is high compared to the magnitude of $Z(s)$ at all frequencies of interest, the gain of this stage is

$$\frac{E_{\text{out}}}{E_{\text{in}}} = -g_m Z(s) \qquad (3.96)$$

If the desired $E_{\text{out}}/E_{\text{in}}$ ratio as a function of s satisfies the realizability conditions for RC driving-point impedances, this circuit configuration can be used. Any voltage-to-current device could of course be used instead of a pentode.

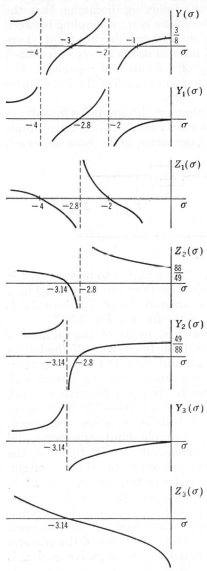

FIG. 3.31. Development of second Cauer form.

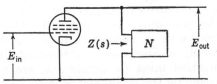

FIG. 3.32. Use of driving-point impedance to realize a transfer function.

3.4. Characteristics of Ladder Networks.
Preliminary to the consideration of techniques for the synthesis of specified transfer functions, it is desirable to consider briefly the characteristics of the most important type of network used in the realization of transfer functions, the ladder

network.   The general form of a ladder network is shown in Fig. 3.33. The final impedance at either end of the ladder may be either a shunt or a series arm.   (In the figure, Z_1 and Z_3 are shown as series arms, Z_2 and Z_4 as shunt arms.)   It is assumed in the following discussion that the term "ladder networks" denotes that there is no mutual coupling between the various impedances; each arm is an isolated driving-point (two-terminal) impedance.   In most cases of interest in the theory of feedback control systems, each arm consists only of resistors and capacitors, and usually at most two elements, although in general each of the impedances shown in Fig. 3.33 may be of any complexity.

It was shown in the preceding section that any driving-point impedance could be realized in the form of a ladder network.   Particularly simple ladder networks resulted from the two Cauer forms, for in those cases each

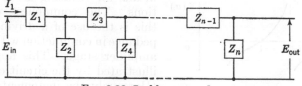

Fig. 3.33. Ladder network.

arm of the ladder was a single element.   The question to be answered in this section is the following: What transfer functions can be realized by a simple ladder?   In other words, what characteristics of E_2/E_1 or E_2/I_1 can be synthesized in a ladder network of the form of Fig. 3.33?

This question is most readily answered in terms of the admissible locations of the poles and zeros of the transfer functions.   If the ladder is of the RC type, the poles must be simple and restricted to the negative real axis in the s plane.   There cannot be a pole at infinity, since at high frequencies the RC network degenerates to simply a resistive network and the output voltage must stay finite.   The permissible behavior at zero frequency depends on the type of transfer function considered. E_2/I_1 may have a pole at the origin (*e.g.*, a simple shunt capacitor would yield this).   If, however, E_2/E_1 is the significant transfer function, the discussion of Sec. 3.2 demonstrated that no pole is permitted at the origin. Practically, poles are never permitted at the origin, for, even if E_2/I_1 is the transfer function considered, a zero-frequency pole implies that z_{11} also possesses a pole at $s = 0$.   Consequently, the driving device must behave as a constant-current source even when working into an open circuit, clearly a physical impossibility.   Thus, the poles of the transfer function must be simple and are restricted to the negative real axis excluding the origin and infinity.

What restrictions are imposed on the location of the zeros of the transfer function?   This question is readily answered if consideration is given to the source of these zeros.   Since there is only one path from input to output through the ladder network, a transmission zero can arise in only two ways: either a series arm must become an open circuit or a shunt arm a short circuit.   In the ladder network shown in Fig. 3.34, for example, there are at most two zeros, one at the value of s at which the R_1C_1 combination presents infinite impedance, the other at infinite frequency, when the C_2 arm is a short circuit.

Thus, the only possible zeros are at the antiresonant frequencies† of the series arms and the resonant frequencies of the shunt arms.   These frequencies, however, are not always transmission zeros.   This statement is clarified by consideration of Fig. 3.34.   If the impedance $Z_a(s)$, seen looking to the right at $a - a'$, possesses a pole at $s = -1/R_1C_1$, the R_1C_1 series arm does not introduce a transmission zero, for the voltage

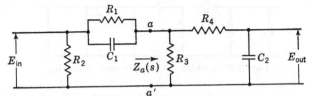

FIG. 3.34. Typical ladder network.

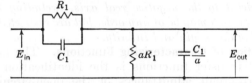

FIG. 3.35. Ladder with voltage ratio independent of frequency.

across $a - a'$ is not zero at a frequency of $-1/R_1C_1$, but rather is determined by the voltage-divider action between the two open circuits.   This phenomenon is illustrated by the simpler example of the ladder of Fig. 3.35.   At the frequency $s = 1/R_1C_1$, both the series and the shunt arms are antiresonant; the voltage ratio is simply

$$\frac{E_2}{E_1} = \frac{a}{1 + a} \tag{3.97}$$

Thus, antiresonance of a series arm of the ladder network produces a transmission zero only if the impedance looking toward the output terminals from the output side of the series arm does not possess a pole at the same value of s.

Likewise, a resonance of a shunt arm produces a transmission zero only if the impedance looking toward the output from the output side of the shunt arm does not possess a zero at the same value of s.   If this condition is not fulfilled, there is simply a current-divider action between the two parallel short circuits, with some current traveling on toward the output.

The above comments concerning the origin of the transmission zeros are perfectly general for a ladder network and valid regardless of the nature of the ladder.   If the further restriction is imposed that the ladder

† The terms "antiresonant frequency" and "resonant frequency" are used here to denote the values of s at which the impedance becomes infinite and zero, respectively.

should be *RC*, it is clear that the transmission zeros are restricted to the negative real axis, for the poles of the series impedances or shunt admittances lie exclusively on this axis.   The zeros may be of any multiplicity, however, for a second-order zero can be created by two series arms, both antiresonant at the same value of *s*, or by two resonant shunt arms, or by a resonant shunt arm and an antiresonant series arm.   A particularly simple example of this is the ladder shown in Fig. 3.36, which has a voltage ratio possessing a triple zero at zero frequency.

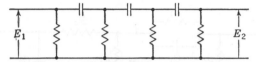

FIG. 3.36. Ladder with triple zero at origin.

The above comments can be summarized by the following statements:

The transfer function of an RC ladder network possesses poles which are simple and restricted to the negative real axis, excluding the origin and infinity, and zeros which may be of any order but are restricted to the negative real axis, including the origin and infinity.

3.5. Identification of Characterizing Functions.   The first step in the synthesis of *RC* transfer functions is the identification of either the appropriate short-circuit admittances or the open-circuit impedances from the specified function.   In other words, if the open-circuit voltage ratio is specified for a network driven from an ideal voltage source, it is shown in Table 3.1 that this ratio can be expressed in terms of the *y* or *z* functions:

$$\frac{E_2}{E_1} = \frac{y_{12}}{y_{22}} \tag{3.98}$$

$$\frac{E_2}{E_1} = \frac{z_{12}}{z_{11}} \tag{3.99}$$

In the statement of the synthesis problem, E_2/E_1 is given as a ratio of two polynomials in *s*.   The first step in the synthesis involves the determination of suitable functions for either y_{12} and y_{22} or z_{12} and z_{11}.

The problem is clarified by a simple example.   In a typical problem, E_2/E_1 might be of the form

$$\frac{E_2}{E_1} = \frac{s(s + 1)}{(s + 2)(s + 4)} \tag{3.100}$$

There exist an infinite number of different pairs of y_{22} and y_{12} functions which yield this voltage ratio.   The selection of one pair is constrained only by the requirement that the two functions satisfy the conditions for realizability as an *RC* network.   Specifically, poles of y_{12} must be poles of y_{22}, and y_{22} must have only simple poles and zeros on the negative real axis, with the poles and zeros interlaced and the lowest critical frequency a zero. The simplest choice in this example is probably

$$y_{22} = \frac{(s + 2)(s + 4)}{s + 3}$$ (3.101)

$$y_{12} = \frac{s(s + 1)}{s + 3}$$ (3.102)

The single finite pole of y_{22} and y_{12} can be chosen anywhere between -2 and -4. In addition, another pole could be chosen outside -4. Latitude in the selection of the y functions is further increased by the possibility of multiplying both y_{22} and y_{12} by any desired factor, subject only to the constraint that y_{22} must be left an RC driving-point admittance.

The optimum choice of the y functions is not clear. The effects of different selections of the two functions are expressed in three ways:

(1) The network complexity is determined by the particular functions chosen. Clearly, it is in general desirable to choose functions without excess common factors in y_{12} and y_{22}.

(2) The spread in element values in the final network is fixed by the choice.

(3) The gain constant realized varies with the selection. The specified voltage ratio E_2/E_1 can in general be realized only within a constant multiplier. The synthesis procedure is independent of this constant multiplier, and the designer must accept the flat loss (or gain) he achieves through the synthesis.†

Unfortunately, there appears to be no simple correlation between realizable gain and element spread on the one hand and the choice of y_{12} and y_{22} functions on the other. As a general rule, the closer the poles and zeros of y_{22}, the greater the spread of element values. In addition, maximum gain is usually realized if one pole of y_{22} is placed at infinity and the others are placed somewhat farther out than the midway point between the zeros. The synthesis procedure is so simple, however, that the vagueness introduced at this point is not a serious handicap, since a wide variety of y_{22} and y_{12} functions can be selected and the corresponding networks found.

3.6. Synthesis of Transfer Functions with Negative Real Zeros.   After the required y or z functions are chosen along the lines indicated in the preceding section, the synthesis proceeds with the determination of a network to realize these functions.   Inspection of Table 3.1 indicates that, in the majority of cases, the specified transfer function serves to determine at most two of the three characterizing impedance or admittance functions. The particular functions of interest are listed in Table 3.4.

Only in the single case when Z_s and Z_L are both specified does the synthesis require the realization of a specified complete set of characterizing functions. This case, however, can ordinarily be reduced to one of the simpler cases by considering either Z_s or Z_L internal to the network

† A. D. Fialkow, Two Terminal-pair Networks Containing Two Kinds of Elements Only, *Proc. of the Symposium on Modern Network Synthesis* 1952, pp. 50–65, Polytechnic Institute of Brooklyn, New York, 1952. This paper contains a summary of the work of Fialkow and Gerst in the study of the maximum gain realizable in RC networks.

and carrying out the synthesis of one of the simpler cases while making certain that the network starts and terminates with the required loading.

Thus, in most cases of interest in the design of feedback systems, the specifications serve to determine only two of the three characterizing functions, either z_{12} or y_{12} and one of the driving-point functions. For example, under the conditions represented in the first line of Table 3.4,

TABLE 3.4
SIGNIFICANT DESCRIBING FUNCTIONS

Source Z	Load Z	Transfer function considered	z or y functions specified
0	∞	$\dfrac{E_2}{E_1}$	z_{12} and z_{11} or y_{12} and y_{22}
0	Z_L	$\dfrac{E_2}{E_1}$	y_{12} and y_{22}
∞	∞	$\dfrac{E_2}{I_1}$	z_{12}
∞	Z_L	$\dfrac{E_2}{I_1}$	z_{12} and z_{22}
Z_s	∞	$\dfrac{E_2}{E_s}$	z_{12} and z_{11}
Z_s	Z_L	$\dfrac{E_2}{E_s}$	$y_{11}, y_{22},$ and y_{12} or $z_{11}, z_{22},$ and z_{12}

y_{12} and y_{22} might be specified. The synthesis job is one of finding a network to realize these two functions without regard to the y_{11} which happens to evolve.

The difficulty of this problem of realizing a given driving-point impedance and transfer function is determined almost exclusively by the location of the zeros of the transfer function. If these zeros all lie on the negative real axis, a ladder network can be used and synthesis is straightforward. If there are complex zeros or zeros in the right-half plane, synthesis is somewhat more difficult. In this section, only the former, simpler case is considered; the consideration of complex zeros is postponed until Sec. 3.7. The following discussion, then, considers this problem: a network is to be found to realize the pair of functions

$$y_{11} = \frac{p(s)}{n(s)q(s)} \tag{3.103}$$

$$y_{12} = \frac{m(s)}{q(s)} \tag{3.104}$$

p, m, n, and q are all polynomials in s with zeros only on the negative real axis. q, n, and p have only simple zeros; m may have zeros of any order. With this description of the functions, all poles of y_{12} are also poles of y_{11}, although y_{11} may have poles not present in y_{12} as a result of the zeros of n.

The simplest synthesis procedure first realizes the poles of y_{11} not present in y_{12}.   These poles are removed in the form of a shunt arm across the input terminals, as shown by y_s in Fig. 3.37.   The admittance y_s does not influence y_{12} in any way, since y_{12} can be measured by determining the current that flows in a shorting bar between the 1-1' terminals when 1 volt is applied to 2-2'.   The shorting bar effectively removes y_s from   the   network.

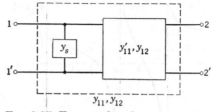

FIG. 3.37. Excess poles of y_{11} removed as shunt admittance.

When this simplification has been effected, the problem is reduced to one of realizing a pair of functions of the form

$$y_{11}' = \frac{p'(s)}{q(s)} \tag{3.105}$$

$$y_{12} - \frac{m(s)}{q(s)} \tag{3.106}$$

The general procedure can be summarized as follows.† y_{11}' is developed in a ladder network in such a way as to realize the desired zeros of y_{12}. The poles of y_{12} are automatically realized since they are identical with poles of y_{11}' as long as no poles of y_{11}' are removed as a shunt network across the input terminals.   The zeros of y_{12} are realized either by suitable antiresonant series arms or by appropriate resonant shunt arms.   To realize a zero at $-\alpha$ by an antiresonant series arm, y_{11}' is manipulated, by partial removal of impedance and admittance poles, until the impedance function possesses a pole at $-\alpha$.   This pole is completely removed. Similarly, to realize a transmission zero by a resonant shunt arm, an admittance pole is created at the desired complex frequency and completely removed.

Details of the procedure are most easily explained by a specific example. The functions considered are

$$y_{11} = \frac{(s+2)(s+4)}{(s+3)(s+5)} \tag{3.107}$$

$$y_{12} = \frac{s(s+1)}{(s+3)(s+5)} \tag{3.108}$$

The ladder network is to possess transmission zeros at $s = 0$ and $s = -1$. The only way, with an RC network, to create a zero at the origin is by a

† E. A. Guillemin, A Note on the Ladder Development of RC Networks, *Proc. IRE,* Vol. 40, No. 4, pp. 482–485, April, 1952.

series capacitor. The zero at -1 can be realized by either a series arm antiresonant at -1 or a shunt arm resonant at -1. In general, either scheme can be used, and, furthermore, the two zeros can be realized in either order. In this example, the zero at -1 is realized first and by an appropriate series arm.

The circumspection of the synthesist is immeasurably increased if a sketch of $y_{11}(\sigma)$ versus the real variable σ is made as shown in Fig. 3.38.

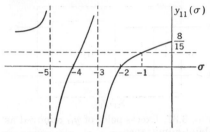

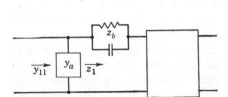

FIG. 3.38. Behavior of y_{11} along real axis.   FIG. 3.39. Desired form of the network.

The form of the network desired is shown in Fig. 3.39. The impedance z_b is to be of the form

$$z_b = \frac{k}{s + 1} \tag{3.109}$$

The impedance z_1 must possess a pole at -1 which can be removed as z_b. In terms of admittances, $y_1 = 1/z_1$ must have a zero at -1. In other words, an admittance y_a is to be removed from y_{11} in order to create an admittance zero at -1.

What sort of an admittance must y_a be? The answer to this question is clear from the sketch of Fig. 3.38. The zeros of the admittance y_{11} can be altered in two ways:

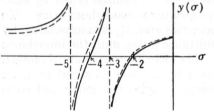

FIG. 3.40. Effect of partial removal of pole at -5.

(1)   Part of a pole can be removed. (If an entire pole were removed as y_a, y_{12} of the final network would not possess the proper poles.) Partial removal of a pole tends to move the neighboring zeros toward the pole. This is demonstrated in Fig. 3.40, where partial removal of the pole at -5 results in a weaker pole with the function not rising so rapidly toward infinity in the vicinity of the pole. Consequently, the zero originally at -4 is moved toward -5. Likewise, partial removal of the pole at -3 would move the zeros at -4 and -2 toward -3.

(2)   A constant value can be subtracted. If the remainder is to be *RC*, the maximum constant which can be removed is $y(0)$ for an admittance [$z(\infty)$ for an impedance]. Removal of more than $y(0)$ leaves the zero-frequency value of the resulting admittance negative. The effect of this modification of the y function is shown in Fig. 3.41. The poles are of course left unaltered, and the zeros are shifted toward the origin.

Either or both of these procedures may be used to create a desired admittance zero in the development of the ladder network. In certain cases, it may be impossible to create the desired admittance zero by either procedure. In such a case, it is necessary to consider first the impedance function and remove part of an impedance pole or part of $z(\infty)$ to transform the admittance function to one which does permit manipulation leading to the realization of the required zero. This two-step procedure

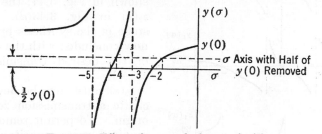

FIG. 3.41. Effect of removal of part of $y(0)$.

for realization of an admittance zero is illustrated in the second example below.

For the specific example considered, Fig. 3.38 indicates that the required admittance zero at -1 can be achieved by removal of a constant shunt conductance. Although the value of the conductance can be determined either graphically or analytically, the easier method is probably the latter. Removal of a conductance equal to $y_{11}(-1)$ results in the translation of a zero to -1. In this example, with $y_{11}(-1)$ equal to $\frac{3}{8}$ mho, removal of this conductance yields the remainder function $y_1(s)$:

$$y_1 = \frac{(s+2)(s+4)}{(s+3)(s+5)} - \frac{3}{8} \quad (3.110)$$

$$y_1 = \frac{5}{8}\frac{(s+1)(s+3.8)}{(s+3)(s+5)} \quad (3.111)$$

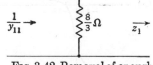

FIG. 3.42. Removal of enough conductance to create an admittance zero at -1.

The first element in the network (Fig. 3.42) is now determined.

This first step is shown graphically in sketches (a) and (b) of Fig. 3.43. The resulting $y_1(\sigma)$ possesses the same poles as y_{11} and zeros moved to -1 and -3.8. Although the entire procedure can be effected graphically, the simplest approach is an analytical procedure with sketches to indicate the general nature of the development.

The function $z_1 = 1/y_1$ is now considered, and the impedance pole at -1 completely removed. The resulting impedance function has only the one pole, at -3.8. The part to be removed is of the form $k/(s+1)$, where k is the residue of z_1 in the pole at -1. Since this residue is $\frac{32}{7}$, the remainder function, after removal of the pole, is

$$z_2 = z_1 - \frac{\frac{32}{7}}{s+1} \quad (3.112)$$

$$z_2 = \frac{8(s+3)(s+5)}{5(s+1)(s+3.8)} - \frac{\frac{32}{7}}{s+1} \quad (3.113)$$

Simplification of the above equation leads to

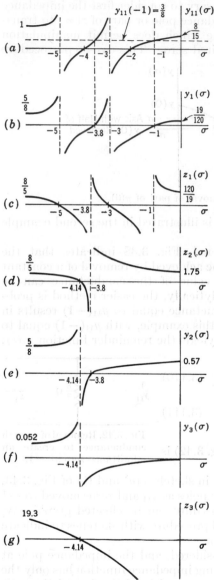

$$z_2 = \frac{8}{5}\frac{s + \frac{29}{7}}{s + 3.8} \qquad (3.114)$$

The network form at this point is shown in Fig. 3.44; the sketch of $z_2(\sigma)$ in Fig. 3.43(d). The first stage of the synthesis procedure is now concluded with the realization of the desired transmission zero at -1.

$z_2(s)$ must now be developed to create a transmission zero at the origin. To permit removal of the required series capacitance, an admittance zero must be created at zero frequency. Fig. 3.43(e) indicates that this can be accomplished by removal of a conductance equal to $y_2(0)$, which can be determined to be $\frac{133}{232}$ by consideration of Eq. (3.114) and the definition of y_2 as $1/z_2$. Removal of this conductance results in the admittance function y_3:

$$y_3 = \frac{5(s + 3.8)}{8(s + \frac{29}{7})} - \frac{133}{232} \qquad (3.115)$$

$$y_3 = \frac{\frac{3}{29}s}{2(s + \frac{29}{7})} \qquad (3.116)$$

The network at this stage is shown in Fig. 3.45.

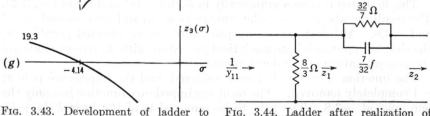

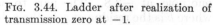

FIG. 3.43. Development of ladder to realize prescribed transmission zeros.

FIG. 3.44. Ladder after realization of transmission zero at -1.

The zero-frequency transmission zero is realized by complete removal of the impedance pole at the origin. The remainder impedance is denoted z_4.

$$z_3 = \frac{58}{3}\frac{s + \frac{29}{7}}{s} \qquad (3.117)$$

$$z_3 = \frac{\frac{1682}{21}}{s} + \frac{58}{3} \tag{3.118}$$

$$z_4 = \frac{58}{3} \tag{3.119}$$

After removal of the zero-frequency pole, the network takes the form shown in Fig. 3.46.

The last question is related to the proper disposition of the impedance z_4. There are evidently two possibilities: z_4 might be placed across the output terminals or in series between the capacitance of $\frac{21}{1682}$ farad and

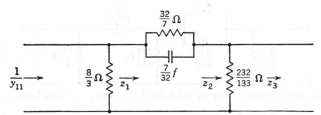

FIG. 3.45. Network prepared for creation of transmission zero at origin.

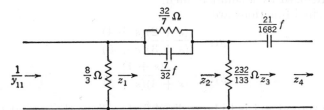

FIG. 3.46. Ladder after realization of both transmission zeros.

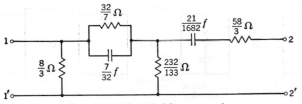

FIG. 3.47. Final ladder network.

the output terminal 2. The decision depends here upon the nature of the original function which is being developed. In this example, the short-circuit admittance y_{11} is the starting point, with the result that if z_4 is to be a part of y_{11} it must be placed in series with the output, and the final form of the network is shown in Fig. 3.47. Insertion of z_4 as a shunt branch means that when y_{11} is measured by shorting the output terminals, z_4 has no effect.

If the original function were the open-circuit driving-point impedance z_{11}, z_4 would be placed across the output terminals, as shown in Fig. 3.48. Use of the network of Fig. 3.47 would mean that the open-circuit input impedance would be unaffected by the $\frac{21}{1682}$-farad capacitance as well as the resistor z_4.

In retrospect, the general procedure in the above example is to create admittance zeros at the frequencies at which transmission zeros are desired. These admittance zeros are manufactured by removal of part of the admittance function as a shunt branch. The transmission zeros are then realized by complete removal of an impedance pole as an anti-resonant series arm. At the beginning of this section it was pointed out that the transmission zeros could equally well be realized by resonant shunt arms. As a second example of this synthesis procedure, the same

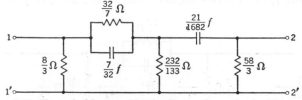

FIG. 3.48. Form ladder would take if starting point had been z_{11}.

functions are considered as in the first example, but the transmission zero at -1 is realized by a shunt branch.

The original functions are

$$y_{11} = \frac{(s+2)(s+4)}{(s+3)(s+5)} \tag{3.120}$$

$$y_{12} = \frac{s(s+1)}{(s+3)(s+5)} \tag{3.121}$$

Again the zero at -1 is to be realized first. Since the zero at the origin can be realized only by a series capacitance, the form of the network will

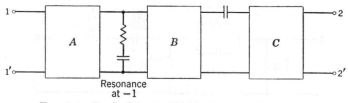

FIG. 3.49. Desired form of ladder for second example.

be as shown in Fig. 3.49. In this figure, block A represents the elements needed to create an impedance zero (admittance pole) at -1, block B those to create an admittance zero at the origin, and block C the remainder of the function.

In order to create the impedance zero at -1, part of an impedance pole or part of $1/y_{11}(\infty)$ can be removed. Inspection of Fig. 3.50(a), displaying the nature of $1/y_{11}(\sigma)$, reveals that partial removal of a pole can never create a zero at -1 since for an RC impedance the lowest critical frequency must be a pole and the lowest pole is at -2. Likewise, removal of some constant value less than $1/y_{11}(\infty)$ cannot create a zero at -1 because $1/y_{11}(-1) > 1/y_{11}(\infty)$. It would appear that the procedure is blocked at this point. The fundamental difficulty arises because the lowest pole is outside -1. This condition can be rectified by moving this pole inside -1 by working on the admittance function. In particular, Fig. 3.50(b) indicates that removal of a constant conductance permits translation of the admittance zero (impedance pole) at -2 in toward the origin as far as desired. Therefore, as the first step in the synthesis, this zero is moved in to $-\frac{1}{2}$. Analytically, this step takes the form of subtraction of a conductance equal to $y_{11}(-\frac{1}{2})$:

$$y_{11}(-\tfrac{1}{2}) = \left[\frac{(s+2)(s+4)}{(s+3)(s+5)}\right]_{s=-\frac{1}{2}}$$

(3.122)

$$y_{11}(-\tfrac{1}{2}) = \tfrac{7}{15}$$ (3.123)

Removal of this conductance of $\frac{7}{15}$ yields $y_1(s)$, shown graphically in Fig. 3.50(c).

$$y_1 = \frac{(s+2)(s+4)}{(s+3)(s+5)} - \frac{7}{15}$$ (3.124)

$$y_1 = \frac{8}{15}\frac{(s+\tfrac{1}{2})(s+\tfrac{15}{4})}{(s^2+8s+15)}$$ (3.125)

The network starts with a shunt resistance of $\frac{15}{7}$ ohms, as in Fig. 3.51.

With this modification, z_1 is in a suitable form for the creation of an impedance zero at -1 through partial removal of the pole at $-\frac{1}{2}$. The

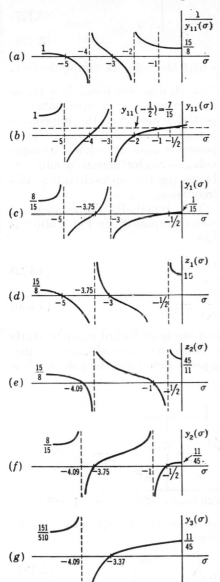

FIG. 3.50. Alternate ladder development of second example.

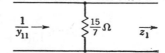

FIG. 3.51. Ladder of second example starts with shunt conductance.

amount of the pole to be removed is expressed analytically by the relation

$$z_1(s) - \frac{A}{s + \frac{1}{2}} = 0 \quad \text{when } s = -1$$ (3.126)

Evaluation of A yields

$$A = \frac{15}{8}\left[\frac{(s+3)(s+5)}{s+\frac{15}{4}}\right]_{s=-1} \tag{3.127}$$

$$A = \frac{60}{11} \tag{3.128}$$

The impedance to be removed is $\dfrac{\frac{60}{11}}{s+\frac{1}{2}}$, with the network taking the form of Fig. 3.52.   The antiresonant series branch does not result in a trans-

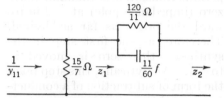

FIG. 3.52. Partial pole removal of z_1 to create impedance zero at -1.

mission zero since it represents only partial removal of the impedance pole at $-\frac{1}{2}$.   The impedance z_2 still possesses a pole at $-\frac{1}{2}$, and a simple voltage-divider action results between the two open-circuits at this frequency.

The remainder impedance z_2, shown graphically in Fig. 3.50(e), is determined from Eqs. (3.125) and (3.128).

$$z_2 = z_1 - \frac{\frac{60}{11}}{s+\frac{1}{2}} \tag{3.129}$$

$$z_2 = \frac{15(s+1)(s+\frac{45}{11})}{8(s+\frac{1}{2})(s+\frac{15}{4})} \tag{3.130}$$

The rest of the synthesis, proceeding in a straightforward manner, starts with removal of the admittance pole at -1 to create the admittance function y_3.   As in the synthesis of driving-point functions, the pole in y/s is

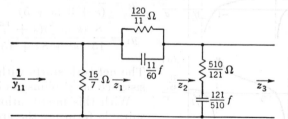

FIG. 3.53. Network at end of first cycle, with transmission zero at -1 realized.

removed, rather than that in y directly, in order to keep both the part removed and the remainder RC-realizable.

$$y_3 = \frac{8(s+\frac{1}{2})(s+\frac{15}{4})}{15(s+1)(s+\frac{45}{11})} - \frac{ks}{s+1} \tag{3.131}$$

Here k, the residue of y_2/s in the pole at -1, is evaluated from Eq. (3.130) to be $\frac{121}{510}$.   The resulting y_3 function is

$$y_3 = \frac{151(s+\frac{510}{151})}{510(s+\frac{45}{11})} \tag{3.132}$$

The network at this stage is shown in Fig. 3.53.

The second part of the development, involving realization of the transmission zero at the origin, proceeds in the same manner as in the first example with $y_3(0)$ removed to create an admittance zero at the origin.

$$y_4 = y_3 - y_3(0) \tag{3.133}$$

$$y_4 = \frac{151(s + \frac{510}{151})}{510(s + \frac{45}{11})} - \frac{11}{45} \tag{3.134}$$

$$y_4 = \frac{79}{1530} \frac{s}{s + \frac{45}{11}} \tag{3.135}$$

The final two elements are the series capacitance and resistance.

$$z_4 = \frac{1530}{79} + \frac{(1530)(45)}{(11)(79)s} \tag{3.136}$$

The final network is shown in Fig. 3.54.

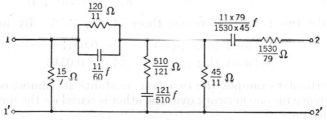

FIG. 3.54. Final ladder, Example 2.

Both the networks developed in the preceding discussion, those shown in Fig. 3.47 and 3.54, realize the specified y_{11}. Both networks realize the proper zeros and poles for y_{12}, but, in general, the specified y_{12} is realized only within a multiplicative gain constant. For example, the y_{12} specified was

$$y_{12} = \frac{s(s + 1)}{(s + 3)(s + 5)} \tag{3.137}$$

Exactly the same procedure would have been followed and the same networks synthesized if the specified y_{12} had been

$$y_{12} = 10 \frac{s(s + 1)}{(s + 3)(s + 5)} \tag{3.138}$$

Because of this possible ambiguity concerning the network gain, it is necessary, at the conclusion of the design, to evaluate the constant multiplier of that y_{12} realized by the network. This can be accomplished by writing the entire y_{12} function by a brute-force circuit analysis, but it is more readily done by inspection of the behavior of the network at either zero or infinite frequency. The procedure is illustrated by the two networks developed above, which are redrawn in Fig. 3.55.

The realized y_{12} is of the form

$$y_{12} = K \frac{s(s+1)}{(s+3)(s+5)} \tag{3.139}$$

The value of y_{12} at infinite frequency is simply the constant K. At very high frequencies, with the degeneration of the capacitors into short

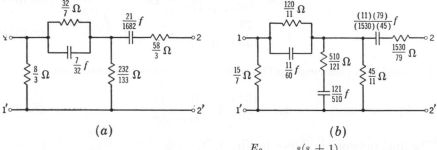

FIG. 3.55. Two ladders to realize $\dfrac{E_2}{E_1} = \dfrac{s(s+1)}{(s+2)(s+4)}$.

circuits, the two networks become those of Fig. 3.56. By inspection,

$$\text{Network } (a): y_{12}(\infty) = \tfrac{3}{58} = 0.0517 \tag{3.140}$$
$$\text{Network } (b): y_{12}(\infty) = \tfrac{79}{1530} = 0.0516 \tag{3.141}$$

In this particular example, the two gain constants are almost equal, and any preference for one network over the other is based on the number and sizes of elements.

Clearly, even after y_{12} and y_{22} are determined, there are a wide variety of networks which can be found to realize these functions, with the two networks derived above only simple examples. There are several points at which the designer is permitted to make an arbitrary choice. At any stage in the ladder development, parts of poles can be removed if desired;

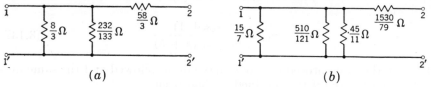

FIG. 3.56. Infinite-frequency behavior of the two ladders.

the impedance and admittance functions can be manipulated at will to yield a tremendous variety of configurations. This freedom in the synthesis is one of the great practical advantages of the method described in this section. Although this very freedom is often disturbing to the engineer, it should be considered not as the source of unpleasant decisions, but as the open gate to a variety of networks all of which will do the job at hand. From this group of networks, one can be selected on the basis of such practical factors as realized gain constant, element spread, availability of components, etc., factors which are not readily phrased analytically.

3.7. Synthesis of Transfer Functions with Complex Zeros.   The ladder development described in Sec. 3.6 for the synthesis of transfer functions with negative real zeros breaks down if there are complex zeros.   The realization of complex zeros in the transmission of a ladder structure requires the use of all three types of elements, R, L, and C, for only with all three elements can the impedance or admittance of one arm become infinite at a complex value of s.   If the specified y_{12} function has complex zeros, there are two general methods for synthesizing the RC network in unbalanced form (*i.e.*, with a common ground from input to output):

(1)   Guillemin's procedure,† using ladders connected in parallel.
(2)   Dasher's procedure,‡ using the tandem connection of bridged twin-T structures.

Both procedures are somewhat limited in their applicability.   Guillemin's procedure can be used with transfer functions having zeros in the right-half plane exclusive of the positive real axis; Dasher's procedure is restricted to functions with zeros on the $j\omega$ axis or in the left-half plane. Dasher's procedure can be used to realize specified impedance functions (z_{11} and z_{12}) as well as admittance functions, while Guillemin's procedure is restricted to the realization of specified admittance functions (y_{11} and y_{12}).   In complicated examples amenable to both procedures, Dasher's method yields fewer elements and often higher gain constants.

Guillemin's Procedure.   Guillemin's procedure, essentially involving the parallel connection of ladder networks, starts from the pair of short-circuit admittance functions y_{11} and y_{12}, which are in general of the form

$$y_{11} = \frac{p(s)}{q(s)} \tag{3.142}$$

$$y_{12} = \frac{a_0 + a_1 s + a_2 s^2 + \cdots + a_n s^n}{q(s)} \tag{3.143}$$

The only requisites for the success of the Guillemin procedure are that the pair of functions satisfy the conditions for realizability in an RC network and that all coefficients in the numerator polynomial of y_{12} be positive. If there are zeros in the right-half plane but off the axis, the coefficients can be made positive in the original transfer function (the voltage ratio, transfer admittance, etc.) by multiplication of both numerator and denominator by an appropriate polynomial with negative real roots.

The first step in the Guillemin procedure involves a rewriting of y_{12} as the sum of simpler functions, as indicated by Eq. (3.144).

$$y_{12} = \frac{a_0 + a_1 s}{q(s)} + \frac{a_2 s^2 + a_3 s^3}{q(s)} + \cdots + \frac{a_{n-1} s^{n-1} + a_n s^n}{q(s)} \tag{3.144}$$

† E. A. Guillemin, Synthesis of RC-Networks, *J. Math. and Phys.*, Vol. 28, No. 1, pp. 22–42, 1949.
‡ B. J. Dasher, Synthesis of RC Transfer Functions as Unbalanced Two Terminal-pair Networks, *Trans. IRE Professional Group on Circuit Theory*, PGCT 1, pp. 20–34, December, 1952.

The numerator of the last term contains either one or two component terms depending upon whether n is even or odd. Each component of y_{12} is now realizable with the prescribed y_{11} in the form of a ladder network, for the transmission zeros are restricted to the negative real axis, including the origin and infinity. The $(n + 1)/2$ [or $(n + 2)/2$ with n even] ladders are synthesized, each realizing the desired y_{11} and one component of the desired y_{12}. These ladders are denoted α, β, γ, $\ldots$, ν in the following discussion.

The desired functions are realized by the parallel connection of these ladders. Before this can be done, however, the gain constants of each network must be adjusted, for each ladder realizes its y_{12} only within a constant multiplier. The various constant multipliers are determined as K_α, K_β, $\ldots$, K_ν. The admittance level of each ladder is then adjusted by multiplication by adjustment factors L_α, L_β, $\ldots$, L_ν, respectively. These L factors are chosen to satisfy the following conditions:

(1) The sum of the L's must equal unity if the parallel connection of the ladders is to yield the desired y_{11}.

$$L_\alpha + L_\beta + \cdots + L_\nu = 1 \tag{3.145}$$

(2) Each component of y_{12} must, after level adjustment, be realized within the same multiplicative factor if the addition of the component y_{12} functions (represented by the parallel connection of the ladders) is to yield an over-all y_{12} with the desired zeros. Thus,

$$L_\alpha K_\alpha = L_\beta K_\beta = L_\gamma K_\gamma = \cdots = L_\nu K_\nu \tag{3.146}$$

The ν equations of (1) and (2) above are solved for the values of the L's. The final parallel connection of the networks then yields the desired y_{11} and the specified y_{12} except for the additional multiplier $L_\alpha K_\alpha$.

As an example of the Guillemin procedure, the functions of Eqs. (3.147) and (3.148) are considered.

$$y_{11} = \frac{(s + 1)(s + 3)}{(s + 2)(s + 4)} \tag{3.147}$$

$$y_{12} = \frac{s^2 + s + 3}{(s + 2)(s + 4)} \tag{3.148}$$

The synthesis is carried out below in a step-by-step method.

(1) y_{12} is written as the sum of functions, each of which is realizable by a ladder.

$$y_{12} = \frac{s^2}{(s + 2)(s + 4)} + \frac{s + 3}{(s + 2)(s + 4)} \tag{3.149}$$

(2) The ladder is found to realize the functions

$$y_{12\alpha} = \frac{s + 3}{(s + 2)(s + 4)} \tag{3.150}$$

$$y_{11\alpha} = \frac{(s + 1)(s + 3)}{(s + 2)(s + 4)} \tag{3.151}$$

There are transmission zeros at -3 and infinity.   The zero at -3 can be realized immediately by removing the impedance pole at this frequency.

$$\frac{1}{y_{11}} = \frac{(s+2)(s+4)}{(s+1)(s+3)}$$ (3.152)

$$\frac{1}{y_{11}} = \frac{s + \frac{5}{2}}{s+1} + \frac{\frac{1}{2}}{s+3}$$ (3.153)

$$z_1 = \frac{s + \frac{5}{2}}{s+1}$$ (3.154)

The zero at infinity is realized by a shunt capacitor.   As a preliminary step, $z_1(\infty)$ is subtracted.

$$z_2 = \frac{s + \frac{5}{2}}{s+1} - 1 = \frac{\frac{3}{2}}{s+1}$$ (3.155)

The final network is shown in Fig. 3.57.

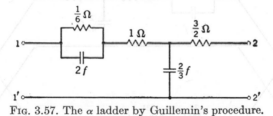

FIG. 3.57. The α ladder by Guillemin's procedure.

(3)   The ladder is found to realize the functions

$$y_{12\beta} = \frac{s^2}{(s+2)(s+4)}$$ (3.156)

$$y_{11\beta} = \frac{(s+1)(s+3)}{(s+2)(s+4)}$$ (3.157)

Since all zeros of $y_{12\beta}$ are at the origin, this network is simply the second-Cauer-form development of $y_{11\beta}$ and is the same as that derived in See. 3.3.   The network is redrawn in Fig. 3.58.

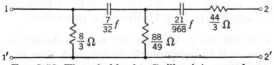

FIG. 3.58. The β ladder by Guillemin's procedure.

(4)   The gain constants of the two networks are determined.   Inspection of the α ladder indicates that at zero frequency the realized y_{12} has a value of $1/(\frac{1}{3} + 1 + \frac{3}{2}) = \frac{3}{8}$, or exactly that specified.   Thus, K_α is unity.   The β ladder has an infinite frequency gain of $\frac{3}{44}$, compared to the value of unity desired; then $K_\beta = \frac{3}{44}$.

(5)   The admittance-level adjustment factors required are deter-

mined. To realize the desired y_{11} it is necessary that

$$L_\alpha + L_\beta = 1 \tag{3.158}$$

Realization of the desired zeros of the over-all y_{12} requires

$$\tfrac{3}{44}L_\beta = L_\alpha \tag{3.159}$$

Solution of the two simultaneous equations yields

$$L_\beta = \tfrac{44}{47} \tag{3.160}$$
$$L_\alpha = \tfrac{3}{47} \tag{3.161}$$

The final over-all gain constant for y_{12} will be $\tfrac{3}{47}$.

(6) The admittance levels of the two ladder networks are adjusted. As an example, the level of ladder α is multiplied by $\tfrac{3}{47}$ by multiplying all

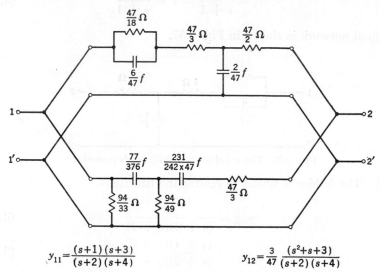

$$y_{11} = \frac{(s+1)(s+3)}{(s+2)(s+4)} \qquad\qquad y_{12} = \frac{3}{47}\frac{(s^2+s+3)}{(s+2)(s+4)}$$

Fig. 3.59. Final network for example of Guillemin's procedure.

capacitances and dividing all resistances by $\tfrac{3}{47}$. The two networks are then connected in parallel, as shown in Fig. 3.59.

In certain special cases, there are two concepts which permit simplification of the networks derived by Guillemin's procedure:

(1) Clearly, if the original y_{12} contains any zeros on the negative real axis or at infinity or the origin, it is advantageous to realize these zeros first by the methods described in Sec. 3.6. When only conjugate complex pairs of zeros are left, Guillemin's procedure can be initiated.

(2) The numerator polynomial in the above example was split into the sum of polynomials, each having only real roots, by the simple method of pairing successive terms. Any other scheme is certainly acceptable, and in special cases other methods result in simpler networks.

Dasher's Procedure. Guillemin's procedure represents an extension of the ladder-development methods for real zeros in one direction, utilizing the parallel connection of ladder networks. The procedure is readily adapted to the handling of admittance functions only. An alternate procedure, developed by Dasher, represents an extension of the ladder-development techniques in a somewhat different direction. The bridged twin T is used as a basic structure to realize a pair of conjugate complex zeros in the left-half plane. The given driving-point impedance or admittance function is developed in the form of a tandem connection of

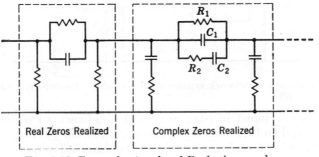

FIG. 3.60. Form of networks of Dasher's procedure.

ladder elements and bridged twin-T structures to realize successively the desired zeros of the transfer function.

Essentially Dasher's procedure represents a ladder development of y_{11} (or z_{11}) to realize the zeros of y_{12} (or z_{12}), a development which is very similar to the ladder synthesis when all transmission zeros lie on the negative real axis. The complex zeros are realized in conjugate pairs and by appropriate antiresonant series arms of the ladder. This realization is accomplished in the form shown in Fig. 3.60. The real transmission zeros are first realized in the usual manner. Each pair of conjugate complex zeros is realized by a structure of the form shown in Fig. 3.60. The series arm, consisting of R_1, R_2, C_1, and C_2, can be made antiresonant at complex values of s by the use of negative elements. For example, the circuit of Fig. 3.61 possesses an impedance

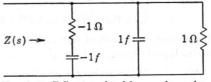

FIG. 3.61. RC network with complex poles.

$$Z(s) = \frac{s + 1}{s^2 + s + 1} \quad (3.162)$$

In Dasher's procedure, the ladder network is developed in this form. Then the π section representing the complex zeros is replaced by an equivalent bridged twin T with all elements positive. The final form of the network is shown in Fig. 3.62. The ability to find an equivalent RC structure with all positive elements is assured by the development of the original ladder network in a prescribed form.

For explicitness, it is assumed in the following discussion that, at the outset of Dasher's procedure, the two functions y_{11} and y_{12} are given. The general procedure involves the development of y_{11} in a ladder network in such a way as to produce the desired transmission zeros. There are nine basic steps in the synthesis:

(1)   Any poles of y_{11} not present in y_{12} are removed as a shunt admittance y_0 across the input terminals, with the remainder admittance denoted y_1, as indicated in Fig. 3.63.

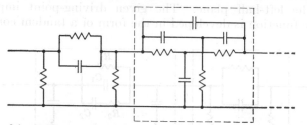

FIG. 3.62. Final form of network synthesized by Dasher's procedure.   (Original form shown in Fig. 3.60.)

(2) y_1 is developed in part in a ladder network to realize the real zeros of y_{12} and to leave the *RC* remainder function y_2 (Fig. 3.64).

(3)   One pair of conjugate complex transmission zeros is considered and denoted as

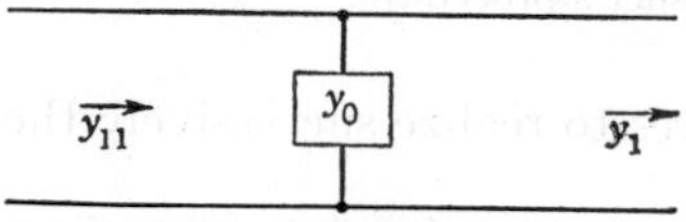

$$s_0 = -\alpha_0 + j\beta_0 = \omega_0 / \theta_0 \qquad (3.163)$$
$$\bar{s}_0 = -\alpha_0 - j\beta_0 = \omega_0 / - \theta_0 \qquad (3.164)$$

FIG. 3.63. Removal of admittance y_0 to create admittance y_1.

The values of $\alpha_0, \beta_0,$ and ω_0 are determined.

(4)   The admittance function y_2 is prepared for the removal of the zero-producing π section.   This step is essential if an equivalent realizable network is to be found for the zero-producing section with negative elements.   This preparation takes the form of

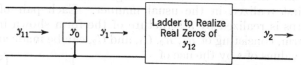

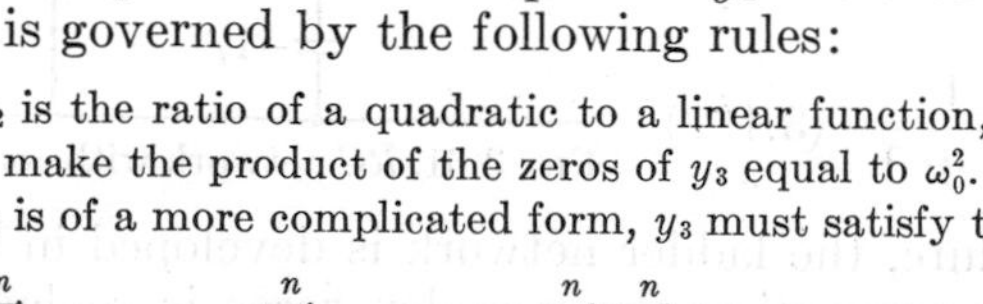

FIG. 3.64. Form of network after first two steps in Dasher's procedure.

the removal of part of one of the poles of y_2 to create the function y_3.   The reduction is governed by the following rules:

(a)   If y_2 is the ratio of a quadratic to a linear function, enough of a pole of y_2 is removed to make the product of the zeros of y_3 equal to ω_0^2.

(b)   If y_2 is of a more complicated form, y_3 must satisfy the equation

$$k_\infty \sum_{\nu=1}^{n} \frac{k_\nu \sigma_\nu}{\rho_\nu^4} - k_0 \sum_{\nu=1}^{n} \frac{k_\nu \sigma_\nu^2}{\rho_\nu^4 \omega_0^2} + \frac{1}{2} \sum_{\nu=1}^{n} \sum_{\mu=1}^{n} \frac{k_\nu k_\mu (\sigma_\nu - \sigma_\mu)^2 (\sigma_\nu \sigma_\mu - \omega_0^2)}{\rho_\nu^4 \rho_\mu^4} = 0 \qquad (3.165)$$

Here,

$$y_3 = k_\infty s + k_0 + \sum_{\nu=1}^{n} \frac{k_\nu s}{s + \sigma_\nu} \qquad (3.166)$$
$$\rho_\nu^2 = \beta_0^2 + (\sigma_\nu - \alpha_0)^2 \qquad (3.167)$$

If Eq. (3.165) cannot be satisfied by reduction of any of the residues of y_2, the equation can be satisfied by removal of part of a pole of s/y_2, corresponding to insertion into the network of a series element. The determination of which pole should be reduced to permit satisfaction of Eq. (3.165) is largely a matter of trial and error.

At this point, the network takes the form shown in Fig. 3.65, and the remainder function y_3 is an admittance function to which the zero-producing technique can be applied.

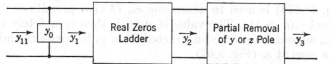

FIG. 3.65. Preparation for zero-producing section.

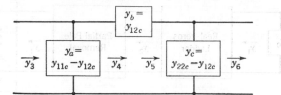

FIG. 3.66. The zero-producing section.

(5)   The zero-producing section is of the form shown in Fig. 3.66. The subscript c is used on the short-circuit driving-point and transfer admittances to indicate that these parameters refer to the characteristics of the zero-producing section only.

A suitable set of short-circuit admittances for the zero-producing section is now selected in the form

$$y_{11c} = c_0 \left[s + \frac{\omega_0^2}{\sigma_0} + a \left(\sigma_0 + \frac{\omega_0^2}{\sigma_0} - 2\alpha_0 \right) \frac{s}{s + \sigma_0} \right] \qquad (3.168)$$

$$y_{12c} = c_0 \left[s + \frac{\omega_0^2}{\sigma_0} - \left(\sigma_0 + \frac{\omega_0^2}{\sigma_0} - 2\alpha_0 \right) \frac{s}{s + \sigma_0} \right] \qquad (3.169)$$

$$y_{22c} = c_0 \left[s + \frac{\omega_0^2}{\sigma_0} + \frac{1}{a} \left(\sigma_0 + \frac{\omega_0^2}{\sigma_0} - 2\alpha_0 \right) \frac{s}{s + \sigma_0} \right] \qquad (3.170)$$

Of the five parameters used in these expressions, ω_0^2 and α_0 are known from the desired transmission zeros; c_0, σ_0, and a are still to be determined.

In order for the zero-producing section (Fig. 3.66) to produce a transmission zero at s_0 by antiresonance in the series arm, y_4 must have a zero at this frequency. In other words,

$$y_a(s_0) = y_3(s_0) \qquad (3.171)$$

The admittance y_a can be written from Eqs. (3.168) and (3.169) in terms of the unknown parameters c_0, σ_0, and a.

$$y_a = y_{11c} - y_{12c} \qquad (3.172)$$

$$y_a = c_0(a + 1) \left(\sigma_0 + \frac{\omega_0^2}{\sigma_0} - 2\alpha_0 \right) \frac{s}{s + \sigma_0} \qquad (3.173)$$

Satisfaction of Eq. (3.171) implies equality of both the magnitude and phase. In other words, if the value of y_a from (3.173) is substituted in (3.171), two equations result:

$$\underline{/y_3(s_0)} = \underline{/\dfrac{s_0}{s_0 + \sigma_0}} \tag{3.174}$$

$$|y_3(s_0)| = c_0(a + 1)\left(\sigma_0 + \dfrac{\omega_0^2}{\sigma_0} - 2\alpha_0\right)\left|\dfrac{s_0}{s_0 + \sigma_0}\right| \tag{3.175}$$

After Eq. (3.174) is used to determine σ_0, (3.175) permits evaluation of the product $c_0(a + 1)$. The value of $y_a(s)$ is then completely known.

(6) y_a, as found above, is subtracted from y_3 to create the admittance y_4, with a zero at s_0 (Fig. 3.67).

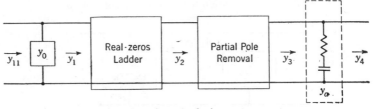

FIG. 3.67. Creation of admittance zero at s_0.

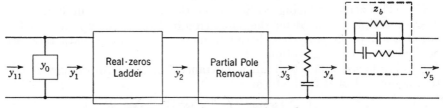

FIG. 3.68. Removal of impedance pole at s_0.

(7)   The impedance pole at s_0 is removed as a series arm. The value of the parameter c_0 is found from the fact that this series arm must have an impedance equal to $1/y_{12c}$, as shown in Fig. 3.66.   With $c_0(1 + a)$ and c_0 known, a can be found, and all three short-circuit admittances of the zero-producing section are completely known. The admittance remaining after the removal of the impedance pole is denoted as y_5 (Fig. 3.68).

(8)   The admittance $y_c = y_{22c} - y_{12c}$ is removed from y_5 to yield y_6. With the remainder function y_6 an *RC* driving-point admittance with numerator and denominator polynomials each two degrees lower than those of y_3, the first cycle of the development is now complete, as shown in Fig. 3.69.

(9)   The zero-producing section with negative elements is replaced by a section with all positive element values. Any network possessing the short-circuit admittance parameters y_{11c}, y_{12c}, and y_{22c} may be used. That such a network can always be found is established by the two networks of Fig. 3.70, with the element values in terms of the location of the desired transmission zeros and the parameters c_0, σ_0, and a found in the above development.

Clearly it is not necessary to go through the complete development described above. The final network can be found as soon as the parameters c_0, σ_0, and a are found. The only tedious or difficult part of the procedure is the satisfaction of the residue condition described above as step (4). In complicated cases, in which the initial admittance functions are polynomials of high degree, this step is time-consuming. However, as pointed out earlier, in most practical cases there are at most two pairs

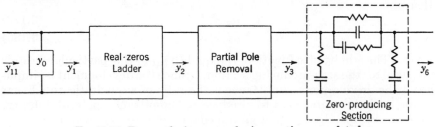

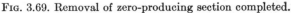

FIG. 3.69. Removal of zero-producing section completed.

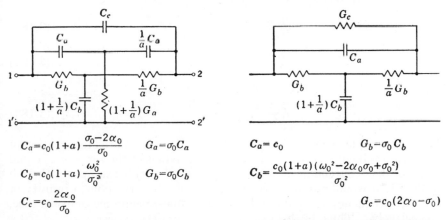

$$C_a = c_0(1+a)\frac{\sigma_0 - 2\alpha_0}{\sigma_0} \qquad G_a = \sigma_0 C_a$$

$$C_b = c_0(1+a)\frac{\omega_0^2}{\sigma_0^2} \qquad G_b = \sigma_0 C_b$$

$$C_c = c_0\frac{2\alpha_0}{\sigma_0}$$

$$C_a = c_0 \qquad\qquad G_b = \sigma_0 C_b$$

$$C_b = \frac{c_0(1+a)(\omega_0^2 - 2\alpha_0\sigma_0 + \sigma_0^2)}{\sigma_0^2}$$

$$G_c = c_0(2\alpha_0 - \sigma_0)$$

(a) Network when $\sigma_0 - 2\alpha_0 \geq 0$ (b) Network when $\sigma_0 - 2\alpha_0 \leq 0$

FIG. 3.70. Equivalent zero-producing sections with all elements positive. (Values in mhos and farads.)

of conjugate complex zeros. If more are present, isolation amplifiers can ordinarily be provided and the over-all transfer function realized as the product of simpler functions.

As an illustration of Dasher's procedure, the example used in the explanation of Guillemin's procedure is synthesized:

$$y_{11} = \frac{(s+1)(s+3)}{(s+2)(s+4)} \tag{3.176}$$

$$y_{12} = \frac{s^2 + s + 3}{(s+2)(s+4)} \tag{3.177}$$

The numbering of the steps below corresponds to the numbering used in the discussion of the procedure.

(1) There are no poles present in y_{11} and not present in y_{12}.

(2) There are no real zeros of y_{12}.

(3) The transmission zeros are located at the roots of the polynomial $s^2 + s + 3$. The root in the upper-half plane is

$$s_0 = -\frac{1}{2} + j\frac{\sqrt{11}}{2} = \sqrt{3} \left/ \arctan \frac{\sqrt{11}}{-1} \right. \tag{3.178}$$

Hence,

$$\alpha_0 = \tfrac{1}{2} \tag{3.179}$$

$$\omega_0^2 = 3 \tag{3.180}$$

(4) The admittance function y_2 (equal to y_{11} in this particular case) is prepared for the zero-producing section. Since the development is simplified if the driving-point admittance is the ratio of a quadratic to a linear factor, it is advantageous to produce an admittance pole at infinity. This can be done by creating an impedance zero by removal, as a series resistance, of $1/y_2(\infty)$. The remainder function y_2' is

$$y_2' = \frac{1}{1/y_2 - 1/y_2(\infty)} \tag{3.181}$$

$$y_2' = \frac{1}{\dfrac{s^2 + 6s + 8}{s^2 + 4s + 3} - 1} \tag{3.182}$$

$$y_2' = \frac{s^2 + 4s + 3}{2s + 5} \tag{3.183}$$

With this simple form of y_2', the admittance can be prepared for creation of the zero-producing section by making the product of the zeros of y_2' equal to ω_0^2, or 3. This condition is already satisfied in this example, although ordinarily it would require partial removal of either the pole at infinity or the zero-frequency constant value as a shunt capacitance or resistance, respectively. Thus, in this example,

$$y_3 = \frac{s^2 + 4s + 3}{2s + 5} \tag{3.184}$$

(5) The short-circuit parameters of the zero-producing section are now determined. In this case, with y_3 the ratio of a quadratic to a linear function, y_3 itself is of a form suitable for use as y_{11c}. Hence an expansion of $y_3 = y_{11c}$ (a partial-fraction expansion of y_3/s) yields a form which can be identified with Eq. (3.168).

$$y_{11c} = \frac{1}{2}\left(s + \frac{6}{5} + \frac{3}{10}\frac{s}{s + \frac{5}{2}}\right) \tag{3.185}$$

Comparison of Eqs. (3.185) and (3.168) yields at once the values of the parameters a, c_0, and σ_0:

$$c_0 = \tfrac{1}{2} \tag{3.186}$$

$$\sigma_0 = \tfrac{5}{2} \tag{3.187}$$

$$a = \tfrac{1}{9} \tag{3.188}$$

(9) Steps (6) through (8) are superfluous since all parameters are already determined.   The final network can be drawn at once on the basis of the relations of Fig. 3.70 and is shown in Fig. 3.71.   The gain constant realized by the network is determined most easily by inspection of the network behavior at infinite frequency.   The desired y_{12} value at

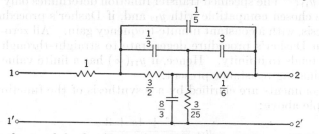

FIG. 3.71. Final network for first illustration of Dasher's procedure.   (Values in ohms and farads.)

infinity is unity and is evidently realized exactly by the network.   (In Guillemin's procedure, it should be recalled, the desired y_{12} was realized only within a constant of $\frac{3}{47}$.)

The above example indicates that, when the driving-point admittance can be put in the form of the ratio of a quadratic to a linear polynomial, the synthesis becomes almost trivial.   The resynthesis of this same example without making this expedient but unnecessary simplification is worth while at this point for two reasons:

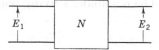

FIG. 3.72. Transfer function of interest, the open-circuit voltage ratio.

(1) This work serves as an illustration of the more general application of Dasher's procedure, the difficulties encountered, and the general procedure which must be used with more than one pair of conjugate complex transmission zeros.

(2) Even if only one pair of conjugate complex zeros is to be realized, the short-circuit driving-point admittance can be written as the ratio of a quadratic to a linear

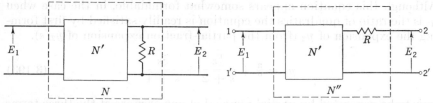

FIG. 3.73. Network N of Fig. 3.72 considered to include N' plus terminating resistance.

FIG. 3.74. Network N'', derived from N of Fig. 3.72.

polynomial only if no terminating resistance is required on the end of the network. Commonly in practice, a voltage ratio is to be realized, as shown in Fig. 3.72.   One simple method is to consider the network terminated in a resistance (Fig. 3.73). Within a multiplicative constant, the voltage ratio of the network N is simply the short-circuit transfer admittance of the network N'' shown in Fig. 3.74.

$$y_{12_{N''}} = \frac{1}{R}\left(\frac{E_2}{E_1}\right)_N \qquad (3.189)$$

Thus, if $y_{12_{N''}}$ is realized by a network with a terminating resistance R, the desired voltage ratio is realized by shorting the output terminals and measuring the output voltage across the terminating resistance.

What does the necessity for this terminating resistance R imply in terms of y_{12} and y_{11}? The specified transfer function determines only y_{12}. Any y_{11} can be chosen compatible with y_{12} and, if Dasher's procedure is used for synthesis, with a constant infinite-frequency gain. All zero-producing sections in Dasher's procedure degenerate to straight-through transmissions as s tends to infinity. Hence, if $y_{11}(\infty)$ has a finite value there will be a terminating resistance present.

These comments are clarified by a resynthesis of the functions used in the example above:

$$y_{11} = \frac{s^2 + 4s + 3}{s^2 + 6s + 8} \tag{3.190}$$

$$y_{12} = \frac{s^2 + s + 3}{s^2 + 6s + 8} \tag{3.191}$$

The first three steps (removal of poles of y_{11} not present in y_{12}, realization of the real transmission zeros, and selection of the pair of conjugate complex zeros to be realized first) are identical with the original example. The remainder driving-point function is

$$y_2 = \frac{s^2 + 4s + 3}{s^2 + 6s + 8} \tag{3.192}$$

The desired transmission zeros are at the roots of $s^2 + s + 3$ or at $-\frac{1}{2} \pm j\sqrt{11}/2$. The next step is denoted by (4) in the original discussion of Dasher's procedure.

(4) Instead of reducing the driving-point function to the ratio of a quadratic to linear function, partial pole removals are now effected to generate a function y_3 which satisfies the residue equation (3.165). Although this equation appears somewhat formidable, in the case when y_2 is the ratio of quadratics the equation is readily satisfied by first forming the expansion of y_2 (from the partial-fraction expansion of y_2/s).

$$y_2 = \frac{3}{8} + \frac{\frac{1}{4}s}{s + 2} + \frac{\frac{3}{8}s}{s + 4} \tag{3.193}$$

y_3 is to be generated by partial removal of one or more of the three terms of y_2. Hence, y_3 will be of the form

$$y_3 = k_0 + \frac{k_1 s}{s + 2} + \frac{k_2 s}{s + 4} \tag{3.194}$$

If the part removed is to be physically realizable, the three inequalities below must be satisfied:

$$k_0 \leq \tfrac{3}{8} \qquad k_1 \leq \tfrac{1}{4} \qquad k_2 \leq \tfrac{3}{8} \tag{3.195}$$

Determination of what and how much to remove from y_2 then involves the simultaneous satisfaction of Eqs. (3.195) and (3.165).

The residue equation (3.165) is written with all terms except k_0, k_1, and k_2 replaced by appropriate numerical values:

$$\alpha_0 = \tfrac{1}{2} \qquad \beta_0 = \frac{\sqrt{11}}{2} \qquad \omega_0 = \sqrt{3}$$

$$\sigma_1 = 2 \qquad \rho_1^2 = \tfrac{11}{4} + (2 - \tfrac{1}{2})^2 = 5$$

$$\sigma_2 = 4 \qquad \rho_2^2 = \tfrac{11}{4} + \tfrac{49}{4} = 15$$

After substitution of these values, the residue equation becomes

$$-k_0(45k_1 + 20k_2) + 3k_1k_2 = 0 \qquad (3.196)$$

Equation (3.196) must be satisfied under the constraints imposed by the inequalities of (3.195). At this stage, the synthesis temporarily degenerates into a trial and error procedure. The simplest attack seems to involve substituting the maximum values of k_1 and k_2 into Eq. (3.196) and determining whether the corresponding value of k_0 is less than the maximum allowable value, $\tfrac{3}{8}$ in this case. With k_1 equal to $\tfrac{1}{4}$ and k_2 equal to $\tfrac{3}{8}$, Eq. (3.196) becomes

$$k_0 = \tfrac{3}{200} \qquad (3.197)$$

Since this value is less than the maximum allowable value and is positive, no further trial and error is required in this example. The admittance to be removed from y_2 is

$$y_{\text{shunt}} = \tfrac{3}{8} - \tfrac{3}{200} = \tfrac{9}{25} \qquad (3.198)$$

The resulting y_3 is

$$y_3 = \tfrac{3}{200} + \frac{\tfrac{1}{4}s}{s+2} + \frac{\tfrac{3}{8}s}{s+4} \qquad (3.199)$$

Collection of terms yields

$$y_3 = \frac{16s^2 + 46s + 3}{25(s^2 + 6s + 8)} \qquad (3.200)$$

The network at this stage in synthesis is shown in Fig. 3.75.

(5) In the fifth step, the value of y_a is determined from the equality of y_a and y_3 at s_0. $y_3(s_0)$ is first determined by substitution of the value for s_0 in Eq. (3.200), with the result

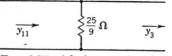
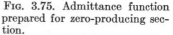

FIG. 3.75. Admittance function prepared for zero-producing section.

$$y_3(s_0) = \frac{6}{25} \frac{-4 + j\sqrt{11}}{1 + j\sqrt{11}} \qquad (3.201)$$

Substitution of $s = s_0$ in Eq. (3.173) for y_a yields

$$y_a(s_0) = c_0(1 + a)\left(\sigma_0 + \frac{\omega_0^2}{\sigma_0} - 2\alpha_0\right)\frac{-1 + j\sqrt{11}}{2\sigma_0 - 1 + j\sqrt{11}} \qquad (3.202)$$

Equating $y_3(s_0)$ and $y_a(s_0)$ yields two equations, one for the angle equality, one the magnitude. The angle equality alone suffices to determine σ_0.

$$\left/ \frac{-4 + j\sqrt{11}}{1 + j\sqrt{11}} \right. = \left/ \frac{-1 + j\sqrt{11}}{2\sigma_0 - 1 + j\sqrt{11}} \right. \tag{3.203}$$

$$\sigma_0 = 2.5 \tag{3.204}$$

With σ_0 known, the determination of y_a is completed by means of the magnitude equality, with the result

$$y_a = \frac{27}{50} \frac{s}{s + 2.5} \tag{3.205}$$

The product $c_0(1 + a)$ can also be found at this point from the known value of y_a and known values of σ_0, ω_0, and α_0.

$$c_0(1 + a) = \tfrac{1}{5} \tag{3.206}$$

(6) In the sixth step in the synthesis, y_a is subtracted from y_3 to create y_4, an admittance possessing a zero at s_0.

$$y_4 = y_3 - y_a \tag{3.207}$$

$$y_4 = \frac{1}{10} \frac{(s^2 + s + 3)(s + 1)}{(s + 2.5)(s^2 + 6s + 8)} \tag{3.208}$$

At this point there is a partial check on the calculations of part (5) since $s^2 + s + 3$ or $(s - s_0)(s - \bar{s}_0)$ must be a factor of the numerator of y_4.

(7) The impedance pole at s_0 is completely removed by subtraction of $1/y_{12c}$. Substitution of the known values of ω_0, σ_0, and α_0 yields an expression for y_{12c} from Eq. (3.169) of the form

$$y_{12c} = c_0 \frac{s^2 + s + 3}{s + 2.5} \tag{3.209}$$

c_0 is chosen to effect complete removal of the pole by subtraction of $1/y_{12c}$ from $1/y_4$.

$$z_5 = \frac{1}{y_4} - \frac{1}{y_{12c}} \tag{3.210}$$

$$z_5 = \frac{(s + 2.5)[10s^2 + (60 - 1/c_0)s + 80 - 1/c_0]}{(s^2 + s + 3)(s + 1)} \tag{3.211}$$

An even stronger check exists here on the calculations of parts (5) and (6), for it must now be possible to find a value of c_0 such that the numerator of z_5, as shown in Eq. (3.211), contains the factor $s^2 + s + 3$. Otherwise, subtraction of $1/y_{12c}$ would not result in complete removal of the pole at s_0 from $1/y_4$. In the above case, a c_0 of $\tfrac{1}{50}$ clearly does the job, and

$$z_5 = 10 \frac{s + 2.5}{s + 1} \tag{3.212}$$

All parameters of the zero-producing section are now known, for, from the value of c_0 and the known value of $c_0(1 + a) = \tfrac{1}{5}$ [Eq. (3.206)], a is 9.

The element values in the zero-producing section are completely determined by the parameters summarized below:

$$\omega_0^2 = 3 \qquad \sigma_0 = 2.5$$
$$\alpha_0 = \tfrac{1}{2} \qquad c_0 = 0.02$$
$$a = 9$$

It should not be inferred, from the ease with which this example has
been carried out, that the synthesis is always so simple. The calculations
of steps (5) and (6) must ordinarily be made with considerable care and
accuracy if in this seventh step it is to be possible to remove the impedance
pole by a subtraction of $1/y_{12c}$ with an appropriate determination of the
multiplying factor c_0. The procedure is straightforward, however, and
there is an early check on the accuracy of the calculations.

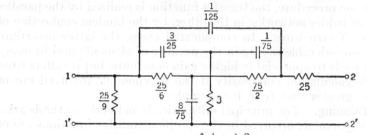

FIG. 3.76. Network to realize $y_{12} = \dfrac{s^2 + s + 3}{25(s^2 + 6s + 8)}$. (Values in ohms and farads.)

(8) The zero-producing section is now completely determined, and
the network can be drawn. However, it is still necessary to determine
the admittance remaining after the zero-producing section. This is done
by subtraction of y_c from y_5. y_c is given by the expression

$$y_c = y_{22c} - y_{12c} \tag{3.213}$$

Substitution of Eqs. (3.169) and (3.170) leads to an expression for y_c in
terms of known parameters:

$$y_c = c_0 \left(1 + \frac{1}{a}\right)\left(\sigma_0 + \frac{\omega_0^2}{\sigma_0} - 2\alpha_0\right)\frac{s}{s + \sigma_0} \tag{3.214}$$

With all parameters known, y_c can be written.

$$y_c = \frac{0.06s}{s + 2.5} \tag{3.215}$$

Subtraction of y_c from y_5 completes removal of the zero-producing section
from the driving-point admittance.

$$y_6 = y_5 - y_c \tag{3.216}$$

$$y_6 = \frac{0.1s + 0.1}{s + 2.5} - \frac{0.06s}{s + 2.5} \tag{3.217}$$

$$y_6 = 0.04 \tag{3.218}$$

(9) The final network can now be drawn, as shown in Fig. 3.76. The
network starts with the shunt resistance of $\tfrac{25}{9}$ ohms needed to create an

admittance function satisfying the residue equation. The zero-producing section follows, with the network terminating with the 25-ohm resistor. The short-circuit admittances of this network are

$$y_{11} = \frac{s^2 + 4s + 3}{s^2 + 6s + 8} \tag{3.219}$$

$$y_{12} = \frac{1}{25} \frac{s^2 + s + 3}{s^2 + 6s + 8} \tag{3.220}$$

The gain constant of $\frac{1}{25}$ realized with y_{12} is determined most readily from the infinite-frequency behavior of the network.

This section has presented the basic elements of two procedures for the realization of transfer functions with conjugate complex zeros by *RC* networks. In one procedure, the transfer function is realized by the parallel connection of ladder networks; in the other, by the tandem connection of bridged twin-T structures. In complicated cases, the latter procedure results in a considerable saving in the number of elements and in many problems it leads to appreciably higher gain constants, but it suffers from considerable calculation complexity if the polynomials involved are of high degree (greater than four, for example).

3.8. Partitioning. The principal difficulties in network synthesis arise when the polynomials involved in the specified transfer functions are of

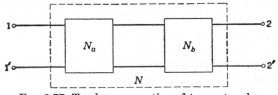

FIG. 3.77. Tandem connection of two networks.

high degree, for in such cases the computations required become annoyingly tedious. In many cases, the synthesis job can be eased by the partitioning of the network.† Instead of starting at one end of the network and developing the specified driving-point impedance function step by step, the designer works from the middle of the network outward toward the two ends.

The possibility of partitioning arises because of the relation between the characteristics of two individual networks (N_a and N_b in Fig. 3.77) and the characteristics of the over-all network N resulting from the tandem connection. The open-circuit transfer impedance and the short-circuit transfer admittance of N are related to the describing impedances and admittances of the component networks by the equations

$$z_{12} = \frac{z_{12a}z_{12b}}{z_{22a} + z_{11b}} \tag{3.221}$$

† L. Weinberg, Synthesis of Transfer Functions with Poles Restricted to the Negative Real Axis, *Trans. IRE Professional Group on Circuit Theory*, PGCT 1, pp. 35–56, December, 1952.

$$y_{12} = \frac{y_{12a}y_{12b}}{y_{22a} + y_{11b}} \tag{3.222}$$

These two important equations are readily derived; the admittance relation serves as an example of the method of derivation.

The over-all y_{12} is the current between the shorted output terminals when 1 volt is applied to the input. With this input voltage, the network is broken between N_a and N_b, and N_a is replaced by the Norton equivalent circuit, as shown in Fig. 3.78. The voltage across the input terminals of N_b is then

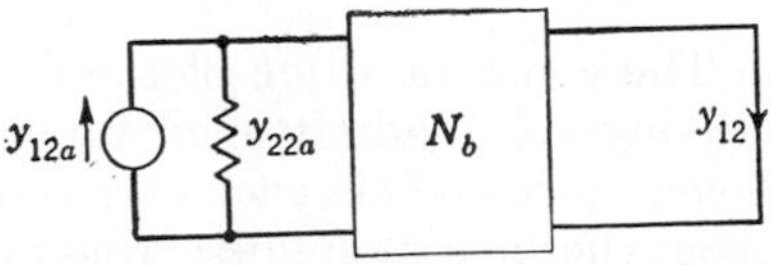

$$E_{1b} = \frac{y_{12a}}{y_{22a} + y_{11b}} \tag{3.223}$$

FIG. 3.78. N_a of Fig. 3.77 replaced using Norton's Theorem.

The output current is y_{12b} times this input voltage, or simply the expression of Eq. (3.222).

If y_{12} alone is specified, Eq. (3.222) can be used to break the synthesis problem down into two separate problems, each of lower complexity. As an example, the short-circuit transfer admittance of Eq. (3.224) is considered:

$$y_{12} = \frac{(s^2 + s + 1)(s^2 + s + 2)}{(s + 1)(s + 3)(s + 5)(s + 7)} \tag{3.224}$$

There are several ways in which y_{12} can be written in a form permitting identification, term by term, with Eq. (3.222). For example, one simple way involves division of both numerator and denominator by a polynomial chosen to leave the denominator rational function realizable as an RC driving-point admittance. One possible choice for the above y_{12} function would be

$$y_{12} = \frac{\dfrac{(s^2 + s + 1)(s^2 + s + 2)}{(s + 2)(s + 4)(s + 6)}}{\dfrac{(s + 1)(s + 3)(s + 5)(s + 7)}{(s + 2)(s + 4)(s + 6)}} \tag{3.225}$$

The denominator rational function y_D is now expanded by a partial-fraction expansion of y_D/s.

$$y_{12} = \frac{\dfrac{(s^2 + s + 1)(s^2 + s + 2)}{(s + 2)(s + 4)(s + 6)}}{s + \dfrac{35}{16} + \dfrac{15s/16}{s + 2} + \dfrac{9s/16}{s + 4} + \dfrac{5s/16}{s + 6}} \tag{3.226}$$

If the N_a network is to be realizable, y_{12a} and y_{22a} must have the same poles. Consequently, as the describing functions for N_a one suitable choice is

$$y_{12a} = \frac{s^2 + s + 1}{s + 2} \tag{3.227}$$

$$y_{22a} = s + \frac{15s/16}{s+2} + \frac{15}{16} \tag{3.228}$$

N_b is then specified by

$$y_{12b} = \frac{s^2 + s + 2}{(s+4)(s+6)} \tag{3.229}$$

$$y_{22b} = \frac{20}{16} + \frac{9s/16}{s+4} + \frac{5s/16}{s+6} \tag{3.230}$$

The constant value of the denominator can be split between the two driving-point admittance functions arbitrarily, as long as each takes some, since y_{12}/s in each case possesses a pole at the origin. In the above case, the pole at infinity was placed in the N_a network, leaving the N_b network with a constant value at infinity. This would permit realization of N_b with a terminating resistance so that the original y_{12} function could be used to realize a specified voltage ratio, as pointed out in the preceding section in the discussion of the second example of Dasher's procedure. If terminating resistances are desired at both ends of the network, the original numerator and denominator polynomials are divided by a quartic rather than a cubic in order that the denominator rational algebraic function may have a constant value at infinite frequency.

The use of partitioning thus permits considerable simplification in the synthesis. Realization of transfer functions involving fourth-degree polynomials is reduced to two problems with second-degree polynomials. Another important application of partitioning occurs in the realization of *RLC* networks by the tandem connection of an *RC* and an *RL* network.

3.9. Conclusion. In this chapter, an attempt has been made to present a few of the more important basic techniques for the synthesis of *RC* networks. Clearly it is impossible to do any more than present an introduction to these methods. Only a few examples have been given to illustrate the techniques. However, throughout the remaining chapters, there are further examples and methods which should assist the reader in the evaluation and interpretation of this chapter. In many ways, so much of the current literature relating to feedback control systems is intimately tied in with network theory that it is difficult to make any sharp distinction.

CHAPTER 4

ROOT-LOCUS METHODS

The past decade has seen a radical change in methods for the design of feedback control systems. One direct consequence of the war and defense efforts in this country has been a strong emphasis on the development of improved techniques for control-system design. Among the many methods presented, the root-locus approach† stands out, for it combines the theoretical advantage of simultaneous control over both transient and frequency responses of the system with a strong appeal to the designer, an appeal which is derived from the simplicity of the method as well as the logic underlying the approach. With the root-locus method, the designer of feedback control systems adopts the tools of the field of network theory and utilizes for the first time the full potentialities of the Laplace transform.

The importance of the root-locus method is indicated by a brief consideration of the state of feedback design theory in 1948, when Evans presented his method. In the early history of servomechanisms, attention was focused on the differential equations describing system behavior. Design entailed a study of the differential equations and the corresponding characteristics of the transient and frequency responses. In such an approach, difficulties arise because of the absence of simple correlation between system parameters and the essential features of system response. Any such correlation must be developed by working through the coefficients of the differential equations.

The work of Harris, Hall, Brown, Campbell, and Nichols, among others, presented design in terms of the sinusoidal frequency response of the system. Based on the earlier work of Nyquist and Bode in the study of feedback systems, this frequency-domain approach involved an adjustment of the open-loop frequency characteristics in order to realize appropriate closed-loop performance. The methods do permit a correlation between parameter values and the nature of the sinusoidal response: *e.g.*, in terms of the gain and phase plots, the break frequencies are related to the parameter values in a straightforward manner.

† The root-locus method was first presented by W. R. Evans in the article, Graphical Analysis of Control Systems, *Trans. AIEE*, Vol. 67, pp. 547–551, 1948; see also his "Control-system Dynamics," McGraw-Hill Book Company, Inc., New York, 1954. Other presentations of the basic principles are given by W. Bollay, Aerodynamic Stability and Automatic Control, *J. Aeronaut. Sci.*, Vol. 18, No. 9, pp. 569–623, 1951; and in the text by G. J. Thaler and R. G. Brown, "Servomechanism Analysis," Chap. 14, McGraw-Hill Book Company, Inc., New York, 1953.

Thus, concentration of attention on the frequency response allows control over such performance characteristics as the bandwidth, the zero-frequency behavior of the system (*e.g.*, the error coefficients), and the general shape of the closed-loop frequency response [for example, M_p, the maximum value of the closed-loop gain $\left| \dfrac{C}{R} (j\omega) \right|$]. Only a very tenuous correlation exists, however, between the frequency response and the transient response of the closed-loop system. This correlation is expressed in terms of several approximate relations, based in part on experience and the study of a number of systems, in part on theoretical derivations. For example, experience has indicated that an M_p of about 1.3 corresponds to a step-function response with an overshoot in the neighborhood of 15 per cent; as another example, the bandwidth is inversely proportional to the rise time of the step-function response, although the constant of proportionality varies rather widely with the shape of the frequency response. Attempts to establish further precise correlations between frequency and transient responses generate very real difficulties as a result of the complexity of the Laplace or Fourier integral relating the two domains.

But this correlation is absolutely essential in a wide variety of design problems (*e.g.*, in the design of antiaircraft-fire-control systems). Thus, design in the frequency domain does not constitute a completely satisfactory theory for linear systems. During the last decade, the majority of the work on the development of design techniques for linear feedback systems has been directed toward methods for simultaneous control over both frequency and transient responses. The basic contributions have been made in three directions: Wiener, in his presentation of statistical design methods, considers the actual input signals described in terms of average statistical properties; Guillemin, applying the concepts of network synthesis to the synthesis of feedback control systems, forces the system to meet specifications in both the frequency and the time domains; Evans, in his root-locus method, adopts one of the basic viewpoints of frequency-domain design, in that he attempts to modify the open-loop system to obtain suitable closed-loop characteristics, but Evans, too, works in terms of both frequency and time domains.

Underlying the work of Wiener, Guillemin, and Evans is the emphasis on the description of the signals and the system components in terms of the Laplace transforms and the transfer functions as functions of the complex frequency variable $s = \sigma + j\omega$. When the Nyquist diagram or the gain and phase plots are the basis of design, use of the Laplace transform is, in many ways, pedantic: at the very outset of the design, s is replaced by $j\omega$, and, thereafter, the $j\omega$ axis is the only part of the s plane of interest. By narrowing the region of interest from the entire s plane down to the $j\omega$ axis, the designer discards the opportunity of maintaining control over both frequency and transient responses. In the methods presented by Wiener, Guillemin, and Evans, the Laplace transform and complex-function theory are basic tools; design is guided by the behavior of both open-loop and closed-loop transfer functions over the entire s plane.

This broadening of viewpoint is achieved by working through the poles and zeros of the relevant transfer functions. As pointed out in Chap. 1, a function of a complex variable is characterized by its singularities. The usual transfer functions of feedback systems are rational algebraic functions and, hence, are described by the poles and the principal parts of the associated Laurent series, or, alternatively, by the poles and zeros. Interpretation of design as adjustment of the poles and zeros of the closed-loop system function permits the designer to maintain control over both transient and frequency responses. The discussion of Secs. 1.4 and 1.5 indicates the nature of the simple correlations between the pole and zero positions and the corresponding frequency and transient responses; the utilization of these concepts is illustrated in the discussion of Evans's work in this chapter, the presentation of Guillemin's philosophy of design in Chap. 5, and the introduction to Wiener's methods in Chaps. 7 and 8. These various methods of design, by virtue of the common emphasis on pole and zero positions, depend to a large extent on the designer's familiarity with the basic principles of Laplace-transform theory and complex-function theory. The very impressive advantages of these methods are fully realized only if the designer is able to make rapid transitions from pole and zero positions to the frequency response, on the one hand, and to the transient response, on the other. Thus, the basic ideas of Secs. 1.4 and 1.5 are introductory to a discussion of any of the three methods.

4.1. The Root-locus Method.
The root-locus method of design is based on the relation between the poles and zeros of the closed-loop system function and those of the open-loop transfer function. Once the relation is established for the

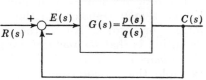

FIG. 4.1. Single-loop feedback system.

system configuration under consideration, design is accomplished by adjusting the poles and zeros and the multiplicative gain factor of the open-loop transfer function in such a way as to yield a closed-loop system function with satisfactory critical frequencies.†

The basic elements of the root-locus method are illustrated by consideration of the system of Fig. 4.1, a single-loop feedback control system with the forward transfer function $G(s)$. The closed-loop system function is given by the relation

$$\frac{C}{R}(s) = \frac{G(s)}{1 + G(s)} \tag{4.1}$$

In the usual feedback control system, $G(s)$ is a rational algebraic function, the ratio of two polynomials in s:

$$G(s) = \frac{p(s)}{q(s)} \tag{4.2}$$

† In this chapter, as in Chap. 1, the term "critical frequencies" is used to denote poles and zeros.

Substitution of Eq. (4.2) in (4.1) gives

$$\frac{C}{R}(s) = \frac{p(s)/q(s)}{1 + p(s)/q(s)} \tag{4.3}$$

$$\frac{C}{R}(s) = \frac{p(s)}{p(s) + q(s)} \tag{4.4}$$

Thus, for the system of Fig. 4.1, the zeros of the closed-loop system function are identical with the open-loop zeros,† and the closed-loop poles are the values of s at which $p(s)/q(s) = -1$. The basic difficulty with design in terms of the Laplace transform arises because the poles of the closed-loop system function are the zeros of the polynomial $p(s) + q(s)$. In any but the simplest cases, the evaluation of these poles for a given $p(s)$ and $q(s)$ is a tedious job; if, in addition, the motion of the poles with changes in a system design parameter is desired, straightforward calculation becomes impractical.

The root-locus method is a graphical technique for determining the zeros of $p(s) + q(s)$ from the zeros of $p(s)$ and $q(s)$, individually. If a system parameter is varied, the corresponding changes in the zeros of $p(s)$ and $q(s)$ are determined (just as would be done if the gain and phase plots were being used for design), and the resulting changes in the zeros of $p(s) + q(s)$ are investigated.

The root loci consist of all points in the s plane at which the phase of the open-loop transfer function is 0° (or 0° + $n360°$, where n is any integer or zero).‡ An alternate, and in many cases more convenient, definition is that *the root loci are plots of the variations of the poles of the closed-loop system function with changes in the open-loop gain.* For example, the configuration of Fig. 4.1 is again considered, and the system is assumed second order, with

$$G(s) = \frac{K}{s(s + 1)} \tag{4.5}$$

In this case,

$$\frac{C}{R}(s) = \frac{K}{s^2 + s + K} \tag{4.6}$$

The root loci are plots of the zeros of the polynomial $s^2 + s + K$ as a function of K. For this simple example, the loci are shown in Fig. 4.2, which also illustrates the form of the root-locus plot. The figure is constructed in the following three steps:

† The term "open-loop zeros" is more accurately written "zeros of the open-loop transfer function." This and similar terms appear so often in a discussion of the root-locus method that the abbreviated form is used throughout this chapter.

‡ Confusion occasionally arises here because of the definition of the term "open-loop transfer function." For the system of Fig. 4.1, for example, the open-loop transfer function is $-p(s)/q(s)$, since the subtraction at the input introduces a minus sign. Thus, for this system, the root loci are the points at which the phase of $p(s)/q(s)$ is 180° + $n360°$, where n is any integer or zero.

(1) In the complex plane, the open-loop poles are marked by x, the open-loop zeros by o.

(2) On the basis of the relation that the closed-loop poles are the roots of the equation $G(s) = -1$, the loci of these poles are plotted as a function of K. (For a multiloop system or any configuration more general than that of Fig. 4.1, the equation defining the loci is more complicated.)

(3) Appropriate values of K are marked along the loci.

In the example of Fig. 4.2, the root loci take such a simple form that they can be drawn by inspection. The next section presents general rules for construction of the loci for more complex systems. Even in this case, however, the loci present the information appropriate for design. In particular, Fig. 4.2 indicates at once the following facts:

(1) As long as K is positive, the system is never unstable.

(2) With the relative damping ratio of the closed-loop poles decreasing as K increases, the value of K for any specified ζ is apparent.

(3) The settling time, or significant time constant, of the system is independent of open-loop gain for all values of K larger than $\frac{1}{4}$.

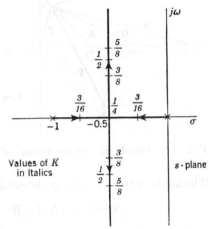

FIG. 4.2. Root loci for $G(s) = \dfrac{K}{s(s+1)}$.

In addition, as described in Sec. 4.4, the loci indicate the nature of the compensation required to meet specifications in a wide variety of forms.

Clearly, the root loci constitute a graphical method for the approximate determination of the zeros of a polynomial. The usefulness of the root loci in the design of feedback control systems depends directly on the ease with which the loci can be constructed. In a design problem, the general shapes of the loci are sketched approximately for a number of different sets of open-loop poles and zeros; with a few appropriate sets determined, the designer must then plot more accurate loci in order to select one set, to adjust system parameters, and to evaluate the effects of changes in these parameters. Construction of the loci is facilitated if a number of special techniques are employed, as described in the following two sections. Once the significance of these simple relations and methods is appreciated, the root loci can be sketched approximately with practically no work for a wide variety of systems, even though the number of poles and zeros may be large.

4.2. Construction of the Root Loci. If attention is again focused on the single-loop system of Fig. 4.1, the root loci are the roots of the equation $G(s) = -1$, as a function of the open-loop gain. In other words, the root loci constitute all s-plane points at which

$$\underline{/G(s)} = 180° + n360° \tag{4.7}$$

where n is any integer, including zero. Equation (4.7) is the basis for all rules and techniques for construction of the root loci.

$\underline{/G(s)}$ at any specific point in the s plane is conveniently measured in terms of the angles contributed by the various poles and zeros. Written in factored form, a typical $G(s)$ for a feedback control system is

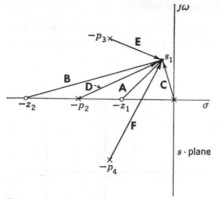

$$G(s) = \frac{K(s + z_1)(s + z_2)}{s(s + p_2)(s + p_3)(s + p_4)}$$
$$(4.8)†$$

At the point s_1, $G(s)$ takes the value

$$G(s_1) = \frac{K(s_1 + z_1)(s_1 + z_2)}{s_1(s_1 + p_2)(s_1 + p_3)(s_1 + p_4)}$$
$$(4.9)$$

The value of $G(s_1)$ can be expressed in terms of the vectors shown in Fig. 4.3,

FIG. 4.3. Graphical interpretation of $G(s_1)$.

$$G(s_1) = K\,\frac{\mathbf{AB}}{\mathbf{CDEF}} \quad (4.10)‡$$

The angle of $G(s_1)$ is simply determined by the angles of the vectors:

$$\underline{/G(s_1)} = \underline{/\mathbf{A}} + \underline{/\mathbf{B}} - \underline{/\mathbf{C}} - \underline{/\mathbf{D}} - \underline{/\mathbf{E}} - \underline{/\mathbf{F}} \qquad (4.11)$$

Thus, construction of the root loci involves the determination of those points, s_j, in the s plane at which

$$\Sigma\underline{/\text{vectors from zeros to } s_j}$$
$$- \Sigma\underline{/\text{vectors from poles to } s_j} = 180° + n360° \quad (4.12)$$

The construction of the root loci does not, however, entail an aimless search for s-plane points satisfying Eq. (4.12). The root loci are continuous curves, since the zeros of a polynomial are continuous functions of the coefficients. Consequently, once sections of the loci are established, the extension of these parts can be effected without lengthy trial and error. The simple rules and relationships listed below permit accurate construction of certain parts of the loci and indicate the approximate location of the other parts.

Rules for Construction of Root Loci. The rules described here are of two general types: those based on the interpretation of Eq. (4.12) in special cases, and those derived from a consideration of Eq. (4.4), which states that the closed-loop poles are the zeros of $p(s) + q(s)$, where the ratio

† The zeros of $G(s)$ are $-z_1$ and $-z_2$; the poles are 0, $-p_2$, $-p_3$, and $-p_4$. Since the zeros and poles of the transfer functions of feedback systems are almost always in the left-half plane, this form usually results in positive numbers for the real parts of z_1, z_2, p_2, p_3, and p_4.

‡ Throughout this chapter, vectors are indicated by boldface roman type.

of the polynomials, $-p(s)/q(s)$, is the open-loop transfer function.†
Accordingly, the rules do not involve any analytical concepts beyond
those already considered, but, rather, they represent the codification of
obvious relationships between the open-loop and the closed-loop transfer
functions. There are a wide variety of rules or special relations which
might be listed, but the eleven below are the most useful.

(1) $K \to 0$. If $G(s)$ is written as $KG_1(s)$, the equation satisfied along
the loci is

$$KG_1(s) = -1 \tag{4.13}$$

Clearly, if K tends to zero, $G_1(s)$ must tend to infinity, or s must approach
the poles of $G(s)$. Hence, if the loci are interpreted as plots of the closed-
loop pole positions when the open-loop gain varies from 0 to $+\infty$, the
loci start at the open-loop poles.

(2) $K \to \infty$. Since Eq. (4.13) indicates that a very large K requires
a $G_1(s)$ tending to zero, or a value of s approaching a zero of $G(s)$, the loci
terminate on the zeros of $G(s)$.

(3) *Number of loci*. From Eq. (4.4) and the fact that a polynomial of
degree n possesses n zeros, it is clear that the number of separate loci
equals the number of poles *or* zeros of $G(s)$, where critical frequencies at
infinity are included and multiple-order critical frequencies are counted
according to the order.

(4) *Conjugate values*. Complex parts of the loci always appear in
conjugate complex pairs if, as is customary in the design of feedback systems, the coefficients of the polynomials $p(s)$ and $q(s)$ are real.

(5) *Loci near infinity*. The behavior of the loci for large values of s is
readily investigated by replacing $p(s)$ and $q(s)$ by the highest powers of
each. Thus, if $G(s)$ possesses an nth-order zero at infinity, the characteristics of the loci near infinity are determined by consideration of an equation of the form

$$K \frac{s^m}{s^{m+n}} = -1 \tag{4.14}$$

$$K \frac{1}{s^n} = -1 \tag{4.15}$$

n of the $m + n$ loci tend to infinity as K becomes large. With K positive,
the 180° angle of K/s^n must be realized by the term s^n. Hence, as the n
loci approach infinity, they tend toward asymptotes at angles of $\pm 180°/n$,
$\pm 540°/n$, $\pm 900°/n$, ... In other words, if n is 3 [a triple zero of $G(s)$
at infinity], the three approaches to infinity are along lines at angles of
60°, $-60°$, and 180° (Fig. 4.4).

The $\pm 60°$ asymptotes do not, in general, intersect at the origin when
extrapolated, but instead meet at a point along the real axis. This point
of intersection must be determined if the asymptotes are to be constructed accurately. The point can be found as follows: the open-loop

† Throughout the remainder of this chapter, the root-locus method is described in
terms of the single-loop configuration of Fig. 4.1. The extension of the method to
other configurations is obvious.

transfer function is written in the form

$$\frac{p(s)}{q(s)} = K \frac{s^m + a_1 s^{m-1} + \cdots + a_m}{s^{m+n} + b_1 s^{m+n-1} + \cdots + b_{m+n}} \tag{4.16}$$

The numerator of the frequency-dependent fraction is divided into the denominator to give

$$\frac{p(s)}{q(s)} = K \frac{1}{s^n + (b_1 - a_1)s^{n-1} + \cdots} \tag{4.17}$$

The loci are described by equating the denominator above to $-K$,

$$s^n + (b_1 - a_1)s^{n-1} + \cdots = -K \tag{4.18}$$

When s is large, the left side of Eq. (4.18) behaves as a polynomial of degree n, with the sum of the zeros $-(b_1 - a_1)$. Consequently, the asymptotes meet at the point

$$s_1 = -\frac{b_1 - a_1}{n} \tag{4.19}$$

In other words,

$$s_1 = \frac{\Sigma \text{ poles} - \Sigma \text{ zeros}}{(\text{number of finite poles}) - (\text{number of finite zeros})} \tag{4.20}\dagger$$

(6) *Loci on real axis.* The parts of the real axis which comprise sections of the loci are readily determined from Eq. (4.12). Along the real axis, the angles of the vectors from any conjugate complex pair of zeros or poles of $G(s)$ cancel, with the result that the total angle of $G(\sigma)$ is made up of the contributions from the real poles and zeros alone. At any given point σ_1 on the real axis, the angle contributed by a pole or zero to the left of σ_1 is zero, while that from a pole or zero to the right of σ_1 is 180°. Hence the loci include those sections of the real axis to the left of an odd number of open-loop critical frequencies.

(7) *Intersections with imaginary axis.* Routh's test‡ frequently permits rapid determination of the points at which the loci cross the $j\omega$ axis and the value of gain at these intersections. The test is applied to the polynomial $p(s) + q(s)$.

(8) *Angles of departure and arrival.* The angles at which the loci leave the poles and arrive at the zeros are readily evaluated from Eq. (4.12). For example, in the configuration of Fig. 4.5(a), the angle of departure of the locus from the pole at $-1 + j1$ is desired. If a test point is assumed only slightly displaced from the pole, the angles con-

---

† It should be noted that it is not possible to say (if $n \geq m + 2$) that $p(s) + q(s)$ behaves as $s^{m+n} + b_1 s^{m+n-1}$ as s tends to infinity, and that, accordingly, the asymptotes meet at $-b_1/(m + n)$. The fallacy here arises from the assumption that in the polynomial $p(s) + q(s)$, as s becomes large, the lower-degree terms (which involve K) are much less than $s^{m+n} + b_1 s^{m+n-1}$.

‡ M. F. Gardner and J. L. Barnes, "Transients in Linear Systems," Vol. I, pp. 197−201, John Wiley & Sons, Inc., New York. 1942.

tributed by all critical frequencies except the pole at $-1 + j1$ are determined approximately by the vectors from these poles and zeros to $-1 + j1$. The angle contributed by the pole at $-1 + j1$ is, then, just sufficient to make the total angle 180°. In the example shown in the figure, the departure angle is found from the relation

$$+45° - (135° + 90° + 26.6° + \theta_1) = 180° + n360° \quad (4.21)$$
$$\underbrace{\hphantom{+45°}}_{/s+2} \quad \underbrace{\hphantom{135°}}_{/s} \quad \underbrace{\hphantom{90°}}_{/s+1+j} \quad \underbrace{\hphantom{26.6°}}_{/s+3} \quad \underbrace{\hphantom{\theta_1}}_{/s+1-j}$$

Solution for θ_1, the angle of locus departure from the pole at $-1 + j1$, gives a value of $-26.6°$. Hence, the locus leaves the pole at an angle of $-26.6°$, as shown in Fig. 4.5(b).

(9) *Point of breakaway from real axis.* The point at which a locus breaks away from the real axis can be readily calculated. Figure 4.6(a) shows the loci for a system with three real open-loop poles; the point $-\alpha$

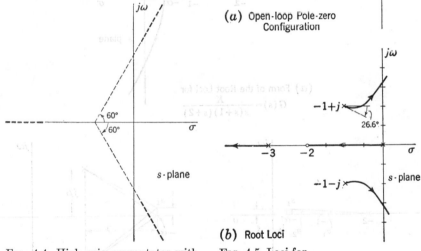

(a) Open-loop Pole-zero Configuration

(b) Root Loci

Fig. 4.4. High-gain asymptotes with triple zero at infinity.

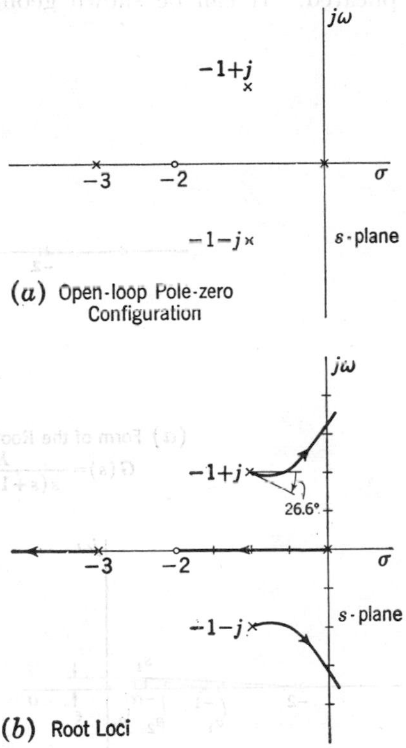

Fig. 4.5. Loci for

$$G(s) = \frac{K(s + 2)}{s(s + 3)(s^2 + 2s + 2)}.$$

at which the two loci leave the axis is to be determined. A point s_1 a small distance (ϵ) off the axis is considered. The transition from $-\alpha$ to s_1 must result in a zero net change in the angle of $G(s)$. The sum of the changes in the angles from the various open-loop critical frequencies is equated to zero, with the appropriate signs depending on the direction of the change and whether the critical frequency is a pole or zero. In this example, Fig. 4.6(b) indicates that

$$\theta_1 + \theta_2 - \theta_3 = 0° \quad (4.22)$$

The small angles can be replaced by the corresponding tangents:

$$\frac{\epsilon}{2-\alpha} + \frac{\epsilon}{1-\alpha} - \frac{\epsilon}{\alpha} = 0 \tag{4.23}$$

After cancellation of ϵ, trial-and-error solution of Eq. (4.23) gives the value

$$\alpha = 0.422 \tag{4.24}$$

If the open-loop transfer function has conjugate complex critical frequencies, the calculation of a breakaway point is slightly more complicated. It can be shown geometrically that, if the notation of Fig.

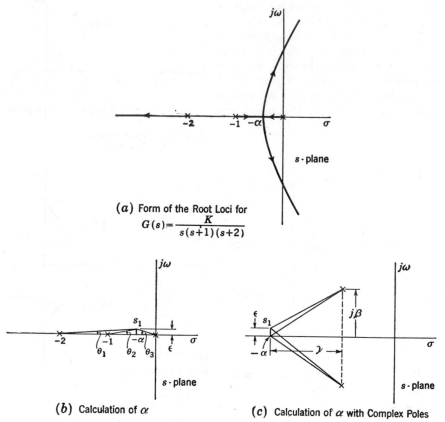

(a) Form of the Root Loci for
$$G(s) = \frac{K}{s(s+1)(s+2)}$$

(b) Calculation of α (c) Calculation of α with Complex Poles

FIG. 4.6. Break-away from real axis.

4.6(c) is used, motion from $-\alpha$ to s_1 results in a decrease of $2\epsilon\gamma/(\beta^2 + \gamma^2)$ in the sum of the angles contributed by the two complex poles. Here γ includes the unknown value of α.

(10) *Sum of the loci.* The loci represent the locations of the zeros of the polynomial $p(s) + q(s)$ as a function of K. If $p(s) + q(s)$ is of degree n and the coefficient of s^n is unity, the coefficient of s^{n-1} is the negative of the sum of the zeros. If the open-loop transfer function

$-p(s)/q(s)$ has at least a double zero at infinity (as is customarily the situation in the study of feedback control systems), the coefficient of s^{n-1} is independent of K. Hence, as certain loci turn to the left in the complex plane, others must turn to the right in order that the sum of the closed-loop poles may be constant.

(11) *Product of the loci.* Likewise, the product of corresponding points on the loci is determined by the constant term of the polynomial $p(s) + q(s)$. If $p(s)/q(s)$ contains a pole at the origin, the constant term of $p(s) + q(s)$ is directly proportional to K.

Application of these eleven rules and relationships to facilitate construction of the loci is illustrated by three examples.

Example 1. In the first example, the open-loop transfer function has three poles on the negative real axis and a triple zero at infinity:

$$G(s) = \frac{K}{s(s + 1)(s + 2)} \tag{4.25}$$

In this case, the polynomial $p(s) + q(s)$ is $s^3 + 3s^2 + 2s + K$. The loci can be drawn approximately on the basis of the eleven rules, which are interpreted as follows:

(1) The loci start from 0, -1, and -2, as shown in Fig. 4.7(a).

(2) The loci all terminate at infinity.

(3) There are three loci.

(4) For all values of K, there must be one locus on the real axis; the other two may be real or conjugate complex.

(5) Since all zeros are at infinity, all three loci approach infinity as K becomes large. These approaches are at angles of $+60°$, $-60°$, and $180°$ [part (b) of Fig. 4.7, where the arrows are directed toward the zeros]. Equation (4.20) indicates that the asymptotes meet at -1.

(6) The parts of the real axis between 0 and -1 and between -2 and $-\infty$ constitute sections of the loci, as indicated in part (c) of the figure. The arrows show the directions of motion of the closed-loop poles as K increases.

(7) The intersections of the loci and the imaginary axis are determined from Routh's test. The Routh table for the given $p(s) + q(s)$ is:

	1	2
s^3	1	2
s^2	3	K
s^1	$\dfrac{6 - K}{3}$	
s^0	K	

Hence, zeros on the $j\omega$ axis occur at the roots of $s^2 + 2 = 0$, or at $s = \pm j\sqrt{2}$, and with a K of 6. Part (d) of the figure shows the appropriate intersections of the loci and the $j\omega$ axis.

(8) Since there are no complex open-loop poles or zeros, no angle of arrival or departure is involved in the loci.

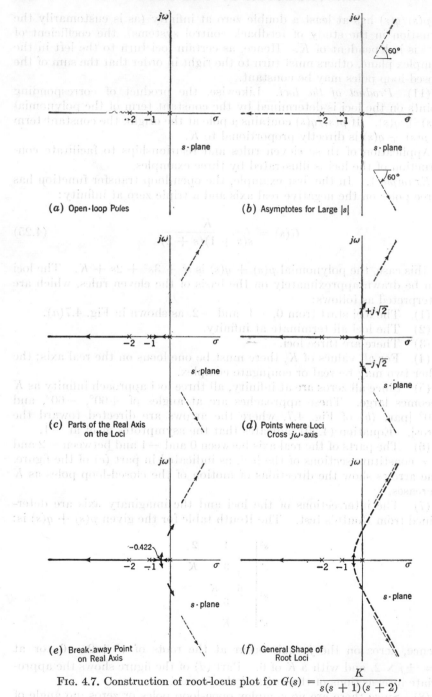

(a) Open-loop Poles

(b) Asymptotes for Large |s|

(c) Parts of the Real Axis
on the Loci

(d) Points where Loci
Cross jω-axis

(e) Break-away Point
on Real Axis

(f) General Shape of
Root Loci

FIG. 4.7. Construction of root-locus plot for $G(s) = \dfrac{K}{s(s + 1)(s + 2)}$.

(9)   The point of breakaway from the real axis occurs between 0 and
-1.   Equation (4.24) gives the point as -0.422, shown in Fig. 4.7(e).
(10)   The sum of the zeros of $p(s) + q(s)$ is constant at -3 as K
varies.   The locus along the real axis to the left of -2 must represent a
monotonic motion of the closed-loop pole as K is increased monotonically

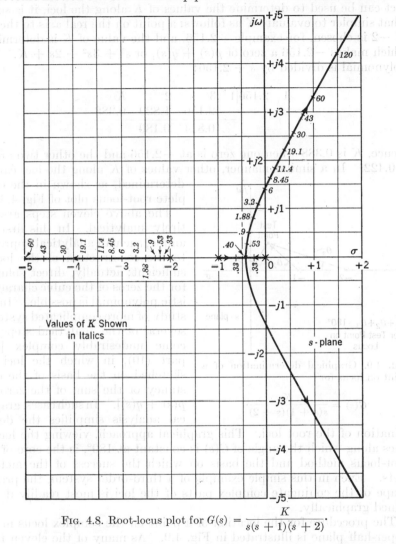

Fig. 4.8. Root-locus plot for $G(s) = \dfrac{K}{s(s+1)(s+2)}$.

from 0 to ∞.   (A given value of s can correspond to only *one* value of K,
since the equation $KG_1(s) = -1$ is linear in K.)   Hence, the conjugate
complex loci leaving the axis at -0.422 must always move to the right.
The over-all root-locus plot can now be sketched, as shown in part (f) of
the figure.   Furthermore, on the basis of the constancy of the sum of the
zeros, equivalent points on the three loci can be determined.   Thus, when

the two loci cross the $j\omega$ axis, the third locus must be at -3; when the two loci break away from the axis, the third must be at $-(3 - 2 \times 0.422)$, or -2.156; when the third locus is at -4, each of the first two has a real part of 0.5; etc.

(11) The product of the three zeros is simply $-K$. Although this fact can be used to determine the values of K along the loci, it is somewhat simpler to evaluate K as follows: a point on the real axis to the left of -2 is chosen, for example -2.156, and the value of K is determined which makes -2.156 a zero of $p(s) + q(s)$, or $s^3 + 3s^2 + 2s + K$. The polynomial is divided by $s + 2.156$:

$$
\begin{array}{r|rrrr}
1 \quad 2.156 & 1 & 3 & 2 & K \\
& & 2.156 & 1.820 & 0.388 \\
\hline
& & 0.844 & 0.180 &
\end{array}
$$

Hence, K is 0.388 when one zero is at -2.156 and the other two are at -0.422. In a similar manner, other values of K along the loci can be determined, as shown in the complete root-locus plot of Fig. 4.8.

The above eleven steps are entirely analytical. In this first example, such an analytical approach to the construction of the loci is sufficient; actually, direct solution for the zeros of the cubic characteristic polynomial is possible. In the study of more complicated systems, several of the analytical steps become undesirably complex [e.g., part (10), in which the loci are sketched on the basis of the constancy of the sum of the zeros of $p(s) + q(s)$]. In such cases, graphical analysis simplifies the determination of the root loci.

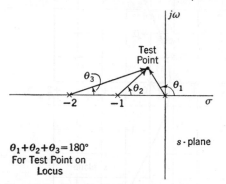

$\theta_1 + \theta_2 + \theta_3 = 180°$
For Test Point on
Locus

Fig. 4.9. Graphical determination of a point on locus for

$$G(s) = \frac{K}{s(s + 1)(s + 2)}.$$

This graphical approach, viewing the loci as lines along which the angle of $G(s)$ is constant at $180°$, is the core of the root-locus method and the basis on which the success of the method rests. Even in this simple example of a third-order system, the precise shape of the conjugate complex parts of the loci is most readily determined graphically.

The procedure for the location of a point on the complex locus in the upper-half plane is illustrated in Fig. 4.9. As many of the eleven relationships as can be readily interpreted are used to obtain an estimate of a point on the locus. The angles of the vectors from 0, -1, and -2 to the trial point are measured. If the sum of these three angles is less than $180°$, the test point is moved in a direction to increase the total angle: e.g., the second trial point might be selected at the same angle, θ_1, but farther from the origin in order to give an increased θ_2 and θ_3.

A graphical procedure is also convenient to determine values of K along the loci. At any given point, K is fixed by the relation

$$K = \frac{1}{|G(s)|} \qquad (4.26)$$

$|G(s)|$ is evaluated in terms of the lengths of the vectors from the open-loop poles and zeros to the point on the locus. For the example previously considered, Fig. 4.10 shows the three measurements required for the evaluation of K at the point at which the ζ of the complex closed-loop poles is 0.707.·

Thus, the construction of the loci is a combination of analytical and graphical techniques. In simple cases, analytical techniques can be used

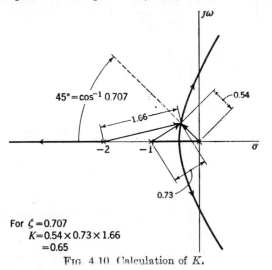

For $\zeta = 0.707$
$K = 0.54 \times 0.73 \times 1.66$
$= 0.65$

FIG. 4.10. Calculation of K.

to determine the entire locus; in more complicated problems, the designer combines the analytical relationships and graphical calculations. If only the general shape of the loci is desired, the simple relations expressed in the eleven rules listed above ordinarily suffice.

Example 2. In the second example, the open-loop transfer function is assumed to have one pair of conjugate complex poles, two real poles, and one finite zero:

$$G(s) = \frac{K(s+2)}{s(s+3)(s^2+2s+2)} \qquad (4.27)$$

Again in this example, all eleven rules outlined previously are applied, although in practice only those relationships of direct usefulness need be considered.

(1) The open-loop poles at 0, -3, and $-1 \pm j1$ are noted in the s plane [Fig. 4.11(a)].

(2) The finite zero at -2 is marked [part (b) of the figure].

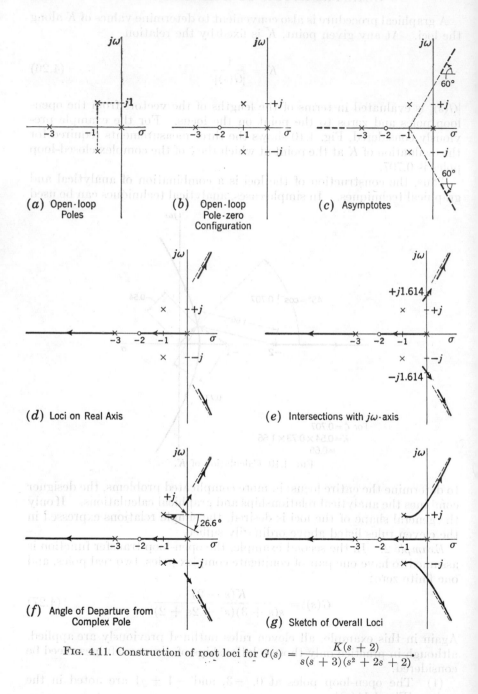

(a) Open-loop Poles

(b) Open-loop Pole-zero Configuration

(c) Asymptotes

(d) Loci on Real Axis

(e) Intersections with $j\omega$-axis

(f) Angle of Departure from Complex Pole

(g) Sketch of Overall Loci

FIG. 4.11. Construction of root loci for $G(s) = \dfrac{K(s + 2)}{s(s + 3)(s^2 + 2s + 2)}$.

(3) There are four loci, since there are four poles of $G(s)$.

(4) Whenever complex, the loci appear in conjugate pairs.

(5) As s tends to infinity, $G(s)$ behaves as K/s^3. Hence, the loci approach infinity at angles of $60°$, $-60°$, and $180°$. The three asymptotes intersect at a point given by substitution of the pole and zero locations in Eq. (4.20):

$$s_1 = \frac{[(0) + (-1 + j) + (-1 - j) + (-3)] - [(-2)]}{4 - 1} \tag{4.28}$$

$$s_1 = -1 \tag{4.29}$$

Thus, the asymptotes are as shown in Fig. 4.11(c).

(6) The sections of the real axis from 0 to -2 and from -3 to $-\infty$ constitute complete loci.† The other two loci, starting from $-1 \pm j1$, are at all times complex and, for large K, tend to infinity along the $\pm 60°$ asymptotes. The root-locus diagram now takes the form shown in part (d) of the figure.

(7) Intersections with the imaginary axis are determined from Routh's test. The polynomial is

$$p(s) + q(s) = s^4 + 5s^3 + 8s^2 + (6 + K)s + 2K \tag{4.30}$$

The first three rows of the Routh table are:

s^4	1	8	$2K$
s^3	5	$6 + K$	
s^2	$34 - K$	$10K$	

The polynomial has imaginary zeros when

$$50K = (6 + K)(34 - K) \tag{4.31}$$

Solution of Eq. (4.34) gives a K of 7.03. The corresponding frequencies at which the loci cross the imaginary axis are $\pm \sqrt{(6 + K)/5}$, or 1.614 rad/sec [Fig. 4.11(e)]. Clearly, if the open-loop transfer function is significantly more complicated than the $G(s)$ of this example, a graphical procedure is desirable for the evaluation of the points at which the loci move into the right-half plane, since the equation analogous to (4.31) becomes undesirably complex.

(8) The angle at which the locus leaves the pole at $-1 + j1$ is given by Eq. (4.21) and is $-26.6°$ [Fig. 4.11(f)].

(9) There is no breakaway from the real axis.

† It is necessary to consider the possibility that the two loci emanating from $-1 \pm j1$ may go to the real axis between 0 and -2 or -3 and $-\infty$. Two loci would then leave the axis at a higher value of gain. With the locations of the real critical frequencies chosen for this example, however, the two loci starting from the complex poles never come close to the real axis. If this is not evident, it can be demonstrated by the remaining steps of this section and a graphical determination of a few points of the loci. In particular, steps (8) and (10) give a strong indication that the complex loci never touch the real axis.

(10)   The sum of the closed-loop poles is the constant value -5, as given by Eq. (4.30).   Since the two loci along the real axis always move from right to left as K is increased, the complex loci must move from left to right, and the form of the over-all diagram can be sketched as indicated in part (g) of the figure.

(11)   The product of the four closed-loop poles is $+2K$.   For the value of K (7.03) when the two complex loci cross the $j\omega$ axis at $\pm j1.614$,

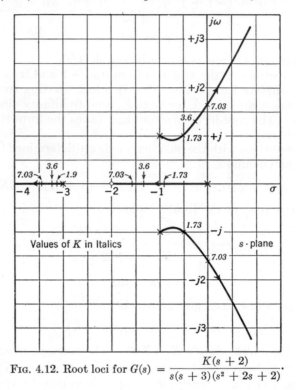

FIG. 4.12. Root loci for $G(s) = \dfrac{K(s+2)}{s(s+3)(s^2+2s+2)}$.

the product of the two real poles must be $2 \times 7.03/(1.614)^2$, or 5.40. The two real poles are, thus, determined from the two equations

$$(-p_1) + (-p_2) = -5 \tag{4.32}$$
$$(-p_1)(-p_2) = 5.40 \tag{4.33}$$

The two poles are at -1.58 and -3.42.

The complete root-locus diagram for this example is shown in Fig. 4.12. After the relationships described above are used to determine the general nature of the loci, graphical analysis permits improvement of the accuracy of the complex loci to any desired degree and, also, the determination of appropriate values of K along the four loci.

Example 3.   The final example of this section demonstrates the problems which arise when a study is desired of the effects of varying system parameters.   The open-loop transfer function considered is

$$G(s) = \frac{20aK_v}{s(s+a)(s^2+4s+20)} \tag{4.34}$$

Here a is a parameter variable from 0.2 to a very large value and K_v is the

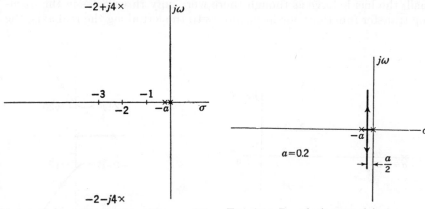

Fig. 4.13. Open-loop poles with $a - 0.2$.   Fig. 4.14. Root loci near origin for

$$G(s) = \frac{4K_v}{s(s+0.2)(s^2+4s+20)}.$$
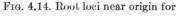

velocity constant.   Root-locus diagrams are to be constructed to portray the effects of varying a.

When a is very small, the open-loop poles are located as shown in Fig. 4.13.   In the region of the s plane very near the origin (*e.g.*, in a circle of radius a), the system appears to have only the two open-loop poles at 0 and $-a$.   The poles at $-2+j4$ are far out in the s plane and, when viewed from the origin, are effectively canceled by two of the zeros at infinity.   The loci, shown in Fig. 4.14, coalesce at approximately $-a/2$, then break away from the real axis normally, as if to follow the vertical line through $-a/2$.   As the gain increases and the loci move away from the real axis, they enter the portion of the plane containing the poles at $-2 \pm j4$.   Then starting to behave as though associated with a fourth-order system, the two loci from 0 and $-a$ break over into the right-half plane to approach

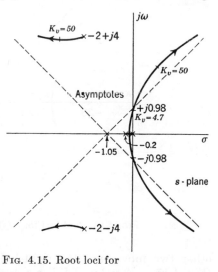

Fig. 4.15. Root loci for

$$G(s) = \frac{4K_v}{s(s+0.2)(s^2+4s+20)}.$$

the $\pm45°$ asymptotes.   Simultaneously, the two loci from $-2 \pm j4$ turn to the left (since the sum of the closed-loop poles is constant) and move toward the $\pm 135°$ asymptotes. The complete diagram is shown in Fig. 4.15 for an a of 0.2.

Figure 4.16 shows the open-loop poles with a very large (compared to $\sqrt{20}$, the distance from the origin to the complex poles). With K_v small, the loci behave as though there were only three poles in the open-loop transfer function: one locus moves to the left along the real axis, the

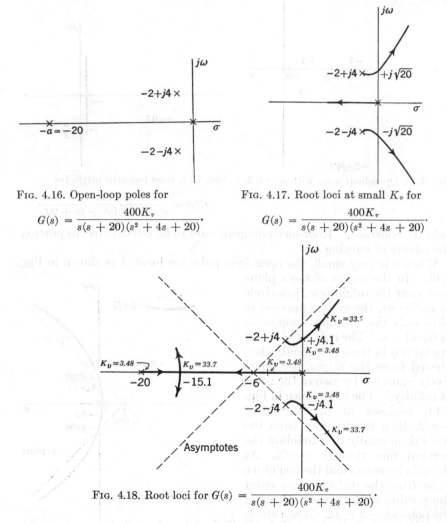

FIG. 4.16. Open-loop poles for
$$G(s) = \frac{400K_v}{s(s + 20)(s^2 + 4s + 20)}.$$

FIG. 4.17. Root loci at small K_v for
$$G(s) = \frac{400K_v}{s(s + 20)(s^2 + 4s + 20)}$$

FIG. 4.18. Root loci for $G(s) = \dfrac{400K_v}{s(s + 20)(s^2 + 4s + 20)}.$

other two move into the right-half plane from the poles at $-2 \pm j4$ (Fig. 4.17). A value of K is reached at which the pole at $-a$ is no longer much farther from the origin than any of the loci, and the locus moving out the real axis meets the fourth locus, with the two then becoming a conjugate complex pair. Figure 4.18 shows the form of the complete diagram.

Thus, for very small values of a, the loci originating from 0 and $-a$ are the ones moving into the right-half plane, while, for large values of a, instability is caused by the motion of the poles starting from $-2 \pm j4$. The transition between the two conditions occurs when a is 4, with the diagram as shown in Fig. 4.19. As a is increased from a very small to a very large value, the loci change as shown by the sequence of Figs. 4.15, 4.19, and 4.18. The apparent order of the system changes from second

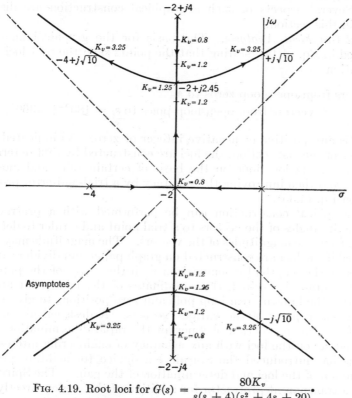

FIG. 4.19. Root loci for $G(s) = \dfrac{80K_v}{s(s+4)(s^2+4s+20)}$.

to fourth to third as the number of poles in the significant part of the s plane is, successively, two, four, and three.

General Comments. The three examples of this section demonstrate the general techniques available for constructing the root loci. On the basis of the simple relationships considered, an approximate picture of the loci can be obtained without any extensive analysis. Refinement of this rough sketch can be effected either by graphical or analytical methods, although ordinarily the graphical approach is easier.

The success of root-locus design depends at the very outset on the ability of the designer to sketch the loci rapidly. As in any design method, the more experienced the engineer, the more efficient use he can make of the analytical tools available. After a few examples, the analyst achieves the ability to picture intuitively the shape of the loci for a wide variety of pole-zero configurations. The previous three examples, combined with the remaining examples of this chapter, are selected in an attempt to give the reader a start toward achieving this very desirable familiarity.

4.3. Graphical Construction of the Loci. As indicated in the last section, the success of the root-locus method is derived from the possibility of plotting the loci from a graphical analysis and with any desired accuracy. Several aspects of such a graphical construction are discussed briefly in this section.

Direct Graphical Analysis. The basis for the graphical analysis is expressed in Eq. (4.12), stating that the points s_j on the root loci satisfy the relation

$$\Sigma / \text{vectors from open-loop zeros to } s_j$$
$$- \Sigma / \text{vectors from open-loop poles to } s_j = 180° + n360° \quad (4.35)$$

Here n is any positive or negative integer or zero. As indicated in the examples of the last section, the loci are constructed by first determining the approximate locations on the basis of certain rules and analytical relations and then improving the accuracy by a trial-and-error procedure based on Eq. (4.35).

The graphical construction can be performed with a protractor to measure the angles of the vectors to a trial point and a ruler to determine the gain from the magnitudes of the vectors. The magnitude may also be measured if the loci are constructed on graph paper and dividers are used to measure the lengths by comparison with the scales of the paper. If greater accuracy is desired, the coordinates of the trial point are combined with the known open-loop pole and zero positions to give the real and imaginary parts of the various vectors. A desk calculator and a table of tan θ as a function of θ permit the rapid determination of particular points on the loci with any accuracy of engineering interest.

Evans has introduced the Spirule,† a device to facilitate graphical construction of the loci and determination of the gain. The Spirule consists of a transparent protractor for addition of the angles directly and a logarithmic spiral for multiplication of the vector lengths to measure gain. The Spirule is particularly convenient if the designer desires to analyze rapidly a very large number of pole-zero configurations; the analytical and graphical techniques described in this chapter suffice if only a few loci are to be drawn. In most cases, the approximate construction of the loci is a rapid process and, in terms of time, a small part of the over-all design.‡

† Available from The Spirule Company, 9728 El Venado, Whittier, California.

‡ The addition of angles and logarithmic magnitudes can also be accomplished electronically for a given pole-zero configuration and a selected point in the s plane. The Complex Plane Analyzer, manufactured by Technology Instrument Corporation and originally designed by A. D. Ehrenfried at MIT, is specifically designed for root-locus construction.

Phase-angle Loci. An alternate method† for the construction of the root loci is based upon the determination of the phase of the forward transfer function (*i.e.*, the negative of the open-loop transfer function) over the entire *s* plane. The total phase is the sum of the individual contributions from each pole and zero. Addition of the components from the various critical frequencies leads to the phase-angle loci, the loci along which the net phase of the forward transfer function, $G(s)$ in Fig. 4.1, is 180°, 170°, 160°, etc. The root loci are only a few of the phase-angle loci, those for angles of $180° + n360°$.

In any simple case, the phase-angle loci are considerably more difficult to construct than the root loci. In more complicated cases, particularly in problems in which the approximate locations of the root loci are not apparent, construction of the phase-angle loci provides a straightforward, logical method of analysis. In addition, the phase-angle loci, including the root loci as one small part, provide significantly more information than is present in the root loci alone. For these reasons, the remainder of this section is devoted to a brief description of the construction and interpretation of the phase-angle loci. The method of construction is illustrated with several simple examples. In each case, the open-loop transfer function is divided into factors sufficiently simple that the corresponding phase-angle loci are known. These various loci are then combined to yield the phase-angle loci for the over-all system.

(1) Single pole. The transfer function considered first has only one pole and no finite zero:

$$G(s) = \frac{K}{s + a} \tag{4.36}$$

The corresponding phase-angle loci are shown in Fig. 4.20. The contours of constant phase are radial lines emanating from the pole at $-a$. If the critical frequency is a zero rather than a pole, the loci are the same but the signs of the angles are changed.

(2) Two poles. The next case in increasing complexity is a transfer function with two finite critical frequencies. If both are poles,

$$G(s) = \frac{K}{(s + a)(s + b)} \tag{4.37}$$

The corresponding phase-angle loci are derived from the relation

$$\underline{/G(s)} = \underline{/\frac{1}{s + a}} + \underline{/\frac{1}{s + b}} \tag{4.38}$$

The total angle at any point is the sum of the two components. The superposition can be effected by plotting the loci of Fig. 4.20 on the same sheet twice, once centered at $-a$, then at $-b$. It is more convenient, however, to plot the loci for a single pole on two sheets of tracing paper. The total phase-angle loci are plotted on a third sheet, placed on top of

† Y. Chu, Synthesis of Feedback Control System by Phase-angle Loci, *Trans. AIEE*, Part II, *Applications and Industry*, Vol. 71, pp. 330–339, 1952.

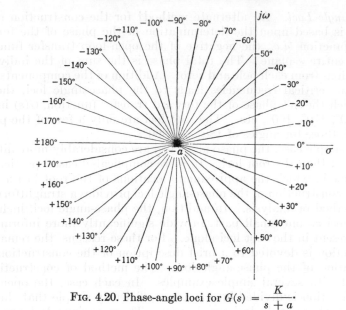

FIG. 4.20. Phase-angle loci for $G(s) = \dfrac{K}{s + a}$.

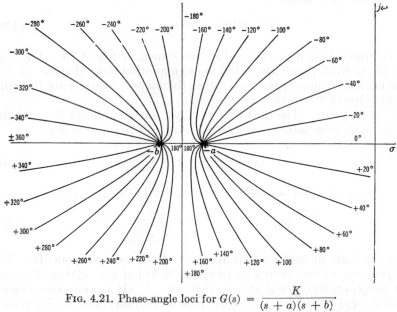

FIG. 4.21. Phase-angle loci for $G(s) = \dfrac{K}{(s + a)(s + b)}$.

the two loci displaced so that the centers lie at $-a$ and $-b$. The exact shape of the loci depends on the separation of the two poles. Figure 4.21 shows the diagram for one possible separation with both poles real. The loci associated with a pair of conjugate complex poles are found by superposing two plots of the form of Fig. 4.20 but with a vertical relative displacement. The result is shown in Fig. 4.22.

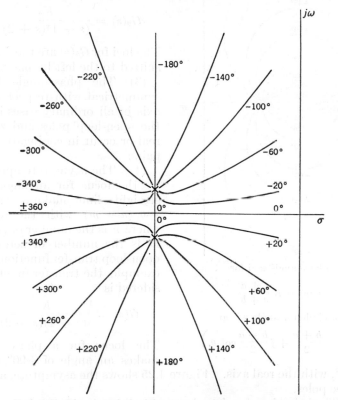

FIG. 4.22. Phase-angle loci for two conjugate complex poles.

(3)   One pole, one zero.   In the same way, the phase-angle loci for one pole and one zero are constructed by graphical superposition of the individual loci.   Figure 4.23 represents the loci in this case.

(4)   Three poles.   The same technique of building up the loci from individual components can be continued. If Figs. 4.20 and 4.21 are combined, with appropriate relative displacements, the plot of Fig. 4.24 results, representing the diagram for a transfer function with three real poles.

The construction of these phase-angle loci is simplified if a few basic relationships are applied:

(1)   The potential analogy described in Sec. 1.3 is useful in visualizing the general shape of the loci.   In terms of this analogy, the phase-angle loci represent the streamlines.

(2) The shape of the phase-angle loci depends only on the relative locations of the open-loop poles and zeros. For example, the loci have the same form for the two transfer functions

$$G_1(s) = \frac{K_1}{s(s+1)} \quad (4.39)$$

$$G_2(s) = \frac{K_2}{(s+1)(s+2)} \quad (4.40)$$

The loci for $G_2(s)$ are those for $G_1(s)$ shifted to the left by one unit.

(3) The phase-angle loci are symmetrical with respect to the σ axis in all ordinary cases in which the open-loop poles and zeros are real or occur in conjugate complex pairs.

(4) The asymptote approached by the locus for an angle θ is a straight line making an angle $-\theta/(n-m)$ with the real axis, where n is the number of poles and m is the number of zeros in the open-loop transfer function. As an example, the transfer function considered is

$$G(s) = \frac{K}{s(s+1)(s+2)} \quad (4.41)$$

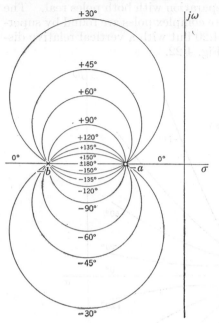

FIG. 4.23. Phase-angle loci for

$$G(s) = K\frac{s+a}{s+b}.$$

(Center of circle for angle θ is at

$$s = -\frac{b+a}{2} + j\frac{b-a}{2}\cot\theta.\Big)$$

The locus for a phase of $-90°$ makes an angle of $+90°/(3-0)$, or $+30°$, with the real axis. Figure 4.25 shows the asymptote, as well as the three poles.

(5) The behavior of a given locus near the poles can be determined by inspection. If the $-90°$ locus for Eq. (4.41) is again considered, the two nonzero poles contribute negligible angles near the pole at the origin; hence, the locus approaches (or leaves) the pole at the origin vertically, as indicated in Fig. 4.26. Near either of the other poles, the zero-frequency pole alone contributes $180°$; consequently, the $-90°$ locus lies entirely to the right of the $j\omega$ axis.†

(6) If extrapolated, the asymptotes all intersect at the point given by the equation

$$s_1 = \frac{\displaystyle\sum_{j=1}^{m} z_j - \sum_{j=1}^{n} p_j}{n-m} \quad (4.42)$$

† In this analysis, the $-450°$ locus is considered distinct from the $-90°$ locus. After the phase-angle loci are constructed, angles of $360°$ can be removed if desired.

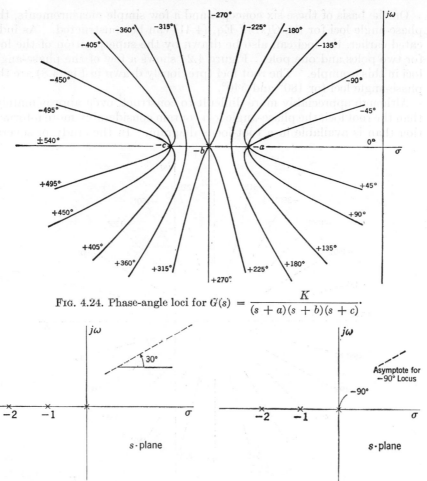

FIG. 4.24. Phase-angle loci for $G(s) = \dfrac{K}{(s+a)(s+b)(s+c)}$.

FIG. 4.25. Asymptote for $-90°$ locus for   FIG. 4.26. Behavior of $-90°$ locus near

$G(s) = \dfrac{K}{s(s+1)(s+2)}$ the origin for $G(s) = \dfrac{K}{s(s+1)(s+2)}$.

Here,

$$G(s) = K \frac{(s+z_1)(s+z_2) \cdots (s+z_m)}{(s+p_1)(s+p_2) \cdots (s+p_n)} \qquad (4.43)$$

That is, the finite zeros are denoted $-z_j$, the poles $-p_j$. For the open-loop transfer function of Eq. (4.41), Eq. (4.42) indicates that the asymptotes originate from the point

$$s_1 = \frac{(0) - (0+1+2)}{3-0} \qquad (4.44)$$

$$s_1 = -1 \qquad (4.45)$$

Hence, the asymptotes are drawn as shown in Fig. 4.27.

On the basis of these six concepts and a few simple measurements, the phase-angle loci for the $G(s)$ of Eq. (4.41) can be constructed. As indicated earlier, the loci can also be drawn by the superposition of the loci for two poles and one pole. Figure 4.24 shows a few of the phase-angle loci in this example. The root loci (previously drawn in Fig. 4.8) are the phase-angle loci for 180° and 540°.

Although appreciably more difficult to construct, even approximately, than the root loci, the phase-angle loci contain considerably more information than is available in a root-locus diagram. In the study of several

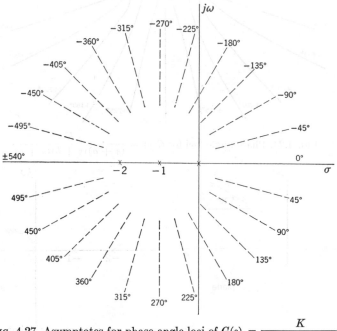

FIG. 4.27. Asymptotes for phase-angle loci of $G(s) = \dfrac{K}{s(s+1)(s+2)}$.

special types of systems, the phase-angle loci are essential: *e.g.*, systems with transportation or distance-velocity lags (Sec. 9.8).

Even in the analysis of an ordinary system with a rational algebraic open-loop transfer function, the phase-angle loci are useful. The most important information available from these loci is the relative effects of gain changes along the various root loci. If the potential analogy is considered again, the equipotential lines (corresponding to contours of constant gain K) are the family of curves orthogonal to the streamlines (analogous to the phase-angle loci). Once the phase-angle loci are constructed, the lines of constant gain can be sketched rapidly and without calculation. In this way, the points on the various root loci corresponding to the same gain can be determined.

Figure 4.28 shows a few of the phase-angle loci for the open-loop transfer function

$$G(s) = \frac{K}{s(s + 1)(s + 2)} \qquad (4.46)$$

The gain corresponding to a closed-loop pole at -2.5 is readily determined from the fact that $G(-2.5)$ is equal to -1. Accordingly,

$$K_{-2.5} = 2.5(-2.5 + 1)(-2.5 + 2) \qquad (4.47)$$
$$K_{-2.5} = 1.875 \qquad (4.48)$$

The corresponding points on the other two loci are found by drawing a contour starting from -2.5 and orthogonal to each of the phase-angle

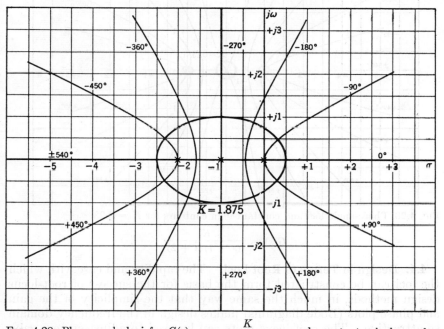

Fig. 4.28. Phase-angle loci for $G(s) = \dfrac{K}{s(s + 1)(s + 2)}$ and constant-gain locus for $K = 1.875$.

loci. Even the few loci shown permit approximate construction of this constant-gain contour, shown in Fig. 4.28. The intersections with the other loci occur at $-0.25 \pm j0.83$.

When the constant-gain contour is in separate parts, at least one point on each part must be determined, and it is more difficult to locate accurately the corresponding points on the various root loci. In such a case, more of the phase-angle loci are required. Figure 4.29 shows the contours for a gain of 0.23 and the same open-loop transfer function previously considered.

Thus, the graphical techniques of construction, and in particular the phase-angle loci, provide the possibility of extending the root-locus plot to obtain a more complete picture of system behavior. The question of whether the work involved in construction of the phase-angle loci is warranted depends on the accuracy desired in the theoretical design. The general concepts associated with the phase-angle loci are important, because, even if the loci are visualized only approximately, the constant-gain contours can often be sketched roughly to indicate the approximate location of corresponding points on the various root loci.

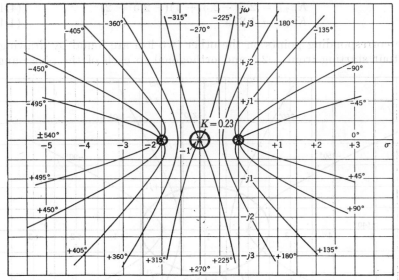

FIG. 4.29. Phase-angle loci and constant-gain contours for $K = 0.23$.

$$G(s) = \frac{K}{s(s+1)(s+2)}.$$

4.4. Design in Terms of Root Loci.　The rapidity and ease with which the loci can be constructed form the basis for the success of root-locus design methods, in much the same way that the simplicity of the gain and phase plots (Bode diagrams) makes design in the frequency domain so attractive.　The root-locus plots can be used to adjust system gain, guide the design of compensation networks, or study the effects of changes in system parameters.

Adjustment of Gain.　The most elementary problem in the design of feedback control systems is the determination of the gain to yield suitable relative stability.　The root-locus diagram places in evidence at once the effect of gain variation on both transient and frequency responses.　The gain can be adjusted to give appropriate dynamic performance as measured by the relative damping ratio associated with a pair of conjugate complex poles or by the significant time constants of the system response. If the diagram is viewed as a picture of loci of variable gain, the problem of gain adjustment is solved directly.

Tandem Compensation.　The transfer functions of appropriate tandem compensation networks can be determined from the root-locus diagram. A simple example, illustrating the general approach, is provided by consideration of a controlled system with the transfer function

$$G_2(s) = \frac{1}{s(s^2 + 2s + 2)} \tag{4.49}$$

A tandem network, with transfer function $G_1(s)$, is to be inserted as in Fig. 4.30 to give an over-all closed-loop system meeting the specifications

$$K_v \geq 10/\text{sec} \tag{4.50}$$

Overshoot of step-function response $< 30\%$ \hfill (4.51)

Before various compensation schemes are considered, it is advantageous to obtain an estimate of the extent of the difficulties presented by the specifications. For example, is a velocity constant of 10 an order of magnitude larger than that realizable by a flat gain in the tandem system,

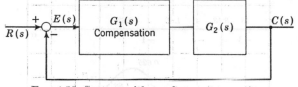

FIG. 4.30. System with tandem compensation.

with the flat gain adjusted to give appropriate overshoot? If $G_1(s)$ is simply K_1, the forward transfer function is

$$G(s) = \frac{K_1}{s(s^2 + 2s + 2)} \tag{4.52}$$

The root loci for the uncompensated system are sketched in Fig. 4.31.

Interpretation of the root loci requires a few specific values of gain and an estimate of the relative locations of the real and complex poles. Routh's test indicates that the system is absolutely unstable for all values of K_1 larger than 4, or K_v larger than 2. Corresponding points on the various loci are readily determined if a point on the real locus is assumed. When the corresponding linear factor is removed from the characteristic polynomial, a quadratic results. For example, when the real pole is at -1, the complex poles are the zeros of $s^2 + s + 1$, and the corresponding value of K_1 is unity ($K_v = 0.5$). Figure 1.22 shows that the corresponding overshoot is less than 2 per cent. When the real pole is at -1.5, the complex poles are the zeros of $s^2 + 0.5s + 1.25$ (an ω_n of about 1.118, a ζ of approximately 0.224), and the associated K_1 is 1.875. The overshoot in this case is approximately 37 per cent. An overshoot of about 30 per cent is realized by a system with K_1 approximately equal to 1.6, or with a velocity constant roughly 0.8. Since these initial considerations are directed at obtaining a picture of the scope of the problem, there is no need for accurate calculations of either the root loci or the overshoot as a function of gain. Without any significant work, it is clear that the compensation network must increase the velocity constant by a factor of about 12 without changing the overshoot.

Integral Compensation. Integral, derivative, and cancellation compensation are the three simple types of compensation which are normally considered before more complex schemes are investigated. The simplest procedure for boosting the velocity constant without adversely affecting

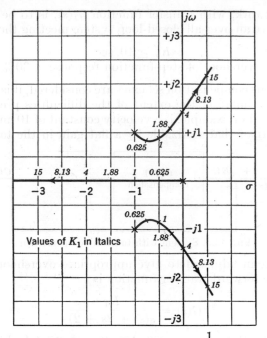

FIG. 4.31. Root-locus diagram for $G(s) = K_1 \dfrac{1}{s(s^2 + 2s + 2)}$ and $K_1 = 2K_v$.

the relative stability involves the insertion of lag or integral compensation. The transfer function of the tandem network is selected as

$$G_1(s) = K_1 \frac{s + k\alpha}{s + \alpha} \tag{4.53}$$

$1/\alpha$ is the larger time constant and k the ratio of the time constants. In general, α and $k\alpha$, the distances of the integrating pole and zero from the origin in the s plane, are chosen small compared to the distances of the other nonzero critical frequencies of the open-loop transfer function, in order that the dipole† may not contribute significant phase lag in the vicinity of the feedback cutoff frequency.

The effect of the dipole is indicated by the root-locus diagrams of Fig. 4.32. The dashed curve represents the complex loci for $K_1G_2(s)$ alone; the solid curve represents the loci for $G_1(s)G_2(s)$, where $G_1(s)$ takes the

† The pole and zero introduced in the open-loop transfer function by the addition of integral compensation are termed a dipole because, from the region of the s plane of interest in the stability analysis (the region in the vicinity of the open-loop poles at $-1 \pm j1$), the pole and zero appear very close together.

form of Eq. (4.53) with an α of 0.01 and a k of 15. If the integrating dipole is added near the origin, the loci in the vicinity of $-1 + j1$ are not changed significantly, since from these points the two poles and the zero near the origin seem to merge into a single simple pole. The open-loop

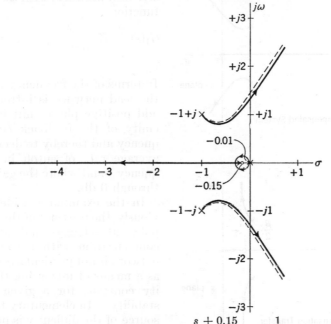

FIG. 4.32. Root loci for $G(s) = K_1 \dfrac{s + 0.15}{s + 0.01} \dfrac{1}{s(s^2 + 2s + 2)}$.

transfer function is now

$$G_1(s)G_2(s) = K_1 \frac{s + k\alpha}{s + \alpha} \frac{1}{s(s^2 + 2s + 2)} \tag{4.54}$$

Thus, although the loci are unchanged around $-1 \pm j1$, the velocity constant corresponding to a given K_1 is

$$K_v = K_1 \frac{k}{2} \tag{4.55}$$

Accordingly, the velocity constant is increased by the multiplicative factor k. In this example, K_v must be multiplied by about 12 to meet the specifications. Consequently, the time-constant ratio of the integrating dipole should be chosen to be at least 12, preferably 15 to allow the dipole to contribute a slight phase lag in the vicinity of cutoff.

This slight phase lag is desirable to avoid the necessity of making α excessively small, with the attendant difficulties of synthesizing the network with practical element sizes. The exact location of the dipole (i.e., the precise value of α) is not critical. As α is increased, the loci begin to change as indicated in Fig. 4.32, where the loci originating at $-1 \pm j1$ are shifted in toward the origin slightly. Thus, it is desirable to select an α less than approximately 0.01.

Lead Compensation. A second possibility for simple compensation is available in the conventional passive lead network, with the transfer function

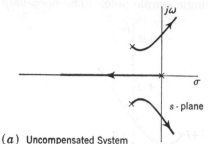

(a) **Uncompensated System**

$$G_1(s) = K_1 \frac{s + \beta}{s + n\beta} \qquad n > 1$$

(4.56)

In terms of the frequency response, the lead network is introduced to add positive phase shift in the vicinity of the feedback cutoff frequency and thereby to decrease the average rate of cutoff in the frequency band where the gain passes through 0 db.

In the example considered previously, the presence of the complex poles at $-1 \pm j1$ indicates that compensation with a simple lead network is not particularly effective as a means of increasing the velocity constant for a given relative stability. In elementary texts, the source of the difficulty is portrayed in the gain and phase plots, where the rapid change of the phase of $G(j\omega)$ through $-180°$ (resulting from the complex open-loop poles) means that a simple lead network, with a maximum positive shift of less than $90°$ regardless of the time-constant ratio, can increase the bandwidth (or velocity constant) only slightly.

The root-locus plots demonstrate the difficulties in a somewhat different manner. Figure 4.33 shows the root loci of the uncompensated open-loop system and the effects of a simple lead network. Part (b) of

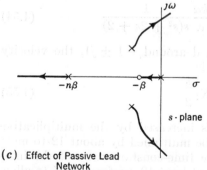

(b) **Compensation Transfer Function, $K_1(s+\beta)$**

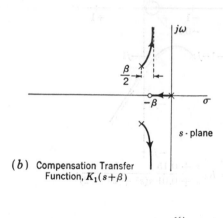

(c) **Effect of Passive Lead Network**

FIG. 4.33. Effect of lead compensation.

the figure shows the loci in the extreme case when the time-constant ratio of the lead transfer function is very high and the compensation behaves as an ideal proportional-plus-derivative network. Even in this idealized situation, the introduction of the simple zero at $-\beta$ can only prevent the closed-loop poles from moving into the right-half plane; regardless of the gain, the relative damping ratio of the complex closed-loop poles is never significantly higher than that of the open-loop poles. If a passive lead network is used [part (c) of the figure], the addition of the lead pole and zero results in complex loci which bend upward before they turn toward the right-half plane. The lead compensation results in only a slight increase in the velocity constant.

If the original poles are distributed along the negative real axis, the simple lead transfer function is more effective in compensation. As shown in Fig. 4.34, for an original system with three real poles, the introduction of a real zero stabilizes the system. Even with the pole of the lead transfer function included, the complex loci turn to the left as they break away from the real axis if the time-constant ratio of the lead network is sufficiently large to make the system, in the vicinity of this break-away, appear to be characterized by only three poles.

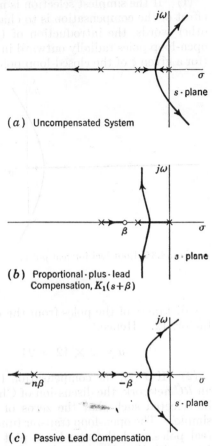

(a) Uncompensated System

(b) Proportional - plus - lead Compensation, $K_1(s+\beta)$

(c) Passive Lead Compensation

Fig. 4.34. Effect of lead compensation if all original poles real.

Cancellation Compensation. The ineffectiveness of simple lead compensation of the open-loop transfer function containing conjugate complex poles, an ineffectiveness which is particularly pronounced if the relative damping ratio of the complex poles is small, suggests the use of a compensation transfer function with two zeros and two poles. On a theoretical basis, the simplest functions of this type have zeros which cancel the poles of the transfer function of the controlled system. In the example considered previously, the resulting open-loop system is still third-order and

$$G(s) = K_1 \underbrace{\frac{s^2 + 2s + 2}{s^2 + as + b}}_{G_1(s)} \underbrace{\frac{1}{s(s^2 + 2s + 2)}}_{G_2(s)} \qquad (4.57)$$

Compensation cancels the poles of $G_2(s)$ and inserts new poles at more advantageous locations in the s plane.

Selection of appropriate values for a and b is governed by the complete specifications, which might restrict such performance characteristics as the bandwidth, the shape of the closed-loop frequency response, the sensitivity of the system transfer function to changes in parameters, etc. In the particular example outlined above, where the only specifications are on the velocity constant and the overshoot of the step-function response, a variety of values for a and b can be used.

(1) If the simplest selection is made, a and b are chosen such that the effect of the compensation is to change the frequency normalization. In other words, the introduction of the compensation network moves the open-loop poles radially outward in the s plane. If the velocity constant (for a given ζ of the closed-loop poles) is to be increased by a factor of 12,

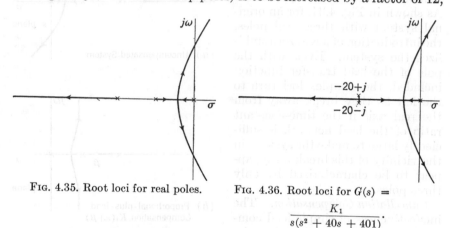

FIG. 4.35. Root loci for real poles.   FIG. 4.36. Root loci for $G(s) =$
$$\frac{K_1}{s(s^2 + 40s + 401)}.$$

the distances of the poles from the origin must be increased by the same factor, 12. Hence,

$$a = 2 \times 12 = 24 \qquad b = 2 \times (12)^2 = 288 \qquad (4.58)$$

(2) If $G_1(s)$, the compensation transfer function, is to be realized by an RC network, the discussion of Chap. 3 demonstrates that a and b must be selected such that the zeros of $s^2 + as + b$ are negative, real, and simple. The open-loop transfer function [Eq. (4.57)] then possesses three real poles, and the root-locus plot takes the form shown in Fig. 4.35. Even with these restrictions, a and b can be varied over wide ranges.

(3) Alternatively, the compensation might be used to move the poles horizontally to the left, in which case a suitable $G_1(s)$ is

$$G_1(s) = K_1 \frac{s^2 + 2s + 2}{s^2 + 40s + 401} \qquad (4.59)$$

The corresponding root-locus diagram is shown in Fig. 4.36, demonstrating that the closed-loop system (for K_1 large enough to make K_v about 10) is behaving as a second-order system. In terms of the root loci, there is no significant difference between this choice of a and b and the selection of (2), where a and b result in real zeros of $s^2 + as + b$. Translation of the complex poles to the left results in a change in the form of the diagram.

with all closed-loop poles real for a range of values of K_1. Determination of the required extent of translation can be effected by a trial-and-error procedure in a few steps. It is clear that the real part (originally at -1) must be made larger than -12 if the velocity constant is to be increased by the factor 12. Actually, the exact amount of the shift is not critical, since the specifications are at best only general guides to desired system behavior. It is largely immaterial whether the K_v realized is 8, 10, or 12.

The particular scheme used to locate the poles of $G_1(s)$ depends on other specifications not considered here or the form desired for the compensation network. If this network is RC, the synthesis procedures of Chap. 3 can be used for the determination of a suitable network. If the transfer function of Eq. (4.59) is selected, the compensation network must involve at least one inductance. The basic principles of synthesis presented in the last chapter can be extended to this case, or a suitable network can be found by inspection. For example, if both numerator and denominator of $G_1(s)$ are divided by s,

$$G_1(s) - K_1 \frac{s + 2 + (2/s)}{s + 40 + (401/s)} \quad (4.60)$$

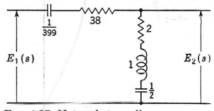

FIG. 4.37. Network to realize
$$\frac{E_2}{E_1}(s) = \frac{s + 2 + (2/s)}{s + 40 + (401/s)}.$$
(Values in ohms, henrys, farads.)

The frequency-dependent part of $G_1(s)$ can be recognized as the voltage ratio of the network shown in Fig. 4.37; the constant multiplier K_1 is realized by amplifiers independent of frequency over the band of interest.

More General Compensation. The cancellation compensation described above does not furnish a completely satisfactory solution to the design problem. The requirement of exact cancellation is frequently wasteful of amplifier gain, and the resulting compensation network often involves undesirable element sizes or an excessive complexity. These disadvantages can often be overcome if more general compensation schemes are considered.

Cancellation compensation is a particular form of generalized lead compensation, with the two lead zeros specified at the outset of the design. The root loci clearly show that there is no necessity to cancel the poles of $G_2(s)$ exactly. For example, the two loci of Fig. 4.38 correspond to essentially the same performance characteristics. The additional closed-loop pole and zero of part (b) of the figure are generated by the inexact cancellation. These two critical frequencies, however, do not contribute significantly to either transient or frequency response.

If the generalization of cancellation compensation is carried one step further, it is clear that all cancellation restrictions on the two compensation zeros may be relaxed. In terms of the example previously considered, poles and zeros are introduced to modify the locus of Fig. 4.39(a) to a more suitable form; any location of the critical frequencies which accomplishes this end can be considered. Figure 4.39(b), for example, indicates that two real zeros and two real poles can be used if the time-constant ratios are sufficiently large. In this figure, the two loci originating at $-1 \pm j1$ are drawn to the left and then downward toward the real axis by the presence of the two real zeros. Whether these loci actu-

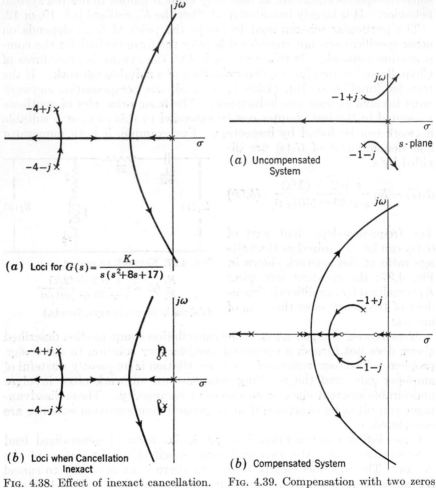

(a) Loci for $G(s) = \dfrac{K_1}{s(s^2 + 8s + 17)}$

(b) Loci when Cancellation Inexact

FIG. 4.38. Effect of inexact cancellation.

(a) Uncompensated System

(b) Compensated System

FIG. 4.39. Compensation with two zeros and two poles. (Not drawn to scale.)

ally reach the axis, as shown in the figure, or only head in this direction before turning back again toward the right-half plane is determined by the locations of the added zeros and poles, but in either case the compensation critical frequencies tend to improve stability or admit a larger velocity constant with the same relative stability.

Thus, in the determination of compensation transfer functions, the root-locus method gives essentially the same freedom as the frequency-domain techniques. With a given transfer function for the controlled system, a wide variety of suitable transfer functions for the tandem compensation network can be derived if the specifications determine only the error constants and the relative stability.   The essential advantages of the root-locus method are based on the presentation of information about the transient response as well as the frequency response.   With a knowledge of the positions of the poles and zeros of the closed-loop transfer function, the designer can determine at once the significant characteristics of the system performance in the time domain.

Final Example.   One final example illustrates the application of the root-locus methods of analysis.   The effect of quadratic lead compensation is considered, when the transfer function of the controlled system is

$$G_2(s) = \frac{K}{s(s^2 + 3.2s + 3.56)} \tag{4.61}$$

The compensation network to be considered has the transfer function

$$G_1(s) = \frac{(s + 1)^2}{(s + 8)(s + 20)} \tag{4.62}$$

Although the compensation as indicated is not particularly effective as a means of increasing the velocity constant for a given relative stability, it does result in increases in bandwidth and speed of response.   Of more importance here, however, the example serves to illustrate the interpretation of the root loci.

Figure 4.40(a) shows the open-loop pole-zero configuration, with simple poles at 0, $-1.6 \pm j1$, -8, and -20 and a double zero at -1. The root loci are sketched in the manner outlined in Sec. 4.2.   For the initial stages of the following analysis, an accurate root-locus diagram is not required, and the rough sketch of Fig. 4.40(b), which can be drawn in large part by inspection, suffices as the starting point.   At a later point in the analysis, the specific sections of the loci which are of particular interest are determined in more detail.

Certain characteristics of the system are at once apparent from the root loci even though the corresponding positions of the poles along the various loci are unknown:

(1)   The step-function response of the system contains a long-duration component (a long tail) as a result of the closed-loop pole on the negative real axis between 0 and -1.   The component amplitude, equal to the residue at this pole in the Laplace transform of the step-function response, depends primarily on the distance between this pole and the double zero at -1.   With the response transform possessing the poles and zeros shown in Fig. 4.40(c), the residue, calculated from the vectors from all other critical frequencies to the pole in question, is always negative, with the result that the long tail tends to be stabilizing, decreasing the overshoot and making the system more sluggish.

(2)   As a result of the closed-loop pole between -1 and -8, there is another real exponential in the step-function response.   Since the corresponding residue is positive, this term tends to counteract the effect of the long-duration term during the first part of the transient.

(3) In the closed-loop step-function response, there is one term with a time constant less than $\frac{1}{20}$ sec. For all practical purposes, this component can be neglected.

(4) If the gain is sufficiently high that the two real poles and the double zero at -1 approximately cancel, the primary characteristics of the transient response are governed by the two conjugate complex poles of the closed-loop system function. These two poles are termed the control poles, because of their importance in fixing

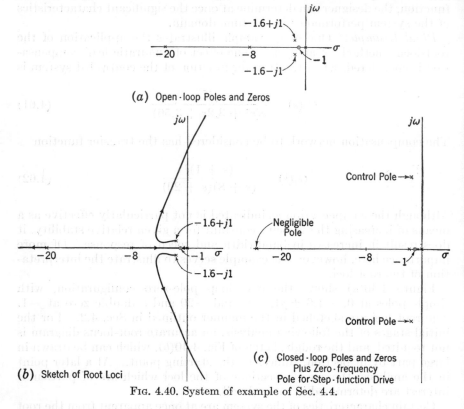

(a) Open-loop Poles and Zeros

(b) Sketch of Root Loci

(c) Closed-loop Poles and Zeros Plus Zero-frequency Pole for-Step-function Drive

FIG. 4.40. System of example of Sec. 4.4.

performance characteristics. The overshoot of the step-function response is somewhat less than the value indicated by the ζ of these complex poles as a result of the stabilizing long-duration component.

A more detailed analysis of the significant characteristics of the transient response for any specified gain or as a function of the gain requires the determination of corresponding points on the various loci. In other words, for a given gain, where are the five closed-loop poles? Or, for a value of gain corresponding to one pole at a particular point, where are the other four poles? In particular, a typical design problem might be: For a given overshoot of the closed-loop step-function response, what value of gain should be used and what is the corresponding transient response?

The significance of these questions is illustrated by a specific numerical investigation of part of the root-locus diagram of Fig. 4.40(b). Since the overshoot is reduced by the long-duration component of the step-function response, a rather small ζ is used for the conjugate complex closed-loop poles. A ζ of 0.316 (corresponding to the closed-loop poles at an angle θ, as shown in Fig. 4.41, where θ is arctan 3) corresponds to an overshoot of about 36 per cent (see Fig. 1.18) when the closed-loop system function has only the two poles. It is not unreasonable to anticipate that this value of 36 per cent is reduced to less than 25 per cent by the stabilizing effect introduced by the other poles and zeros. Hence, the points at which the complex loci cross the lines for $\zeta = 0.316$ are investigated in more detail.

Figure 4.42 indicates that these intersections occur at approximately $-2.61 \pm j7.83$. Again in the evaluation of these points, exact calculations are not particularly important;† a short trial-and-error procedure with a protractor suffices to determine the points along the lines AB of Fig. 4.42 at which the net phase angle contributed by the five open-loop poles and the double zero is 180°. Likewise, the lengths of the vectors from the open-loop critical frequencies to $-2.61 + j7.83$ can be found with a ruler.

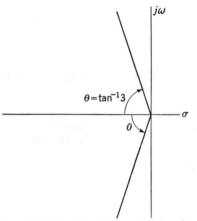

Fig. 4.41. Location of complex closed-loop poles.

From the six vectors shown in Fig. 4.43,

$$K = \frac{8.25 \times 6.90 \times 8.89 \times 9.51 \times 19.07}{(7.99)^2} = 1438 \qquad (4.63)$$

The other closed-loop poles for the same K are now determined. The pole on the negative real axis between 0 and -1 is found most readily by a trial-and-error procedure. Since the predominant factor in determining this pole is the length of the vector from the double zero at -1, two steps of trial and error ordinarily suffice. For example, if a value -0.7 is assumed, the corresponding K is

$$K = \frac{0.7 \times 7.3 \times 19.3 \times \sqrt{1.81} \times \sqrt{1.81}}{(0.3)^2} \qquad (4.64)$$

$$K = 1983 \qquad (4.65)$$

The numerator factors in the right side of Eq. (4.64) represent the magnitudes of the vectors from the five open-loop poles to -0.7; the denomi-

---

† The three significant figures used in locating the poles and throughout the remainder of this example represent an accuracy which is excessive for the usual design problem, where the specifications and equipment characteristics are often known only very approximately. The accuracy is carried through this example to illustrate the possibility of utilizing the root-locus approach even when very accurate calculations are required.

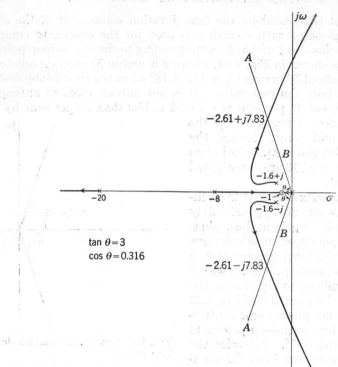

FIG. 4.42. Root loci and complex closed-loop poles with $\zeta = 0.316$.

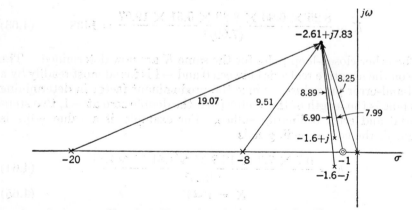

FIG. 4.43. Vector lengths for evaluating K.

nator factor, the vector from the double zero at -1. Since the numerator factors are nearly constant if the value of -0.7 is changed slightly, the proper value for a K of 1438 can be determined from the equation

$$\frac{(1 + x)^2}{(0.3)^2} = \frac{1983}{1438} \tag{4.66}$$

Here, x is the closed-loop pole for a gain of 1438. Solution of Eq. (4.66) gives

$$x = -0.648 \qquad (4.67)$$

This value of x can be checked by calculating the corresponding gain.

In the same manner, the closed-loop pole between -1 and -8 is evaluated as -1.352. The pole to the left of -20 can be neglected, and the resulting closed-loop system function is

$$\frac{C}{R}(s) = \frac{59.7(s + 1)^2}{(s + 0.648)(s + 1.352)(s^2 + 5.22s + 68.1)} \qquad (4.68)$$

The factor 59.7, used to make $\dfrac{C}{R}(0)$ equal to unity, is not the gain, 1438,

because the pole to the left of -20 is not included in Eq. (4.68).†

The corresponding transient response can now be evaluated by consideration of Fig. 4.44, the pole-zero configuration for the closed-loop system function. The following characteristics of the step-function response can be deduced directly, without calculating the exact inverse transform.

(1) The time constant of the primary component of the transient response is $1/2.61$, or 0.383 sec.

(2) The time required for this primary component of the output to reach the first maximum is $\pi/7.83$, or approximately 0.4 sec.

(3) If just the two complex poles were present in $\dfrac{C}{R}(s)$, the overshoot of the step-function response would be 36 per cent. The contribution of the two complex poles of the actual system function to the overshoot is somewhat different than 36 per cent as a result of the fact that the presence of the other poles and zeros of $\dfrac{C}{R}(s)$ affects both the magnitude and phase of the resi-due of $\dfrac{1}{s}\dfrac{C}{R}(s)$ in the pole at $-2.61 + j7.83$.

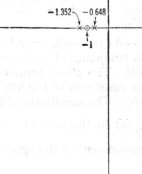

FIG. 4.44. Closed-loop poles and zeros.

These changes can be determined graphically as shown in Fig. 4.45. The

† The pole outside -20 can be found readily if desired, since it is at $-1438/59.7$, or -24.1.

residue is changed by the factor

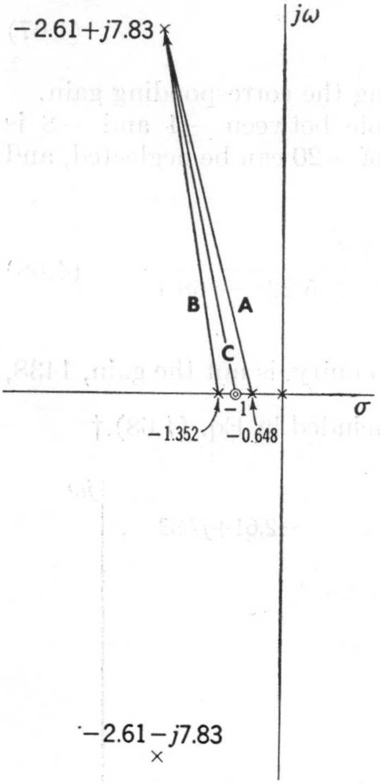

$$\frac{k_{-2.61+j7.83}}{k'_{-2.61+j7.83}} = (0.648)(1.352)\frac{\mathbf{C}^2}{\mathbf{AB}} \quad (4.69)$$

where $k_{-2.61+j7.83}$ = residue of $\dfrac{1}{s}\dfrac{C}{R}(s)$ in the pole at $-2.61 + j7.83$

$k'_{-2.61+j7.83}$ = residue of

$$\frac{1}{s}\frac{68.1}{s^2 + 5.22s + 68.1} \text{ in}$$

the pole at $-2.61 + j7.83$

$\mathbf{A}$, $\mathbf{B}$, and $\mathbf{C}$ = vectors shown in Fig. 4.45

$(0.648)(1.352)$ = a factor introduced because $\dfrac{C}{R}(s)$ of Eq. (4.68) has a multiplying factor of 59.7 rather than 68.1

Substitution of the values of $\mathbf{A}$, $\mathbf{B}$, and $\mathbf{C}$, as determined graphically from Fig. 4.45, yields

$$\frac{k_{-2.61+j7.83}}{k'_{-2.61+j7.83}} = 0.85\underline{/0°} \quad (4.70)$$

FIG. 4.45. Vectors for evaluating change in residue at $-2.61 + j7.83$.

Hence, the overshoot introduced by the damped sinusoid is reduced to $0.85 \times 36 = 31$ per cent, even before the decrease resulting from the long-duration component is considered.

(4) The other, exponential terms of the step-function response have time constants of $1/0.648 = 1.54$ sec and $1/1.352 = 0.740$ sec.

(5) The amplitude of the long-duration term is simply the residue of $\dfrac{1}{s}\dfrac{C}{R}(s)$ in the pole at -0.648 and can be found from Eq. (4.68) and measurement of the appropriate vectors:

$$k_{-0.648} = 59.7\frac{(0.352)^2}{(-0.648)(0.704)(8.07\underline{/-75.9°})(8.07\underline{/+75.9°})} \quad (4.71)$$

$$k_{-0.648} = -0.25 \quad (4.72)$$

(6) The amplitude of the term in $e^{-1.352t}$ is the residue of $\dfrac{1}{s}\dfrac{C}{R}(s)$ in the pole at -1.352. Evaluation of the five vectors gives

$$k_{-1.352} = +0.12 \quad (4.73)$$

(7) The total response is the sum of four terms: a step function, a damped sinusoid, and the two exponentials. The total overshoot is determined roughly as follows: it was shown in (2) above that the peak value of the response occurs at approximately 0.4 sec. At this time, the sum of the two exponential terms is approximately the same as at $t = 0$; hence, because of the exponential terms, the overshoot is reduced by slightly more than $25 - 12$ or 13 per cent. Accordingly, the overshoot of the over-all response is slightly less than 18 per cent, and the maximum value occurs about 0.4 sec after initiation of the transient.

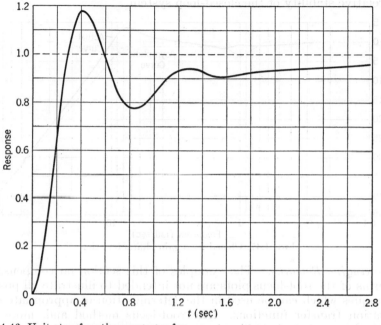

Fig. 4.46. Unit-step-function response for

$$\frac{C}{R}(s) = \frac{59.7(s + 1)^2}{(s + 0.648)(s + 1.352)(s^2 + 5.22s + 68.1)}.$$

(8) The over-all transient response can be sketched, as shown in Fig. 4.46. Clearly, the response in this example has been determined in considerably more detail than is ordinarily required in the design of feedback control systems. In most cases, evaluation of corresponding points on the root loci, and hence of the set of closed-loop poles, is sufficient to indicate the general nature of the transient response within the accuracy required for design. The detailed analysis of this example is presented to illustrate the type of information which can be drawn from the root-locus plots with essentially no laborious calculations.

Once the closed-loop poles are determined, the closed-loop frequency response can be sketched with the asymptotic plots.† Alternatively, the

† A brief discussion of the asymptotic gain-frequency plots is given in Sec. 6.4. More detailed presentations can be found in standard servo texts: e.g., G. S. Brown

gain and phase characteristics can be determined graphically as described in Sec. 1.2. For the above example, with $\dfrac{C}{R}$ (s) given by Eq. (4.68), the gain characteristic is shown in Fig. 4.47. The very slight dip in the characteristic in the vicinity of 0.7 rad/sec indicates the long tail in the response, while the dip near 1.5 rad/sec represents the partially compensating effect of the term $+0.12e^{-1.352t}$. The M_p of 3.8 db (or the amplitude ratio of 1.55), corresponding to a second-order system with a ζ of 0.34 or an overshoot of 33 per cent, is not particularly indicative of the relative stability of the closed-loop system.

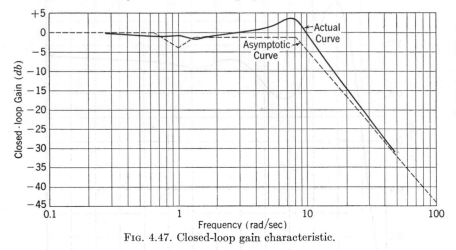

Fig. 4.47. Closed-loop gain characteristic.

Concluding Remarks. The examples of this section on compensation in terms of the root-locus plots are not intended to illustrate all possible techniques which can be used in the determination of appropriate compensation transfer functions. The root-locus method and, more generally, the concept of working in terms of the pole and zero positions in the complex plane afford powerful techniques for design, because one picture of the poles and zeros presents the salient characteristics of both transient and frequency responses.

4.5. Other Uses of the Root-locus Method. The root loci constitute a graphical method for the approximate determination of the zeros of a polynomial. In the analysis of the single-loop feedback system of Fig. 4.48, the root-locus plot permits the evaluation of the zeros of $p(s) + q(s)$, where $p(s)$ and $q(s)$ are the polynomials forming the numerator and denominator, respectively, of the forward transfer function. The zeros of $p(s) + q(s)$ are located from the known zeros of the individual components $p(s)$ and $q(s)$. The root-locus method, including the rules and

and D. P. Campbell, "Principles of Servomechanisms," Chap. 8, John Wiley & Sons, Inc., New York, 1948; or H. Chestnut and R. W. Mayer, "Servomechanisms and Regulating System Design," Vol. I, Chap. 11, John Wiley & Sons, Inc., New York, 1951.

techniques for determining the loci, is useful in a variety of analysis problems, some quite distinct from the design of feedback systems.

Factoring Polynomials. In a variety of situations, the root-locus method can be applied in the approximate determination of the zeros of a polynomial. In particular, the root-locus approach provides a useful adjunct to conventional procedures (*e.g.*, Lin's method), for the rapid convergence of these more accurate methods often depends on the selection of a first approximation which is reasonably close to the correct value.

One example suffices to illustrate the application of the root-locus method. The polynomial selected is

$$p(s) = s^5 + 5s^4 + 11s^3 + 14s^2 + 10s + 4 \qquad (4.74)$$

The zeros of $p(s)$ can be found either by Lin's method† or by a combination of Horner's method and Routh's test. In the latter approach, the zeros are shifted to the right in the complex plane until Routh's test reveals one or more zeros on the imaginary axis. The Routh table also indicates the location of imaginary zeros. These zeros are then removed, and the procedure is repeated with the reduced polynomial. In the case of Eq. (4.74), the following steps are used:

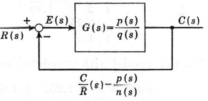

FIG. 4.48. Single-loop system.

(1) The Routh test is used to determine if $p(s)$ is Hurwitz (*i.e.*, if all zeros are in the left-half plane):

s^5	1	11	10
s^4	~~5~~	~~14~~	~~4~~
	1	2.8	0.8
s^3	~~8.2~~	~~9.2~~	
	1	1.12	
s^2	~~1.68~~	~~0.8~~	
	1	0.476	
s^1	~~0.644~~		
	1		
s^0	~~0.476~~		
	1		

Here, each row is divided by the number required to make the first entry unity, and, since the number of zeros in the right-half plane is not of interest, the table is formed only until a minus sign appears. In most

† G. S. Brown and D. P. Campbell, *op. cit.*, pp. 89–91.

cases, no more than slide-rule accuracy is required unless zeros are very close to the $j\omega$ axis. The above table indicates that $p(s)$ is Hurwitz.

(2)   The sum of the five zeros is -5, and all zeros are in the left-half plane. Hence, unless there are five zeros with a real part of -1, there must be at least one zero with a real part between 0 and -1. The zeros are moved to the right by an amount 0.75 in order to determine whether there are any zeros between $\sigma = 0$ and $\sigma = -0.75$. This translation to the right is accomplished by Horner's method:

1	5	11	14	10	4	$\underline{\smash{0.75}}$
	0.75	3.188	5.86	6.11	2.92	
1	4.25	7.812	8.14	3.89	1.08	
	0.75	2.625	3.89	3.19		
1	3.5	5.19	4.25	0.70		
	0.75	2.06	2.35			
1	2.75	3.13	1.90			
	0.75	1.50				
1	2	1.63				
	0.75					
1	1.25					

The polynomial with translated zeros is

$$p_1(s) = s^5 + 1.25s^4 + 1.63s^3 + 1.90s^2 + 0.70s + 1.08 \qquad (4.75)$$

(3)   The Routh test is applied to $p_1(s)$:

s^5	1	1.63	0.70
s^4	~~1.25~~	~~1.90~~	~~1.08~~
	1	1.52	0.86
s^3	0.11	-0.16	

Since a minus sign appears, formation of the table can be stopped at this point with the knowledge that $p_1(s)$ is not Hurwitz. The shift of 0.75 is too large and a smaller translation must be used.

(4)   The original polynomial is reconsidered, and the zeros are shifted to the right by an amount 0.5.

1	5	11	14	10	4	$\underline{\smash{0.5}}$
	0.5	2.25	4.375	4.8125	2.59375	
1	4.5	8.75	9.625	5.1875	1.40625	
	0.5	2	3.375	3.125		
1	4	6.75	6.25	2.0625		
	0.5	1.75	2.5			
1	3.5	5	3.75			
	0.5	1.5				
1	3	3.5				
	0.5					
1	2.5					

The resulting polynomial is

$$p_2(s) = s^5 + 2.5s^4 + 3.5s^3 + 3.75s^2 + 2.0625s + 1.40625 \quad (4.76)$$

(5) The Routh table for $p_2(s)$ is:

s^5	1	3.5	2.0625
s^4	~~2.5~~	~~3.75~~	~~1.40625~~
	1	1.5	0.5625
s^3	~~2~~	~~1.5~~	
	1	0.75	
s^2	~~0.75~~	~~0.5625~~	
	1	0.75	

The polynomial $p_2(s)$ has a pair of zeros on the $j\omega$ axis at

$$\pm j\sqrt{0.75} = \pm j0.866$$

(6) These zeros are removed from $p_2(s)$ to yield the reduced polynomial $p_3(s)$:

```
                1   2.5  2.75  1.875
     1  0  0.75|1   2.5  3.5   3.75   2.0625  1.40625
               |1   2.5  0.75  1.875
                    2.75 1.875 2.0625 1.40625
                    2.75 1.875 2.0625 1.40625
```

Thus, $p_2(s)$ can be written

$$p_2(s) = (s^2 + 0.75)p_3(s) \quad (4.77)$$
$$p_3(s) = s^3 + 2.5s^2 + 2.75s + 1.875 \quad (4.78)$$

(7) The polynomial $p_3(s)$ is next considered. Application of the same procedure results in the factoring

$$p_3(s) = (s + 1.5)(s^2 + s + 1.25) \quad (4.79)$$

(8) The zeros of $p_2(s)$ are then at $\pm j0.866$, -1.5, and $-0.5 \pm j1$. The zeros of the original polynomial $p(s)$ are located 0.5 unit to the left of the zeros of $p_2(s)$, or at $-0.5 \pm j0.866$, -2, and $-1 \pm j1$. Thus,

$$p(s) = (s^2 + s + 1)(s + 2)(s^2 + 2s + 2) \quad (4.80)$$

The complexity of the procedure outlined above can be reduced in the general case if it is possible to obtain a rough estimate of the shift required to move the zeros farthest to the right over to the imaginary axis. Likewise, if Lin's method is used, the procedure is considerably simplified if an initial trial factor can be found which approximates a true factor of the polynomial. In either of these cases, the root-locus method can be used to indicate the approximate locations of the zeros. The accuracy of the root-locus analysis depends only on the effort expended; generally, it is more efficient to switch to an analytical procedure more amenable to the use of a desk calculator once the roots are located approximately.

In the example used above, the original polynomial is

$$p(s) = s^5 + 5s^4 + 11s^3 + 14s^2 + 10s + 4 \qquad (4.81)$$

Emphasis is switched from the zeros of $p(s)$ to the zeros of $1 + m(s)/n(s)$, where $m(s) + n(s)$ is identical with $p(s)$. In other words, $p(s)$ is separated into two additive components m and n, preferably chosen such that the zeros of m and n can be determined either by inspection or with as little work as possible. There are a number of ways in which $p(s)$ can be divided:

(1) One method is to allot the highest powers to $n(s)$, the lowest to $m(s)$:

$$m(s) = 14s^2 + 10s + 4 \qquad n(s) = s^5 + 5s^4 + 11s^3 \qquad (4.82)$$

(2) If $p(s)$ is divided according to its even and odd parts, $m(s)/n(s)$ is a ratio of the form even/odd or odd/even. If $p(s)$ is Hurwitz, $m(s)/n(s)$ is a reactance function, with all poles and zeros simple and alternating along the $j\omega$ axis.

(3) A particularly simple division of $p(s)$ involves the selection of $n(s)$ as a polynomial of the form

$$n(s) = s^5 + 5s^4 + 11s^3 + as^2 + bs \qquad (4.83)$$

The first three coefficients of $n(s)$ are made identical with those of $p(s)$ by selecting the zeros of $n(s)$ according to the conditions

$$\begin{aligned} \text{Sum of zeros of } n(s) &= -5 \\ \text{Sum of zeros taken two at a time} &= +11 \end{aligned} \qquad (4.84)$$

The five zeros of $n(s)$ are chosen as follows: one zero is placed at the origin; two additional real zeros are selected to add to -5: e.g., -1 and -4; the other two zeros, which must have a sum of zero, are chosen to make the sum of all the zeros taken two at a time equal to $+11$. If these two are denoted $\pm a$, the quantity a is determined by the condition

$$0[(-1) + (-4) + (a) + (-a)] + (-1)[(-4) + (a) + (-a)]$$
$$+ (-4)[(a) + (-a)] + (a)(-a) = +11 \qquad (4.85)$$
$$a = \pm j \sqrt{7} \qquad (4.86)$$

The five zeros of $n(s)$ are then 0, -1, -4, and $\pm j \sqrt{7}$, and $n(s)$ is

$$n(s) = s(s + 1)(s + 4)(s^2 + 7) \qquad (4.87)$$

The corresponding $m(s)$ is $p(s) - n(s)$, or

$$m(s) = -21(s + 1.04)(s - 0.183) \qquad (4.88)$$

Regardless of the method used to separate $p(s)$ into $m(s)$ and $n(s)$, the function $1 + m(s)/n(s)$ is now formed. In order to complete the example, the separation described by Eqs. (4.87) and (4.88) is considered. The zeros of the original polynomial $p(s)$ are identical with the zeros of the expression

$$1 + \frac{m(s)}{n(s)} = 1 + \frac{-21(s + 1.04)(s - 0.183)}{s(s + 1)(s + 4)(s^2 + 7)} \tag{4.89}$$

If the root loci are considered as plots of the motion of the zeros of $1 + m(s)/n(s)$ as a function of the gain K, Eq. (4.89) is rewritten

$$1 + \frac{m(s)}{n(s)} = 1 + \frac{K(s + 1.04)(s - 0.183)}{s(s + 1)(s + 4)(s^2 + 7)} \tag{4.90}$$

The zeros are to be determined when K is -21.

The root loci, shown in Fig. 4.49, are constructed by the usual procedure, initiated by location of the poles and zeros of $m(s)/n(s)$ in the

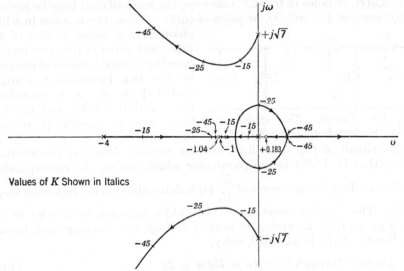

Values of K Shown in Italics

FIG. 4.49. Root loci for factoring polynomial.

s plane. The loci desired are for negative values of gain—*i.e.*, the loci represent the points at which the phase of $\dfrac{(s + 1.04)(s - 0.183)}{s(s + 1)(s + 4)(s^2 + 7)}$ is $0°$.
Thus, those sections of the real axis which constitute parts of the loci are to the left of an *even* number of singularities, and, as s tends to infinity, the loci approach the asymptotes at $0°$, $+120°$, and $-120°$. As indicated previously, if the loci are used only to determine a rough approximation for the zeros, the loci are constructed with just enough care to indicate the general characteristics.

In the specific example considered here, the loci of Fig. 4.49 demonstrate the approximate location of the zeros. Lin's method or the combination of Horner's method and Routh's test can then be employed for a more accurate factoring of the polynomial. Alternatively, the root-locus method can be employed as a complete procedure for the factoring of polynomials if the loci are constructed with more accuracy in the vicinity of the points corresponding to the appropriate value of gain. If the original polynomial is of a high degree, the two components (m and n) can individually be factored using the root-locus techniques.

Parameter Variations. The root-locus method can be used for the study of the effects of the variation of a single parameter in a network. If x is the changing parameter, the root-locus method is most easily applied if the transfer function of the network is written in the form

$$G(s) = f(x)G_c(s) \frac{1 + xG_a(s)}{1 + xG_b(s)} \tag{4.91}$$

Here $G_a(s)$, $G_b(s)$, and $G_c(s)$ are independent of x, and $f(x)$ is independent of frequency s. Poles of $G(s)$ may be generated by poles of $G_c(s)$, zeros of $1 + xG_b(s)$, or poles of $G_a(s)$. Likewise, the zeros of $G(s)$ may be zeros of $G_c(s)$, zeros of $1 + xG_a(s)$, or poles of $G_b(s)$. Thus, the manner in which changes in x cause motion of the poles and zeros of $G(s)$ can be analyzed by a consideration of the zeros of the two functions $1 + xG_a(s)$ and $1 + xG_b(s)$. x is considered as a variable gain, and $G_a(s)$ or $G_b(s)$ as the open-loop transfer function.

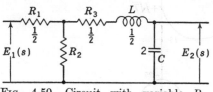

FIG. 4.50. Circuit with variable R_2. (Values in ohms, henrys, and farads.)

The circuit of Fig. 4.50 illustrates the specific details of the analysis. If G_2 (that is, $1/R_2$) is the parameter which varies, the corresponding motion of the poles and zeros of $\frac{E_2}{E_1}(s)$ is determined in the following steps.

(1) The transfer function of the ladder network is derived in the usual manner, by assuming an output voltage and working back toward the input. If E_2 is assumed unity,

Current through $C = I_C = E_2Cs = 2s$ \hfill (4.92)

Voltage across $R_2 = E_{R_2} = E_2 + I_C(R_3 + Ls)$

$$= 1 + 2s(\tfrac{1}{2} + \tfrac{1}{2}s)$$
$$= s^2 + s + 1 \tag{4.93}$$

Current through $R_2 = I_{R_2} = \frac{E_{R_2}}{R_2} = G_2(s^2 + s + 1)$ \hfill (4.94)

Current through $R_1 = I_1 = I_{R_2} + I_C = G_2s^2 + (G_2 + 2)s + G_2$ \hfill (4.95)

Input voltage $= E_1 = E_{R_2} + I_1R_1 = (s^2 + s + 1)$
$$+ [G_2s^2 + (G_2 + 2)s + G_2]\tfrac{1}{2}$$
$$= \left(1 + \frac{G_2}{2}\right)s^2 + \left(2 + \frac{G_2}{2}\right)s + 1 + \frac{G_2}{2} \tag{4.96}$$

Transfer function $= \frac{E_2}{E_1}(s)$

$$= \frac{1}{(1 + G_2/2)s^2 + (2 + G_2/2)s + 1 + G_2/2} \tag{4.97}$$

(2)   The transfer function is written in the form of Eq. (4.91) by rewriting the numerator and denominator polynomials as a sum of the form $p_1(s) + xp_2(s)$, where $p_1(s)$ and $p_2(s)$ are polynomials in s and independent of the variable x.   In this example, the appropriate form is

$$\frac{E_2}{E_1}(s) = \frac{1}{s^2 + 2s + 1 + G_2[\frac{1}{2}(s^2 + s + 1)]} \tag{4.98}$$

The polynomial $s^2 + 2s + 1$ is now factored from the denominator to yield

$$\frac{E_2}{E_1}(s) = \frac{1}{s^2 + 2s + 1} \frac{1}{1 + G_2 \dfrac{s^2 + s + 1}{2(s^2 + 2s + 1)}} \tag{4.99}$$

Comparison of Eqs. (4.91) and (4.99) indicates that, in this case,

$$x = G_2 \tag{4.100}$$
$$f(x) = 1 \tag{4.101}$$
$$G_c(s) = \frac{1}{s^2 + 2s + 1} \tag{4.102}$$
$$G_a(s) = 0 \tag{4.103}$$
$$G_b(s) = \frac{1}{2}\frac{s^2 + s + 1}{s^2 + 2s + 1} \tag{4.104}$$

(3)   The only root-locus plot required here is that for

$$1 + xG_b(s) = 1 + \frac{G_2}{2}\frac{s^2 + s + 1}{s^2 + 2s + 1} \tag{4.105}$$

$G_b(s)$ is considered as the open-loop transfer function, and $G_2/2$ is associated with the gain along the loci, as shown in Fig. 4.51.   As G_2 varies from zero to infinity, the two poles of $\dfrac{E_2}{E_1}(s)$ move along the paths shown and the two zeros remain at infinity.

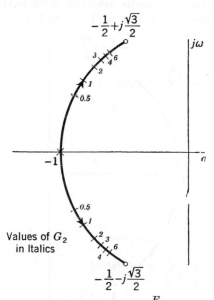

FIG. 4.51. Motion of poles of $\dfrac{E_2}{E_1}(s)$ with changes in G_2.

If the variation of G_2 about a normal operating value G_{20} is of interest, the procedure can be modified slightly.   After the transfer function $\dfrac{E_2}{E_1}(s)$ is determined, G_2 is replaced by the quantity $G_{20} + \Delta G_2$.   The analysis is then carried through as described above, but with ΔG_2 considered as the variable parameter.   For example, if in the analysis of the circuit of Fig. 4.50 the variations of G_2 about a normal value of 2 are to be studied, Eq. (4.97) is rewritten

$$\frac{E_2}{E_1}(s) = \frac{1}{[1 + \frac{1}{2}(2 + \Delta G_2)]s^2 + [2 + \frac{1}{2}(2 + \Delta G_2)]s + 1 + \frac{1}{2}(2 + \Delta G_2)}$$

(4.106)

The denominator of the transfer function is written as a sum of the form $p_1(s) + \Delta G_2\, p_2(s)$:

$$\frac{E_2}{E_1}(s) = \frac{1}{2s^2 + 3s + 2 + \frac{1}{2}\Delta G_2(s^2 + s + 1)}$$

(4.107)

Equation (4.107) is written

$$\frac{E_2}{E_1}(s) = \frac{1}{2(s^2 + 1.5s + 1)} \; \frac{1}{1 + \frac{1}{4}\Delta G_2 \dfrac{s^2 + s + 1}{s^2 + 1.5s + 1}}$$

(4.108)

The root-locus diagram, with both positive and negative values of ΔG_2 now of interest, is shown in Fig. 4.52 for ΔG_2 varying over the range from

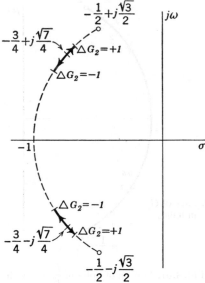

FIG. 4.52. Effect of small variations of G_2 around 2.

−1 to +1. The form is similar to that of Fig. 4.51, except that the "open-loop" poles are now at the zeros of $s^2 + 1.5s + 1$, rather than $s^2 + 2s + 1$. Exactly the same information is carried in Figs. 4.51 and 4.52. In the analysis of a complicated network, when the loci must be constructed graphically, consideration of the variation about a normal operating value occasionally simplifies the analysis.

The example considered above is sufficiently simple that the study can be carried out without the root-locus techniques. In a more complex case, however, use of the loci systematizes the analysis. The method is useful if both transient and frequency responses are desired as a function of a circuit parameter. When the frequency response only is to be studied, analysis is more simply effected in terms of the asymptotic plots of the gain $\left|\dfrac{E_2}{E_1}(j\omega)\right|$ versus frequency, if the variable parameter enters into the determination of only one or two break frequencies.

Other Applications. There are a number of other problems in which the root-locus techniques are useful. In network theory, for example, the realization of a specified transfer impedance (output voltage/input current) by a reactive network terminated in a resistance is based on the equation

$$Z_{12}(s) = \frac{z_{12}(s)}{1 + Gz_{22}(s)} \qquad (4.109)$$

The various terms are described in Fig. 4.53: G is the load conductance $1/R$; $z_{12}(s)$ and $z_{22}(s)$ are the open-circuit transfer and driving-point impedances of the lossless network. In a typical problem, the poles of $z_{12}(s)$ and $z_{22}(s)$ are identical, with the result that the zeros of $Z_{12}(s)$ are the zeros of $z_{12}(s)$, and the poles of $Z_{12}(s)$ are the zeros of $1 + Gz_{22}(s)$.

If the coupling network consists only of inductors and capacitors, the poles and zeros of $z_{22}(s)$ are simple and interlaced along the $j\omega$ axis. With the network working into an open-circuit ($G = 0$), the poles of $Z_{12}(s)$ are those of $z_{12}(s)$

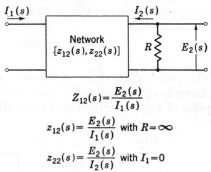

$$Z_{12}(s) = \frac{E_2(s)}{I_1(s)}$$

$$z_{12}(s) = \frac{E_2(s)}{I_1(s)} \text{ with } R = \infty$$

$$z_{22}(s) = \frac{E_2(s)}{I_2(s)} \text{ with } I_1 = 0$$

FIG. 4.53. Definition of transfer impedance $Z_{12}(s)$.

or $z_{22}(s)$. As the network is loaded (G increased), the poles are shifted into the left-half plane and then toward the zeros of $z_{22}(s)$. A root-locus

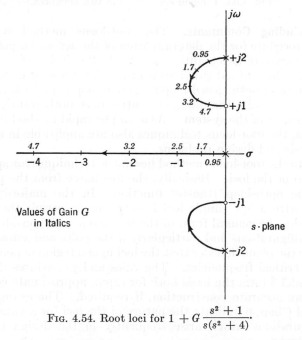

Values of Gain G in Italics

FIG. 4.54. Root loci for $1 + G\dfrac{s^2 + 1}{s(s^2 + 4)}$.

investigation of $1 + Gz_{22}(s)$ demonstrates the manner in which the loading of the network leads to this shift of the poles of the transfer function. For example, Fig. 4.54 shows the root loci when

$$z_{22}(s) = \frac{s^2 + 1}{s(s^2 + 4)} \tag{4.110}$$

The root-locus method is also useful in the analysis of the transfer function of a tandem combination of networks. The discussion of partitioning in Sec. 3.8 demonstrates that the over-all transfer function for the configuration of Fig. 4.55 is

$$z_{12}(s) = \frac{z_{12a}z_{12b}}{z_{22a} + z_{11b}} \tag{4.111}$$

The poles of $z_{12}(s)$ are the zeros of $z_{22a}(s) + z_{11b}(s)$, or $1 + (1/z_{22a})z_{11b}$. Accordingly, if the poles and zeros of both z_{22a} and z_{11b} are known, the poles of $z_{12}(s)$ can be found from the root loci.

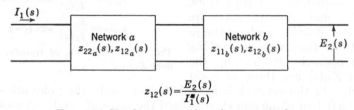

$$z_{12}(s) = \frac{E_2(s)}{I_1^*(s)}$$

Fig. 4.55. Tandem connection of two networks.

4.6. Concluding Comments. The root-locus method represents a graphical procedure for the determination of the zeros of a polynomial in terms of the zeros of two additive parts. In the design of feedback control systems, the method provides a means for working in terms of the poles and zeros of both closed-loop and open-loop transfer functions and, consequently, permits the designer control over both transient and frequency responses of the system. As a simple, rapid method for factoring polynomials, the root-locus techniques also are applicable in a variety of other analysis and design problems.

The key to the root-locus method lies in the techniques for approximate construction of the loci. Basically, the loci move from the poles to the zeros of the open-loop transfer function. In the majority of cases, familiarity with a few simple loci is sufficient to permit the analyst to sketch rapidly the general form of the loci, even with considerably more complex configurations and particularly if the poles and zeros are spread widely over the plane in order that the loci in one region depend on only a few of the critical frequencies. The rules and procedures described in Secs. 4.2 and 4.3 form the basis both for rapid, approximate construction and for more accurate construction, if required. The examples of this chapter and Chap. 6 indicate the nature of the loci for a variety of pole-zero configurations which arise frequently in the design of feedback control systems.

There are a number of questions which logically arise in the use of the root-locus method:

(1)   How is the root-locus approach used to guide the design of a system to control the effect of disturbing signals entering at points other than the input?

(2)   Since the root-locus method is based on the transfer functions as descriptions of the system components, how are the transfer functions derived from experimental measurements?

(3)   Can the root-locus techniques be applied in the design of a-c servomechanisms?

Discussion of these questions is postponed until Chap. 6, since the same questions arise in connection with Guillemin's synthesis procedure, presented in the next chapter.

CHAPTER 5

SYNTHESIS THROUGH
POLE-ZERO CONFIGURATIONS

The root-locus method of synthesis represents a radical departure in philosophy from the more conventional methods of design working in terms of the frequency-domain behavior of the open-loop transfer function. By working through the poles and zeros of the various transfer functions, the designer is able to control simultaneously the frequency response and the transient response. He need no longer depend on rather tenuous relationships between frequency and time domains. It is certainly true that, in the vast majority of feedback control systems, realization of a value of M_p of 1.3 leads to a system with a suitable step-function response. Unfortunately, however, it is all too often the unusual system that the designer is called upon to consider. The emphasis on fire-control equipment and other high-performance systems attaches even greater significance to transient performance. Indeed, often in fire-control problems the transient response is the only acceptable measure of system performance; frequency response is primarily of interest in the investigation of the noise power coming through the system.

The wide acceptance in the feedback-control field of design through poles and zeros is based largely upon three advantages:

(1) The ability of the designer to control transient response.
(2) The ability of the designer to control the effect of load-torque disturbances or other corrupting signals. This facet of the design problem is discussed in detail in Chap. 6.
(3) The circumspection such a method affords the designer.

The principal disadvantage of this method of design lies in the extent of the requirements imposed on the designer: familiarity with Laplace-transform methods and with the significance of various pole and zero configurations in terms of transient response.

Frequently in the design of feedback systems, problems arise where it is highly desirable to work in a more logical synthesis pattern. The word *synthesis* rigorously implies a logical procedure for the transition from specifications to system. In pure synthesis, the designer is able to take the specifications and in a straightforward path proceed to the final system. In this sense, neither the conventional methods of servo design nor the root-locus method is pure synthesis, for in each case the designer attempts to modify and to build up the open-loop system until he has

278

reached a point where the system, after the loop is closed, will be satisfactory.

In many ways, this state of the art of servo design is analogous to the conventional filter theory of the communications engineer. Conventional filter theory, characterized by the constant-k and m-derived sections, essentially involves a building-up of the filter, section by section, until satisfactory characteristics are obtained. On the other hand, modern filter theory, typified by Darlington's procedure for the synthesis of filters for prescribed insertion loss, has taken an approach which involves two steps:

(1) A transfer function in the complex frequency s is determined from the specifications.
(2) The transfer function is realized by a network.

Guillemin† in 1947 proposed that the synthesis of feedback control systems take the same form. Because of the closed-loop nature of the servo problem, three steps are necessary:

(1) The closed-loop transfer function is determined from the specifications.
(2) The corresponding open-loop transfer function is found.
(3) The appropriate compensation networks are synthesized.

Such an approach to the synthesis of closed-loop systems represents a complete change in basic thinking. No longer is the designer working inside the loop and trying to splice things up so that the over-all system will do the job required. On the contrary, he is now saying, "I have a certain job that has to be done. I will force the system to do it."

In practice, of course, no one method of synthesis is always optimum, regardless of the problem. Certain types of problems are best suited to certain techniques. Guillemin's philosophy and the details of the methods to carry it out are widely useful tools in the feedback-control field. In the last analysis, the capable engineer has at his command as many different techniques as possible; on the basis of his experiences and the nature of the problem, he uses those techniques which are appropriate. Indeed, in any one system design, a variety of techniques may be useful, particularly if the system is complicated with a number of different loops to be designed or if the specifications relate to specific characteristics of the performance in both time and frequency domains. It is the purpose of this chapter to present the methods associated with Guillemin's approach and to indicate the types of problems in which these methods are of greatest assistance.

5.1. Determination of the Closed-loop System Function from the Specifications. The initial step in Guillemin's procedure involves the determination of the closed-loop system function from the specifications. Essentially what is required is an analytical statement of the specifica-

---

† J. G. Truxal, Servomechanism Synthesis through Pole-zero Configurations, *MIT Research Laboratory of Electronics Tech. Rept.* 162, August 25, 1950; and M. R. Aaron, Synthesis of Feedback Control Systems by Means of Pole and Zero Location of the Closed Loop Function, *Trans. AIEE*, Vol. 70, Part II, pp. 1439–1445, 1951.

tions and, in particular, a statement in such a form that it is readily interpreted in terms of the poles and zeros of the closed-loop system function.   This part of the design is in many ways the most difficult part of the problem, for, in the feedback-control field as in most other branches of engineering, specifications may take a wide variety of forms and be undesirably vague.   It is impossible here to consider more than the commonest specifications.   When unusual specifications arise in particular problems, a heavy burden is placed on the designer to interpret these into analytical forms.   This difficulty is, of course, not a disadvantage of Guillemin's approach; rather, it is characteristic, regardless of the design method used.

The choice of an over-all system function is governed by two general factors: the fixed components and the performance specifications.   By

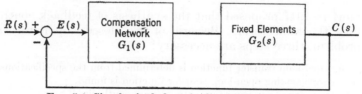

FIG. 5.1. Simple single-loop feedback control system.

the term "fixed components" is meant those components (commonly the elements of the controlled system and the motor, gear train, and power members) which must be used for economic or availability reasons.   In general, the nature of these fixed components determines the excess of poles over zeros required for the closed-loop system function $C(s)/R(s)$, while the performance specifications determine suitable regions in which these poles and zeros may lie.

The manner in which the nature of the transfer function, $G_2(s)$, of the fixed components constrains the selection of C/R is illustrated by Fig. 5.1, representing a simple unity-feedback single-loop system with tandem compensation. C/R is related to $G_2(s)$ by the expression

$$\frac{C}{R}(s) = \frac{G_1(s)G_2(s)}{1 + G_1(s)G_2(s)} \tag{5.1}$$

Here $G_1(s)$ is the transfer function of the compensation network.   In any physical system, the open-loop transfer function tends to zero at high frequencies, with the result that

$$\frac{C}{R}(s) \xrightarrow[s \to \infty]{} G_1(s)G_2(s) \tag{5.2}$$

If the compensation is to be easily realized by a physical system, it is desirable that $G_1(s)$ not possess a pole at infinity.†   Consequently, C/R

† It is mathematically permissible for $G_1(s)$ to possess poles at infinity, and theoretically such a network could be built, or at least constructed to any desired accuracy over any specified finite portion of the frequency spectrum.   Any design procedure

must tend to zero, as s approaches infinity, at least as fast as $G_2(s)$. In other words,

$$(N_p - N_z)_{C/R} \geq (N_p - N_z)_{G_2} \tag{5.3}$$

The excess of poles over zeros for C/R must at least equal the excess for G_2.

The second factor determining the choice of C/R is the set of performance specifications. The commonest specifications are those discussed in Sec. 1.7 and include the error constants, the bandwidth, and the general characteristics of the transient response. In each case, it is necessary to be able to interpret specifications of these types in terms of the poles and zeros of the closed-loop transfer function. Although particularly applicable in Guillemin's approach, the relationships derived below are basic and of importance regardless of the synthesis procedure used.

The error constants of interest are the position, velocity, and acceleration constants. Interpretations of these constants in terms of the steady-state errors, frequency response, sensitivity, and time delay and rise time of the step-function response were developed in Sec. 1.8. These error constants are determined completely by the positions of the poles and zeros of the closed loop system function.

As shown in Eq. (1.250), the generalized position, velocity, and acceleration constants are defined in terms of the Maclaurin expansion of the transfer function $E(s)/R(s)$, the ratio of the transform of the actuating signal to the transform of the input:†

$$\frac{E}{R}(s) = \frac{1}{1 + K_p} + \frac{1}{K_v} s + \frac{1}{K_a} s^2 + \cdots \tag{5.4}$$

As a result of the relation between C/R and E/R, the error constants also serve to define the Maclaurin expansion of C/R:

$$\frac{C}{R}(s) = 1 - \frac{1}{1 + K_p} - \frac{1}{K_v} s - \frac{1}{K_a} s^2 - \cdots \tag{5.5}$$

The relation between K_p, K_v, and K_a and the poles and zeros of C/R is readily determined if C/R is written in factored form:

$$\frac{C}{R}(s) = K \frac{(s + z_1)(s + z_2) \cdots (s + z_m)}{(s + p_1)(s + p_2) \cdots (s + p_n)} \tag{5.6}$$

With this notation, the zeros lie at $-z_j$, the poles at $-p_j$.

---

which admits this possibility immediately permits the selection of the ideal over-all system function $C/R = 1$, regardless of the nature of the fixed components. This difficulty simply means that engineering judgment must be used to restrict the admissible class of functions.

† If the system does not possess unity feedback, the generalized error constants are ordinarily defined in terms of the E_1/R transfer function, where E_1 refers to the equivalent unity-feedback system: that is, E_1 is $I - C$. where I is the desired value of the output.

(1) K_p: K_p is simply related to $\dfrac{C}{R}$ (0), as shown in Eq. (5.5).

$$\frac{C}{R}(0) = \frac{K_p}{1 + K_p} \tag{5.7}$$

Solution for K_p in terms of $\dfrac{C}{R}$ (0) and substitution of pole and zero values for $\dfrac{C}{R}$ (0) yields

$$K_p = \frac{K \prod\limits_{j=1}^{m} z_j}{\prod\limits_{j=1}^{n} p_j - K \prod\limits_{j=1}^{m} z_j} \tag{5.8}\dagger$$

(2) K_v: The derivative of $C(s)/R(s)$ at the origin is equal to $-1/K_v$. In most servo systems, $\dfrac{C}{R}$ (0) = 1, with the result that $1/K_v$ can be written

$$\frac{1}{K_v} = - \frac{\left[\dfrac{d}{ds}\left(\dfrac{C}{R}\right)\right]_{s=0}}{\left(\dfrac{C}{R}\right)_{s=0}} \tag{5.9}$$

$$\frac{1}{K_v} = - \left\{\frac{d}{ds}\left[\ln \frac{C}{R}(s)\right]\right\}_{s=0} \tag{5.10}$$

The operation of taking the logarithm replaces the multiplication of factors in C/R by an addition. Substitution of Eq. (5.6) into (5.10) yields

$$\frac{1}{K_v} = - \left\{\frac{d}{ds}\left[\ln K + \ln (s + z_1) + \cdots + \ln (s + z_m)\right.\right.$$
$$\left.\left. - \ln (s + p_1) \cdots - \ln (s + p_n)\right]\right\}_{s=0} \tag{5.11}$$

$$\frac{1}{K_v} = - \left(\frac{1}{s + z_1} + \cdots + \frac{1}{s + z_m} - \frac{1}{s + p_1} - \cdots - \frac{1}{s + p_n}\right)_{s=0} \tag{5.12}$$

$$\frac{1}{K_v} = \sum_{j=1}^{n} \frac{1}{p_j} - \sum_{j=1}^{m} \frac{1}{z_j} \tag{5.13}\star$$

$\dagger$ The symbol $\prod\limits_{j=1}^{m}$ indicates the product of all factors from $j = 1$ to and including $j = m$. For example, $\prod\limits_{j=1}^{3} a_j = a_1 a_2 a_3$.

(3) K_a: Equation (5.5) indicates that $-2/K_a$ is equal to the zero-frequency value of the second derivative of $\dfrac{C}{R}$ (s). For the clearest interpretation in terms of the poles and zeros of C/R, K_a is also written in terms of the logarithmic derivative.

$$\frac{d^2}{ds^2}\left[\ln\frac{C}{R}(s)\right] = \frac{(C/R)''}{C/R} - \left[\frac{(C/R)'}{C/R}\right]^2 \tag{5.14}$$

Consequently, if $\dfrac{C}{R}$ (0) is equal to unity,

$$-\frac{2}{K_a} = \left\{\frac{d^2}{ds^2}\left[\ln\frac{C}{R}(s)\right]\right\}_{s=0} + \frac{1}{K_v^2} \tag{5.15}$$

Differentiation of the right side of Eq. (5.12) and substitution of $s = 0$ yields, with K_v as given in Eq. (5.13),

$$-\frac{2}{K_a} = \frac{1}{K_v^2} + \sum_{j=1}^{n}\frac{1}{p_j^2} - \sum_{j=1}^{m}\frac{1}{z_j^2} \tag{5.16}\star$$

If K_v is infinite, K_a is expressible directly in terms of the squared reciprocals of the poles and zeros.

Equations (5.13) and (5.16) are of basic importance in servo synthesis for they represent the correlation between the error constants and the system response characteristics. Indeed, these two equations are simply another way of stating the relationship between the velocity and acceleration constants and the time delay and rise time of the step-function response of the system. In addition, the two equations place in evidence the manner in which lead and integral equalization permit control over K_v and K_a without affecting relative stability, and, by presenting the effects of conventional compensation schemes in a somewhat different light, the equations indicate more general methods of compensation. These interpretations of Eqs. (5.13) and (5.16) are clarified by the following comments.

Independence of K_v and K_a. The two equations indicate that there exists the possibility for more or less independent control over K_v and K_a. One simple example points this up rather forcefully. If a simple second-order servo system is considered, $\dfrac{C}{R}$ (s) is given by the equation

$$\frac{C}{R}(s) = \frac{\omega_n^2}{s^2 + 2\zeta\omega_n s + \omega_n^2} \tag{5.17}$$

$1/K_v$, the sum of the reciprocals of the negatives of the poles, is simply the ratio of the last two coefficients of the denominator:

$$\frac{1}{K_v} = \frac{2\zeta}{\omega_n} \tag{5.18}$$

Determination of K_a can be effected either by making a direct Maclaurin expansion of $\dfrac{C}{R}(s)$ by long division or by use of Eq. (5.16), with the result

$$\frac{1}{K_a} = \frac{1 - 4\zeta^2}{\omega_n^2} \tag{5.19}$$

Clearly, K_a is infinite if

$$\zeta = \tfrac{1}{2} \tag{5.20}$$

Certainly from the standpoint of system performance, there is little choice between relative damping ratios of 0.4, 0.5, or 0.6, although judgment of the system characteristics from K_a would indicate that 0.5 was far and away the best choice.   This example, as well as the discussion of Sec. 1.8, reaffirms the dangers associated with attaching too much significance to the higher-order error constants.

Pole-zero Configurations for Infinite Velocity Constant.   The expression for K_v in terms of the poles and zeros is

$$\frac{1}{K_v} = \sum_{j=1}^{n} \frac{1}{p_j} - \sum_{j=1}^{m} \frac{1}{z_j} \tag{5.21}$$

On the basis of this equation, the relationship between the velocity constant and a variety of simple pole-zero configurations can be readily deduced.   As an example, the various configurations which yield an infinite velocity constant are determined.

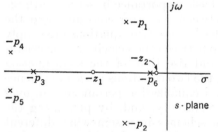

FIG. 5.2. Principal pole-zero configuration.

The pole-zero configurations considered in detail in the following discussion are all characterized by the fact that the principal characteristics of the transient response of the system are fixed by one pair of conjugate complex poles, $-p_1$ and $-p_2$ in Fig. 5.2.†   All other poles are placed either so far out to the left in the complex plane (as $-p_3$, $-p_4$, and $-p_5$) or so close to a zero (as $-p_6$) that they contribute negligibly to the transient response.   To a first order, the system characteristics are determined by the two control poles $-p_1$ and $-p_2$ and any zeros in the significant part of the plane.   Extensive consideration of this apparently oversimplified case is justifiable on at least three grounds:

First, even if classical methods of design were used, the majority of feedback control systems, in their final form, degenerate, at least to a rough approximation, to essentially this simple system.   Control of the system characteristics by one pair of poles is synonymous, in terms of the

† J. H. Mulligan, Jr., The Effect of Pole and Zero Locations on the Transient Response of Linear Dynamic Systems, *Proc. IRE*, Vol. 37, pp. 516–529, May, 1949.

Nyquist-diagram approach, with a nice, clean tangency to the desired M_p circle.

Second, if system synthesis is carried out using Guillemin's approach, restriction of significant critical frequencies to one pair of conjugate complex control poles plus one or more zeros gives the designer all the freedom he can intelligently use. Intelligent design, whether by the root-locus method or through Guillemin's approach, requires that the designer be able to interpret effects of the motion of the poles and zeros in terms of the consequent changes in the transient response. Thus, in a practical case, although a suitable system might be designed using a large number of significant poles and zeros, the designer is ordinarily better off to yield some of this freedom and go to a simple system which he can handle.

Third, in certain specific cases, it is admittedly not feasible to reduce to two the number of significant poles in the over-all system function. This

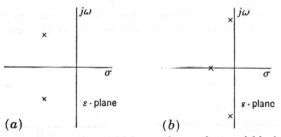

Fig. 5.3. Two pole configurations which can be made to yield similar transient responses.

difficulty does not mean that satisfactory dynamic performance cannot be realized. Essentially similar characteristics, for example, can be obtained from the two pole configurations of Fig. 5.3. The decreased relative stability indicated by the diminished relative damping ratio of the complex poles as the transition is made from part (a) of the figure to part (b) is offset by the introduction of a pole on the negative real axis. The difficulty in reduction of system complexity is encountered, for example, in the design of aircraft control systems, in which the aerodynamical, mechanical, and hydraulic components lead to a relatively complex system before any compensation or stabilization is introduced. Even in higher-order systems, however, the basic ideas of this analysis are valid. The consideration of the simple two-pole system suffices to describe the fundamental features of the method.

There is an even more decisive reason for considering this particular configuration, for by the use of this configuration, Guillemin guarantees that the poles of the open-loop transfer function lie on the negative real axis, with the result that tandem compensation can be accomplished by RC networks. This aspect of the configuration is discussed in detail in Sec. 5.3. In these characteristics of this configuration lie one of the novel features of Guillemin's approach and, to a very great extent, the keystone of the success of this method of synthesis. Therefore, the following discussion considers only the simplest type of pole-zero configuration, that shown in Fig. 5.2, and the appropriate positions of the zeros for infinite velocity constant are investigated.

For a control system in which $\frac{C}{R}(0) = 1$, the velocity constant is simply related to the logarithmic derivative of the system function at the origin by Eq. (5.10), repeated below.

$$\frac{1}{K_v} = - \left\{ \frac{d}{ds} \left[\ln \frac{C}{R}(s) \right] \right\}_{s=0} \tag{5.22}$$

Visualization of those pole and zero positions which lead to an infinite velocity constant is aided by the use of a potential analogy.   If the poles are considered as electric line unit charges of one polarity, the zeros of the opposite polarity, the derivative of $\frac{C}{R}(s)$ corresponds to the electric field, or the force on a unit charge.   The velocity constant, consequently, is analogous to the inverse of the electric field at the origin, an infinite

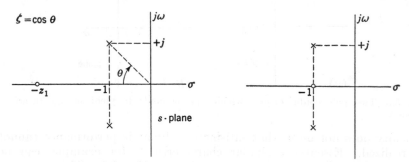

FIG. 5.4. Configuration to illustrate potential analogy.

FIG. 5.5. Configuration yielding infinite velocity constant.

velocity constant to zero electric field.   The use of the analogy is illustrated by Fig. 5.4, portraying a very simple pole-zero configuration.   A pair of conjugate complex poles is placed at $-1 \pm j$, corresponding to an ω_n of $\sqrt{2}$, a ζ of 0.707.   One finite zero (at $-z_1$) is to be used to make the velocity constant infinite.   The required value of z_1 is desired.

In the potential analogy, there is no vertical field at the origin regardless of the value of z_1 since the vertical components of the two conjugate line charges cancel.   The two horizontal components of the field at the origin add, however.   Each field component is of the form $(\cos \theta)/\omega_n$, since the electric field due to a unit positive line charge is of the form $1/r$, where r is the vector from the charge to the point of interest.   The net horizontal field due to the two pole charges is then $(2 \cos \theta)/\omega_n$ or unity.   The zero causes a horizontal field component in the opposite direction and of magnitude $1/z_1$.   Realization of infinite velocity constant thus requires that z_1 be equal to unity, as shown in Fig. 5.5.

Variation of the relative damping ratio associated with the conjugate poles results in a variation in the required zero position. As the poles approach the $j\omega$ axis (ζ tending to zero), the horizontal field component decreases and the required zero position moves farther to the left in the complex plane. The variation of z_1 with ζ is shown graphically in Fig. 5.6.

The introduction of additional poles complicates the picture somewhat. The addition of one pole on the negative real axis (Fig. 5.7) modifies slightly the required zero position. Addition of the pole at $-p_3$ requires motion of the zero inward toward the imaginary axis in order that the zero-frequency component of the electric field resulting from the line

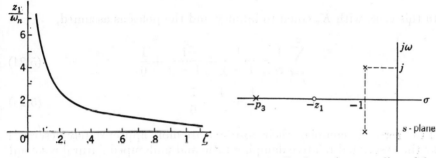

FIG. 5.6. For configuration of Fig. 5.4, z_1 required to give infinite velocity constant.

FIG. 5.7. Configuration complicated by addition of one pole.

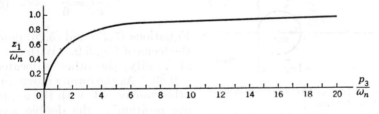

FIG. 5.8. Zero required for infinite velocity constant with $\zeta = 0.5$ and one extra pole.

charge at $-z_1$ may be increased enough to offset the component resulting from the charge at $-p_3$. For a pair of conjugate complex poles with a relative damping ratio of $\frac{1}{2}$, the required value of z_1 varies with p_3 in the manner shown in Fig. 5.8. It should be noted that Fig. 5.8, as well as Fig. 5.6, is drawn only to indicate the general trends of the various effects described. In any specific problem, appropriate curves or specific points on the curve are quickly determined on the basis of the potential analogy or the analytical expression [Eq. (5.21)] for the velocity constant in terms of the pole and zero positions.

Figure 5.8 indicates that the addition of the pole on the negative real axis has little effect on the value of z_1 required for infinite velocity constant unless the pole position is of the same order of magnitude as ω_n. The presence of a number of poles, rather than merely one, increases the effect on the required position of z_1.

In the preceding paragraphs, the infinite velocity constant was realized by a single zero on the negative real axis. A somewhat more complex scheme with certain advantages discussed later involves the use of a pair of finite zeros either on the negative real axis or at conjugate points. As an example, poles are assumed to lie at $-1 \pm j$ and -6. A pair of zeros is to be added to make K_v infinite. Suitable locations for these zeros can be determined either from the potential analogy or directly from the equation for K_v in terms of the pole and zero positions:

$$\frac{1}{K_v} = \sum_{j=1}^{n} \frac{1}{p_j} - \sum_{j=1}^{m} \frac{1}{z_j} \tag{5.23}$$

In this case, with K_v equal to infinity and the poles as assumed,

$$\sum_{j=1}^{2} \frac{1}{z_j} = \frac{1}{1+j} + \frac{1}{1-j} + \frac{1}{6} \tag{5.24}$$

$$\frac{1}{z_1} + \frac{1}{z_2} = \frac{7}{6} \tag{5.25}$$

If the zeros are complex, their positions are more appropriately described by the associated relative damping ratio and undamped natural resonant frequency,

$$\frac{2\zeta}{\omega_n} = \frac{7}{6} \tag{5.26}$$

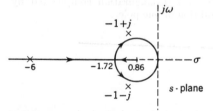

FIG. 5.9. Locus of two zeros for infinite velocity constant.

Equations (5.25) and (5.26) describe the locus of Fig. 5.9. With one zero at infinity, the other is located at -0.86. As the former moves in, the other moves out, with the appropriate position of the double zero at -1.72. The locus is completed by the two semicircular arcs shown. Zeros at any pair of values on this locus result in an infinite velocity constant.[†]

Clearly the number of zeros and poles considered could be increased still further, but it appears that a system of the complexity of Fig. 5.9 is approaching the limit of the designer's ability of interpretation. It was pointed out in Sec. 1.4 that even in a case of this complexity the general characteristics of the transient response are not always obvious.

The above discussion is an attempt to indicate a line of reasoning and a way of looking at the design of feedback control systems. The relationships between the error constants, particularly the velocity constant, and the poles and zeros of the closed-loop system function are material aids in

† The negative real axis between -0.86 and the origin and the positive real axis are also paired as part of the complete locus, but in most feedback control systems it is desirable to avoid nonminimum-phase system functions (*i.e.*, functions with zeros in the right-half plane).

increasing the designer's circumspection, regardless of the design technique he may choose to use.   The zero loci for infinite velocity constant are one example of methods of manipulation of these relationships. Even though an infinite velocity constant may not be desired in a specific problem, the loci and the potential analogy indicate the general nature of the pole-zero configurations leading to a high K_v.   Combination of this relationship between the configuration and K_v with the obvious relationships between the pole and zero positions and the bandwidth, relative stability, and significant time constants in the transient response permits the choice of a pole-zero configuration to meet the common types of specifications.

Compensation in Terms of Pole-zero Configurations.   Regardless of the design method used, compensation of a feedback control system can be viewed as a boost in the velocity constant (or open-loop gain) while maintaining the relative stability roughly constant.   Conventionally, compensation is either or both of two types: integral or lead.   The effects of integral or lead compensation on the open-loop transfer function are well known and discussed in considerable detail in any of the basic servo texts.   It is helpful, in addition, if the designer is aware of the effects of various methods of compensation on the closed-loop system function.

In the preceding paragraphs, it was shown that one method of boosting the velocity constant entailed the addition of a simple zero on the negative real axis.   In more conventional terms, the addition of this zero corresponds to lead or derivative compensation.   Addition of the zero boosts both the bandwidth and the velocity constant.   Since the numerator polynomial of the over-all system function is identical with that of the open-loop transfer function, the zero added to the pole-zero configuration appears as the zero of the lead-compensation network.   The

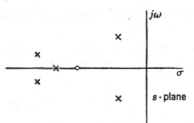

FIG. 5.10. Basic pole-zero configuration.

relative positions of the pole and zero of the lead-network transfer function depend upon the location of this zero in the over-all pole-zero configuration.

An alternate method for increasing the velocity constant is evident from a consideration of the relation between K_v and the pole and zero positions:

$$\frac{1}{K_v} = \sum_{j=1}^{n} \frac{1}{p_j} - \sum_{j=1}^{m} \frac{1}{z_j} \tag{5.27}$$

One basic pole-zero configuration is shown in Fig. 5.10. K_v, as given by Eq. (5.27), can be changed significantly without appreciable effect on either the transient or frequency response if a dipole is added near the origin (Fig. 5.11).   The zero at $-z_i$ and the pole at $-p_i$ are placed sufficiently close together that the residue of the transfer function in the pole at $-p_i$ is made negligible. This can be done since the residue is proportional to the separation of the pole and zero. Even though p_i and z_i are nearly equal, there may be a significant contribution to $1/K_v$ in Eq. (5.27) because the inverse values, $1/p_i$ and $1/z_i$, are large numbers compared to the other terms in the equation.

As a specific example of this method of raising K_v, the configuration of Fig. 5.12 is considered. Poles are located at $-1 \pm j1$ and -5, and a zero is at -4, with the resulting system function

$$\frac{C}{R}(s) = \frac{2.5(s + 4)}{(s^2 + 2s + 2)(s + 5)} \tag{5.28}$$

The velocity constant, computed from Eq. (5.27), is 1.05. A dipole is added near the origin on the negative real axis. Since the velocity constant is to be increased, the zero must be inside the pole (in order that

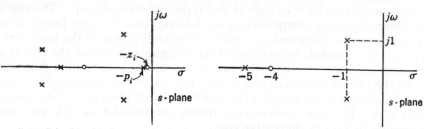

FIG. 5.11. Dipole added to configuration of Fig. 5.10.   FIG. 5.12. Configuration for example of integral equalization.

$1/p_i$ may be less than $1/z_i$ to result in a decrease in $1/K_v$, an increase in K_v). The resulting over-all system function is

$$\frac{C}{R}(s) = 2.5 \frac{p_i}{z_i} \frac{(s + 4)(s + z_i)}{(s^2 + 2s + 2)(s + 5)(s + p_i)} \tag{5.29}$$

The amplitude of the added term in the unit step-function response is the residue of $\dfrac{1}{s}\dfrac{C}{R}(s)$ in the pole at $-p_i$:

$$k_{-p_i} = 2.5 \frac{p_i}{z_i} \frac{(4 - p_i)(z_i - p_i)}{(-p_i)(p_i^2 - 2p_i + 2)(5 - p_i)} \tag{5.30}$$

If p_i is much smaller than any of the poles or zeros in the original configuration, the residue is approximately

$$k_{-p_i} = 2.5 \frac{1}{(-z_i)} \frac{4(z_i - p_i)}{10} \tag{5.31}$$

$$k_{-p_i} = -1 + \frac{p_i}{z_i} \tag{5.32}$$

If the added transient term resulting from the addition of the pole is to have an initial amplitude less than 5 per cent, it is necessary that p_i/z_i lie between 1 and 1.05.

If p_i and z_i are chosen to yield a ratio satisfying the above condition, the transient response of the system is not appreciably affected by the addition of the dipole. Specifically, the response to a unit step function is changed in two ways:

(1) The term $(-1 + p_i/z_i)e^{-p_i t}$ is added.
(2) The original terms are modified, but only slightly because, as a result of the fact that the fraction $(s + z_i)/(s + p_i)$ is essentially unity at the original poles, the residues at these poles are almost unchanged by the dipole addition.

Thus, p_i and z_i must be chosen subject to the above constraint $(p_i/z_i$ less than 1.05) and placed so as to yield the desired K_v. With the dipole, K_v is given by the expression

$$\frac{1}{K_v} = \frac{1}{1.05} + \frac{1}{p_i} - \frac{1}{z_i} \qquad (5.33)$$

As an example, a K_v of 10 is chosen. Then,

$$\frac{1}{z_i} - \frac{1}{p_i} = \frac{17}{20} \qquad (5.34)$$

$$\frac{1}{p_i}\left(\frac{p_i}{z_i} - 1\right) = \frac{17}{20} \qquad (5.35)$$

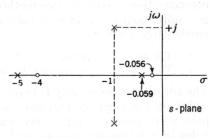

If the maximum allowable value, 1.05, is selected for p_i/z_i, the pole and zero positions are found to be

$$p_i = 0.059 \qquad (5.36)$$
$$z_i = 0.056 \qquad (5.37)$$

FIG. 5.13. Final configuration for example of integral compensation. (Not drawn to scale.)

The final pole-zero configuration is that of Fig. 5.13; the final system function is

$$\frac{C}{R}(s) = \frac{2.64(s + 0.056)(s + 4)}{(s^2 + 2s + 2)(s + 5)(s + 0.059)} \qquad (5.38)$$

This method of increasing K_v by the addition of a dipole is the familiar integral compensation. A dipole with the zero inside the pole in the over-all system function corresponds to a dipole with the pole inside the zero in the open-loop transfer function. (This rather unusual relation between open-loop and closed-loop transfer functions is clarified in Sec. 5.3.) It is of interest to compare the effect of the addition of the dipole to the $\frac{C}{R}(s)$ configuration and the known effects of the addition of integral compensation to the open-loop transfer function. It is clear that from either viewpoint the K_v is increased. Inspection of the closed-loop pole-zero configuration would seem to indicate that the dipole tended to increase the bandwidth slightly since the zero is inside the pole. However, for the same relative stability, the bandwidth is somewhat decreased as a result of the fact that the dipole tends to make the transient response slightly more sluggish.   A sharper cutoff results when this added sluggishness is equalized by a slight decrease in the relative damping ratio associated with the conjugate complex poles.

Consideration of integral equalization in terms of the closed-loop pole-zero configuration does indicate that the transient response contains a long tail of small amplitude.   The term $k_{-p_i}e^{-p_i t}$, which is added to the system step-function response, has a time constant of $1/p_i$, which is large compared to the original time constants of the system.   Thus, although it can be made of small amplitude, a long-duration tail will always exist when integral compensation is used.

Generalized Picture of Compensation.   The fourth significant result based on the equations relating the error constants to the positions of the poles and zeros of the over-all system function is the generalized picture of compensation as the modification of pole-zero configurations to meet specifications on the error constants as well as the general characteristics of transient and frequency responses.   In this light, lead and integral compensation are simply two methods of effecting the desired end.   More generally, compensation can take a number of forms, of which two are particularly simple:

(1)   The addition of zeros.
(2)   The addition of zeros and poles in combination.

The addition of zeros only is typified by lead equalization, with one zero added on the negative real axis, but more generally includes the use of pairs of conjugate complex zeros as well as real zeros.   The zeros and poles in combination can take the form of dipoles or, more generally, quadripoles and higher-order systems.   In terms of the open-loop transfer function, these generalized concepts of lead and integral equalization correspond to the use of generalized compensation transfer functions, including both complex and real poles and zeros.

5.2. Examples of Selection of Over-all System Function.   The method of selection of the over-all system function C/R is illustrated by three examples which are purposely chosen simple to facilitate understanding of the basic elements of the procedure.

Example 1.   For the first example, the specifications considered are the following:

(1)   The fixed part of the system is described by the transfer function

$$G_2(s) \; = \; \frac{K_2}{s(s + a)} \tag{5.39}$$

(2)   The frequency response and transient response are to be generally governed by a bandwidth less than 100 rad/sec and a relative damping ratio of the control poles of about 0.7, corresponding to a system with a step-function response having an overshoot less than 5 per cent.

(3)   The error constants are to satisfy the following inequalities:

$$K_v \geq 50/\text{sec} \tag{5.40}$$
$$K_a \geq 100/\text{sec}^2 \tag{5.41}$$

The selection of a suitable C/R is divided into four steps.

(1)   If C/R is chosen consistent with the pole-zero configuration in which one pair of conjugate complex control poles governs the response, the bandwidth and velocity constant of the system are determined principally by the locations of the two control poles and any finite zeros. The first step in determining the configuration involves a decision as to the necessity of using zeros.

If C/R possesses no finite zeros, the bandwidth of the system, defined as the frequency at which the gain is 3 db down from the zero-frequency value, is directly related to ω_n and ζ of the control poles by the relation

$$\text{Bandwidth} = \omega_n(1 - 2\zeta^2 + \sqrt{2 - 4\zeta^2 + 4\zeta^4})^{\frac{1}{2}} \qquad (5.42)$$

With a relative damping ratio of 0.7, the bandwidth in rad/sec is equal to ω_n; if ζ is 0.5, the bandwidth is $1.27\omega_n$. The velocity constant, on the other hand, is also directly proportional to ω_n (again under the assumption that the response is governed by only the two control poles).

$$K_v = \frac{\omega_n}{2\zeta} \qquad (5.43)$$

Inspection of Eqs. (5.42) and (5.43) reveals that, for systems with the simple pole configuration under consideration, a bandwidth/velocity-constant relationship exists, with the ratio a function of the relative damping ratio only. Specifically, in two common cases, the two quantities are related by the equations

$$\zeta = 0.7 \qquad K_v = 0.71 \text{ (bandwidth)} \qquad (5.44)$$
$$\zeta = 0.5 \qquad K_v = 0.79 \text{ (bandwidth)} \qquad (5.45)$$

In both above equations, the bandwidth is expressed in radians per second.

The specifications in the example under consideration are sufficiently lenient, therefore, to permit realization of the required velocity constant and bandwidth without the use of finite zeros.

(2)   The two control poles are placed at $-70 \pm j70$, yielding a bandwidth of about 100 rad/sec and a relative damping ratio of 0.7.

(3)   The resulting K_v is evaluated from the expression for K_v in terms of the pole and zero positions [Eq. (5.27)] and found to be 70/sec. The system possesses a K_a of approximately 10^4/sec,[2] with the result that all specifications are met by the C/R with these poles.

(4)   The fixed components possess a transfer function with two more poles than zeros, so that C/R must have an excess of poles over zeros of two. A suitable C/R is then

$$\frac{C}{R}(s) = \frac{9800}{s^2 + 140s + 9800} \qquad (5.46)$$

Example 2.   As a second example, the same specifications are used, with the exception that the allowable bandwidth is dropped to 50 rad/sec. Finite zeros are now required, for the desired velocity constant, 50/sec, is greater than that permitted by the allowable bandwidth if no zeros are used.   If lead compensation is used (a simple zero on the negative real axis), the specifications can be met by the use of one real zero.   Figure 5.14 presents graphically the increase in both the velocity constant and the bandwidth resulting from the addition of one finite zero.   It is clear from the curves that the addition of the zero increases the velocity constant more than the bandwidth and permits meeting the more stringent

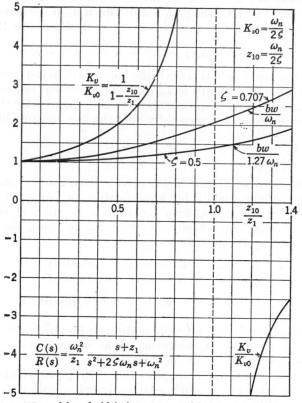

Fig. 5.14. K_v and bandwidth for system with two poles and one zero.

performance specifications of this example.   In particular, with $\zeta = 0.7$, the bandwidth is never more than approximately twice ω_n, even if the zero is brought in until the velocity constant becomes infinite.   Consequently, the control poles can be chosen at $-20 \pm j20$ with the certainty that the bandwidth specification will be met.

(2)   The required location of the zero is determined by the specified velocity constant:

$$\frac{1}{z_1} = \frac{2\zeta}{\omega_n} + \frac{1}{p_3} - \frac{1}{K_v} \tag{5.47}$$

If p_3 is arbitrarily chosen as 160 (it can be shown that if this pole is to contribute negligibly to the transient response, p_3 must be roughly six times ω_n), the above equation gives a z_1 of 27.6.

(3)   With poles at $-20 \pm j20$ and -160 and a zero at -27.6, the infinite-frequency behavior of C/R is consistent with that of the fixed components and the resulting bandwidth is about 45 rad/sec. The resulting C/R is

$$\frac{C}{R}(s) = \frac{4640(s + 27.6)}{(s^2 + 40s + 800)(s + 160)} \tag{5.48}$$

The corresponding step-function response is shown in Fig. 5.15.

Example 3.   For the third example, the same specifications as in Example 2 are met by integral compensation.   Since the bandwidth is

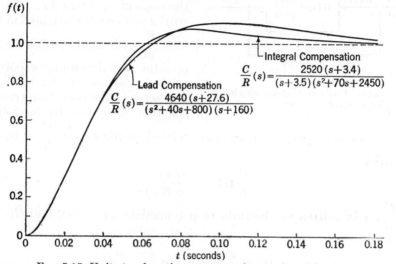

FIG. 5.15. Unit-step-function response of examples of Sec. 5.2.

not appreciably increased by the addition of the dipole, the two control poles can be placed at $-35 \pm j35$, yielding a relative damping ratio of 0.7 and a maximum bandwidth of 50 rad/sec.

Either the pole or the zero of the compensation dipole can be arbitrarily placed, or the dipole separation can be specified, as in the preceding section, to control the amplitude of the long-time-constant tail in the transient response.   If the pole is placed at -3.5, the zero is located from the specified value of K_v:

$$\frac{1}{z_i} = \frac{2\zeta}{\omega_n} + \frac{1}{p_i} - \frac{1}{K_v} \tag{5.49}$$

$$z_1 = 3.40 \tag{5.50}$$

The resulting $\frac{C}{R}(s)$ is

$$\frac{C}{R}(s) = \frac{2520(s + 3.4)}{(s^2 + 70s + 2450)(s + 3.5)} \tag{5.51}$$

The associated transient response is shown in Fig. 5.15.   The close similarity between the transient responses of the two systems of Examples

2 and 3 is noteworthy, particularly in view of the apparently striking dissimilarity between the two system functions.

5.3. Determination of the Open-loop Transfer Function from the Closed-loop System Function.   The second step in a synthesis along the lines suggested by Guillemin is a determination of the open-loop transfer function corresponding to the closed-loop system function chosen to meet the performance specifications.   It is this step which was the stumbling block to successful logical synthesis of servomechanisms before Guille-

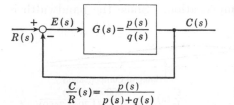

$$\frac{C}{R}(s) = \frac{p(s)}{p(s)+q(s)}$$

FIG. 5.16. Unity-feedback, single-loop feedback control system.

min's work, for in its basic form this step involves the evaluation of the roots of a polynomial.   The essential problem is illustrated in Fig. 5.16. $\frac{C}{R}(s)$ is known, with the numerator and denominator polynomials in factored form; the poles and zeros of the open-loop transfer function $G(s)$ are to be found.

These unknown poles and zeros are related to the known $\frac{C}{R}(s)$ by the equation

$$\frac{C}{R}(s) = \frac{G(s)}{1 + G(s)} \tag{5.52}$$

If $\frac{C}{R}(s)$ is written as the ratio of polynomials, $p(s)/n(s)$, and $G(s)$ as $p(s)/q(s)$,

$$\frac{C}{R}(s) = \frac{p}{n} = \frac{p/q}{1 + p/q} = \frac{p}{p + q} \tag{5.53}$$

$$n(s) = p(s) + q(s) \tag{5.54}$$

$$q(s) = n(s) - p(s) \tag{5.55}$$

In other words, the zeros of the open-loop transfer function are identical with the zeros of the closed-loop system function, while the poles of the open-loop transfer function are the zeros of the polynomial $n(s) - p(s)$. In general, determination of these zeros involves solution of a polynomial of the degree of $n(s)$.   It was this problem of zero determination which, until Guillemin's work, discouraged design through this method of working from the over-all system inward toward the compensation networks.

The foundation for the success of Guillemin's method lies in the procedure he presented to ensure a simple solution to the zero-determination problem.   He proposed that the pole-zero configuration for $\frac{C}{R}(s)$ be chosen not only to meet the specifications, but also to ensure that all zeros of $q(s)$ lie on the negative real axis.   If this condition is satisfied, the zeros of $q(s)$ can be determined graphically by plots of $n(s)$ and $p(s)$ (polynomials with known zeros) for real values of s and by graphical subtraction according to the equation

$$q(s) = n(s) - p(s) \tag{5.56}$$

The imposition of the additional constraint that all poles of the open-loop transfer function lie on the negative real axis is not only necessary if the synthesis is to be simple, but also frequently desirable to ensure that the transfer functions of the compensation networks be realizable by RC networks.

The critical part of the procedure is, then, the choice of the original pole-zero configuration for C/R. The configuration discussed in Sec. 5.1 and shown again in Fig. 5.17 is characterized by one pair of conjugate complex control poles, one or more dipoles, poles far to the left in the s plane, and one or more finite

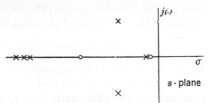

FIG. 5.17. Pole-zero configuration proposed by Guillemin.

zeros. A configuration of this type meets the two basic requirements:

(1) Ordinary specifications can be met by choice of the critical frequencies.
(2) The poles of the open-loop transfer function can be made to lie on the negative real axis.

Although not general, this configuration is not so narrowly specialized as might at first glance appear. As pointed out in Sec. 5.1, not only do the vast majority of systems designed by any other method essentially reduce to this configuration, but in this system the designer has all the freedom he can intelligently use, while at the same time he possesses a

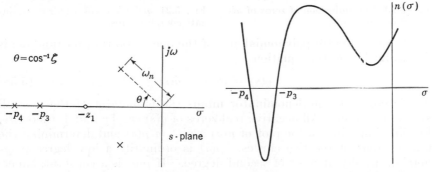

FIG. 5.18. Configuration without dipoles.   FIG. 5.19. General characteristics of $n(\sigma)$ for configuration of Fig. 5.18.

clear concept of the nature of the transient response and those factors which are significant in determining this response.

The statement was made above that with the use of the pole-zero configuration of Fig. 5.17 it is possible to guarantee that all poles of the open-loop transfer function lie on the negative real axis. This startling phenomenon is demonstrated by sketches of the form of the polynomials $n(\sigma)$ and $p(\sigma)$, evaluated for real values of σ. Initially any integral-compensation dipole is ignored, and the configuration is that in Fig. 5.18. There are one pair of conjugate complex control poles and a group of poles far to the left in the s plane on the negative real axis. Figure 5.19 indicates the general shape of $n(\sigma)$, the denominator polynomial of the over-all system function. For the four-pole case shown, $n(\sigma)$ is a quartic with two real zeros, at $-p_3$ and $-p_4$. If these two poles of C/R are far to the left in the s plane (*e.g.*, at least five or six times as far from the imaginary axis as the complex poles), the control poles lead to a dip in $n(\sigma)$ near the origin. The location of this dip is clear from the form of $n(\sigma)$:

$$n(\sigma) = (\sigma^2 + 2\zeta\omega_n\sigma + \omega_n^2)(\sigma + p_3)(\sigma + p_4) \tag{5.57}$$

If p_3 and p_4 are both appreciably larger than $\zeta\omega_n$, the first minimum of $n(\sigma)$ occurs in the vicinity of $-\zeta\omega_n$. The larger the value of ζ, the more pronounced the dip (with $\zeta = 1$, a double root exists and the minimum lies on the axis).

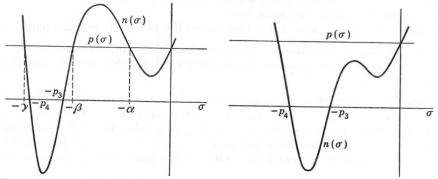

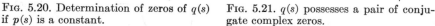

Fig. 5.20. Determination of zeros of $q(s)$ if $p(s)$ is a constant.

Fig. 5.21. $q(s)$ possesses a pair of conjugate complex zeros.

The denominator polynomial $q(s)$ of the open-loop transfer function is determined from the equation

$$q(s) = n(s) - p(s) \tag{5.58}$$

$q(s)$ is equal to the denominator minus the numerator of the over-all system function. All negative real zeros of $q(s)$ can be found, therefore, by superimposing on the plot of $n(\sigma)$ a plot of $p(\sigma)$ and determining the intersections of the two curves. $p(\sigma)$ is ordinarily a low-degree polynomial, usually at most of second degree. If $p(\sigma)$ is a constant, super-position of $p(\sigma)$ and $n(\sigma)$ takes the form shown in Fig. 5.20. The two curves intersect at $\sigma = 0$ if, as is ordinarily the case in a servomechanism, $q(s)$ possesses a zero at the origin. The other zeros of $q(s)$ are at $-\alpha$, $-\beta$, and $-\gamma$. Furthermore, these are all the zeros since $q(s)$, like $n(s)$, is a quartic.

What conditions must be satisfied if all zeros of $q(s)$ are to be negative real? In terms of Fig. 5.20, four intersections of the two curves must occur. This can be assured by a suitable choice of p_3 and p_4, in particular by making p_3 and p_4 sufficiently large. If p_3 is allowed to become too small, the situation portrayed in Fig. 5.21 exists: $q(s)$ has one pair of conjugate complex zeros which cannot be determined by sketches of $n(\sigma)$ and $p(\sigma)$. But in the synthesis procedure and in meeting the specifications, the exact values of p_3 and p_4 are not critical.   The only requirement is that both be sufficiently large to guarantee that the corresponding poles do not contribute significantly to the transient response. Thus, if $p(s)$ is a constant, the pole-zero configuration under consideration here can be made to lead to negative real zeros, exclusively, for $q(s)$.

Much the same situation exists if $p(s)$ is a linear or quadratic function, the two cases shown in Figs. 5.22 (a) and (b).   In each case, four intersections of the two curves can be assured by appropriate selection of p_3 and p_4, simultaneously with satisfaction of the condition that p_3 and p_4 should be sufficiently large.   Furthermore, the same conditions prevail when $n(s)$ is of degree higher than four and regardless of the degree of

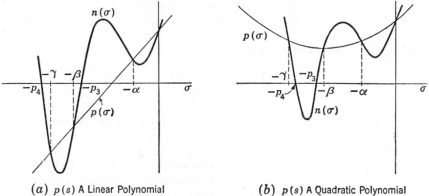

(a) $p(s)$ A Linear Polynomial (b) $p(s)$ A Quadratic Polynomial

FIG. 5.22. Determination of open-loop poles.

$p(s)$ [except for the obvious constraint that $p(s)$ must be of no higher degree than $n(s)$].

The diagrams of Figs. 5.20 and 5.22 indicate the general procedure for a graphical determination of the negative real poles of the open-loop transfer function from the poles and zeros of the closed-loop system function.   The figures represent the essential features of the second step of feedback-control-system synthesis according to Guillemin's procedure. In addition, this general approach of obtaining as much information as possible by plots of the functions along the negative real axis is useful in establishing correlations between open-loop and closed-loop characteristics regardless of the design procedure that may be used.   In the following section a number of special techniques and relationships are presented to permit full utilization of plots of this type.   In addition, the discussion considers the difficulties encountered when an integral-compensation dipole is introduced in C/R.

5.4. Additional Correlations between Open-loop and Closed-loop Characteristics.   The graphical procedure for the determination of the open-loop characteristics from the closed-loop system function was described in detail in the last section.   There are five additional comments which should be made in connection with this procedure.

K_v *in Terms of the Real-axis Plots.*   The velocity constant K_v is placed directly in evidence by plots of $n(\sigma)$ and $p(\sigma)$. As shown in Sec. 5.1, Eq. (5.9), K_v is related to the derivative of $\dfrac{C}{R}(s)$:

$$\frac{1}{K_v} = - \left\{ \frac{d}{ds}\left[\frac{C}{R}(s)\right]\right\}_{s=0} \tag{5.59}$$

In terms of the numerator and denominator polynomials of C/R,

$$\frac{1}{K_v} = - \left\{ \frac{d}{ds}\left[\frac{p(s)}{n(s)}\right]\right\}_{s=0} \tag{5.60}$$

$$\frac{1}{K_v} = - \left[\frac{p'(0)}{n(0)} - \frac{p(0)n'(0)}{n^2(0)}\right] \tag{5.61}$$

With $\dfrac{C}{R}(0)$ equal to unity, Eq. (5.61) becomes

$$\frac{1}{K_v} = \frac{n'(0) - p'(0)}{n(0)} \tag{5.62}$$

In a plot of $p(\sigma)$ and $n(\sigma)$, the two curves intersect at the origin if the open-loop transfer function has a pole at zero frequency. In addition, the difference in the slopes of $n(\sigma)$ and $p(\sigma)$ at the origin is a measure of the velocity constant of the system. For example, an infinite velocity constant implies that $n'(0)$ is equal to $p'(0)$, or, in other terms, that a double zero of $q(s)$ is at the origin, which agrees with the familiar criterion of a zero-frequency double pole in the open-loop transfer function.

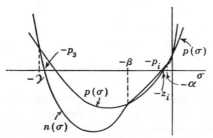

FIG. 5.23. Determination of open-loop poles when integral dipole present.

Integration Dipoles. The graphical procedure described in the preceding section for the determination of the open-loop poles becomes impractical when integral compensation is used to increase the velocity constant. With C/R possessing a dipole near the origin, both $p(\sigma)$ and $n(\sigma)$ possess zeros for slightly negative values of σ. The plots of $p(\sigma)$ and $n(\sigma)$ take the form shown in Fig. 5.23, with the near equality of the two zero-frequency slopes leading to the possibility of large errors in any graphical determination of the intersection.

The integrating zero of $q(s)$ can easily be found analytically once the other zeros are known. From the known poles and zeros of the over-all system function C/R, the value of the velocity constant can be determined by use of the expression

$$\frac{1}{K_v} = \sum_{j=1}^{n} \frac{1}{p_j} - \sum_{j=1}^{m} \frac{1}{z_j} \tag{5.63}$$

A second expression for K_v is available from the definition in terms of the open-loop transfer function:

$$K_v = \lim_{s \to 0} \left[s \frac{p(s)}{q(s)} \right] \qquad (5.64)$$

With K_v, $p(s)$, and all but one zero of $q(s)$ known, Eq. (5.64) yields the remaining zero, the integrating pole of the open-loop transfer function.

This method for the determination of one zero is illustrated by the system function of Eq. (5.38),

$$\frac{C}{R}(s) = 2.64 \frac{(s + 0.056)(s + 4)}{(s^2 + 2s + 2)(s + 5)(s + 0.059)} \qquad (5.65)$$

Here,

$$p(s) = 2.64(s + 0.056)(s + 4) \qquad (5.66)$$
$$n(s) = (s^2 + 2s + 2)(s + 5)(s + 0.059) \qquad (5.67)$$

A sketch of the form of Fig. 5.24 places in evidence at once three poles of the open-loop transfer function, at $s = 0$, -1.885, and -5.168. Thus, the open-loop transfer function is of the form

$$\frac{p(s)}{q(s)} = \frac{2.64(s + 0.056)(s + 4)}{s(s + 1.885)(s + 5.168)(s + \alpha)} \qquad (5.68)$$

The poles and zeros of the closed-loop system function were initially chosen to make the velocity constant equal to 10. Hence, the un-
known open-loop pole $-\alpha$ is given
by the equation

$$10 = \frac{(2.64)(0.056)(4)}{(1.885)(5.168)\alpha} \qquad (5.69)$$
$$\alpha = 0.00607 \qquad (5.70)$$

*Simplification of Graphical Pro-
cedure.* There are several short
cuts that can be used to simplify
the graphical procedure for the determination of the zeros of $q(s)$:

(1) Obviously $n(\sigma)$ and $p(\sigma)$
need be plotted only in the vicinity
of a zero of $q(s)$. A rough sketch
of $n(\sigma)$ and $p(\sigma)$ suffices to determine

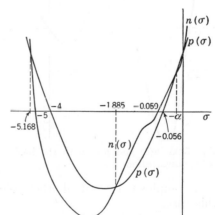

FIG. 5.24. Form of the plot for the determination of the zeros of $q(s)$.

approximately the intersections and, consequently, the regions of interest.

(2) The pair of relationships for K_v [Eqs. (5.63) and (5.64)] can be used to determine any one of the zeros of $q(s)$ or to check on the accuracy of the graphical calculations.

(3) Other analytical relations are available to determine other zeros or to check the calculations. The simplest of these is the relation between the sums of the zeros of $n(s)$ and $q(s)$. The numerator and denominator

polynomials of the over-all system function can be written

$$n(s) = s^n + \left(\sum_{j=1}^{n} p_j\right) s^{n-1} + \cdots + \prod_{j=1}^{n} p_j \tag{5.71}$$

$$p(s) = K\left[s^m + \left(\sum_{j=1}^{m} z_j\right) s^{m-1} + \cdots + \prod_{j=1}^{m} z_j\right] \tag{5.72}$$

$q(s)$ is the difference of these two functions. In all cases of interest, n is at least equal to $m + 2$, with the result that the first two terms of $q(s)$ have the form

$$s^n + \left(\sum_{j=1}^{n} p_j\right) s^{n-1}$$

Consequently, the sum of the zeros of $q(s)$ is identical with the sum of the poles of the over-all system function. From this relation, any one of the zeros of $q(s)$ can be found once the other zeros are known. (The relationship is of little value for the determination of the integrating zero, or any small zero, because of the inaccuracy introduced in the subtraction of nearly equal large numbers.)

Analytical Determination of Two Zeros. The above relation yielding the value of the sum of the zeros of $q(s)$ and the two expressions for the velocity constant, yielding the value of the product of the zeros of $q(s)$, can be used together to find, very simply, any two zeros of $q(s)$.

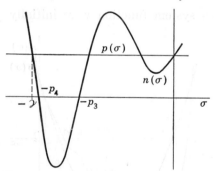

Approximate Determination of Large Zeros. The approximate determination of the real zeros of $q(s)$ lying far from the $j\omega$ axis is particularly easy if $p(s)$ is a constant. Figure 5.25 illustrates the general shape of $n(\sigma)$ if the system response is controlled by one pair of conjugate complex poles and all other poles are placed far from the $j\omega$ axis. In this case,

FIG. 5.25. $n(\sigma)$ and $p(\sigma)$ with the basic pole configuration.

$$\frac{C}{R}(s) = \frac{\omega_n^2 p_3 p_4}{(s^2 + 2\zeta\omega_n s + \omega_n^2)(s + p_3)(s + p_4)} \tag{5.73}$$

In the vicinity of p_4, $n(\sigma)$ behaves as $-p_4^3(\sigma + p_4)$. If p_4 is large, the slope of $n(\sigma)$ has a large negative value. Consequently, the intersection of $p(\sigma)$ and $n(\sigma)$, actually occurring at $-\gamma$, can be considered to occur at $-p_4$, with a negligible error in the system characteristics.

5.5. Realization of Required Open-loop Transfer Function. The final step in synthesis along the lines proposed by Guillemin for feedback control systems entails realization of the open-loop transfer function, determined as outlined in Secs. 5.3 and 5.4. The problem is complicated by the existence of certain fixed components which must be used for economic or other practical reasons. Thus, in the simple case of the design of a tandem servomechanism, the compensation network, represented by the transfer function $G_1(s)$ in Fig. 5.26, must be designed in such a way that the desired open-loop transfer function results from the tandem

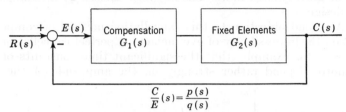

$$\frac{C}{E}(s) = \frac{p(s)}{q(s)}$$

FIG. 5.26. Single-loop system with tandem compensation.

combination of compensation network and fixed components. Analytically, $G_1(s)$ must be chosen such that

$$G_1(s)G_2(s) = \frac{p(s)}{q(s)} \tag{5.74}$$

The required $G_1(s)$ is then

$$G_1(s) = \frac{1}{G_2(s)} \frac{p(s)}{q(s)} \tag{5.75}$$

In alternate system configurations (*e.g.*, with minor loops), the required transfer functions for the compensation networks are determined in a similar manner.

What is the significance of Eq. (5.75)? With this approach the designer is basically coercing the system into behaving as required to meet the specifications. The coercion, furthermore, is not at all subtle, for $G_1(s)$ is essentially chosen to cancel out all the poles and zeros of $G_2(s)$ and reinsert a satisfactory set of critical frequencies. The dynamic characteristics of the motor, gear train, load, etc., are completely modified by the compensation network. There are certain apparent objections to such a blatant scheme of design:

(1) The commonest objection rests on the argument that one cannot cancel out motor time constants and expect the motor to behave in anything like a linear mode. Of course, this is true. If a motor possesses the transfer function $1/s(0.1s + 1)$, it is unreasonable to suppose that a tandem network with a transfer function $(0.1s + 1)/(0.001s + 1)$ is likely to result in an over-all system with a controlling time constant of 1 msec. Trouble arises because of inaccuracy in the original description of the motor, small neglected time lags present in the motor but neglected in the original characterization, and, most important, nonlinearity in motor operation.

This whole argument, however, is not a valid objection to Guillemin's method of design. The nature of the performance demanded from the motor and the fixed components of the system can be considered to be

determined by the specified characteristics of the output.   Regardless,
then, of the design method, the degree to which the motor is driven is
determined by the specifications.   Failure of the motor to operate
properly or on a linear basis with the actual input signals and with the
system designed by Guillemin's procedure simply means that a large
enough or good enough motor has not been chosen at the outset of the
system design.

(2)   A second objection to this cancellation method of compensation
is based on the impossibility of ever achieving perfect cancellation.   It is
well known, for example, that the significant time constants of a two-
phase motor depend rather strongly on the amplitude of the driving

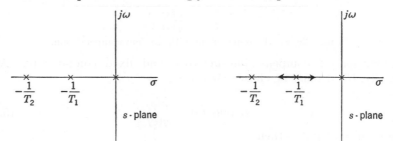

FIG. 5.27. Pole configuration for approxi-   FIG. 5.28. Variation of the time constant
mate transfer function of two-phase T_1.
motor.

signal as well as the output impedance of the amplifier and other parameters which vary during operation.   Clearly, then, it is impracticable to
design a compensation network which results in complete cancellation
of the poles and zeros of $G_2(s)$ under all conditions.   Fortunately, however, complete cancellation is not necessary; the necessary condition is
one of approximate cancellation.

As an example, one transfer function used frequently to describe a two-
phase motor is of the form

$$G_2(s) = \frac{K}{s(T_1 s + 1)(T_2 s + 1)} \tag{5.76}$$

The corresponding pole configuration is shown in Fig. 5.27.   Application
of Guillemin's synthesis procedure might result in a compensation-network transfer function of the form

$$G_1(s) = \frac{(T_1 s + 1)(T_2 s + 1)}{(T_a s + 1)(T_b s + 1)} \tag{5.77}$$

The resulting open-loop transfer function, $G_1(s)G_2(s)$, would have poles
at 0, $-1/T_a$, and $-1/T_b$ and no finite zeros.   If T_1 varies during operation over the interval shown in Fig. 5.28, imperfect cancellation occurs,
and the open-loop transfer function is of the form

$$\frac{p(s)}{q(s)} = \frac{K(T_{10} s + 1)}{s(T_a s + 1)(T_b s + 1)(T_1 s + 1)} \tag{5.78}$$

Here T_{10} is used to denote the value of T_1 for which the compensation network is designed. Although it is difficult to be quantitative here concerning the permissible variation in T_1, it is clear that appreciable variation in T_1 does not affect adversely the dynamic characteristics of the open-loop transfer function. Such variation results in the addition of an extra zero and pole to the over-all system function C/R, but these two critical frequencies are close together, with the result that the residue at this pole is very nearly zero and the residues at all other poles are not significantly altered.

Thus, if the variations in the characteristics of $G_2(s)$ are kept small, the cancellation approach to compensation is still valid. The difficulties inherent in this approach are neither worse nor better than those encountered with more conventional design techniques. Any design method for linear systems must be modified if large variations in system parameters occur, as for example the 100:1 or greater change in gain of an aircraft control surface as the aircraft speed and altitude vary over the flight regime.

(3) The third objection most commonly raised to the cancellation method of compensation expresses dislike for the unnecessary complexity of the transfer functions of the compensation network. Any synthesis method requiring complete cancellation of the critical frequencies of $G_2(s)$ and insertion of selected poles and zeros is generally going to require complicated compensation networks. Actually the situation is not so undesirable as might at first appear. In the first place, the realization of rather complicated transfer functions by suitable networks is frequently not troublesome. The discussion of Chap. 3 on network-synthesis procedures indicates that the synthesis problem is in many cases not a major difficulty of the over-all system design. Secondly, the transfer function of the compensation network is required to cancel out only those poles and zeros of $G_2(s)$ which are not also poles and zeros, respectively, of the desired open-loop transfer function. A utiliza tion of at least some of the poles of $G_2(s)$ in $p(s)/q(s)$ is possible in most cases because of the flexibility permitted in the determination of the over-all system function C/R to meet the specifications. In other words, in the usual case, the poles and zeros of C/R can be chosen anywhere within limited regions and still meet the performance specifications. The situation might be that of Fig. 5.29, where any location of the poles and zeros within the appropriate shaded regions would result in a satisfactory system. As a result of the simplicity of the method for determining the open-loop poles and zeros from the closed-loop system function, it is not difficult to select specific positions within these regions in such a way that several of the poles of the desired open-loop system function are already present in G_2.

Techniques for this adjustment of the zeros of $q(s)$ are apparent from the example of Fig. 5.30, which illustrates the situation for which the over-all system function C/R has no finite zeros [$p(\sigma)$ a constant] and four poles, two negative real and two conjugate complex. If one pole of G_2 is in the vicinity of $-p_4$, $-p_4$ can be adjusted slightly to make $-\gamma$

equal to this pole. System performance is not significantly changed by variation of p_4, since the large magnitude means that this pole has little effect on either transient or frequency response. If another pole of G_2 is in the neighborhood of $-\beta$, variation of either p_3 or the ζ of the conjugate poles permits equalization of $-\beta$ and the pole of G_2.

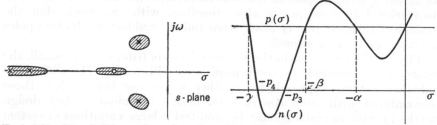

FIG. 5.29. Permissible regions for the poles and zeros.

FIG. 5.30. Determination of zeros of $q(s)$ when $p(s)$ is a constant.

One specific example illustrates the application of these ideas. The specifications considered are

$$G_2(s) = \frac{K_m}{s(s + 0.615)(s + 1.625)(s + 11.62)}$$ (5.79)

$$K_v \geq 0.9/\text{sec}$$

$$\zeta \cong 0.5, \ \omega_n \cong 1.2 \ \text{rad/sec} \quad \text{for} \ \frac{C}{R} \ (s)$$

Since the desired values of ω_n, ζ, and K_v indicate that K_v is to be appreciably less than the bandwidth, the specifications can be met by a C/R

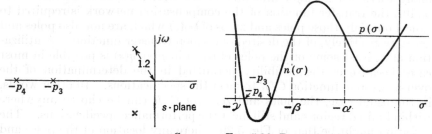

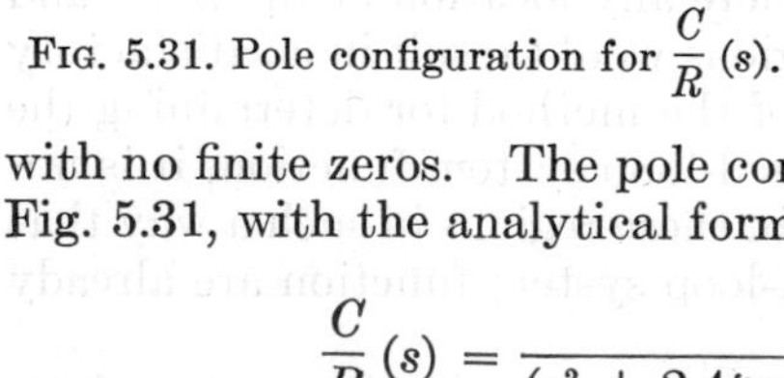

FIG. 5.31. Pole configuration for $\frac{C}{R}$ (s).

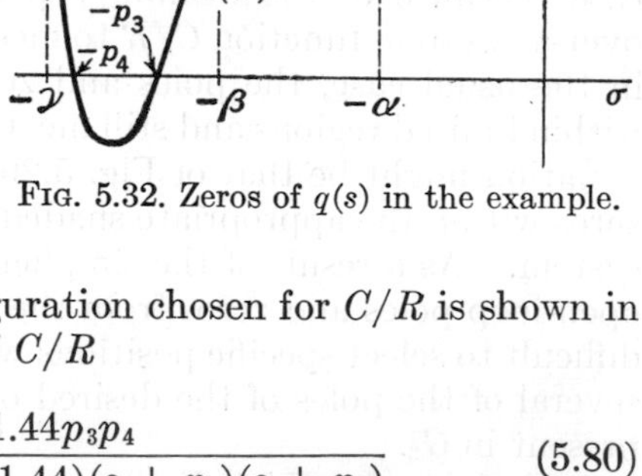

FIG. 5.32. Zeros of $q(s)$ in the example.

with no finite zeros. The pole configuration chosen for C/R is shown in Fig. 5.31, with the analytical form of C/R

$$\frac{C}{R}(s) = \frac{1.44 p_3 p_4}{(s^2 + 2.4\zeta s + 1.44)(s + p_3)(s + p_4)}$$ (5.80)

The sketch for the determination of the zeros of $q(s)$ is shown in Fig. 5.32. If p_3 and p_4 are chosen much larger than unity, $n(\sigma)$ behaves near the origin approximately as $p_3 p_4(\sigma^2 + 2.4\zeta\sigma + 1.44)$. This function has a minimum at $\sigma = -1.2\zeta$. The specified value of ζ of 0.5 leads to a first minimum of $n(\sigma)$ occurring in the vicinity of $\sigma = -0.6$. If the zeros of $n(\sigma)$ at $-p_3$ and $-p_4$ were not present [i.e., if $n(\sigma)$ were quadratic], $-\alpha$, the intersection with $p(\sigma)$, would occur at $\sigma = -2.4\zeta = -1.2$. The effect of p_3 and p_4 is to pull down the $n(\sigma)$ curve in the vicinity of $-\alpha$. Consequently, the value of α is always greater than 2.4ζ and approaches 2.4ζ as p_3 and p_4 tend to infinity.

To simplify the complexity of the compensation network, it is desired to choose a C/R in such a manner that $q(s)$ incorporates as zeros as many of the poles of $G_2(s)$ as possible. $G_2(s)$ is given by Eq. (5.79); $q(s)$ is of the form

$$q(s) = s(s + \alpha)(s + \beta)(s + \gamma) \tag{5.81}$$

Since $\alpha \geq 2.4\zeta$, no zero of $q(s)$ can occur at -0.615. It is possible, however, to place zeros of $q(s)$ at -1.625 and -11.62. If p_4 is chosen to be approximately 11.5, γ can be made as close as desired to 11.62, and one of the poles of $G_2(s)$ is utilized in the open-loop transfer function.

Either α or β can be chosen equal to 1.625, but if α is chosen, $-p_3$ will lie farther to the left and the pole at $-p_3$ will have less effect on the frequency-domain and time-domain characteristics of C/R. To make $\alpha = 1.625$, either ζ or p_3 can be arbitrarily chosen, with the other properly adjusted. A graphical sketch of $n(\sigma)$ and $p(\sigma)$ indicates that ζ can be adjusted slightly to make $\alpha = 1.625$ without violating the approximate specification on ζ. If p_3 is chosen as 8,

$$n(s) = (s^2 + 2.4\zeta s + 1.44)(s + 8)(s + 11.5) \tag{5.82}$$
$$p(s) = 132.5 \tag{5.83}$$

ζ is determined from the relationship

$$n(s) = 132.5 \qquad \text{for } s = -1.625$$

The resulting value of ζ is 0.506, and the final form for C/R, realizing a K_v of 0.95, is

$$\frac{C}{R}(s) = \frac{132.5}{(s^2 + 1.22s + 1.44)(s + 8)(s + 11.5)} \tag{5.84}$$

The open-loop transfer function is already known to a large extent; i.e.,

$$\frac{p(s)}{q(s)} = \frac{132.5}{s(s + 11.62)(s + 1.625)(s + \beta)} \tag{5.85}$$

Only β remains to be determined. This can be done graphically, as shown in Fig. 5.33, or analytically from either of the two relationships previously discussed in this section:

(a) From the sum of the zeros of $n(s)$ and $q(s)$

$$11.62 + 1.625 + \beta = 1.22 + 8 + 11.5 \tag{5.86}$$
$$\beta = 7.48 \tag{5.87}$$

(*b*) From the known value of K_v and the relation for K_v in terms of the poles and zeros of $p(s)/q(s)$,

$$0.95 = \frac{132.5}{11.62 \times 1.625\beta} \tag{5.88}$$

$$\beta = 7.37 \tag{5.89}$$

The discrepancy between Eqs. (5.87) and (5.89) is in part a result of rounding off numbers throughout the calculation, in part due to the fact -11.62 is not the exact value of the pole of the open-loop transfer function if C/R is given by Eq. (5.84).

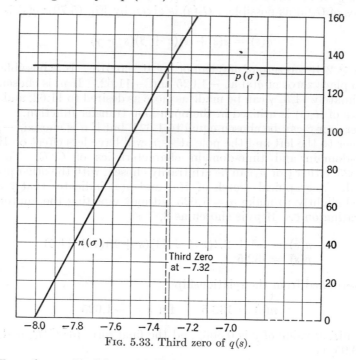

FIG. 5.33. Third zero of $q(s)$.

(*c*) From the graphical determination,

$$\beta = 7.32 \tag{5.90}$$

Thus, $p(s)/q(s)$ is completely determined as

$$\frac{p(s)}{q(s)} = \frac{132.5}{s(s + 1.625)(s + 7.35)(s + 11.62)} \tag{5.91}$$

(4) A last objection arises when $G_2(s)$ is a nonminimum-phase transfer function, *i.e.*, contains zeros in the right-half plane. This situation occasionally arises when the output of the fixed part of the system is the result of the subtraction of signals entering along two parallel paths. Under these conditions it is clearly impracticable to force the poles and zeros of the compensation-network transfer function to cancel the critical frequencies of $G_2(s)$, for this cancellation would necessitate a pole of $G_1(s)$

in the right-half plane, an unstable compensation network. Although unstable transfer functions can be realized theoretically by the use of feedback amplifiers, practical difficulties make this solution completely undesirable.

If $G_2(s)$ is nonminimum-phase, the simplest procedure is to include the right-half-plane zeros of G_2 in the open-loop transfer function $p(s)/q(s)$. The initial selection of the poles and zeros of the closed-loop system function C/R is modified to force this configuration to include the right-half-plane zeros. The other critical frequencies are chosen in such a way as to lead to a system meeting the specifications. The synthesis procedure is essentially unchanged in this case, the plot of $n(\sigma)$ and $p(\sigma)$ to determine the open-loop poles taking the usual form.

5.6. Comments on Guillemin's Method of Synthesis. The preceding sections have attempted to delineate the basic philosophy of Guillemin's synthesis procedure. The first step in synthesis involves an interpretation of the specifications in terms of the pole and zero positions for the over-all system function. In the second step, the open-loop transfer function is determined. The third step includes realization of the required compensation networks. Although the basic pattern is a fundamental evolution from specifications to final system, there is inevitably a certain amount of anticipation in the design. For example, the poles and zeros of C/R are chosen only approximately in the initial step; final adjustment can be made to simplify the compensation network by at least partial utilization of the poles of G_2.

The system designed along these lines is in many cases essentially the same as the system which results from more conventional methods of synthesis. Guillemin's procedure, just as Evans's root-locus method, provides a different viewpoint for the designer. Familiarity with these two general techniques gives the designer tools with which he can handle many of the unusual systems or systems with uncommon specifications. In particular, the two methods present for the first time the possibility of achieving throughout the design complete control over characteristics of the system transient response. In many applications, presentation of the principal specifications in terms of time-domain characteristics makes this control over the transient response essential. As an example, the discussion of Chap. 6 emphasizes the difficulty of trying to relate the frequency and transient characteristics of subsidiary transmissions. In other words, the significant effects of load-torque disturbances or other corrupting signals entering the system at points other than the input may be measurable only in the time domain; design on a frequency basis leaves the designer with the difficult and onerous task of trying to determine relations between frequency-domain and time-domain characteristics. A second example of the type of problems in which Guillemin's procedure is particularly useful lies in systems designed by statistical methods. The examples of Chap. 8 point out this close correlation between the philosophy behind statistical design methods and that of Guillemin's procedure. Essentially the two methods differ only in the type of input signals considered.

Neither Guillemin's procedure nor any of the familiar design methods is a panacea for all the problems associated with linear design. Indeed, perhaps the strongest impression the feedback-control-systems engineer acquires is the desirability of combining the various techniques in any one problem. Not only must the successful designer be able to draw upon his knowledge of a variety of engineering fields (mechanical, hydraulic, electrical, etc.), but he must in a narrower sense be able to combine the various techniques for system design to realize a final system meeting specifications which may take a tremendous variety of forms.

The following section presents an example of synthesis using Guillemin's techniques, an example which is purposely chosen sufficiently simple to illustrate the basic elements of this approach. In this case, a pair of systems is determined, each of which meets the performance specifications.

5.7. Example of Guillemin's Procedure. Synthesis is initiated by a determination of the specifications, including the transfer function of the fixed part of the system and the performance characteristics. The following specifications are considered:

(1) The fixed part of the system is described by the transfer function

$$G_2(s) = \frac{7200}{s(s + 10)(s + 30)} \tag{5.92}$$

(2) The performance characteristics are specified by the bandwidth, velocity constant, and relative damping ratio associated with the control poles:

Bandwidth: less than 60 rad/sec
K_v: greater than 60/sec
ζ: approximately 0.7

If a pole-zero configuration other than the type discussed in the preceding sections was to be used, the specification of ζ would be replaced by one describing the relative stability.

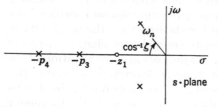

FIG. 5.34. Configuration for example of Guillemin's procedure.

As the first step in the synthesis, the over-all system function C/R is chosen. Since the specified velocity constant exceeds the allowable bandwidth, at least one zero must be used in C/R. If noise or similar considerations do not preclude the use of lead networks, the specifications can be met by a C/R with the pole-zero configuration shown in Fig. 5.34. If ζ is roughly 0.7, the value of ω_n and the location of the zero are set by the bandwidth and velocity-constant specifications. With no zeros, an ω_n of 60 rad/sec would satisfy the bandwidth specification. Addition of the zero necessitates a decrease in ω_n to realize the same bandwidth. In anticipation of the effect of the zero, ω_n is chosen as 28.3 rad/sec. (The bandwidth must be determined after C/R is completely known, to ensure satisfaction of the specifications, but this choice of ω_n leaves an appreciable margin of safety.)

The location of the zero is determined from the relation for K_v in terms of the pole and zero positions:

$$\frac{1}{K_v} = \frac{2\zeta}{\omega_n} + \frac{1}{p_3} + \frac{1}{p_4} - \frac{1}{z_1} \tag{5.93}$$

If the poles at $-p_3$ and $-p_4$ are neglected, a satisfactory value of z_1 is 30. The zero is placed at -25 to allow a margin of safety to permit realization of the required K_v when the poles at $-p_3$ and $-p_4$ are included. The form of C/R is then

$$\frac{C}{R}(s) = 32p_3p_4 \frac{s + 25}{(s^2 + 56.6\zeta s + 800)(s + p_3)(s + p_4)} \tag{5.94}$$

The choices of p_3 and p_4 are largely arbitrary, subject only to the constraints that $1/p_3 + 1/p_4$ must not appreciably influence $1/K_v$ and that p_3 and p_4 must differ sufficiently to yield real zeros of $q(s)$. A rough sketch of $n(\sigma)$ and $p(\sigma)$ (Fig. 5.35) indicates that satisfactory values are

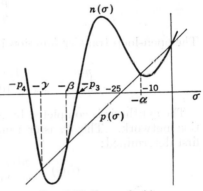

FIG. 5.35. Zeros of $q(s)$.

$$p_3 = 150 \qquad (5.95)$$
$$p_4 = 400 \qquad (5.96)$$

From the general shape of $p(\sigma)$ and $n(\sigma)$ shown in Fig. 5.35, it is apparent that, by slight adjustment of the parameter ζ, it is possible to make $\alpha = 10$ without appreciably affecting system performance. The appropriate value of ζ is most readily determined analytically:

$$(s^2 + 56.6\zeta s + 800)(s + 150)(s + 400) = 32 \times 150 \times 400(s + 25)$$
$$\text{at } s = -10 \quad (5.97)$$
$$\zeta = 0.656 \tag{5.98}$$

Thus, the final value of C/R is

$$\frac{C}{R}(s) = \frac{32 \times 150 \times 400(s + 25)}{(s^2 + 37.1s + 800)(s + 150)(s + 400)} \tag{5.99}$$

The resulting K_v is 65/sec, and the bandwidth is less than 55 rad/sec.

Determination of the open-loop transfer function constitutes the second step in the synthesis. From the sketch of Fig. 5.35 and the method used to select ζ, it is evident that

$$\frac{p(s)}{q(s)} = \frac{32 \times 150 \times 400(s + 25)}{s(s + 10)(s + \beta)(s + \gamma)} \tag{5.100}$$

The values of β and γ can be determined either graphically or analytically, although in this simple case the analytical procedure is probably easier. The product $\beta\gamma$ is known from the specified K_v and Eq. (5.100).

$$65 = \frac{32 \times 150 \times 400 \times 25}{10\beta\gamma} \tag{5.101}$$

$$\beta\gamma = 73,800 \tag{5.102}$$

The sum $\beta + \gamma$ can be found from the equality of the sum of the zeros of $h(s)$ and $q(s)$:

$$37.1 + 150 + 400 = 10 + \beta + \gamma \tag{5.103}$$
$$\beta + \gamma = 577 \tag{5.104}$$

Simultaneous solution of Eqs. (5.102) and (5.104) yields the values of β and γ.

$$\beta = 191 \tag{5.105}$$
$$\gamma = 386 \tag{5.106}$$

The open-loop transfer function is

$$\frac{p(s)}{q(s)} = \frac{1.92 \times 10^6(s + 25)}{s(s + 10)(s + 191)(s + 386)} \tag{5.107}$$

The synthesis is completed by a determination of a suitable compensation network. The transfer function of the compensation network is first determined:

$$G_1(s) = \frac{p(s)}{q(s)} \frac{1}{G_2(s)} \tag{5.108}$$

$$G_1(s) = 267 \frac{(s + 25)(s + 30)}{(s + 191)(s + 386)} \tag{5.109}$$

As an example of the method for realization of this compensation, the tandem compensation network is synthesized as an open-circuit transfer impedance of a ladder network by the methods discussed in Sec. 3.6. The open-circuit transfer impedance is set equal to the desired function of frequency, $G_1(s)$ of Eq. (5.109). An appropriate driving-point impedance is chosen with the same poles as z_{12} and the zeros are interlaced to satisfy the conditions for realizability as an RC network.

$$z_{11} = \frac{(s + 250)(s + 500)}{(s + 191)(s + 386)} \tag{5.110}$$

The driving-point impedance is now developed in a ladder network in such a way as to realize the desired transmission zeros. If these zeros are realized by antiresonant series arms, the final network takes the form shown in Fig. 5.36. This network, shown in its simplest form and without any adjustment in impedance level, is by no means necessarily the best network, but is shown only to complete the problem.

The final compensation network represents the tandem connection of two lead networks. Objection might be raised to the solution to the design problem on the basis of the difficulties inherent in the practical realization of two lead networks, each with time-constant ratios of the order of 10, especially in the presence of noise. The high time-constant ratios, however, are a direct consequence of the high K_v required by the

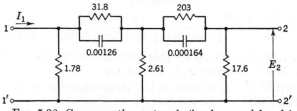

FIG. 5.36. Compensation network (in ohms and farads).

specifications. The final system would be subject to the same objections regardless of the design method used, if compensation were effected by lead networks.

This objection can be overcome by using a combination lead-lag network for compensation, corresponding to the use of a dipole in the C/R pole-zero configuration to meet the specification on K_v. Simultaneously, the bandwidth can be appreciably reduced, if desired. With this approach, the synthesis takes the following form:

Rather arbitrarily, the ω_n of the control poles is chosen as 15 (the actual ω_n which would be used in practice would depend upon how much the bandwidth was to be decreased by the use of integral rather than lead compensation). The over-all system function is then of the form

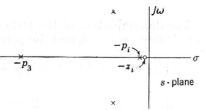

FIG. 5.37. Configuration for alternate system.

$$\frac{C}{R}(s) = \frac{(225 p_i p_3 / z_i)(s + z_i)}{(s^2 + 30\zeta s + 225)(s + p_i)(s + p_3)} \qquad (5.111)$$

The pole-zero configuration is shown in Fig. 5.37.

The zero and poles of C/R are determined. If the long tail in the unit-step-function response is to have an amplitude less than 0.05, the dipole critical frequencies must satisfy the condition derived in Sec. 5.1,

$$z_i = 0.95 p_i \qquad (5.112)$$

The values of z_i and p_i are found from the above equation and the specified velocity constant, given by the equation

$$\frac{1}{K_v} = \frac{2\zeta}{\omega_n} + \frac{1}{p_3} + \frac{1}{p_i} - \frac{1}{z_i} \qquad (5.113)$$

If ζ is approximately 0.7 and p_3 of the order of 100, Eq. (5.113) becomes

$$\frac{1}{z_i}\left(1 - \frac{z_i}{p_i}\right) = \tfrac{13}{150} \tag{5.114}$$

Simultaneous solution of (5.112) and (5.114) yields

$$z_i = 0.577 \tag{5.115}$$
$$p_i = 0.607 \tag{5.116}$$

$$\frac{C}{R}(s) = \frac{225 \times 100 \times 20}{19}\ \frac{s + 0.577}{(s^2 + 21s + 225)(s + 0.607)(s + 100)} \tag{5.117}$$

The velocity constant realized by this system function is 60, the relative damping ratio is 0.7, and the ω_n is 15 rad/sec.

The next step in the synthesis is the determination of the open-loop transfer function, which is of the form

$$\frac{p(s)}{q(s)} = \frac{100 \times 225 \times 20(s + 0.577)}{19s(s + \alpha)(s + \beta)(s + \gamma)} \tag{5.118}$$

The denominator polynomial $q(s)$ is given by the equation

$$q(s) = n(s) - p(s) \tag{5.119}$$

$$q(s) = (s + 0.607)(s^2 + 21s + 225)(s + 100)$$
$$\qquad - \frac{100 \times 225 \times 20}{19}(s + 0.577) \tag{5.120}$$

The determination of the zeros of $q(s)$ is simplified if the integrating zero is first neglected and the polynomial $q_1(s)$ is considered, where

$$q_1(s) = s(s^2 + 21s + 225)(s + 100) - \frac{100 \times 225 \times 20}{19}s \tag{5.121}$$

$$q_1(s) = s\left[(s^2 + 21s + 225)(s + 100) - \frac{100 \times 225 \times 20}{19}\right] \tag{5.122}$$

With this simplification, the zeros of $q_1(s)$ can be found by a graph of the form of Fig. 5.38, in which the two components inside the brackets in Eq. (5.122) are subtracted graphically. The zeros of $q_1(s)$ are found to lie approximately 0, $+0.496$, -23.3, and -97.2. These are also zeros of the actual denominator polynomial $q(s)$, if the assumption can be made that the magnitude of s is much larger than 0.577 and 0.607 in the vicinity of these zeros. Thus, two zeros of $q(s)$ are very nearly -23.3 and -97.2.

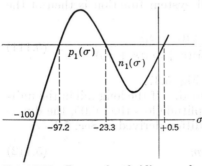

Fig. 5.38. Zeros of subsidiary polynomial, $q_1(s)$.

$q(s)$ also possesses a zero at the origin. The fourth, or integrating, zero can be determined from the known value of K_v and the definition of K_v. Thus Eq. (5.118) with the two known finite zeros yields

$$K_v = \frac{100 \times 225 \times 20}{19} \frac{0.577}{23.3 \times 97.2\alpha} \qquad (5.123)$$

With K_v equal to 60, α is about 0.10. The final expression for the open-loop transfer function in factored form is

$$\frac{p(s)}{q(s)} = 23,700 \frac{s + 0.577}{s(s + 0.10)(s + 23.3)(s + 97.2)} \qquad (5.124)$$

It should be noted here that analytical methods for the determination of the integrating zero are apt to lead to the same pitfall as a graphical method, i.e., difficulty with maintaining accuracy when relatively large, nearly equal numbers are subtracted. Determination of this integrating pole by use of the defining equation for K_v eliminates this difficulty.

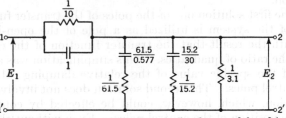

FIG. 5.39. Compensation network (in ohms and farads).

The transfer function of the compensation network is determined from the specified fixed components and the desired open-loop transfer function:

$$G_1(s) = 3.29 \frac{(s + 0.577)(s + 10)(s + 30)}{(s + 0.10)(s + 23.3)(s + 97.2)} \qquad (5.125)$$

The appropriate tandem compensation network is designed on the basis of the techniques presented in Chap. 3. If the transfer function is to be realized as an open-circuit voltage ratio, the identification is made

$$\frac{y_{12}}{y_{22}} = \frac{(s + 0.577)(s + 10)(s + 30)}{(s + 0.10)(s + 23.3)(s + 97.2)} \qquad (5.126)$$

Division of both numerator and denominator by the factor $(s + 0.577)$ $(s + 30)$ yields appropriate values of y_{12} and y_{22}:

$$y_{12} = s + 10 \qquad (5.127)$$

$$y_{22} = \frac{(s + 0.10)(s + 23.3)(s + 97.2)}{(s + 0.577)(s + 30)} \qquad (5.128)$$

Expansion of y_{22} (by a partial-fraction expansion of y_{22}/s) gives

$$y_{22} = s + 13.1 + \frac{61.5s}{s + 0.577} + \frac{15.2s}{s + 30} \qquad (5.129)$$

Since y_{22}, as shown in Eq. (5.129), can be identified as y_{12} plus an admittance function, the network, before adjustment of impedance level, takes the form of Fig. 5.39. A variety of alternate networks, some with better element spreads, can be found by changing the common factor by which both numerator and denominator of the voltage ratio were divided in the first step in the network synthesis.

The networks of Figs. 5.36 and 5.39 constitute two possible solutions to the synthesis problem. The example, as pointed out earlier, was purposely chosen simple to illustrate the basic elements of the approach to servomechanism synthesis proposed by Guillemin. Certain comments relative to this example are appropriate at this time:

(1)   Two solutions were developed for the compensation network on the basis of two pole-zero configurations for the over-all system function C/R. Clearly, a large number of other systems may be easily designed simply by using other variations of the pole-zero configurations for the closed-loop system function. In the first example, lead compensation was used, while the second solution emphasized the use of integral compensation.

(2)   In the first solution one of the poles of the transfer function of the fixed part of the system is utilized as a pole of the open-loop transfer function, with the result that the transfer function of the compensation network is the ratio of quadratics. This simplification was accomplished by choice of the specific value of the relative damping ratio associated with the control poles. The second solution does not involve any similar pole utilization, which, however, could be effected by control over the choice of the position of the control poles. Even without this simplification, the compensation network is not unduly complex.

(3)   The choice of the original pole-zero configuration involves a certain amount of experience. Even with the simple specifications considered in this example, the choices of the positions of the control poles and that of the compensation zero or dipole are interdependent, the selection of one affecting the other if the bandwidth and velocity-constant specifications are both to be met. The relative stability also depends on both the choices since the position of the lead-compensation zero as well as the ζ of the control poles determines the overshoot in the step-function response of the system. Such an interdependence of the various parameters would lead to troublesome difficulties in design if the specifications were rigid (e.g., if K_v had to be exactly 10). Fortunately, in the design of feedback control systems, the specifications can always be interpreted liberally; there is insignificant difference between systems with velocity constants of 8 and 10, for example. Indeed, in many cases, the parameters describing system characteristics are only specified within a tolerance of 20 per cent or more.

(4)   In each solution presented above, only the appropriate tandem compensation network was developed. Suitable minor-loop feedback compensation networks or networks for more complicated schemes of compensation could be designed using the same general techniques. In any case, determination of the open-loop transfer function is followed by determination of the transfer functions of the various compensation networks. The examples of Sec. 6.2 illustrate the procedure when the compensation is to be divided between a tandem network and a minor loop.

CHAPTER 6

DESIGN IN THE s PLANE

The two preceding chapters present the basic elements of Evans's root-locus method and Guillemin's synthesis procedure. Both methods emphasize the behavior of the pertinent transfer functions throughout the entire s plane. In each approach, the transfer functions, both closed-loop and open-loop, are characterized by the pole and zero locations. Knowledge of the positions of the critical frequencies permits rapid approximate determination of the transient and frequency responses of the system. The effects of varying gain or changing parameter values are studied by evaluating the corresponding motion of the poles and zeros.

Throughout the two chapters, attention is directed toward the classical design problem in feedback theory: the design of a system which meets certain performance specifications and at the same time incorporates certain components which must be used for economic or availability reasons. Thus, the problem of direct concern is essentially the filter problem—the design of a system with a suitable over-all closed-loop transfer function $\frac{C}{R}(s)$. In the design, it is assumed either that $G_2(s)$, the transfer function of the controlled system, is completely known, or at least that the appropriate constraints on $G_2(s)$ are specified.

Application of the concept of synthesis in the s plane, whether the details of the synthesis are carried out with Evans's or Guillemin's approach, raises certain questions. For example, the design of a practical system often involves the realization of control over not only the filtering characteristics, described by $\frac{C}{R}(s)$, but also the transmission to the output from a point other than the primary input (in other words, control over the effect of a disturbing signal).

An additional difficulty may arise because both Evans's and Guillemin's procedures are based on the transfer functions. Frequently, the characteristics of the controlled system are known only from experimental measurements, either sinusoidal or transient tests. Before design can be carried out in the s plane, a transfer function must be found to describe the experimental data.

Finally, the prevalence of a-c or carrier servomechanisms makes it desirable to be able to extend the techniques of design in the s plane to a-c systems. In the general case, such an extension encounters certain difficulties, but in special cases (*e.g.*, the design of narrow-band systems) the extension is straightforward.

In this chapter, these rather unrelated aspects of s plane design are considered. Sections 6.1 to 6.3 present the basic elements of the design of systems with multiple inputs; the approximation problem is considered briefly in Secs. 6.4 to 6.6; and the chapter concludes with a brief discussion of the problems peculiar to the design of a-c systems. Thus, this chapter serves as a continuation of either Chap. 4 or Chap. 5.

6.1. Systems with Multiple Inputs. One of the strongest advantages of design in terms of the poles and zeros of the various transfer functions rests in the possibility of controlling both the transient and frequency responses of not only the closed-loop system used as a filter, but also the system used to reject corrupting or unwanted signals entering at points

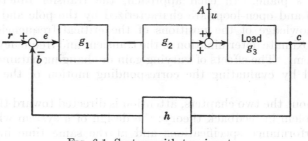

Fig. 6.1. System with two inputs.

other than the reference input. One of the primary motivations for the use of *closed-loop* systems is the opportunity of controlling such disturbances. For example, Fig. 6.1 is a possible block diagram of a servo-mechanism for the positioning of a radar antenna. The output is corrupted by the wind forces $u(t)$ entering the system as load-torque disturbances on the output shaft. The use of a closed-loop system permits independent control of the transmission from point A to the output and the primary transmission from reference input to output. Extreme examples of systems with such corrupting disturbances are afforded by certain regulators in which the only type of disturbance to which the system is subjected is variation in the load.†

Thus, a feedback control system must be considered an n-terminal-pair configuration, with the output, the primary or reference input, and a number of secondary inputs. In this section, the particular secondary input considered is a load-torque disturbance, but the analysis is applicable when the corrupting signal enters at any point except the reference input. The signal may be random noise, potentiometer noise, etc. In very general terms, the design of a system subject to multiple disturb-

† G. S. Brown and D. P. Campbell, "Principles of Servomechanisms," pp. 293–294, John Wiley & Sons, Inc., New York, 1948. Chapter IX of this reference, containing a discussion of systems subjected to multiple disturbances, points out the relation between $\dfrac{C}{R}(s)$ and $\dfrac{C}{U}(s)$ for a tandem system.

ances involves the realization of suitable dynamic characteristics for several different transmissions.

Basic Problem. The basic problem is illustrated by Fig. 6.2, the block diagram of a system with two inputs. The relation between $\frac{C}{R}(s)$ and $\frac{C}{U}(s)$ is evident from either the simultaneous equations describing the block diagram or the analysis techniques presented in Chap. 2. Each transfer function is the appropriate forward gain divided by the return difference: for the primary system, the forward gain is $G_1(s)G_2(s)G_3(s)$;

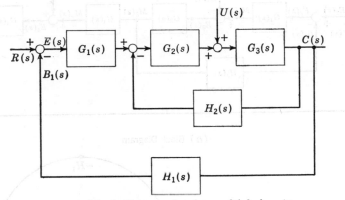

FIG. 6.2. Block diagram showing multiple inputs.

for the secondary system, $G_3(s)$. In each case the return difference is $1 + G_2(s)G_3(s)H_2(s) + G_1(s)G_2(s)G_3(s)H_1(s)$. Hence,

$$\frac{C}{R}(s) = \frac{G_1(s)G_2(s)G_3(s)}{1 + G_2(s)G_3(s)H_2(s) + G_1(s)G_2(s)G_3(s)H_1(s)} \tag{6.1}$$

$$\frac{C}{U}(s) = \frac{G_3(s)}{1 + G_2(s)G_3(s)H_2(s) + G_1(s)G_2(s)G_3(s)H_1(s)} \tag{6.2}$$

Equation (6.2) is more conveniently written in the form

$$\frac{C}{U}(s) = \frac{1}{G_1(s)G_2(s)} \left[\frac{C}{R}(s) \right] \tag{6.3}$$

In other words, the transfer function from the point of disturbance input to the output is the over-all system function divided by the transfer function from actuating signal to disturbance input, with the path broken just beyond the disturbance input. In Eq. (6.3), $G_1(s)$ and $G_2(s)$ may represent transfer functions of multiloop systems: in Fig. 6.3(a), for example, $\frac{C}{U}(s)$ is given by the equation

$$\frac{C}{U}(s) = \left[\frac{1 + G_1(s)G_2(s)H_2(s)}{G_1(s)G_2(s)G_3(s)} \right] \left[\frac{C}{R}(s) \right] \tag{6.4}$$

The first bracketed term again represents the reciprocal of the total transmission from the actuating signal to the disturbance input without leaving the disturbance input [in terms of the signal-flow diagram of Fig. 6.3(b), it represents the transfer function from E_1 to M_3 without leaving the node M_3].

Equation (6.3) is the basis for the design of systems with multiple inputs. The equation places in evidence the possibility of arbitrarily

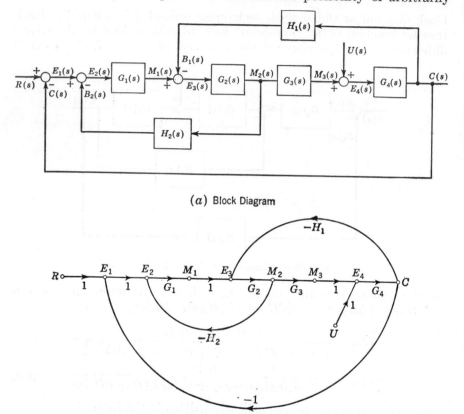

(a) Block Diagram

(b) Signal-flow Diagram

Fɪɢ. 6.3. Multiloop system.

specifying both $\dfrac{C}{R}(s)$ and $\dfrac{C}{U}(s)$. In other words, theoretically it is possible to select a $\dfrac{C}{R}(s)$ which gives suitable primary characteristics and then to choose, completely independently, a $\dfrac{C}{U}(s)$ to yield an appropriate secondary transfer function. The configuration of Fig. 6.4 can be used to illustrate the manner in which this independent control is achieved. The specifications fix $G_2(s)$, representing the load, for example; from the other specifications, $\dfrac{C}{R}(s)$ and $\dfrac{C}{U}(s)$ are determined. The ratio fixes $G_1(s)$, the tandem part of the compensation. With $G_1(s)$ and $G_2(s)$ known, either $\dfrac{C}{R}(s)$ or $\dfrac{C}{U}(s)$ suffices to determine an appropriate $H(s)$, the transfer function of the feedback elements. In other words, $\dfrac{C}{R}(s)$ specifies the compensation required. The introduction of the two compensation transfer functions $G_1(s)$ and $H(s)$ permits the division of the

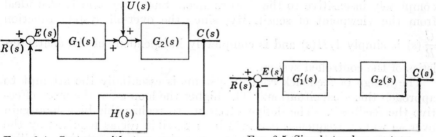

FIG. 6.4. System with two compensation networks.

FIG. 6.5. Simple tandem system.

compensation between the two in such a way that not only is $\dfrac{C}{R}(s)$ realized, but also $\dfrac{C}{U}(s)$ is controlled.

One application of the s-plane approach to the design of a system such as that of Fig. 6.4 is readily apparent. The root loci are used to determine the total tandem compensation needed to realize suitable dynamic characteristics for the primary system $\left[\,i.e.,\ \text{for }\dfrac{C}{R}(s)\right].$ This single tandem block (Fig. 6.5) is now split into the tandem and feedback blocks of Fig. 6.4. The values of $G_1(s)$ and $H(s)$ to ensure the equivalence of the two configurations can be determined in a variety of ways. In many cases, $G_1(s)$ can be chosen on the basis of the known $\dfrac{C}{R}(s)$ and the desired $\dfrac{C}{U}(s)$, and the corresponding value of $H(s)$ can then be found from a root-locus plot. The details of this type of analysis are illustrated by the examples of this and the following two sections.

In the majority of cases, the design problem is primarily concerned with minimizing the effects of the disturbing signals, a minimization which is achieved by placing upper bounds on the transfer function $\dfrac{C}{U}(s)$. These upper bounds may take the form of specifications in either the frequency or the time domain. For example, specifications may include the maximum value of $\left|\dfrac{C}{U}(j\omega)\right|$ in a frequency band of interest or, alternatively, the maximum value of $c(t)$ when $u(t)$ is a unit step function. In problems of this type, the optimum system is clearly one in which $\dfrac{C}{U}(s)$ is identically zero. Consideration of Fig. 6.4 indicates that this ideal situation can be realized in this configuration if $G_1(s)$ is infinite and $\dfrac{C}{R}(s)$ is simply $1/H(s)$. In other words, with infinite forward gain between the actuating signal and the disturbance input, the output is completely insensitive to the disturbance. Such a system is also ideal from the viewpoint of sensitivity, since the over-all system function $\dfrac{C}{R}(s)$ is simply $1/H(s)$ and is completely independent of the characteristics of the controlled system.

The design of feedback control systems is essentially the attempt to approach this ideal situation. The higher the loop gain, the more effective the feedback. The design attempts to realize this high loop gain over as wide a frequency bandwidth as possible (or as required by the specifications), while at the same time ensuring suitable relative stability for the system. The problems of design arise because, although the open-loop gain can be made essentially infinite over a finite frequency band, the gain eventually must drop off with frequency. The average rate of cutoff (where cutoff is measured by the maximum frequency at which the gain is 0 db) is limited to less than 12 db/octave if the system is to be stable, somewhat less if a degree of relative stability is desired. Thus, design involves a compromise between high loop gain and relative stability. Design of a system with multiple inputs entails the determination of how this ideal of high loop gain can be compromised without the loss of the tendency for the feedback to reject the disturbance. This compromise analytically involves the choice of a function, $G_1(s)$ in Fig. 6.4, which is finite and for which the gain is as low as possible, but which still yields an appropriate $\dfrac{C}{U}(s)$. In the following paragraphs, the choice of $G_1(s)$ is considered first in terms of the classical frequency-domain design and then in terms of design in the s plane.

Frequency-domain Design. If the feedback control system is designed in the frequency domain (*i.e.*, with the aid of a Nyquist diagram or plots of gain and phase versus frequency), it is logical to attempt to introduce frequency-domain specifications on the effects of disturbances. The spectrum of the disturbance is determined from experimental measurements or theoretical analysis. On the basis of this spectrum, an allowable variation of $\left|\dfrac{C}{U}(j\omega)\right|$ is derived. In a simple example, if the disturbing signal contains a significant amount of energy in a known frequency band, the maximum value of $\left|\dfrac{C}{U}(j\omega)\right|$ in this band might be specified.

This maximum is determined from a desire to keep the output resulting from the disturbance small compared to the output resulting from the reference input.

Clearly, it is difficult to be specific in regard to a procedure for the determination of a maximum value for $\left|\dfrac{C}{U}(j\omega)\right|$. Meeting a quantitative specification depends in large measure on the ingenuity and experience

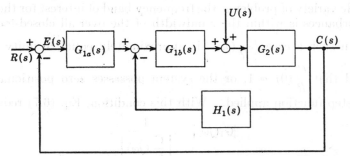

FIG. 6.6. System which can be made equivalent to Fig. 6.4.

of the designer. The procedure can be placed on a more logical basis if the statistical methods of Chaps. 7 and 8 are used; in particular, the allowable variation of $\left|\dfrac{C}{U}(j\omega)\right|$ over the frequency band of interest can be determined from the specification of the permissible mean-square value of the output resulting from the disturbance (*cf.* Sec. 8.1).

Once the allowable variation (or the maximum value) of $\left|\dfrac{C}{U}(j\omega)\right|$ is determined, the corresponding constraints on the transfer functions of the compensation networks can be determined directly. The block diagram of Fig. 6.4 is used throughout this section to illustrate the general method of analysis. It is assumed that $G_2(s)$ is specified and $G_1(s)$ and $H(s)$ are to be chosen to yield the desired characteristics for $\dfrac{C}{R}(s)$ and $\dfrac{C}{U}(s)$. Other configurations which might be considered can be designed in exactly the same manner. For example, in terms of both $\dfrac{C}{R}(s)$ and $\dfrac{C}{U}(s)$, the configuration of Fig. 6.6 is equivalent to that of Fig. 6.4 if the following relations are satisfied:

$$G_1(s) = G_{1a}(s)G_{1b}(s) \tag{6.5}$$

$$H(s) = 1 + \frac{H_1(s)}{G_{1a}(s)} \tag{6.6}$$

Thus, if $G_{1b}(s)$ and $G_2(s)$ represent the controlled system set by the specifications, $G_{1a}(s)$ and $H_1(s)$ (the transfer functions of the compensation networks) can be found from the two equations above after the configuration of Fig. 6.4 has been designed.

The system of Fig. 6.4 satisfies the equation

$$|G_1(j\omega)| = \frac{1}{\left|\dfrac{C}{U}(j\omega)\right|} \left|\frac{C}{R}(j\omega)\right| \tag{6.7}$$

In a wide variety of problems, the frequency band of interest for the study of disturbances is within the bandwidth of the over-all closed-loop system. In such a case, $\left|\dfrac{C}{R}(j\omega)\right|$ is approximately equal to unity if it is assumed that $\dfrac{C}{R}(0) = 1$, or the system possesses zero positional error with a step function applied. With this condition, Eq. (6.7) reduces to

$$|G_1(j\omega)| = \frac{1}{\left|\dfrac{C}{U}(j\omega)\right|} \tag{6.8}$$

The maximum value of $\left|\dfrac{C}{U}(j\omega)\right|$ determines directly the minimum value that $|G_1(j\omega)|$ may assume in the frequency band of interest.

Once the minimum value of $|G_1(j\omega)|$ is fixed, design can take a variety of forms. One simple procedure is to assume the frequency-dependent portion of $G_1(s)$ and determine the corresponding multiplicative gain constant from the specified minimum value. $H(s)$, the transfer function of the feedback elements, is then used to realize the desired $\dfrac{C}{R}(s)$ with the known values for $G_1(s)$ and $G_2(s)$. Since in any practical case, the specifications on the effects of disturbing signals always govern certain characteristics of the time-domain response of the system, more detailed discussion of the design procedure is postponed until the time-domain specifications are considered.

Time-domain Specifications. Complete control over the effects of disturbances can theoretically be achieved by shaping the frequency response $\dfrac{C}{U}(j\omega)$, but attempts to interpret the variation of $\dfrac{C}{U}(j\omega)$ in terms of time-domain characteristics encounter almost insurmountable difficulties because of the absence of simple correlations between frequency and time domains. The difficulties arise even in the consideration of a simple system: *e.g.*, one with a closed-loop system function given by the equation

$$\frac{C}{R}(s) = \frac{K(s + z_1)}{(s^2 + 2\zeta\omega_n s + \omega_n^2)(s + p_3)} \tag{6.9}$$

If the block diagram of the system is that shown in Fig. 6.7,

$$\frac{C}{U}(s) = \frac{1}{G_1(s)} \frac{K(s + z_1)}{(s^2 + 2\zeta\omega_n s + \omega_n^2)(s + p_3)} \tag{6.10}$$

The characteristics of $\frac{C}{U}(s)$ depend markedly on the $G_1(s)$ used to realize the closed-loop system function. If $G_1(s)$ is the transfer function

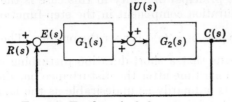

FIG. 6.7. Tandem single-loop system.

of a simple lead or lag network,

$$\frac{C}{U}(s) = \frac{s + p_g}{K_g(s + z_g)} \frac{K(s + z_1)}{(s^2 + 2\zeta\omega_n s + \omega_n^2)(s + p_3)} \tag{6.11}$$

The response $c(t)$ to a step function of disturbance exhibits very poor relative stability if $G_1(s)$ describes a lag network (with p_g much smaller than z_g). For example, if $z_g = z_1$ and $p_g = \frac{1}{10}z_1$,

$$\frac{C}{U}(s) = \frac{K}{K_g}$$

$$\frac{s + \frac{1}{10}z_1}{(s^2 + 2\zeta\omega_n s + \omega_n^2)(s + p_3)} \tag{6.12}$$

Substitution of specific numerical values illustrates the effect possible here. The poles and zeros of $\frac{C}{R}(s)$ are chosen as shown in Fig. 6.8(a), and those of $G_1(s)$ as indicated in part (b) of the figure. The closed-loop system has a step-function response with approximately 21 per cent overshoot (cf. Fig. 1.21). With these values, $\frac{C}{U}(s)$ has the pole-zero configuration shown in Fig. 6.8(c). The corresponding step-function response exhibits an overshoot of almost 600 per cent. Thus, although the final value of $c(t)$, with $u(t)$ a step function, depends on K_g and may be small, the overshoot is excessive.

If, in contrast, $G_1(s)$ represents a lead network, the system from dis-

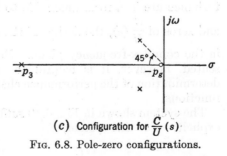

(a) Configuration for $\frac{C}{R}(s)$

(b) Configuration for $G_1(s)$

(c) Configuration for $\frac{C}{U}(s)$

FIG. 6.8. Pole-zero configurations.

turbance to output is more stable than the system from reference input to output. The corresponding pole-zero configuration for $\dfrac{C}{U}$ (s) is shown in Fig. 6.9. The principal difficulty in this case is the possibility of an extremely long-duration component in the step-function response if the zero of $G_1(s)$ $\left[\text{the pole of } \dfrac{C}{U} \ (s)\right]$ is near the origin. The existence of such a component means that a short-duration disturbing signal may excite the system for a long time after the disturbance has died out. Clearly, such a condition is ordinarily as undesirable as the large overshoot previously considered.

Thus, complete control over the effect of disturbing signals must

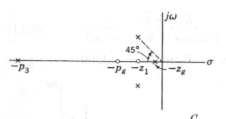

FIG. 6.9. Pole-zero configuration of $\dfrac{C}{U}$ (s) when g_1 is a lead network.

include a knowledge of the characteristics of $\dfrac{C}{U}$ (s) not only in the frequency domain, but also in terms of the transient response. Typical specifications govern certain aspects of both descriptions of system performance. As described above, the frequency-domain specifications govern the magnitude of $\left|\dfrac{C}{U} \ (j\omega)\right|$.

The time-domain specifications vary widely from problem to problem, but commonly include the following three characteristics of the response of the system to a unit step function of disturbance:

(1) The final value
(2) The settling time (or longest significant time constant)
(3) The maximum overshoot

The first quantity measures the zero-frequency, or steady-state, error with a constant disturbing signal; the second, the speed of response, or the speed with which the system settles down after a disturbance; and the third, the relative stability.

Principles of Analysis. If the specifications on the effects of the disturbance are in a form amenable to interpretation in terms of the poles and zeros of $\dfrac{C}{U}$ (s), the design of the complete system can be carried out in the complex-frequency plane. Before the approach to design is presented, however, it is helpful to consider the analysis problem: the determination of the performance characteristics from the system transfer functions.

The system shown in Fig. 6.10 suffices to make the following discussion explicit. For this system,

$$\frac{C}{U} \ (s) = \frac{1}{G_1(s)G_2(s)} \left[\frac{C}{R} \ (s)\right] \tag{6.13}$$

The analysis problem can be stated as follows: From a knowledge of the poles and zeros of $\dfrac{C}{R}$ (s) and $G_1(s)G_2(s)$, what facts can be deduced simply about the frequency and transient responses associated with $\dfrac{C}{U}$ (s)?

Since the poles and zeros of $\dfrac{C}{U}$ (s) are known, any desired transient response can be evaluated exactly by an inverse Laplace transform, but the objective of this analysis is not an exact expression for the transient response, but rather an approximate, qualitative picture easily deduced.

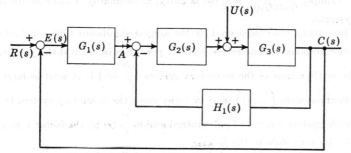

FIG. 6.10. System with disturbance input.

Thus, the analysis is logically divided into two parts: determination of the poles and zeros of $\dfrac{C}{U}$ (s), and interpretation of these pole and zero positions in terms of significant characteristics of the frequency and transient responses.

The poles and zeros of $\dfrac{C}{U}$ (s) are those of $\dfrac{C}{R}$ (s) and $1/[G_1(s)G_2(s)]$ (unless cancellation occurs). The possibility of such cancellation is clear if $\dfrac{C}{R}$ (s) is written in terms of the component transfer functions,

$$\frac{C}{R}(s) = \frac{G_1(s)G_2(s)G_3(s)}{1 + G_2(s)G_3(s)H_1(s) + G_1(s)G_2(s)G_3(s)} \qquad (6.14)$$

Substitution of Eq. (6.14) in (6.13) demonstrates that zeros of $\dfrac{C}{R}$ (s) may be generated by zeros of $G_1(s)G_2(s)$ and, hence, may not appear in $\dfrac{C}{U}$ (s). The expression for $\dfrac{C}{U}$ (s) is left in the form of Eq. (6.13), however, because it is convenient to determine the settling time and relative stability of $\dfrac{C}{U}$ (s) in terms of the known characteristics of the over-all system described by $\dfrac{C}{R}$ (s).

Once the poles and zeros of $\dfrac{C}{U}$ (s) are known, the frequency response $\left|\dfrac{C}{U} (j\omega)\right|$ can be found in the usual way: either by the asymptotic plots or by consideration of the vectors in the s plane from the various poles and zeros to a point moving along the $j\omega$ axis. The three characteristics of the unit-step-function response (the steady-state value, the settling time, and the overshoot) are determined as follows:

(1)   Equation (6.13) indicates that the final value of this subsidiary step-function response is simply $\dfrac{1}{G_1(0)G_2(0)}$ if $\dfrac{C}{R}$ (0) is unity, as ordinarily is the case for feedback control systems.

(2)   The settling time (measured by the longest significant time constant) for the step-function response is determined by that pole of $\dfrac{C}{U}$ (s) nearest the $j\omega$ axis. Ordinarily, the settling time of the secondary system $\left(\dfrac{C}{U} (s)\right)$ is at least as large as that of the primary system $\left(\dfrac{C}{R} (s)\right)$, and in many cases the secondary system is appreciably more sluggish as a result of poles introduced in $\dfrac{C}{U}$ (s) by the factor $1/[G_1(s)G_2(s)]$, poles which lie very close to the $j\omega$ axis.

(3)   An approximate picture of the relative stability of the secondary system can be deduced from the known relative stability of the primary system and the location of the poles and zeros of $1/[G_1(s)G_2(s)]$. The concepts presented in Sec. 1.4 apply directly here.

6.2. Design of a System with Multiple Inputs.   The design of a system with specified transmission characteristics $\left[\text{represented by } \dfrac{C}{R} (s)\right]$ and also with a controlled susceptibility to disturbing signals can be effected with the root-locus method or Guillemin's procedure. The specific problem considered here is illustrated in Fig. 6.10. The two transfer functions $G_2(s)$ and $G_3(s)$ are given, and $G_1(s)$ and $H_1(s)$ are to be determined.

The design can be started in several ways. For example, an $H_1(s)$ might be sought such that $\dfrac{G_2(s)G_3(s)}{1 + G_2(s)G_3(s)H_1(s)}$, the transfer function from point A (Fig. 6.10) to the output, is of such a nature that an appropriate tandem network for $G_1(s)$ results in values of both $\dfrac{C}{R}$ (s) and $\dfrac{C}{U}$ (s) meeting the specifications. A more direct and considerably simpler procedure breaks the problem into two parts:

(1)   It is first assumed that tandem compensation only is to be used (as shown in Fig. 6.11), and $G_{1a}(s)$ is determined to yield an appropriate closed-loop system function $\dfrac{C}{R}$ (s). The determination of $G_{1a}(s)$ is conveniently effected in terms of the poles and zeros, particularly since the critical frequencies are needed in the second part of the design.

(2)   The second stage of the design involves a division of the compensation, with part effected in the tandem network and part by the feedback elements.   Thus the single transfer function $G_{1a}(s)$ of Fig. 6.11 is replaced by the two transfer functions $G_1(s)$ and $H_1(s)$ in Fig. 6.10.   The manner of separation of the tandem compensation is governed by the specifications on $\frac{C}{U}$ (s).

Illustrative Example.   The details of the design procedure as outlined above are clarified by a simple example.   Since the second stage of the procedure is of primary interest in this section, it is assumed that the first part is completed with the transfer functions, defined in Fig. 6.10,

$$G_2(s) = \frac{1}{s + 1.15} \tag{6.15}$$

$$G_3(s) = \frac{0.5}{s(s + 0.5)} \tag{6.16}$$

$$\frac{C}{R}(s) = \frac{200(s + 2)}{(s^2 + 2s + 2)(s + 10)(s + 20)} \tag{6.17}$$

$G_2(s)$ and $G_3(s)$ characterize the controlled system and are given in the

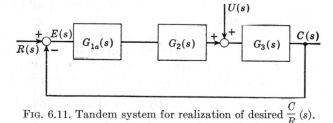

FIG. 6.11. Tandem system for realization of desired $\frac{C}{R}$ (s).

original specifications for the problem. $\frac{C}{R}$ (s) represents the results of s-plane design to meet the over all system specifications of a velocity constant of 1.5, an overshoot in the step-function response of approximately 7 per cent, and a bandwidth of less than 1.9 rad/sec.†
The transfer function of a tandem compensation network which can be used to give the above $\frac{C}{R}$ (s) in the presence of $G_2(s)$ and $G_3(s)$ is

$$G_{1a}(s) = \frac{400(s + 2)(s + 0.5)}{(s + 12.1)(s + 18.8)} \tag{6.18}$$

The large lead ratios required in $G_{1a}(s)$ are a result of the wide bandwidth and high velocity constant desired for $\frac{C}{R}$ (s) even though the controlled system has a transfer function, $G_2(s)G_3(s)$, with a magnitude which decreases rapidly with frequency.

† The values here and throughout this problem are those existing after the frequency has been normalized to place the principal poles of $\frac{C}{R}$ (s) at $-1 \pm j1$.

At this point, the second part of the system design is initiated, the control over the system response to disturbing signals entering between the $G_2(s)$ and $G_3(s)$ blocks of Fig. 6.10. In this example, the specifications governing this secondary system describe the following three characteristics of the response to a $u(t)$ which is a unit step function:

(1) The final value of the output must be less than $\frac{1}{10}$.
(2) The settling time must be approximately the same as for a reference input $r(t)$.
(3) The overshoot is to be less than 25 per cent.

From these specifications, a configuration is selected and the required transfer functions determined.

Selection of a Configuration. The choice of a configuration is largely arbitrary. A tandem system, with $G_{1a}(s)$ the transfer function of the compensation network, would be the simplest solution, but it is not difficult to demonstrate that the specifications cannot be met with this configuration. The torque constant,† which must be at least 10, is

$$G_{1a}(0)G_2(0) \bigg/ \frac{C}{R}\,(0)$$ for the tandem system. Substitution of the values from Eqs. (6.15), (6.17), and (6.18) yields a value of 1.53. Even if this value were adequate, the settling time and overshoot would have to be considered for the tandem system.

Once the simple tandem system is rejected, a number of alternate configurations can be considered. Any configuration in which the compensation is effected in two independent parts always permits meeting the specifications, since the two degrees of freedom can be utilized to control $\frac{C}{R}\,(s)$ and $\frac{C}{U}\,(s)$ independently. In this example, the system considered is that of Fig. 6.10, containing the two unknown transfer functions $G_1(s)$ and $H_1(s)$.

Partial Determination of $G_1(s)$ and $H_1(s)$. $G_1(s)$ and $H_1(s)$ can be determined to a large extent from simple logical reasoning and the knowledge of the required open-loop transfer function $G_{1a}(s)G_2(s)G_3(s)$, which is given explicitly by the equation

$$\frac{C}{E}\,(s) = \frac{200(s + 2)}{s(s + 1.15)(s + 12.1)(s + 18.8)} \tag{6.19}$$

Certain factors of $G_1(s)$ and $H_1(s)$ are apparent at once or can be chosen arbitrarily without significant loss of freedom.

(1) The simplest way to introduce a zero in $\frac{C}{E}\,(s)$ is by a zero of $G_1(s)$. Hence, $G_1(s)$ contains the numerator factor $s + 2$. This zero might also be introduced as a pole of $H_1(s)$, but this possibility is discarded in the following discussion.

---

† The torque constant K_t is defined as the reciprocal of the steady-state error when the only input is a unit step of load-torque disturbance. In other words, for a system with unity over-all feedback,

$$K_t = \lim_{s \to 0} \frac{1}{E(s)/U(s)}$$

(2) The poles of $G_2(s)G_3(s)$ which are also to be poles of $\dfrac{C}{E}$ (s) are made zeros of $H_1(s)$. Hence, $H_1(s)$ contains the numerator factor $s(s+1.15)$.

(3) If $H_1(s)$ is to be simply realized (e.g., by a tachometer and RC network), it must have at most a simple pole at infinity.

(4) The infinite-frequency behavior of $\dfrac{C}{E}$ (s) is identical with that of $G_1(s)G_2(s)G_3(s)$ if $H_1(s)$ does not have a third-order pole at infinity, since the minor-loop gain

$$G_2(s)G_3(s)H_1(s)$$

approaches zero as s tends to infinity. Hence,

$$G_1(s) \xrightarrow[s\to\infty]{} 400 \qquad (6.20)$$

(5) A pole of $H_1(s)$ produces a zero in the over-all open-loop transfer function. This zero must be canceled by a pole of $G_1(s)$.

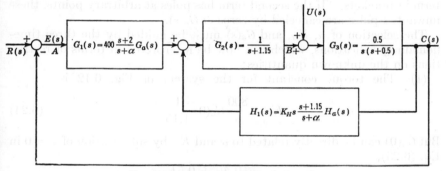

FIG. 6.12. System partially designed.

The most general form of compensation satisfying these five requirements is shown in Fig. 6.12. In this block diagram, $G_a(s)$ and $H_a(s)$ are arbitrary transfer functions, with $G_a(s)$ approaching unity and $H_a(s)$ approaching unity or zero as s tends to infinity. The corresponding open-loop transfer function is

$$\frac{C}{E}(s) = \frac{200(s+2)}{s(s+1.15)} G_a(s) \frac{1}{(s+0.5)(s+\alpha)+0.5K_H H_a(s)} \qquad (6.21)$$

By variation of $G_a(s)$, it is possible to produce a variety of poles and zeros in the transfer function from A to B in Fig. 6.12 [the transfer function which determines the relation between $\dfrac{C}{R}$ (s) and $\dfrac{C}{U}$ (s)]. There is still considerably more freedom here than required to meet the specifications. In order to reduce this freedom, it is assumed here that it is desirable to simplify the feedback network by selecting $H_a(s)$ identically unity. The resulting transfer function for the feedback elements is simply

$$H_1(s) = K_H s \frac{s+1.15}{s+\alpha} \qquad (6.22)$$

Introduction of Time-domain Specifications. α, K_H, and $G_a(s)$ must be selected to make the open-loop transfer function of Eq. (6.21) identical with the desired value of Eq. (6.19), or, if the two expressions are equated and like factors canceled,

$$\left[\frac{G_a(s)}{(s+\alpha)(s+0.5)}\right]\left[\frac{1}{1+\dfrac{0.5K_H}{(s+\alpha)(s+0.5)}}\right]$$

$$= \frac{1}{(s+12.1)(s+18.8)} \qquad (6.23)$$

In spite of the numerous arbitrary assumptions already made, there still is considerably more freedom than required to guarantee the proper open-loop transfer function. The poles at -12.1 and -18.8 in the right side of Eq. (6.23) can be generated in the left side by either $G_a(s)$ or the second term in brackets. If the second term has poles at arbitrary points, these unwanted poles are canceled by zeros of $G_a(s)$.

The selection of α, K_H, and $G_a(s)$ must be guided by the three time-domain specifications, which can now be interpreted in terms of restrictions on the unknown quantities:

(1) The torque constant for the system of Fig. 6.12 is

$$K_t = \frac{800}{\alpha} G_a(0) \frac{1}{1.15} \qquad (6.24)$$

But $G_a(0)$ can be directly related to α and K_H by substitution of $s = 0$ in Eq. (6.23),

$$G_a(0) = \frac{0.5\alpha + 0.5K_H}{12.1 \times 18.8} \qquad (6.25)$$

Substitution of Eq. (6.25) in (6.24) gives

$$K_t = 1.53 + 1.53\frac{K_H}{\alpha} \qquad (6.26)$$

If K_t is to be greater than 10,

$$\frac{K_H}{\alpha} > 5.54 \qquad (6.27)$$

(2) The settling time of the secondary system (C/U) is determined by the poles of the transfer function,

$$\frac{C}{U}(s) = \underbrace{\frac{(s+\alpha)(s+1.15)}{400(s+2)G_a(s)}}_{\frac{1}{G_1(s)G_2(s)}} \underbrace{\frac{200(s+2)}{(s^2+2s+2)(s+10)(s+20)}}_{\frac{C}{R}(s)} \qquad (6.28)$$

Any zeros of $G_a(s)$ [poles of the second term in brackets of Eq. (6.23)] must be to the left of -1 if the settling time of the secondary system is to be at least as short as that of the primary system described by $\frac{C}{R}(s)$ with poles at $-1 \pm j1$.

(3)   The overshoot specification requires that, except for the zero at -1.15, all zeros of $\dfrac{C}{U}\,(s)$ lie well to the left of -1, since the zero already present at -1.15, when combined with the poles at $-1 \pm j1$, generates an overshoot of nearly 20 per cent (*cf.* Fig. 1.21).   Additional zeros around -1 or farther to the right would increase the overshoot beyond the 25 per cent allowed by the specifications.   The zeros, excluding -1.15, are at $-\alpha$ and at the poles of $G_a(s)$.   But the poles of $G_a(s)$, if present at all, are at -12.1 and -18.8; accordingly, the overshoot specification is met if α is of the order of magnitude of 5 or larger.

Thus, the time-domain specifications reduce to the restrictions that

$$K_H > 5.54\alpha$$
$$\alpha > 5 \tag{6.29}$$

Poles of $\dfrac{1}{1 + \dfrac{0.5 K_H}{(s + \alpha)(s + 0.5)}}$ lie to the left of -1

In addition, realization of the desired open-loop transfer function requires that K_H, α, and $G_a(s)$ be chosen such that Eq. (6.23) is satisfied.   Thus, α and K_H can be selected to meet Eq. (6.29), and $G_a(s)$ is then determined from (6.23).

Final Selection of $G_1(s)$ *and* $H_1(s)$. The poles of

$$\left[1 + \dfrac{0.5 K_H}{(s + \alpha)(s + 0.5)} \right]$$

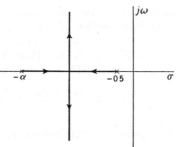

FIG. 6.13. Root-locus plot for $\dfrac{0.5 K_H}{(s + 0.5)(s + \alpha)}$.

can be determined by a root-locus plot as shown in Fig. 6.13, where the poles vary along the loci shown as a function of the value of K_H.   The simplest choice of α and K_H results in the two poles lying at -12.1 and -18.8, for in this case $G_a(s)$ is simply unity, as indicated by Eq. (6.23).   These values for the poles are realized with a value of α given by the fact that the sum of the poles is always $-0.5 - \alpha$,

$$\alpha = 12.1 + 18.8 - 0.5 \tag{6.30}$$
$$\alpha = 30.4 \tag{6.31}$$

The corresponding value of K_H can be found graphically from the root-locus plot or analytically by equating the constant terms in the two denominators of Eq. (6.23).

$$0.5\alpha + 0.5 K_H = 12.1 \times 18.8 \tag{6.32}$$
$$K_H = 425 \tag{6.33}$$

These values of α and K_H satisfy the specifications of Eq. (6.29) with a considerable safety factor. Although this is analytically the simplest choice for the two variables, the resulting system is wasteful of gain. For example, the torque constant realized is about 23, in comparison with the required value of 10. In addition, the gain of the feedback transfer function is considerably larger than required to meet the specifications, since K_H is appreciably larger than 5.54α, and the time constant $(1/\alpha)$ associated with $G_1(s)$ and $H_1(s)$ is unnecessarily short. Admission of a

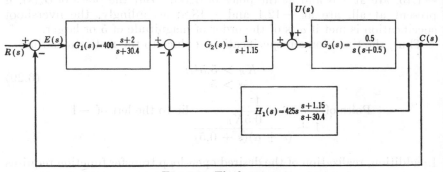

FIG. 6.14. Final system.

slightly more complex function for $G_1(s)$—that is, $G_a(s)$ not unity—would permit reduction of α to 5 and K_H to 5.54α.

If the simple set of values is used, with $G_a(s)$ unity, the final system is shown in Fig. 6.14. Here the torque constant realized is 23 and the secondary transfer function is

$$\frac{C}{U}(s) = \frac{(s + 30.4)(s + 1.15)}{2} \cdot \frac{1}{(s^2 + 2s + 2)(s + 10)(s + 20)} \quad (6.34)$$

The pole-zero configuration, shown in Fig. 6.15, indicates that the pre-dominant time constant associated

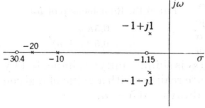

FIG. 6.15. Pole-zero configuration for $\frac{C}{U}(s)$.

with $\frac{C}{U}(s)$ is the same (1 sec) as that with $\frac{C}{R}(s)$, and that the overshoot of the secondary system is controlled by the zero at -1.15 and the poles at $-1 \pm j1$ and, accordingly, is approximately 16 per cent (cf. Fig. 1.21). Thus, all specifications are met by the system of Fig. 6.14.

Recapitulation. At this point, it is appropriate to summarize the significant features of the design procedure as outlined in the above example:

(1) The system is first designed to meet the specifications on the primary transfer function $\frac{C}{R}(s)$. Here, the assumption is made that the

compensation is to be effected solely by a tandem network and that the transfer function $G_{1a}(s)$ of this network is determined.

(2) The specifications on the effects of disturbances are now considered. A suitable configuration to meet these specifications is selected. Generally, this configuration must contain at least two unknown transfer functions.

(3) On the basis of physical reasoning, as much as possible of the unknown transfer functions is determined. The basis for this determination is the required form for the over-all open-loop transfer function.

(4) Enough arbitrary selections are made to reduce the degrees of freedom to a number which the designer can handle intelligently. These selections are guided by a desire to keep the net complexity of the unknown transfer functions as low as possible.

(5) The specifications on the effects of the disturbance are considered quantitatively and are interpreted, as far as possible, in terms of the unknown parameters remaining in the two transfer functions.

(6) A set of values is chosen for these unknown parameters. Ideally, this set is always chosen to result in a system meeting all specifications. In general, however, a certain amount of trial-and-error analysis is necessary, especially if the specifications are not readily phrased simply in terms of the unknown parameters. The use of the root-locus method to analyze the minor loops permits rapid investigation of the effect of varying parameters on the poles and zeros of the closed-loop transfer function.

(7) Ordinarily, a number of satisfactory sets of values for the unknown parameters can be determined without difficulty. One set is selected on the basis of practical considerations which are not conveniently stated analytically, such considerations as limitations on amplifier gain, required size of components, system susceptibility to noise, etc.

Consideration of these seven steps (particularly the third through sixth) indicates that the fundamental philosophy is very similar to that of classical servo design theory. An attempt is made to find a set of open-loop transfer functions yielding an appropriate closed-loop characteristic (in this case C/U). Such an approach is satisfactory in the majority of problems, but, when unusual specifications are encountered, the determination of an appropriate set of compensation transfer functions can become extremely tedious in the absence of a logical procedure.

These difficulties can be circumvented if Guillemin's procedure (Chap. 5) is used for the division of the compensation between $G_1(s)$ and $H_1(s)$. With this approach, $\dfrac{C}{U}(s)$ is arbitrarily selected *at the outset of the design* to meet the specifications on the effects of the disturbing signal. $G_1(s)$ is determined at once from the ratio $\dfrac{C/R}{C/U}$. $H_1(s)$ is then evaluated from either $\dfrac{C}{R}(s)$ or $\dfrac{C}{U}(s)$ and the known $G_1(s)$, $G_2(s)$, and $G_3(s)$ by the procedure described in detail in Chap. 5. In this way, all trial-and-error steps are removed from the design. If the $H_1(s)$ resulting from such a straightforward approach is undesirably complicated, the poles and zeros selected for $\frac{C}{U}(s)$ and $\frac{C}{R}(s)$ can be adjusted slightly in order to obtain cancellation of numerator and denominator factors of $H_1(s)$. The adjustment follows the lines indicated in Sec. 5.4. In general, if the specifications are not strict, the intuitive, trial-and-error procedure outlined in this section is desirable; it is only when the specifications become more difficult to meet that the logical nature of Guillemin's procedure is most rewarding.

6.3. Example of s-plane Design. The example of the last section was presented to explain the general approach used in the design of a system to control a secondary transmission as well as the primary transmission from reference input to the output. In this section, another example demonstrates certain slightly different aspects of the same

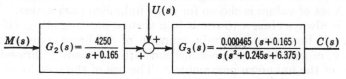

FIG. 6.16. Controlled system for Sec. 6.3.

approach and also emphasizes the simplicity of the design once the general techniques are understood. In this case, the complete design is considered, rather than just the realization of a suitable secondary transmission.

Specifications. The specifications include a description of the controlled system, the desired performance characteristics of the over-all system, and certain constraints on the response of the system to a disturbance.

(1) The controlled system is described by Fig. 6.16; the complete transfer function is

$$G_2(s)G_3(s) = \frac{1.975}{s(s^2 + 0.245s + 6.375)} \qquad (6.37)\dagger$$

The conjugate complex poles of $G_2(s)G_3(s)$ are described by an ω_n of 2.52 rad/sec and a ζ of 0.049. The disturbance enters the controlled system in such a way that $G_3(s)$, the transfer function from disturbance input to system output, is

$$G_3(s) = \frac{0.000465(s + 0.165)}{s(s^2 + 0.245s + 6.375)} \qquad (6.38)$$

Hence,

$$G_2(s) = \frac{4250}{(s + 0.165)} \qquad (6.39)$$

† Again in this example, it is assumed that an appropriate frequency normalization has been introduced.

(2)   The performance specifications require a system with an overshoot of less than 5 per cent, a velocity constant greater than 0.8, and a bandwidth less than 1.5 rad/sec.

(3)   The response of the system to a disturbance which is a unit step function is to have the following characteristics: a final value less than $\frac{1}{3000}$, a maximum time constant essentially the same as that associated with the primary system, and an overshoot less than 25 per cent.

Design of the Primary System.   The first step involves the design of the primary system: *i.e.*, the determination of a tandem compensation network (Fig. 6.17) to yield a $\frac{C}{R}$ (s) meeting the specifications.   If the highly underdamped, complex poles of $G_2(s)G_3(s)$ are canceled by zeros

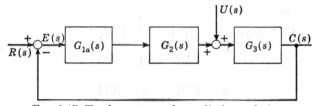

FIG. 6.17. Tandem system for preliminary design.

of $G_{1a}(s)$, the open-loop transfer function takes the form

$$\frac{C}{E}(s) = \frac{1.975K_a}{s(s+a)(s+b)} \qquad (6.40)$$

where K_a is the constant multiplier in $G_{1a}(s)$.

The poles $-a$ and $-b$ must be chosen such that closing of the loop results in a $\frac{C}{R}$ (s) meeting the performance specifications on overshoot, velocity constant, and bandwidth.   If a and b are sufficiently different and the open-loop gain is large enough, the characteristics of $\frac{C}{R}$ (s) are almost completely determined by the pair of complex poles indicated by the complex loci of Fig. 6.18.   A ζ of 0.707 for these poles results in a suitable overshoot

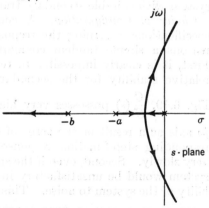

FIG. 6.18. Root loci if a and b are real.

of the step-function response.   The ω_n, which for this ζ must be less than the maximum allowable bandwidth [*cf.* Eq. (5.42)], is chosen as 1.41 rad/sec.   If it is arbitrarily assumed that the real closed-loop pole is at -10 when the gain is such that the complex poles are at $-1 \pm j1$, the closed-loop system function is

$$\frac{C}{R}(s) = \frac{20}{(s^2 + 2s + 2)(s + 10)} \tag{6.41}$$

The corresponding K_v is 0.91, and all specifications on $\dfrac{C}{R}(s)$ are met.†

Thus, a and b must be chosen to give closed-loop poles at $-1 \pm j1$ and -10. In this simple case, the appropriate values of a and b can be determined from the root-locus diagram directly: the sum of $-a$ and $-b$ must be equal to the sum of the closed-loop poles, or

$$a + b = 12 \tag{6.42}$$

The product ab must be equal to the sum of the closed-loop poles taken two at a time, or

$$(-a)(-b) = (-1 + j)(-1 - j) + (-1 + j)(-10) \\ + (-1 - j)(-10) \tag{6.43}$$
$$ab = 22 \tag{6.44}$$

Hence,

$$a = 2.26 \qquad b = 9.74 \tag{6.45}‡$$

The appropriate transfer function for the tandem compensation network is

$$G_{1a}(s) = \frac{10.13(s^2 + 0.245s + 6.375)}{(s + 2.26)(s + 9.74)} \tag{6.46}$$

With $G_{1a}(s)$ and $\dfrac{C}{R}(s)$ determined, the performance specifications have been met, and attention can now be concentrated on realization of a system with suitable secondary transmission.

Choice of Configuration. A configuration is selected to meet the specifications governing the response to the disturbance. For several reasons a simple tandem configuration (Fig. 6.19) is unsatisfactory. First, it is clearly impossible to realize a tandem system with suitable relative stability for the secondary transmission. For the system of Fig. 6.19, $\dfrac{C}{U}(s)$ possesses very highly underdamped poles close to the $j\omega$ axis as a result of the zeros of $G_{1a}(s)$ at $-0.123 \pm j2.52$. The corresponding step-function response exhibits oscillations which die out very slowly. Second, even if the specifications could be met, the tandem system would be unsatisfactory in many cases because of the susceptibility of the system to noise. This difficulty arises because realization of

---

† If the K_v determined at this point is not large enough, a different closed-loop pole-zero configuration is used. The particular configuration can be selected by trial and error or, more logically, by the methods described in Sec. 5.1.

‡ When the transfer functions are of higher order, the methods of Sec. 5.3 are useful in determining graphically the appropriate open-loop poles from the known closed-loop poles and zeros.

$G_{1a}(s)$ by either a mechanical or an electric circuit is most simply effected by the use of a set of elements tuned to the resonant frequency (2.52 rad/sec) and with very little damping. Consequently, any pickup of noise (in the electric system) or vibration (in the mechanical system) at this resonant frequency would be amplified tremendously by the sharply resonant $G_2(s)G_3(s)$.

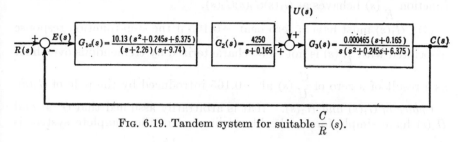

FIG. 6.19. Tandem system for suitable $\dfrac{C}{R}$ (s).

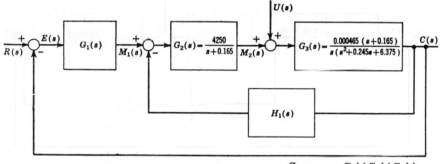

FIG. 6.20. System with two compensation networks. $\quad \dfrac{C}{E}(s) = \dfrac{G_1(s)G_2(s)G_3(s)}{1 + G_2(s)G_3(s)H_1(s)}$.

These disadvantages can be avoided if the configuration of Fig. 6.20 is considered. The design problem is now one of selecting values for $G_1(s)$ and $H_1(s)$ which meet the specifications on $\dfrac{C}{U}$ (s) and, at the same time, yield the required forward transfer function

$$\frac{C}{E}(s) = \frac{20}{s(s + 2.26)(s + 9.74)} \tag{6.47}$$

Basic Characteristics of $G_1(s)$ and $H_1(s)$. Certain characteristics of $G_1(s)$ and $H_1(s)$ can be deduced at once:

(1) $H_1(s)$ has a zero at $s = 0$, since both $\dfrac{C}{E}$ (s) and $G_2(s)G_3(s)$ have poles at the origin. If $H_1(s)$ did not have a zero at the origin, $\dfrac{C}{M_1}$ (s) would not have a pole at $s = 0$ and the synthesis of $G_1(s)$ would be unnecessarily complicated by the necessity of introducing the zero-frequency pole.

(2) $G_1(s)$ and $H_1(s)$ have coincident finite poles if the poles of $H_1(s)$ are not to introduce zeros in $\dfrac{C}{E}$ (s).

(3)   As s tends to infinity, $G_1(s)$ approaches 10.13, since at high frequencies the minor-loop gain tends to zero and the forward transfer function $\dfrac{C}{E}$ (s) behaves as $G_1(s)G_2(s)G_3(s)$.

(4) $G_1(s)$ must have a zero near -0.165 if the step-function response associated with $\dfrac{C}{U}$ (s) is not to be characterized by tremendous overshoot as a result of a zero of $\dfrac{C}{U}$ (s) at -0.165 introduced by the pole of $G_2(s)$.

Choice of $G_1(s)$ and $H_1(s)$. If it is arbitrarily assumed that $G_1(s)$ and $H_1(s)$ have simple forms, the block diagram of the complete system is

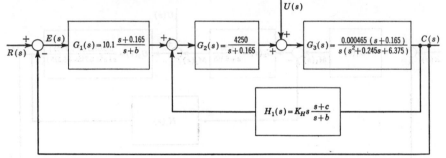

Fig. 6.21. $G_1(s)$ and $H_1(s)$ partially evaluated.

shown in Fig. 6.21. The question now arises: Is this simple configuration sufficiently general to permit satisfaction of the specifications on $\dfrac{C}{U}$ (s)? The secondary transfer function is

$$\frac{C}{U} (s) = \frac{1}{G_1(s)G_2(s)} \frac{C}{R} (s) \tag{6.48}$$

Substitution of the values for the component functions gives

$$\frac{C}{U} (s) = \frac{s + b}{10.1(s + 0.165)} \frac{s + 0.165}{4250} \frac{20}{(s^2 + 2s + 2)(s + 10)} \tag{6.49}$$

The characteristics of $c(t)$ when $u(t)$ is a step function can be determined from Eq. (6.49):

(1) The final value is $b/42,900$. If this is to be less than $\frac{1}{3000}$, b must be less than 14.3.

(2) The longest time constant is 1 sec and meets the specifications.

(3) The overshoot depends on the relation between the zero at $-b$ and the poles at $-1 \pm j1$. If b is larger than unity, the overshoot is less than the specified 25 per cent (cf. Fig. 1.21). Hence, any value of b between 1 and 14.3 results in a system

satisfying the specifications. If this range of b does not permit realization of the required forward transfer function [Eq. (6.47)], more complex functions must be chosen for $G_1(s)$ and $H_1(s)$.

Equating the open-loop transfer function of Fig. 6.21 with the desired value of Eq. (6.47) gives

$$\left[10.1 \frac{s + 0.165}{s + b} \frac{1.975}{s(s^2 + 0.245s + 6.375)}\right]$$

$$\left[\frac{1}{1 + K_H \dfrac{1.975(s + c)}{(s + b)(s^2 + 0.245s + 6.375)}}\right]$$

$$= \frac{20}{s(s + 2.26)(s + 9.74)} \quad (6.50)$$

The parameters b, c, and K_H must be found such that the second term in brackets of the left side of this equation has poles at -0.165, -2.26, and

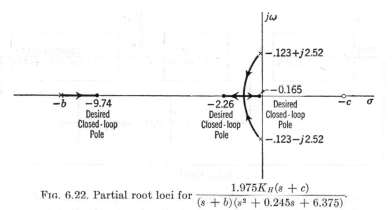

Fig. 6.22. Partial root loci for $\dfrac{1.975K_H(s + c)}{(s + b)(s^2 + 0.245s + 6.375)}$.

-9.74. Figure 6.22 shows the significant part of the root-locus plot for the forward transfer function† $\dfrac{1.975K_H(s + c)}{(s + b)(s^2 + 0.245s + 6.375)}$.

In the construction of these loci, realization of the three loci simultaneously at -9.74, -2.26, and -0.165 requires that the pole at $-b$ must be far enough to the left and the zero at $-c$ far enough to the right (actually in the right-half plane) that the two loci originating on the complex poles hit the axis between -0.165 and -2.26. The appropriate value of b is easily found from the equality of the sums of open-loop and closed-loop poles:

$$b + 0.245 = 0.165 + 2.26 + 9.74 \quad (6.51)$$
$$b = 11.92 \quad (6.52)$$

Since b lies between 1 and 14.2, all specifications are met.

The determination of the transfer functions is completed with the

† The loop referred to in the discussion of Fig. 6.22 is the minor loop of Fig. 6.21.

evaluation of c and K_H. The two parameters can be found analytically by equating coefficients of like powers of s in Eq. (6.50),

$$(s + 11.92)(s^2 + 0.245s + 6.375) + 1.975K_H(s + c)$$
$$= (s + 0.165)(s + 2.26)(s + 9.74) \quad (6.53)$$

The result is

$$c = -4.92 \quad (6.54)$$
$$K_H = 7.44 \quad (6.55)$$

The complete system, shown in Fig. 6.23, uses two compensation networks with transfer functions

$$G_1(s) = 10.1 \frac{s + 0.165}{s + 11.92} \quad (6.56)$$

$$H_1(s) = 7.44s \frac{s - 4.92}{s + 11.92} \quad (6.57)$$

The system shown is certainly not optimum in any sense. The very

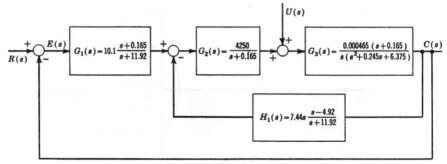

Fig. 6.23. Final system.

large time-constant ratio of the lead network represented by $G_1(s)$ and the nonminimum-phase character of $H_1(s)$ (that is, the fact the function has a zero in the right half of the s plane) are a direct consequence of the rather stringent specifications and the restriction to simple compensation transfer functions. The specifications require the realization of a closed-loop system with an overshoot of less than 5 per cent while utilizing components with a transfer function having complex poles with a ζ of less than 0.05. The minor-loop feedback then is forced to pull the poles almost on the $j\omega$ axis around to the negative real axis. In addition, the desire for the zero of $G_1(s)$ at -0.165, in order to neutralize the pole of $G_2(s)$ at the same point, means that the zero of $H_1(s)$ must lie in the right-half plane (as shown in the root-locus plot of Fig. 6.22).

Synthesis of the Compensation Networks. The final step in the design is the synthesis of networks to realize the compensation transfer functions $G_1(s)$ and $H_1(s)$. The former represents a conventional lead network and can be realized by the usual circuits or by the techniques outlined in Chap. 3. $H_1(s)$, however, is more difficult because of the nonminimum-phase character. If the factor s, representing a pole at infinity, is realized by any conventional method (*e.g.*, with a tachometer), the rest of the frequency-dependent part, $(s - 4.92)/(s + 11.92)$, must be realized by a balanced network.   The lattice,[†] shown in Fig. 6.24(a), is the simplest network from a theoretical viewpoint.   For the lattice driven from a

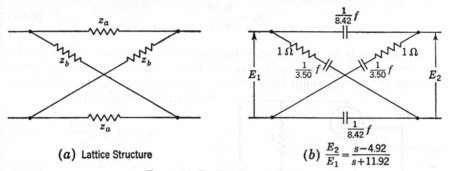

(a) Lattice Structure

(b) $\dfrac{E_2}{E_1} = \dfrac{s-4.92}{s+11.92}$

FIG. 6.24. Realization of $H_1(s)$.

voltage source and into an open circuit,

$$\frac{E_2}{E_1} = \frac{z_b - z_a}{z_b + z_a} \tag{6.58}$$

If the lattice is driven by an ideal current generator and into an open circuit, the transfer impedance is

$$z_{12}(s) = \frac{E_2}{I_1} = \frac{z_b - z_a}{2} \tag{6.59}[‡]$$

In either case, appropriate values can be found for z_b and z_a by identifying the expressions of Eq. (6.58) or (6.59) with the desired transfer function.   If in this example the lattice is driven by a generator with zero internal impedance,

$$\frac{z_b - z_a}{z_b + z_a} = \frac{s - 4.92}{s + 11.92} \tag{6.60}$$

The numerator and denominator of the right side are divided by a polynomial $q(s)$, and the identifications are made:

$$z_b - z_a = \frac{s - 4.92}{q(s)} \tag{6.61}$$

$$z_b + z_a = \frac{s + 11.92}{q(s)} \tag{6.62}$$

[†] J. L. Bower and P. F. Ordung, The Synthesis of Resistor-Capacitor Networks, *Proc. IRE*, Vol. 38, pp. 263–269, 1950.

[‡] If the lattice is to work into a finite resistance or from a generator with a finite, nonzero internal impedance, the simplest synthesis procedure is to assume that the terminating impedances are infinite or zero.   The polynomial $q(s)$, as defined in Eqs. (6.61) and (6.62), is chosen to ensure that resistances can be pulled out of the lattice at both ends.   This removal of resistance is described by Bower and Ordung, *op. cit.*

Addition and subtraction of the two equations give

$$z_b = \frac{s + 3.50}{q(s)} \tag{6.63}$$

$$z_a = \frac{8.42}{q(s)} \tag{6.64}$$

If the lattice is to contain only resistors and capacitors, $q(s)$ must be chosen such that both z_b and z_a satisfy the realizability conditions (Sec. 3.2) for RC driving-point impedances. Among the many suitable forms for $q(s)$, the simplest is s:

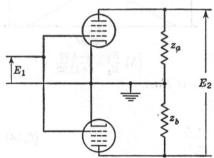

$$z_b = 1 + \frac{3.50}{s} \tag{6.65}$$

$$z_a = \frac{8.42}{s} \tag{6.66}$$

The lattice is shown in Fig. 6.24(b). The transfer function is unchanged if the impedance level is adjusted to any desired value by dividing all capacitances and multiplying all resistances by any desired constant.

FIG. 6.25. Incremental circuit for realization of E_2/E_1 proportional to $z_b - z_a$.

The lattice, although very simple from a synthesis viewpoint, is not a particularly satisfactory network in practical systems because of the large number of elements required (each element size appears twice) and the necessity for achieving an accurate balance, since the lattice is a bridge circuit. If tubes or equivalent current generators can be used, the transfer function realized by the lattice can also be realized by the system indicated in Fig. 6.25. The input is unbalanced to ground, but the output contains no ground terminal. There are a number of other schemes for circumventing the large number of elements required by the use of a lattice structure.

6.4. Determination of Transfer Functions. The root-locus method is frequently criticized because the starting point of the design is the transfer function of the controlled system, or the fixed components which must be incorporated in the system. If the characteristics of these fixed elements are known only in terms of experimental measurements with test input signals, either root-locus design or Guillemin's synthesis of the over-all system must be preceded by the determination of an appropriate transfer function for the controlled system.

There are three general methods by which the characteristics of physical equipment may be determined:

(1) System analysis leads to a transfer function in terms of system parameters which are evaluated by experimental tests. In the analysis of a translational hydraulic pilot valve and power piston, for example, the behavior of the various components is described by a set of equations based on physical laws. On the basis of the prob-

able excitation and load, suitable linearizing assumptions are made; the transfer function is derived from these linear equations; and, finally, the parameters (the oil compressibility, the flow/displacement ratio of the pilot valve, the load mass, spring constant, damping, etc.) are evaluated either experimentally or theoretically.

(2)   The sinusoidal characteristics of the system are determined. With the components excited by a variable-frequency sine-wave generator, the input and output amplitude and phase are measured to yield the frequency response and phase characteristic of the controlled system.

(3)   Transient tests are used, with the response of the system determined when the input is a step function, an impulse function, or a more general transient input. The system is characterized in the time domain.

If the first method is used, the transfer function which results is often in a form appropriate for direct application of the root-locus method or Guillemin's procedure.   The transfer function is ordinarily in factored form, or at least partially factored, and the poles and zeros characterizing the controlled system are determined at once.   If the second approach (involving frequency measurements) is the basis for describing the controlled elements, the data are in a form directly amenable to frequency-domain design methods (the Nyquist diagram or the gain and phase plots).   Application of the root-locus method or Guillemin's procedure necessitates the approximation of the given gain and phase characteristics by means of a rational algebraic transfer function.   In the third case, with the components characterized in the time domain, application

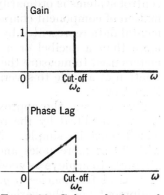

FIG. 6.26. Gain and phase of ideal low-pass filter (time delay permissible).

of the root-locus method requires determination of a suitable transfer function, while use of frequency-domain design involves either a Fourier transform of the time function or the derivation of a transfer function and the subsequent plotting of gain and phase curves.

Thus, there are two problems which may arise when either the root-locus method or Guillemin's method is used for system design:

(1)   Derivation of a transfer function from plots of gain and phase versus frequency.
(2)   Derivation of a transfer function from the transient response.

In this and the following section, the first of these problems is considered; Sec. 6.6 contains a brief discussion of approximation in the time domain.

Approximation in the Frequency Domain.   The determination of a transfer function to represent specified gain and phase characteristics is one of the basic aspects of network theory.   For example, the classical problem of network theory involves the determination of a network with characteristics approximating the ideal low-pass filter function, with the gain and phase curves of Fig. 6.26.   Modern network theory breaks the problem into two parts: approximation of the given characteristics by a rational algebraic function, and realization of this transfer function by a network. The approximation here is a very special case of the more general problem which arises in the design of feedback control systems, where the gain and phase characteristics to be approximated may take a wide variety of shapes.

The literature in the field of network theory provides a number of possible approaches to the problem of approximating simultaneously both a specified gain curve and a given phase characteristic.† These powerful approximation techniques are not generally applicable in the study of feedback control systems, however, as a consequence of certain basic considerations. First, the accuracy desired for the approximation is not the small fractions of a decibel or of a degree so often described in connection with problems of filter and equalizer design. The designer of control systems is ordinarily more interested in the rapid, rough approximation of component characteristics. Indeed, in many cases, the experimental data represented by the gain and phase curves are not accurate to more than a decibel or a few degrees. For example, the phase-angle meters used to measure the phase characteristic of a servo system from a fraction of a cycle to several cycles frequently have accuracies no better than 1 or 2°.

Furthermore, the approximation problem in feedback-control theory is often modified by the requirement that the transfer function determined must be simple. While the network designer may be working with 30 or more poles and zeros, the control-system engineer usually attempts to achieve as good an accuracy as possible with a small number of critical frequencies (*e.g.*, three or four). The nonlinearities of the equipment and the variations of component characteristics with time, temperature change, and drift of supply voltages make accurate and complicated approximations unnecessary. Indeed, one of the strongest motivations for the use of feedback is the continuous system calibration in the presence of changes in system parameters.

In one additional way the approximation problem confronting the control-system engineer is often simpler than that with which the network theorist deals. In network theory, the desired gain and phase characteristics may be highly incompatible, but in the usual approximation problem in feedback-control theory, the two characteristics are compatible. The significance of this qualitative term *compatibility* depends on two facts:

(1) Bode has demonstrated‡ that over any finite frequency band both gain and phase can be specified arbitrarily and approximated with any desired accuracy.§

† For example, *cf.* the two articles by S. Darlington: The Potential Analog Method of Network Synthesis, *Bell System Tech. J.*, Vol. 30, pp. 315–365, April, 1951; Network Synthesis Using Tchebycheff Polynomial Series, *Bell System Tech. J.*, Vol. 31, pp. 613–665, July, 1952.

‡ H. W. Bode, "Network Analysis and Feedback Amplifier Design," D. Van Nostrand Company, Inc., New York, 1945.

§ The statement is true if the term "accuracy" is interpreted properly. The Paley-Wiener criterion (*cf.* G. E. Valley and H. Wallman, "Vacuum Tube Amplifiers,"

(2) If the gain is specified at all frequencies, the phase is completely determined if nonminimum-phase systems are excluded.

The validity of these two statements can be shown from the Hilbert transform relating the real and imaginary parts of a function of a complex variable. In particular, this transform shows that the phase at any frequency ω_1 depends on the derivative of the gain at all frequencies, with the significance of the value of gain at a frequency ω decreasing as $|\omega - \omega_1|$ becomes larger. The actual weighting function is shown in Fig. 6.27.

A definition of compatible gain and phase characteristics can now be given. Figure 6.28(a) shows possible forms for the desired gain and phase curves, specified between the two frequencies ω_a and ω_b. If the specified characteristics are compatible, approximation results in over-all gain and phase curves as shown in part (b) of the figure. If the gain curve is first approximated by a simple transfer function, the resulting phase characteristic of this approximation does not differ radi-

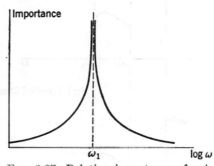

Fig. 6.27. Relative importance of gain derivative at ω in determining phase at ω_1.

cally from the specified phase between ω_a and ω_b. In a case in which the specified characteristics are incompatible, the over-all gain and phase resulting from the approximation are shown in part (c) of the figure. After the gain is approximated, meeting the phase specifications necessitates a large, rapid gain variation outside the frequency band of interest. This large variation is required because gain variations outside the band are ineffective as a means of controlling phase within the band.

Clearly, if gain and phase curves are arbitrarily specified or are given by certain specifications which do not implicitly satisfy the Hilbert transform, incompatibility is very likely to arise. In the study of feedback control systems, however, the measured gain and phase correspond to a physical piece of equipment. Accordingly, in many cases approximation of the gain alone results in a phase characteristic which is very close to that desired. Slight adjustment of the poles and zeros of the approximation often permits a satisfactory compromise between gain and phase accuracy.

Thus, in a number of cases of significance, determination of a suitable transfer function for the controlled elements can be resolved to the

MIT Radiation Laboratory Series, Vol. 18, Appendix I, McGraw-Hill Book Company, Inc., New York, 1948) implies that the gain of a physically realizable network cannot be zero over a nonzero band of frequencies. The statement that the gain characteristic of the ideal low-pass filter can be approximated within any desired "accuracy" over a frequency band from zero to twice the cutoff frequency, for example, does not mean within a specified number of decibels, but rather within a specified magnitude of gain.

approximation of a given gain curve.   The phase characteristic is automatically realized with sufficient accuracy.   Probably the simplest method of determining a rational algebraic function approximating a specified gain characteristic is a reverse application of the asymptotic techniques for plotting gain versus frequency from a given transfer function.   The following discussion presents the basic features of this

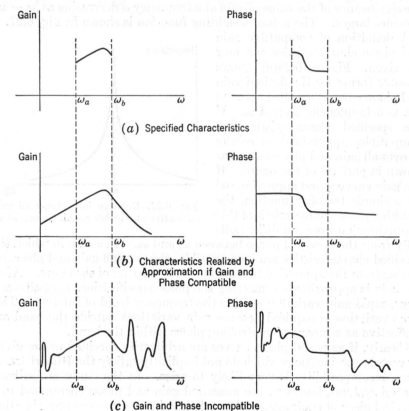

FIG. 6.28. Definition of compatibility.

asymptotic procedure; more complete descriptions can be found in most servomechanism texts.†

Construction of Gain Characteristic from Transfer Function.   It is desired to plot $|G(j\omega)|$ versus frequency, with the function $G(s)$ given. $G(s)$ is in general the ratio of two polynomials in s, each polynomial containing both real and conjugate complex zeros.   A typical form for $G(s)$ is

† G. S. Brown and D. P. Campbell, "Principles of Servomechanisms," Chap. 8, John Wiley & Sons, Inc., New York, 1948; and H. Chestnut and R. W. Mayer, "Servomechanisms and Regulating System Design," Chap. 12, John Wiley & Sons, Inc., New York, 1951.

$$G(s) = K \frac{(T_a s + 1)(T_e^2 s^2 + 2\zeta_e T_e s + 1)}{s(T_b s + 1)(T_c s + 1)(T_d^2 s^2 + 2\zeta_d T_d s + 1)} \qquad (6.67)$$

The associated pole-zero configuration is shown in Fig. 6.29.

The magnitude of the gain along the $j\omega$ axis is desired:

$$|G(j\omega)| = K \frac{|1 + j\omega T_a||1 + j\omega 2\zeta_e T_e - \omega^2 T_e^2|}{|j\omega||1 + j\omega T_b||1 + j\omega T_c||1 + j\omega 2\zeta_d T_d - \omega^2 T_d^2|} \qquad (6.68)$$

The multiplication and division of the various numerator and denominator factors representing the zeros and poles are transformed to addition

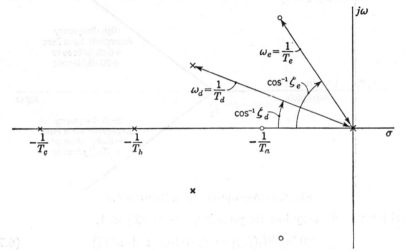

FIG. 6.29. Pole-zero configuration for $G(s)$ of Eq. (6.67).

and subtraction by consideration of $\log_{10} |G(j\omega)|$, rather than $|G(j\omega)|$ directly.

$$\log |G(j\omega)| = \log K + \log |1 + j\omega T_a| + \cdots \\ - \log |j\omega| - \log |1 + j\omega T_b| - \cdots \quad (6.69)\dagger$$

Ordinarily it is convenient to plot the gain in decibels:

$$20 \log |G(j\omega)| = 20 \log K + 20 \log |1 + j\omega T_a| \\ + 20 \log |1 + j\omega 2\zeta_e T_e - \omega^2 T_e^2| - 20 \log |j\omega| - 20 \log |1 + j\omega T_b| \\ - 20 \log |1 + j\omega T_c| - 20 \log |1 + j\omega 2\zeta_d T_d - \omega^2 T_d^2| \quad (6.70)$$

Thus, a plot of the gain versus frequency can be made by simple point-by-point addition of the gains of each individual term in the summation on the right side of Eq. (6.70). For the general rational algebraic transfer function, this sum includes terms of four types:

(1)   A constant term, $20 \log K$
(2)   Terms arising from real zeros or poles and of the form

$$20 \log |G_2(j\omega)| = \pm 20 \log |1 + j\omega T_2| \qquad (6.71)$$

† All logarithms in this discussion are to the base 10.

(3) Terms arising from a zero or pole at the origin and of the form

$$20 \log |G_3(j\omega)| = \pm 20 \log \omega \qquad (6.72)†$$

(4) Terms arising from conjugate complex zeros or poles and of the form

$$20 \log |G_4(j\omega)| = \pm 20 \log |1 + j\omega 2\zeta_4 T_4 - \omega^2 T_4^2| \qquad (6.73)$$

In each case, the plus sign is used for zeros, the minus sign for poles.

Terms of type (2) above, arising from linear factors, are readily plotted approximately if the behavior at both high and low frequencies is

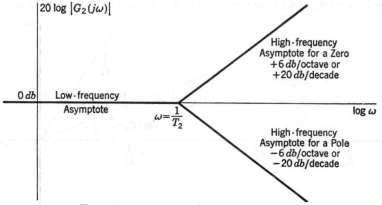

Fig. 6.30. Asymptotes for a linear factor.

considered. At very low frequencies, where $\omega T_2 \ll 1$,

$$20 \log |G_2(j\omega)| = \pm 10 \log (1 + \omega^2 T_2^2) \qquad (6.74)$$

$$20 \log |G_2(j\omega)| \xrightarrow[\omega \to 0]{} \pm \frac{10}{2.3} \omega^2 T_2^2 \qquad (6.75)$$

If all terms in $(\omega T_2)^3$ and higher degrees are neglected, Eq. (6.75) indicates that the gain is essentially 0 db for all frequencies low enough that $\omega T_2 < 0.1$. At very high frequencies, with $\omega T_2 \gg 1$,

$$20 \log |G_2(j\omega)| = \pm 20 \left[\log \omega T_2 + \log \left(1 + \frac{1}{\omega^2 T_2^2} \right)^{\frac{1}{2}} \right] \qquad (6.76)$$

$$20 \log |G_2(j\omega)| \xrightarrow[\omega \to \infty]{} \pm 20 \log \omega T_2 \qquad (6.77)$$

If the gain is plotted versus $\log \omega$ instead of ω, Eq. (6.77) states that the characteristic is essentially linear at high frequencies, for

$$20 \log |G_2(j\omega)| \xrightarrow[\omega \to \infty]{} \pm 20 \log \omega \pm 20 \log T_2 \qquad (6.78)$$

$$\frac{d}{d \log \omega} [20 \log |G_2(j\omega)|] \xrightarrow[\omega \to \infty]{} 20 \qquad (6.79)$$

Thus, at very low and very high frequencies, the gain follows the low-frequency and high-frequency asymptotes shown in Fig. 6.30. The

† If the zero or pole is of order n, the gain in decibels is $\pm 20 \log \omega^n$, or $\pm 20n \log \omega$.

intersection of the two asymptotes can be found by equating the high-frequency asymptote [Eq. (6.77)] to zero:

$$\pm 20 \log \omega T_2 = 0 \tag{6.80}$$

$$\omega = \frac{1}{T_2} \tag{6.81}$$

The slope of the high-frequency asymptote is found from Eq. (6.79), which indicates that, for a zero factor (when the plus sign is used), multiplying the frequency by a factor of 10 increases the gain by 20 db, or doubling the frequency results in a 6-db increase in gain.

Clearly, the two asymptotes can be drawn rapidly once the linear factor is known. The construction of the curve follows three rules:

(1) The low-frequency asymptote is 0 db.

(2) The high-frequency asymptote has a slope of ±6 db/octave, the plus sign being used for a zero factor, the minus sign for a pole factor.

(3) The two asymptotes intersect at $\omega = 1/T_2$.

An example is shown in Fig. 6.31.

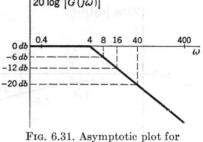

FIG. 6.31. Asymptotic plot for $G(s) = 4/(s + 4)$.

Accuracy of the Asymptotes. How accurate an approximation is this asymptotic plot to the actual gain curve? This question is readily interpreted by a few simple calculations, summarized in Table 6.1. In

TABLE 6.1
ACCURACY OF ASYMPTOTIC PLOT FOR LINEAR FACTOR

Frequency	Actual value of gain, db	Asymptotic value, db	Error db
$\omega = \dfrac{1}{T_2}$ (break frequency)	±3	0	±3
$\omega = \dfrac{0.5}{T_2}$	±1.0	0	±1
$\omega = \dfrac{2}{T_2}$	±7.0	±6	±1
$\omega = \dfrac{0.76}{T_2}$	±2	0	±2
$\omega = \dfrac{1.31}{T_2}$	±4.3	±2.3	±2

the case of a zero factor, with the plus signs used in the table, the actual curve lies entirely above the asymptotic curve. For a pole, the actual curve falls below the asymptotes. The difference between the actual and asymptotic curves is a maximum at the break frequency and is

geometrically symmetrical about this break frequency.   The error is 3 db
at the break, 2 db at 0.76 and 1.31 times the break frequency, and 1 db at
one half and twice the break frequency.   The situation for a pole is
shown graphically in Fig. 6.32.

The logarithmic-gain curve corresponding to any linear factor can thus
be sketched with essentially no computation.   The procedure is as
follows:

(1)   The asymptotes are determined, with the break frequency at $\omega = 1/T_2$.
(2)   The actual values are determined at five frequencies (those shown in Fig. 6.32).
(3)   A smooth curve is drawn on the basis of the five points and the two asymptotes.

Zero-frequency Poles and Zeros.   The plotting is even simpler in the
case of a critical frequency at the origin.   If the pole or zero is simple, the

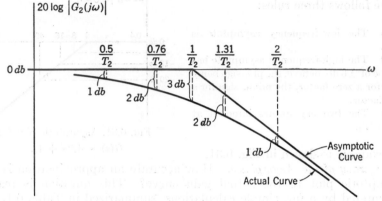

FIG. 6.32. Error of asymptotic gain for $G_2(s) = 1/(T_2 s + 1)$.

logarithmic gain is

$$20 \log |G_3(j\omega)| = \pm 20 \log \omega \tag{6.82}$$

The curve plotted versus log ω is merely a straight line with a slope of
± 6 db/octave.   The location of this line is determined by the fact that
for $\omega = 1$ the gain is 0 db.

Complex Poles or Zeros.   The situation is slightly complicated in the
consideration of conjugate complex pairs of zeros or poles.   Equation
(6.73) states that in this case

$$20 \log |G_4(j\omega)| = \pm 20 \log |1 + j\omega 2\zeta_4 T_4 - \omega^2 T_4^2| \tag{6.83}$$

The low-frequency asymptote is again 0 db, but the high-frequency
asymptote has a slope of ± 12 db/octave, twice the slope of the simple
pole or zero case, for at high frequencies

$$20 \log |G_4(j\omega)| \xrightarrow[\omega \to \infty]{} \pm 20 \log (\omega T_4)^2 \tag{6.84}$$

The two asymptotes intersect at the frequency at which

$$\pm 20 \log (\omega T_4)^2 = 0 \tag{6.85}$$

$$\omega = \frac{1}{T_4} \quad \text{(also denoted } \omega_4) \tag{6.86}$$

The asymptotic plots for both the zero and pole cases are shown in Fig. 6.33.

The difference between the asymptotic plot and the actual curve depends on the value of ζ, with a variety of shapes realizable for the actual curve. A family of these actual curves is shown in Fig. 6.34. Regardless of the value of ζ_4, the actual curve approaches the asymptotes at both high and low frequencies. In addition, the error between the asymptotic plot and the actual curve is geometrically symmetrical about the break frequency ω_4. As a result of this symmetry, the curves of Fig. 6.34 are plotted only for $\omega \leq \omega_4$. The error for $\omega = \alpha\omega_4$ is identical with the error at an ω of ω_4/α.

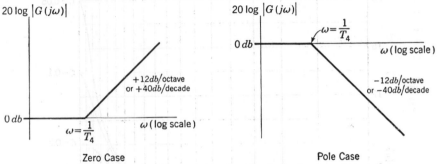

Zero Case   Pole Case

FIG. 6.33. Asymptotes for a conjugate complex pair of zeros or poles.

The necessity for curves as shown in Fig. 6.34 can be avoided if each quadratic term is divided by s.† Consideration of a term of the form $s^2 + 2\zeta_4\omega_4 s + \omega_4^2$ is then replaced by plots for the two terms: s and $(s^2 + 2\zeta_4\omega_4 s + \omega_4^2)/s$. When the quadratic term is divided by s, the actual curve has an extremum at the break frequency ω_4 (a maximum for quadratic poles, a minimum for zeros) and the extremum differs from the asymptotic value by $\pm 20 \log (1/2\zeta)$. The error decreases on either side of the break frequency.

Construction of Complete Gain Curve. The procedure for drawing a complete logarithmic gain-frequency curve is now fully established. The asymptotic plots of the various pole and zero components are added together. The errors for each of the components are included, and a smooth curve is drawn through the resultant points. Alternatively, the errors of the individual components can be inserted and the accurate individual curves added point by point.

One example illustrates the procedure. The transfer function considered is

$$G(s) = \frac{s(s + 10)}{(s + 20)(s^2 + 0.6\sqrt{2}\,s + 2)} \tag{6.87}$$

(1) $G(s)$ is rewritten to make the constant term of each factor equal to unity:

† This possibility was pointed out to the author by Dr. E. J. Angelo.

$$G(s) = \frac{10}{40} \frac{s(0.1s + 1)}{(0.05s + 1)(0.5s^2 + 0.3\sqrt{2}\,s + 1)} \tag{6.88}$$

(2) The break frequencies of the asymptotic factors are determined:
Break up at 6 db/octave at $\omega = 10$ because of $0.1s + 1$
Down at 6 db/octave at $\omega = 20$ because of $0.05s + 1$
Down at 12 db/octave at $\omega = 1.414$ with a ζ of 0.3 because of $0.5s^2 + 0.3\sqrt{2}\,s + 1$

(3) The constant terms and the critical frequency at the origin are determined. There is a rise at 6 db/octave because of the s factor in the

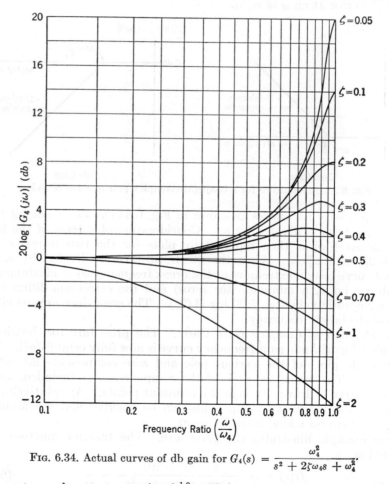

FIG. 6.34. Actual curves of db gain for $G_4(s) = \dfrac{\omega_4^2}{s^2 + 2\zeta\omega_4 s + \omega_4^2}$.

numerator and a constant gain of $\frac{10}{40}$. If these two factors are considered together, $G_1(j\omega) = \frac{10}{40}j\omega$ intersects 0 db at $\omega = 4$. Thus, the asymptotic plot starts at low frequencies as a line rising at 6 db/octave toward 0 db at an ω of 4.

(4) The asymptotic plot is sketched in Fig. 6.35.

(5) The error component of the quadratic term, representing the lowest break frequency, is added. From Fig. 6.34, with $\zeta = 0.3$, the error is 4.44 db at the break frequency, a maximum of 4.85 db at 0.91 and 1.10 times the break frequency, 4.05 db at 0.75 and 1.33 times the break, and 1.8 db at 0.5 and 2.0 times the break. The addition of the error leads to a curve of the form shown by the solid line of Fig. 6.36(a).

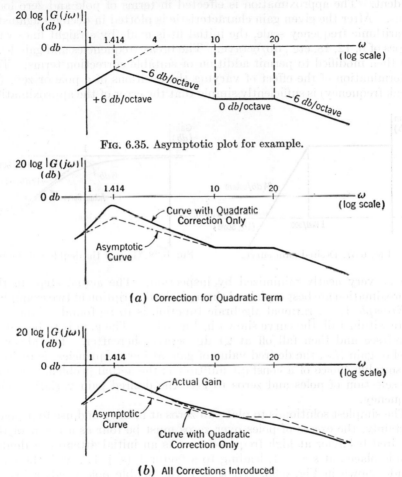

Fig. 6.35. Asymptotic plot for example.

(a) Correction for Quadratic Term

(b) All Corrections Introduced

Fig. 6.36. Actual gain characteristic in example.

(6) The corrections associated with the breaks at $\omega = 10$ and $\omega = 20$ are added. At $\omega = 5$, there is a correction of 1 db to be added; at $\omega = 10$, a correction of 3 db because of the break at 10 and a correction of -1 db because of the break at 20. At 20, the total correction is $-3 + 1 = -2$ db. At 40, the correction is -1 db. The resultant approximate curve is sketched in Fig. 6.36(b).

Clearly, difficulty is experienced if the break frequencies are so close together that the proper correction term at any given frequency is the sum of components resulting from a large number of different breaks. If the break frequencies are closely spaced, the smooth curve is most easily constructed in steps, where each step involves addition of all the correction associated with a single break frequency.

Approximation. The general procedure for the approximation of a given gain characteristic by a suitable rational algebraic function is now evident. The approximation is effected in terms of pole and zero locations. After the given gain characteristic is plotted in decibels against a logarithmic frequency scale, the initial fit is made by straight lines with slopes of 6, 12, 18, etc., db/octave. The break frequencies and gain level are then modified to permit addition of suitable correction terms. The determination of the effect of varying the positions of a pole or zero (or break frequency) is sufficiently simple that the error of the approximation

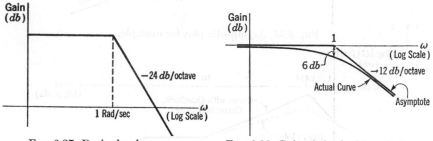

FIG. 6.37. Desired gain curve.   FIG. 6.38. Gain of the double-pole factor.

can be very nearly minimized by inspection. The actual steps in the approximation are best explained through the description of two examples.

Example 1. A rational algebraic function is to be found to approximate within 1 db the curve shown in Fig. 6.37. The gain is to be flat to 1 rad/sec and then fall off at 24 db/octave thereafter. The absolute level of gain (*i.e.*, the desired value of gain at low frequencies) is realized by suitable choice of a constant multiplier; the actual problem concerns the selection of poles and zeros to give the desired gain variation with frequency.

The simplest solution is to place all zeros at infinity and use four poles. Certainly, the excess of poles over zeros must be four as a result of the required behavior at high frequencies. As an initial attempt, a double pole is placed at $s = -1$, leading to a factor $1/(s + 1)^2$, with the magnitude shown in Fig. 6.38. At $\omega = 1$, the double pole yields a loss of 6 db. This unwanted attenuation can be compensated with one pair of conjugate complex poles with an undamped natural resonant frequency of 1 rad/sec and a relative damping ratio sufficiently small to yield a gain of 6 db at 1 rad/sec. Inspection of Fig. 6.34 reveals that a ζ of about 0.25 meets this requirement well within the 1-db tolerance allowed. As a first trial, then, the quadratic factor $1/(s^2 + 0.5s + 1)$ is selected. The corresponding gain curve is shown in Fig. 6.39.

Whether this combination of a double pole and a quadratic factor meets the specifications can be readily determined by adding the two gain components represented by Figs. 6.38 and 6.39. The sum has the appearance shown in Fig. 6.40 and stays within approximately 1 db of the desired value. If necessary, a somewhat lower peak error can be obtained by slight adjustment of the ζ of the complex poles. If the ζ of 0.25 is satisfactory, the final system function is

$$G(s) = \frac{K}{(s + 1)^2(s^2 + 0.5s + 1)} \qquad (6.89)$$

Example 2. The transfer function of a system is found by measurement to exhibit the characteristic shown by the solid curve of Fig. 6.41. A rational algebraic function approximating this curve is to be found.

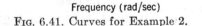

Fig. 6.39. Gain of the quadratic factor.   Fig. 6.40. Final approximation for Example 1.

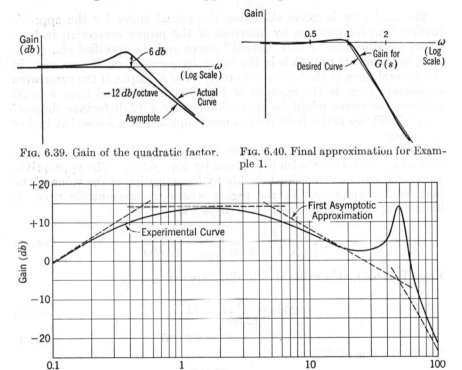

Fig. 6.41. Curves for Example 2.

At low frequencies, the gain increases at 6 db/octave. An approximate asymptote is drawn, and the first break frequency is estimated to be at the frequency at which this asymptote deviates from the measured curve by 3 db—in this example, at 0.5 rad/sec. From this point, a horizontal asymptote is drawn and extended again to the point of 3-db error, $\omega = 5$ rad/sec. At high frequencies, the gain falls off at -18 db/octave (although more of the experimental curve should be shown to make this clear). The peak indicates at least one pair of conjugate poles. Thus, at 5 rad/sec the asymptotic curve is broken down at -6 db/octave.

The peak is sufficiently high to indicate that the corresponding break frequency occurs at about the same frequency as the peak amplitude, or at $\omega = 50$ rad/sec. The asymptotic curve is then completed as shown by the dotted curve of Fig. 6.41.

The first approximating transfer function is completely determined by selection of a ζ to give the proper peak amplitude. The curves of Fig. 6.34 demonstrate that when ζ is about 0.05 the peak is about 20 db above the break. The transfer function is then

$$G(s) = \frac{Ks}{(s + 0.5)(s + 5)(s^2 + 5s + 2500)} \tag{6.90}$$

The next step involves sketching the actual curve for the approximating transfer function by insertion of the proper correction factors. From a comparison of this "actual" curve and the specified characteristic, adjustments are made in the break frequencies, or, if necessary, in the general form of the asymptotic plot. For example, if the error were excessively large in the example of Fig. 6.41 in the band from 5 to 50 rad/sec, the curve might be approximated by a 12-db/octave drop-off above 5 rad/sec and a 6-db/octave break upward at a somewhat higher frequency.

For the completion of this example, it is assumed that the first approximation is satisfactory, with $G(s)$ given by Eq. (6.90). The appropriate value of K can be determined readily by investigation of the value of the horizontal asymptote. In the region where the asymptotic curve is horizontal, the asymptotic value of $|G(j\omega)|$ is

$$\left| \frac{Ks}{s \times 5 \times 2500} \right|_{s=j\omega} = \frac{K}{12,500} \tag{6.91}$$

From Fig. 6.41, this value is $+14$ db. Hence,

$$20 \log \frac{K}{12,500} = 14 \tag{6.92}$$

$$K = 62,600 \tag{6.93}$$

The final value of $G(s)$ is

$$G(s) = \frac{62,600s}{(s + 0.5)(s + 5)(s^2 + 5s + 2500)} \tag{6.94}$$

Phase Characteristic. If a transfer function is to be determined to represent specified gain and phase characteristics, the simplest approach is to approximate the gain alone by the procedure outlined in the preceding section. In the initial selection of the number of poles and zeros to be used and the choice of break frequencies, consideration can be given to the nature of the phase characteristic in order to realize, if possible, a transfer function with a phase characteristic which does not deviate radically from the desired curve. The phase of the approximating transfer function is then plotted in the conventional way, by addition

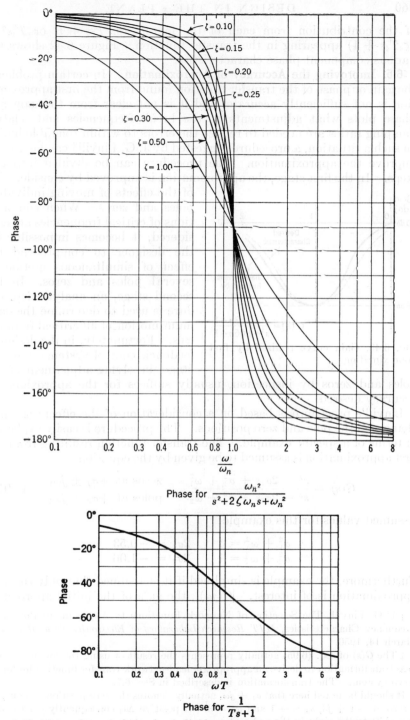

FIG. 6.42. Phase characteristics for individual factors of a transfer function. (*From H. M. James, N. B. Nichols, and R. S. Phillips, "Theory of Servomechanisms," MIT Radiation Laboratory Series, Vol. 25, p. 144, McGraw-Hill Book Company, Inc., New York, 1949.*)

of the contribution from each of the factors (s, $T_2s + 1$, or $T_4^2s^2 + 2\zeta_4T_4s + 1$) appearing in the transfer function. Figure 6.42 shows the various component phase characteristics.

6.5. Improving the Accuracy of Approximation. In certain problems, the gain or phase of the transfer function found from the first approximation is not sufficiently accurate, and it is not clear from the gain and phase plots what adjustments of the break frequencies and relative damping ratios are needed to reduce the errors to within tolerable limits. In such a situation, a procedure suggested by J. G. Linvill[†] can be used to improve the approximation. The procedure can be divided into two steps. In the first stage, the approximation is improved by consideration of the effects of moving individual poles and zeros. When combinations of critical frequencies are considered, it becomes impossible for the designer to comprehend the effect of simultaneous motion of several poles and zeros. In the second stage, an analytical procedure is used to determine the optimum motion of all critical frequencies. Fortunately, in the design of feedback control systems, the first stage, involving adjustment of the poles and zeros by inspection, usually suffices for the approximation accuracy desired.

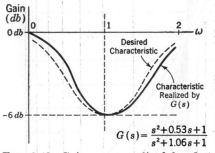

$$G(s) = \frac{s^2 + 0.53s + 1}{s^2 + 1.06s + 1}$$

FIG. 6.43. Gain curve realized by first approximation.

Linvill's procedure is based on a consideration of the effects of small changes in the pole and zero positions. The procedure is easily explained in terms of a specific example. The transfer function resulting from the first approximation is assumed to be given by the equation

$$G(s) = \frac{s^2 - 2\sigma_1 s + \sigma_1^2 + \omega_1^2}{s^2 - 2\sigma_2 s + \sigma_2^2 + \omega_2^2} \qquad \begin{array}{l} \text{zeros at } +\sigma_1 \pm j\omega_1 \\ \text{poles at } +\sigma_2 \pm j\omega_2 \end{array} \qquad (6.95)\ddagger$$

Assumed values for this example:

$$\begin{array}{ll} \sigma_1^2 + \omega_1^2 = 1 & 2\sigma_1 = -0.53 \\ \sigma_2^2 + \omega_2^2 = 1 & 2\sigma_2 = -1.06 \end{array}$$

Furthermore, the example is simplified if it is assumed that only the gain approximation is of interest. $|G(j\omega)|$, the gain of the initial approxima-

[†] J. G. Linvill, The Selection of Network Functions to Approximate Prescribed Frequency Characteristics, *MIT Research Laboratory of Electronics Tech. Rept.* 145, March 14, 1950.

[‡] The $G(s)$ of Eq. (6.95) actually represents the result of using the low pass–band pass transformation to derive an appropriate lead-network transfer function for an a-c servo system. The transformation is described in Sec. 6.7.

It should be noted here that $\sigma_1 + j\omega_1$ actually denotes the zero position. Thus, for a zero at $-1 + j3$, $\sigma_1 = -1$ and $\omega_1 = 3$. A positive $\Delta\sigma_1$ consequently corresponds to a shift to the right in the s plane.

tion, is shown in Fig. 6.43, which also includes the desired characteristic. The problem is to determine appropriate *changes* of σ_1, ω_1, σ_2, and ω_2 [that is, translations of the poles and zeros of $G(s)$] to improve the accuracy of the gain approximation.

The keystone of Linvill's procedure is the description of the effects of small shifts in the pole and zero positions in terms of the partial derivatives of the gain function. In particular, if the logarithmic gain, 20 log $|G(j\omega)|$, is termed $F(\omega)$, the change in $F(\omega)$ resulting from changes of the poles and zeros is given by the expression

$$\Delta F(\omega) = \int_0^{\Delta\sigma_1} \frac{\partial F}{\partial \sigma_1} \, d\sigma_1 + \int_0^{\Delta\omega_1} \frac{\partial F}{\partial \omega_1} \, d\omega_1 + \int_0^{\Delta\sigma_2} \frac{\partial F}{\partial \sigma_2} \, d\sigma_2$$
$$+ \int_0^{\Delta\omega_2} \frac{\partial F}{\partial \omega_2} \, d\omega_2 \quad (6.96)$$

If the changes of the four parameters (σ_1, ω_1, σ_2, and ω_2) are small, the partial derivatives are constant, and

$$\Delta F(\omega) = \frac{\partial F}{\partial \sigma_1} \Delta\sigma_1 + \frac{\partial F}{\partial \omega_1} \Delta\omega_1 + \frac{\partial F}{\partial \sigma_2} \Delta\sigma_2 + \frac{\partial F}{\partial \omega_2} \Delta\omega_2 \quad (6.97)$$

In other words, once the partial derivatives are evaluated for the original values of the four parameters, Eq. (6.97) permits determination of the effects of changes $\Delta\sigma_1$, $\Delta\omega_1$, $\Delta\sigma_2$, and $\Delta\omega_2$. In addition, consideration of the logarithmic gain, rather than $|G(j\omega)|$, allows separation of the various zeros and poles: that is, $\partial F/\partial \sigma_1$ depends only on σ_1 and ω_1 and is independent of the poles at $+\sigma_2 \pm j\omega_2$. In an analogous fashion, an equation similar to (6.97) can be written for the change in the phase angle of $G(j\omega)$ as a sum of linear functions of $\Delta\sigma_1$, $\Delta\omega_1$, $\Delta\sigma_2$, and $\Delta\omega_2$.

Utilization of Eq. (6.97) involves the following steps:

(1)   From the actual and desired gain curves (Fig. 6.43) a plot is made of the error-frequency function which is to be realized by the shift in the pole and zero positions.   The error curve, shown in Fig. 6.44(a), is the desired $\Delta F(\omega)$ of Eq. (6.97).

(2)   The frequency variations of the four partial derivatives of Eq. (6.97) are evaluated at the given values of σ_1, ω_1, σ_2, and ω_2.   Typical curves of these derivatives versus frequency are shown in Fig. 6.44(b).

(3)   A combination of the four partial-derivative curves must be selected to approximate the desired error function over the frequency band of interest.   In many cases, an appropriate combination can be found merely by inspection; in this problem, for example, it is clear that $(\partial F/\partial \omega_1) \Delta\omega_1$ can be made to approximate the known variation of error with frequency if an appropriate negative value of $\Delta\omega_1$ is chosen.   Alternatively, ω_2, the imaginary part of the pole, might be increased to improve the accuracy.

(4)   The gain corresponding to the new pole and zero positions is determined, and the new error-frequency function is plotted.   The adjustment process is continued in this way until sufficient accuracy is

obtained or until it is no longer apparent what combination of changes ($\Delta\sigma_1$, $\Delta\omega_1$, etc.) leads to an improved accuracy.

(5)   When the appropriate values of $\Delta\sigma_1$, etc., are not apparent from the plots of the partial derivatives and the error function, an analytical procedure† can be used to minimize the mean-square value of the error evaluated at n different frequencies by adjustment of the m quantities $\Delta\sigma_1$, $\Delta\omega_1$ etc. (where $n \geq m$).   This procedure is not described in detail here because of the limited application in the design of feedback control systems.

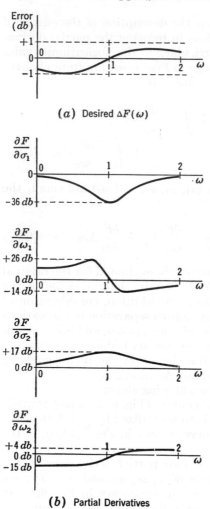

(a) Desired $\Delta F(\omega)$

(b) Partial Derivatives

Although Linvill's procedure is straightforward, the calculation and plotting of the partial derivatives are a tedious process.   Fortunately, curves are available which give the frequency variation of the partial derivatives for all cases of practical interest.   These curves are shown in Fig. 6.45.   The normalization of the curves is described below.

Parts (a) and (b) of the figure represent the partial derivative of the logarithmic gain with respect to the position of a real pole or zero.   If the critical frequency is real, the factor in $G(s)$ is of the form

$$G_r(s) = (s - \sigma_r)^{\pm 1} \quad (6.98)$$

The plus sign is used for a zero, the minus sign for a pole.   The corresponding term in the logarithmic gain, $F_r(\omega)$, is

Fig. 6.44. Curves for adjustment of first approximation.

$$F_r(\omega) = \pm 20 \log |j\omega - \sigma_r| \quad (6.99)$$

The partial derivative of $F_r(\omega)$ with respect to σ_r gives

$$\frac{\partial F_r}{\partial \sigma_r} = \pm 20 \frac{\sigma_r}{\omega^2 + \sigma_r^2} \quad (6.100)$$

† J. G. Linvill, The Approximation with Rational Functions of Prescribed Magnitude and Phase Characteristics, *Proc. IRE*, Vol. 40, pp. 711–721, June, 1952.

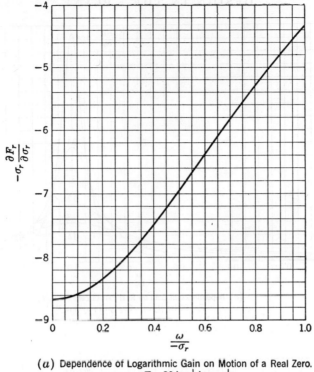

(a) Dependence of Logarithmic Gain on Motion of a Real Zero.
$$F_r = 20 \log \left| j\omega - \sigma_r \right|$$

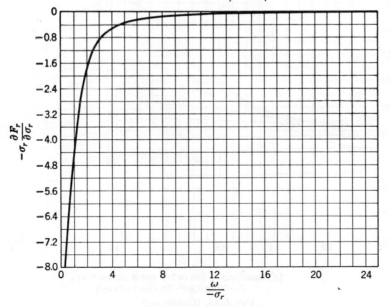

(b) Dependence of Logarithmic Gain on Motion of a Real Zero.
$$F_r = 20 \log \left| j\omega - \sigma_r \right|$$

FIG. 6.45. Partial derivatives for Linvill's procedure. (*From J. G. Linvill, The Selection of Network Functions to Approximate Prescribed Frequency Characteristics, MIT Research Laboratory of Electronics Tech. Rept. 145, March 14, 1950.*)

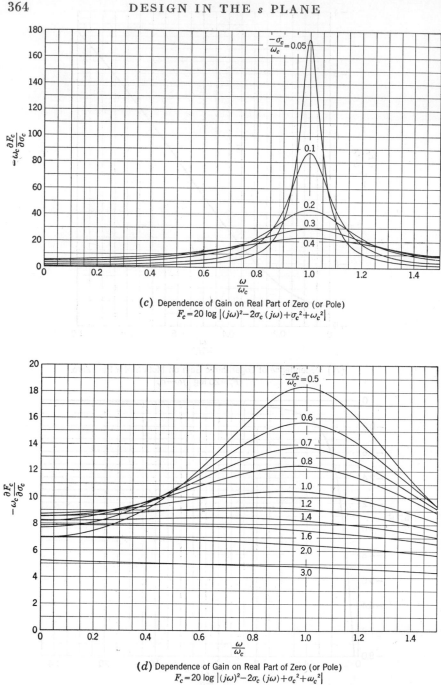

(*c*) Dependence of Gain on Real Part of Zero (or Pole)
$$F_c = 20 \log \left| (j\omega)^2 - 2\sigma_c (j\omega) + \sigma_c{}^2 + \omega_c{}^2 \right|$$

(*d*) Dependence of Gain on Real Part of Zero (or Pole)
$$F_c = 20 \log \left| (j\omega)^2 - 2\sigma_c (j\omega) + \sigma_c{}^2 + \omega_c{}^2 \right|$$
FIG. 6.45. (*Continued*)

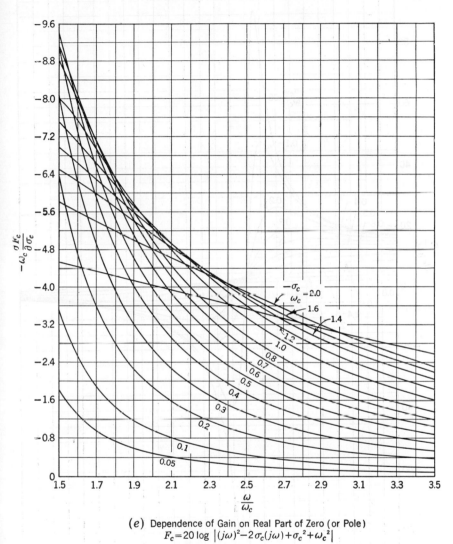

(e) Dependence of Gain on Real Part of Zero (or Pole)
$$F_c = 20 \log \left| (j\omega)^2 - 2\sigma_c(j\omega) + \sigma_c{}^2 + \omega_c{}^2 \right|$$
Fig. 6.45. (Continued)

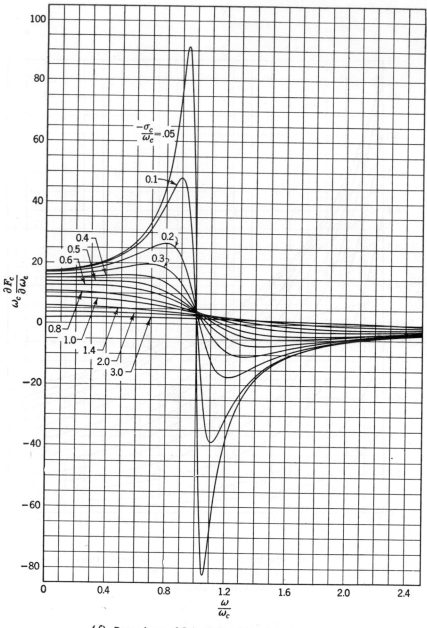

(*f*) Dependence of Gain on Imaginary Part of Zero (or pole)

$$F_c = 20 \log \left[(j\omega)^2 - 2\sigma_c (j\omega) + \sigma_c^2 + \omega_c^2 \right]$$

Fig. 6.45. (*Continued*)

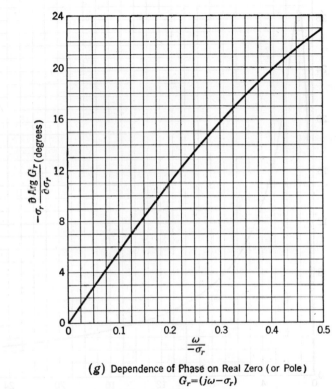

(**g**) Dependence of Phase on Real Zero (or Pole)

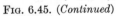

$$G_r = (j\omega - \sigma_r)$$

FIG. 6.45. (*Continued*)

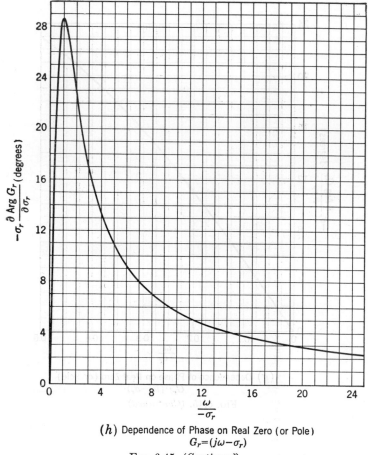

(*h*) Dependence of Phase on Real Zero (or Pole)

$$G_r = (j\omega - \sigma_r)$$

FIG. 6.45. (*Continued*)

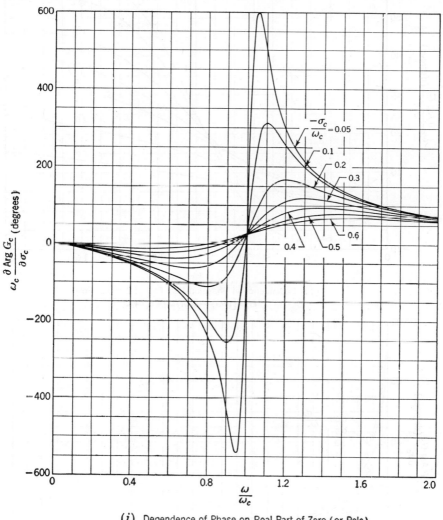

(*i*) Dependence of Phase on Real Part of Zero (or Pole)

$$G_c = [(j\omega)^2 - 2\sigma_c(j\omega) + \sigma_c^2 + \omega_c^2]$$

FIG. 6.45. (*Continued*)

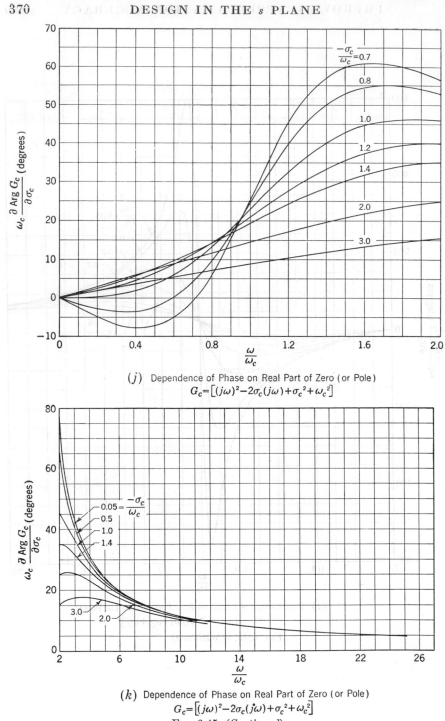

(j) Dependence of Phase on Real Part of Zero (or Pole)

$$G_c = \left[(j\omega)^2 - 2\sigma_c(j\omega) + \sigma_c^2 + \omega_c^2\right]$$

(k) Dependence of Phase on Real Part of Zero (or Pole)

$$G_c = \left[(j\omega)^2 - 2\sigma_c(j\omega) + \sigma_c^2 + \omega_c^2\right]$$

FIG. 6.45. (Continued)

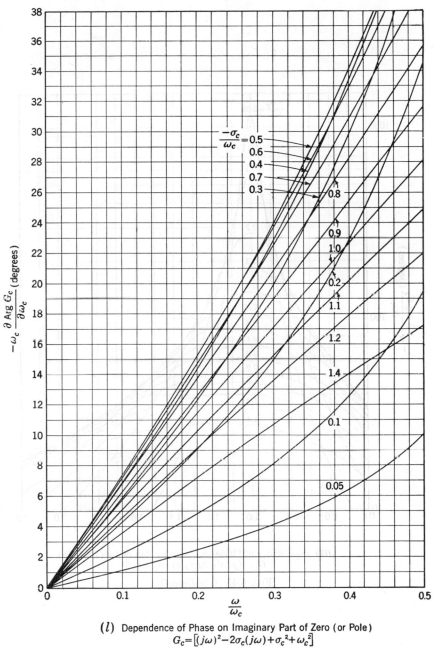

(l) Dependence of Phase on Imaginary Part of Zero (or Pole)
$$G_c = \left[(j\omega)^2 - 2\sigma_c(j\omega) + \sigma_c^2 + \omega_c^2 \right]$$

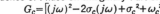

Fɪɢ. 6.45. (Continued)

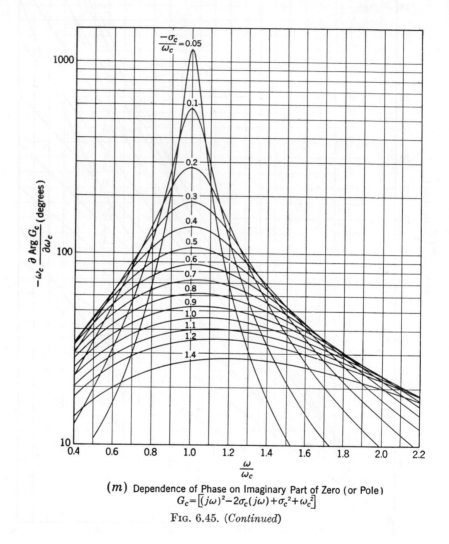

(m) Dependence of Phase on Imaginary Part of Zero (or Pole)

$$G_c = \left[(j\omega)^2 - 2\sigma_c(j\omega) + \sigma_c^2 + \omega_c^2\right]$$

FIG. 6.45. (*Continued*)

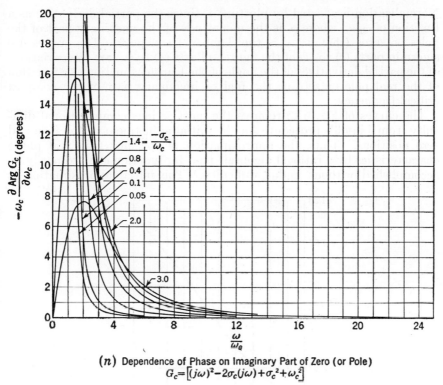

(*n*) Dependence of Phase on Imaginary Part of Zero (or Pole)

$$G_c = \left[(j\omega)^2 - 2\sigma_c(j\omega) + \sigma_c^2 + \omega_c^2\right]$$

FIG. 6.45. (*Concluded*)

Equation (6.100) can be rewritten

$$-\sigma_r \frac{\partial F_r}{\partial \sigma_r} = \mp 20 \frac{1}{1 + (\omega/\sigma_r)^2} \qquad (6.101)$$

Thus, if $-\sigma_r(\partial F_r/\partial \sigma_r)$ is plotted as a function of $\omega/(-\sigma_r)$,† a single curve suffices for any σ_r. Figures 6.45(*a*) and (*b*) represent this plot when σ_r is a zero of the transfer function. The same curves can be used for a pole if the signs of the ordinates are changed.

Utilization of these curves is straightforward. If, for example, σ_r represents a zero in the *s* plane at -3 ($\sigma_r = -3$), the horizontal scale is relabeled as shown in Fig. 6.46, and the vertical scale is converted to values of the partial derivative by dividing the ordinates by $-\sigma_r$, or 3.

In a similar manner, expressions for the partial derivatives with respect to the real and imaginary parts of complex poles or zeros can be obtained.

† The frequency is normalized with $-\sigma_r$ as a base (rather than σ_r), since poles and zeros usually lie in the left-half plane (and, hence, σ_r is negative). The gain function along the $j\omega$ axis is unchanged if a critical frequency is reflected about the $j\omega$ axis (*i.e.*, the real part changed in sign). Hence, the same curve can be used for the two factors $s + 1$ and $s - 1$. The phase for $s - 1$, however, is 180° minus the phase of $s + 1$. The change in phase, with a shift in zero or pole position, is an odd function of $\omega/(-\sigma_r)$.

Normalization is effected by plotting ω_c times the partial derivative as a function of ω/ω_c, where ω_c is the magnitude of the imaginary part of the poles or zeros (that is, ω_c is the damped frequency). The curves are shown in parts (c) to (f) of the figure. Parts (g) to (n) are the variations of the partial derivatives of the angle of the transfer function as a function of the real pole or zero or the real or imaginary part of the complex critical frequency.

The curves of Fig. 6.45 remove the most serious computational difficulty from Linvill's procedure for the initial adjustment of the pole and zero positions. Thus, the approximation of specified gain and phase characteristics by a rational algebraic transfer function can ordinarily be accomplished without undue difficulty. The initial approximation is

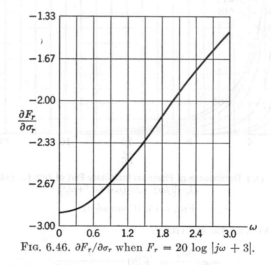

FIG. 6.46. $\partial F_r/\partial \sigma_r$ when $F_r = 20 \log |j\omega + 3|$.

made on the basis of the asymptotic gain plots. The corresponding phase, if required, is plotted, and the poles and zeros are adjusted slightly to yield a suitable compromise between gain and phase accuracy. This adjustment of pole and zero positions can be further refined if the partial derivatives of the gain and phase are considered as functions of the pole and zero positions. Inspection of these partial-derivative plots ordinarily indicates small motions of the critical frequencies, which result in improved approximation accuracy. If successive applications of this adjustment-by-inspection procedure do not result in the required accuracy, an analytical procedure can be initiated to determine the best fit on a mean-square-error basis, with the error evaluated at discrete points.

In exceptional cases, even the analytical procedure may not result in adequate accuracy, since Linvill's entire procedure is concerned with finding the optimum approximation with a specified number of poles and zeros and with the critical frequencies allowed to move only slightly in the vicinity of the initial positions. If the approximation cannot be made satisfactory, a different number of poles and zeros can be chosen and the procedure repeated. Linvill's procedure, accordingly, while not useful in certain network-theory problems in which very high accuracy is demanded, is appropriate for control-system design, where an approximation is desired which is the best obtainable with a transfer function of reasonable complexity.

6.6. Approximation in the Time Domain.   The two preceding sections include a brief description of methods for obtaining a transfer function representing experimentally measured curves of gain and phase versus frequency.   A problem of equal importance involves the determination of a transfer function from the transient response of the system.   During the last few years, the increasing use of transient signals (impulses and step functions, for example) for the measurement of the characteristics of physical equipment has emphasized the importance of methods of approximation in the time domain.   Even if the conventional frequency-domain methods are to be used for design, characterizations of the controlled system in terms of transient response must be interpreted in terms of gain and phase variations with frequency.

The increased familiarity of control engineers with Laplace-transform methods and the extension of feedback-system analysis to more diverse fields have led to the increased importance associated with time-domain testing.   A single transient test can yield all the information contained in an extensive frequency analysis.   In the experimental evaluation of the control characteristics of piloted aircraft, for example, sinusoidal measurements involve lengthy tests which are uncomfortable for personnel. Furthermore, very small test signals applied to the rudder, elevator, and ailerons may lead to undesirably strong oscillation of the aircraft.   These disadvantages can be overcome by application of short pulses and measurement of the corresponding transient response.†   During the test, the airplane operates very near the equilibrium condition.

Such transient tests are a logical extension of methods used for measuring the response characteristics of low-frequency mechanical-hydraulic systems, where the dominant resonances are determined by giving the system an initial displacement and then allowing it to oscillate toward rest.   Transient tests have been used for a number of years for characterizing certain electronic systems; in these tests, square-wave generators, with a half period which is long compared to the system response time, can be used to apply a series of step functions to the system.   The response can be measured on a cathode-ray oscilloscope or a recorder. The interpretation of transient response has become even more important in recent years as a result of the presentation of a method of testing a system by application of a small noise signal.   The technique, described in Sec. 7.10, results in the unit-impulse response of the system.

In all these applications, the experimental measurements characterize the system in the time domain.   In the design of feedback control systems, the engineer must interpret the time-domain description in more familiar terms, either as a frequency response or as a transfer function.

† R. C. Seamans, Jr., B. P. Blasingame, and G. C. Clementson, The Pulse Method for the Determination of Aircraft Performance, *J. Aeronaut. Sci.*, Vol. 17, No. 1, pp. 22–38, January, 1950.

Clearly, the most direct interpretation is developed by a Fourier transform of the transient response and the test signal. The ratio of these two transforms is $G(j\omega)$, the transfer function evaluated at real frequencies. The Fourier transformation can be accurately performed with the use of digital computers, but such a solution involves undesirably extensive equipment. A number of methods have been proposed for carrying out the Fourier transformation approximately, most of the procedures depending on the approximation of the actual time functions by a series of simpler functions: *e.g.*, step functions, rectangular pulses, or

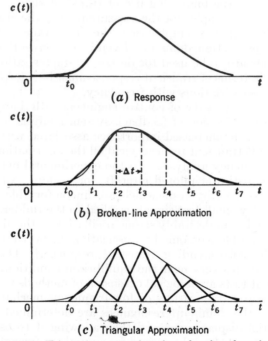

(*a*) Response

(*b*) Broken-line Approximation

(*c*) Triangular Approximation

Fig. 6.47. Triangular approximation of a time function.

triangular pulses. Once the transform of one component function is determined, the total transform is found as the sum of the individual components.

The approximation of the measured response by a series of triangles†
illustrates the general procedure used. The discussion of the analysis is logically divided into four parts:

(1) The approximation of the given response by triangular pulses
(2) The transform of a single triangular pulse
(3) The addition of component transforms
(4) The limitations on accuracy

Approximation. The first step involves the approximation of the measured response by a series of triangular pulses. Figure 6.47(*a*) shows

† *Ibid.*

a typical system response to a very short test pulse.   The response is negligible until the time t_0, increases to a maximum, and finally decreases to zero.   The response can be approximated by a series of straight lines connecting regularly spaced points along the curve, as shown in Fig. 6.47(b).   But this set of straight lines is equivalent to approximation by a series of pulses of the shape of isosceles triangles.   The triangles, shown in part (c) of the figure, are centered at regular intervals of time and have bases equal to the width of two intervals.   The equivalence of the triangular and straight-line approximations is clear if a given interval t_2 to t_3 is considered.   In this interval, the sum of the two nonzero triangles must be a linear function of time, since the sum of two linear functions is

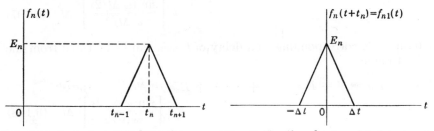

Fig. 6.48. A single triangular pulse centered at t_n.

Fig. 6.49. nth pulse translated to $t = 0$.

again linear.   Hence, the sum of the two triangles must be a straight line connecting the points on the response at t_2 and t_3.   Thus, the measured response is approximated by the series of triangles shown in Fig. 6.47(c).

Transform of a Triangular Pulse.   The transform of a single triangular pulse can be evaluated directly from the Fourier integral.   For the pulse $f_n(t)$ of Fig. 6.48, which is denoted the nth pulse since it is centered about t_n, the corresponding spectrum function is

$$F_n(\omega) = \int_{-\infty}^{\infty} f_n(t) e^{-i\omega t} dt \qquad (6.102)$$

If t is replaced by $t + t_n$, the triangular pulse is centered about $t = 0$ as shown in Fig. 6.49, and Eq. (6.102) becomes

$$F_n(\omega) = e^{-i\omega t_n} \int_{-\Delta t}^{\Delta t} f_{n1}(t) e^{-i\omega t} dt \qquad (6.103)$$

Since $f_{n1}(t)$ is an even function of t, $F_n(\omega)$ can be written

$$F_n(\omega) = 2e^{-i\omega t_n} \int_{0}^{\Delta t} f_{n1}(t) \cos \omega t \, dt \qquad (6.104)$$

Substitution of the analytical expression for $f_{n1}(t)$ gives

$$F_n(\omega) = 2e^{-i\omega t_n} E_n \int_{0}^{\Delta t} \left(1 - \frac{t}{\Delta t}\right) \cos \omega t \, dt \qquad (6.105)$$

The integration is now straightforward, and algebraic manipulation of the result yields an expression for $F_n(\omega)$:

$$F_n(\omega) = E_n \, \Delta t \left[\frac{\sin (\omega \, \Delta t/2)}{\omega \, \Delta t/2} \right]^2 e^{-j\omega t_n} \qquad (6.106)$$

Addition of Component Transforms. The approximate transform of the response is the sum of the transforms of the component triangular pulses. The various individual transforms differ in the amplitude E_n and the phase shift ωt_n. If the total transform is denoted $F(\omega)$,

$$F(\omega) = (E_1 e^{-j\omega t_1} + E_2 e^{-j\omega t_2} + \cdots + E_n e^{-j\omega t_n} + \cdots)$$
$$\left[\frac{\sin (\omega \, \Delta t/2)}{\omega \, \Delta t/2} \right]^2 \Delta t \quad (6.107)$$

A term $e^{-j\omega t_0}$, corresponding to a delay of t_0 sec, can be factored from the series to give

$$F(\omega) = (E_1 e^{-j\omega \, \Delta t} + E_2 e^{-j\omega 2 \, \Delta t} + \cdots + E_n e^{-j\omega n \, \Delta t} + \cdots) e^{-j\omega t_0}$$
$$\left[\frac{\sin(\omega \, \Delta t/2)}{\omega \, \Delta t/2} \right]^2 \Delta t \quad (6.108)$$

The series can be summed graphically, with the nth term represented by a vector of length E_n and at an angle $-\omega n \, \Delta t$ with respect to the real axis. Each vector lags the preceding in the series by the amount $\omega \, \Delta t$.

Manual summation of the series is a tedious job because the sum must be evaluated as a function of frequency over the band of interest. Seamans, *et al.*, describe a simple electrical computer to perform the required operations. Resolvers and attenuators are used to sum the real and imaginary series derived by replacing the exponentials by the cosine and sine equivalents.

Limitations on Accuracy. The triangular approximation is equivalent to sampling the response every Δt sec. Hence, the approximate transformation gives no significant information about frequency components of the response at frequencies larger than $\pi/\Delta t$ rad/sec. (The component at this frequency is sampled twice per cycle.) Furthermore, as pointed out in detail in Sec. 9.1, if there are significant frequency components at frequencies above $\pi/\Delta t$ rad/sec, the information obtained at lower frequencies is erroneous. Thus, Δt should be selected less than π/ω_{max}, where ω_{max} is the maximum frequency at which the response transform may have a significant component. As in any sampling process, difficulty occasionally arises because the required sampling frequency is most readily evaluated in terms of the spectrum to be measured.

Determination of $G(j\omega)$. The above procedure or any of the similar approximations used to determine the frequency function from the time function yields the transform of the transient response. The transfer function $G(j\omega)$ is the ratio of the transform of the response to the transform of the input, or driving function. If the input is a unit-impulse function, $G(j\omega)$ is simply the transform of the output; otherwise, the transform of the input must be determined in the usual manner, and the ratio $C(j\omega)/E(j\omega)$ is formed to obtain $G(j\omega)$. If the approximate transformation described above is used and the same Δt is selected for both input and output functions, the transfer function is simply the ratio of the series:

$$G(j\omega) = \frac{C_1 e^{-j\omega\,\Delta t} + C_2 e^{-j\omega 2\,\Delta t} + \cdots + C_n e^{-j\omega n\,\Delta t} + \cdots}{E_1 e^{-j\omega\,\Delta t} + E_2 e^{-j\omega 2\,\Delta t} + \cdots + E_n e^{-j\omega n\,\Delta t} + \cdots} \qquad (6.109)$$

Guillemin's Impulse Method of Approximation. Guillemin[†] has suggested a somewhat different method for the approximate evaluation of the Laplace integrals. The technique is applicable to the determination of the frequency response from the transient response or vice versa. If $g(t)$, the transient response, is given and the corresponding transform $G(j\omega)$ is desired, the following steps are used:

(1) $g(t)$ is approximated by a sequence of straight lines, parabolic curves, cubic curves, or curves of higher powers of t.

(2) The approximate function $g^*(t)$ is differentiated enough times (ν) to make $g^{*(\nu)}(t)$ a sequence of impulses. For example, if $g^*(t)$ is formed by a broken-line approximation of $g(t)$, two differentiations suffice, and $g^{*(2)}(t)$ consists of impulses only.

(3) The transform of $g^*(t)$ can then be written by inspection as the sum of n terms, where n is the number of impulses contained in $g^{*(\nu)}(t)$.

Thus, the essential characteristic of the method is the conversion of the integrand of the Laplace integral to a set of impulses in order that the integral may be evaluated without numerical methods. The philosophy underlying this approach is very similar to that described in Sec. 1.6, where the convolution of two time functions is simplified by the use of impulse functions. The impulse method for the determination of $g(t)$ from the frequency function follows an analogous procedure, based on the fact that the inverse Laplace integral is similar to the direct integral if the Re $G(j\omega)$ is considered, rather than the entire $G(j\omega)$ function.

The three steps described above are first clarified and illustrated by a very simple transformation from the time domain to the frequency domain. The section concludes with an example of the inverse problem, evaluation of the time function from the frequency function.

If $g(t)$ is given and $G(j\omega)$ is desired, the first step involves the approximation of $g(t)$ by a sequence of polynomials. If $g(t)$ can be satisfactorily approximated by straight lines, $g^*(t)$ can be formed by inspection. If parabolas or higher-order curves are to be used, the choice of an appropriate set of curves ordinarily cannot be visualized easily. For example, Fig. 6.50 shows a possible $g(t)$. The broken-line approximation indicated is evidently about the best that can be done with three line segments. The breaks and slopes of the three segments might be determined by minimization of the mean-square error or a similar analytical procedure, but the improvement would not be significant. It is much more difficult,

[†] E. A. Guillemin, Computational Techniques which Simplify the Correlation between Steady-state and Transient Responses of Filters and Other Networks, *Proc. Nat. Electronics Conf.* 1953, Vol. 9, 1954.

however, to determine a set of three parabolas which approach the best fit.

This difficulty is circumvented in Guillemin's method by differentiating $g(t)$ and then approximating the derivative by straight lines. Figure 6.51(*a*) shows the $g(t)$ of the previous figure, and the curve of part (*b*) is the first derivative. With the broken-line approximation to $g^{(1)}(t)$ indicated in (*b*), the original function is approximated by the parabolic segments drawn in (*c*). The differentiation tends to yield a curve with sharper peaks; a moderately poor approximation of $g^{(1)}(t)$ corresponds to a very good fit to $g(t)$, since the integration smoothes the errors of approximation. Clearly, higher-order derivatives of $g(t)$ can be formed before the approximation is made if increased accuracy is desired. If the original $g(t)$ is given analytically, the derivatives can be evaluated exactly and plotted, and the accuracy of the method is limited only by

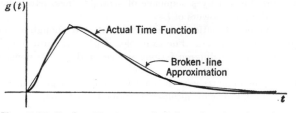

Fig. 6.50. Broken-line approximation of a time function.

the number of differentiations the analyst is willing to make and the number of straight-line segments he is willing to use (corresponding to the number of terms in the final frequency function). Each derivative requires an additional line segment to effect a good approximation, since each successive derivative involves one additional inflection point in the time function. If $g(t)$ is only known graphically [a common situation in the design of feedback control systems, where $g(t)$ is the measured impulse response of a part of the system], the allowable number of differentiations before approximation is limited by the error introduced in graphical differentiation, unless an excess amount of labor is used in evaluation of the derivative. In most cases arising in the design of feedback control systems, one differentiation seems sufficient to ensure the accuracy required. This differentiation can be effected by using the differentiation formulas of numerical analysis.†

Once the broken-line approximation is obtained, the second step in Guillemin's impulse method involves two more differentiations, which generate a set of impulses. The example of Fig. 6.51(*b*) is differentiated once to obtain the step functions of Fig. 6.51(*d*); the second differentiation results in the impulses of part (*e*) of the figure.

In the third step, the frequency function $G(j\omega)$ is written. If ν differentiations *in all* are required before the impulses are obtained, the impulses represent an approximation of the νth derivative of $g(t)$. But

† F. W. Bubb, A New Linear Operational Calculus, *Air Force Tech. Rept.* 6581, WADC, pp. 9–13, May, 1951.

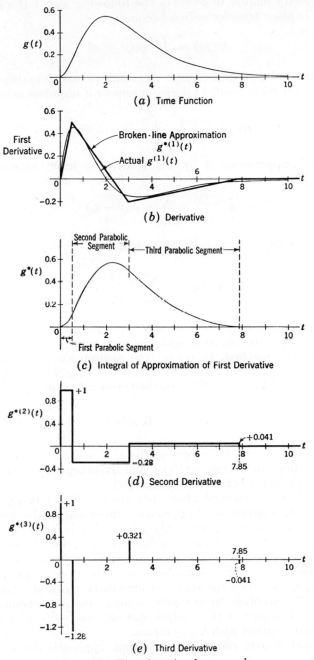

(a) Time Function

(b) Derivative

(c) Integral of Approximation of First Derivative

(d) Second Derivative

(e) Third Derivative

FIG. 6.51. Time function for example.

$G(j\omega)$ is directly related to $g^{(\nu)}(t)$ in the following way. If s is replaced by $j\omega$, the Laplace transformation becomes

$$G(j\omega) = \int_0^\infty g(t)e^{-i\omega t}\, dt \tag{6.110}$$

Differentiation of $g(t)$ with respect to t corresponds to multiplication of $G(j\omega)$ by $j\omega$ [the term $-g(0+)$ does not appear if impulses are admitted]. Hence,

$$G(j\omega) = \frac{1}{(j\omega)^\nu} \int_0^\infty g^{(\nu)}(t)e^{-i\omega t}\, dt \tag{6.111}$$

The $g^{(\nu)}(t)$ is approximated by the train of n impulses occurring at $t_1, t_2, \ldots, t_n$:

$$g^{*(\nu)}(t) = \sum_{k=1}^n a_k u_0(t - t_k) \tag{6.112}$$

Substitution of Eq. (6.112) in (6.111) yields

$$G^*(j\omega) = \sum_{k=1}^n \frac{a_k e^{-i\omega t_k}}{(j\omega)^\nu} \tag{6.113}\dagger$$

The real and imaginary parts of $G^*(j\omega)$ can be found from Eq. (6.113) by writing the exponential in rectangular form.

In Guillemin's method, therefore, the assumption is made that the impulses $g^{*(\nu)}(t)$ actually represent the νth derivative of $g(t)$. In the simple example of Fig. 6.51, $G^*(j\omega)$, the transform of $g^*(t)$, is

$$G^*(j\omega) = \frac{1}{(j\omega)^3}\,(1 - 1.28e^{-i\omega 0.5} + 0.321e^{-i\omega 3} - 0.041e^{-i\omega 7.85}) \tag{6.114}$$

This $G^*(j\omega)$ is the *exact* transform of the $g^*(t)$ shown in part (c) of the figure. The difference between $G^*(j\omega)$ and the actual $G(j\omega)$ is exclusively the result of the error between $g^*(t)$ and $g(t)$.

The procedure as outlined above possesses several advantages when compared to the conventional approaches described in the first part of this section. The accuracy with only a few terms is much better in this method than in any of the usual procedures. The differentiation essentially permits approximation of the time function by curves of higher order than can ordinarily be considered by inspection. The problem of plotting $|G(j\omega)|$, or even the real and imaginary parts of $G(j\omega)$, versus frequency still involves appreciable computational difficulties. The tediousness of this part of the analysis can only be reduced by obtaining a better approximation with fewer terms.

As indicated above, essentially the same approach can be used to

---

† $G(j\omega)$ approaches a finite value as $\omega \to 0$ because the broken-line approximation was chosen to yield a time function $g^*(t)$ which is zero for all t larger than 7.85. Consequently, there is no d-c component of $g^*(t)$, and $G(0)$ is finite.

evaluate the inverse Fourier integral for the determination of $g(t)$ from $G(j\omega)$:

$$g(t) = \frac{1}{2\pi} \int_{-\infty}^{\infty} G(j\omega)e^{j\omega t}\, d\omega \tag{6.115}$$

If the integrand is written in rectangular form,

$$g(t) = \frac{1}{2\pi} \int_{-\infty}^{\infty} \{\text{Re}[G(j\omega)]\cos \omega t - \text{Im}[G(j\omega)]\sin \omega t\}\, d\omega$$

$$+ \frac{j}{2\pi} \int_{-\infty}^{\infty} \{\text{Re}\,[G(j\omega)]\sin \omega t + \text{Im}\,[G(j\omega)]\cos \omega t\}\, d\omega \tag{6.116}$$

The second integral is zero because the integrand is an odd function of ω [if the integral were not zero, $g(t)$ would be complex and a nonphysical time function].   The first integral consists of an odd and an even function of time.   If $g(t)$ is zero for t negative, the two components must be equal and opposite for $t < 0$ and hence equal for $t > 0$.   Thus,

$$g(t) = \frac{1}{\pi} \int_{-\infty}^{\infty} \text{Re}\,[G(j\omega)]\cos \omega t\, d\omega = -\frac{1}{\pi} \int_{-\infty}^{\infty} \text{Im}\,[G(j\omega)]\sin \omega t\, d\omega$$

$$\text{for } t > 0 \tag{6.117}$$

Since each integrand is an even function of ω,

$$g(t) = \frac{2}{\pi} \int_{0}^{\infty} \text{Re}\,[G(j\omega)]\cos \omega t\, d\omega = -\frac{2}{\pi} \int_{0}^{\infty} \text{Im}\,[G(j\omega)]\sin \omega t\, d\omega$$

$$\text{for } t > 0 \tag{6.118}$$

The integrals of this equation have exactly the same form as the expressions for the real and imaginary parts of $G(j\omega)$ in terms of $g(t)$.   For example, if $g(t)$ is zero for t negative, Eq. (6.110) implies the relation

$$\text{Re } G(j\omega) = \int_{0}^{\infty} g(t)\cos \omega t\, dt \tag{6.119}$$

Thus, $g(t)$ can be evaluated from $\text{Re } G(j\omega)$, denoted $G_1(\omega)$, in the following steps:†
(1) $G_1(\omega)$ is differentiated $\nu - 2$ times and approximated by a set of straight-line segments.   The appropriate value of ν depends on considerations similar to those described previously.
(2)   Two more differentiations (ν in all) yield a set of impulses as the approximation of the νth derivative of $G_1(\omega)$.
(3) $g(t)$ is written by inspection as the sum of sinusoidal or cosinusoidal terms divided by t^{ν}.
Step (3) is the only one differing at all from the procedure used to pass from the time domain to the frequency domain.   If $G_1(\omega)$ is given and $g(t)$ is to be found, the equation corresponding to (6.111) is

† Use of the imaginary part rather than the real part involves exactly the same steps, although the formulas of step (3) are slightly different.

$$
g(t) = \begin{cases} \dfrac{2}{\pi} \dfrac{(-1)^{\nu/2}}{t^{\nu}} \displaystyle\int_0^{\infty} G_1^{(\nu)}(\omega) \cos \omega t \, d\omega & \nu \text{ even, } t > 0 \\[2em] \dfrac{2}{\pi} \dfrac{(-1)^{(\nu+1)/2}}{t^{\nu}} \displaystyle\int_0^{\infty} G_1^{(\nu)}(\omega) \sin \omega t \, d\omega & \nu \text{ odd, } t > 0 \end{cases} \qquad (6.120)\dagger
$$

The νth derivative of $G_1(\omega)$ is a set of impulses, occurring at both positive and negative frequencies. Since $G_1(\omega)$ is an even function of ω, the νth derivative is an even function of ω if ν is even, an odd function of ω if ν is odd. Thus, the νth derivative takes the form

$$
G_1^{(\nu)}(\omega) = \sum_{k=1}^{n} a_k[u_0(\omega - \omega_k) + (-1)^{\nu} u_0(\omega + \omega_k)] \qquad (6.121)
$$

Guillemin demonstrates that a real part consisting of a pair of equal impulses occurring at $+j\omega_k$ and $-j\omega_k$ corresponds to a cosinusoidal time function.‡ Accordingly,

$$
g(t) = \begin{cases} \dfrac{2}{\pi} \dfrac{(-1)^{\nu/2}}{t^{\nu}} \displaystyle\sum_{k=1}^{n} a_k \cos \omega_k t & \nu \text{ even, } t > 0 \\[2em] \dfrac{2}{\pi} \dfrac{(-1)^{(\nu+1)/2}}{t^{\nu}} \displaystyle\sum_{k=1}^{n} a_k \sin \omega_k t & \nu \text{ odd, } t > 0 \end{cases} \qquad (6.122)
$$

† Equation (6.120) follows directly from the theorem in Laplace-transform theory which states that differentiation of the transform with respect to s (or $j\omega$ in this discussion) corresponds to multiplication of the time function by $-t$. In Eq. (6.120), $G_1^{(\nu)}(\omega)$ represents the νth derivative with respect to ω.

‡ The proof follows by considering the transform pair

$$
\frac{1}{\pi(s + \alpha - j\omega_0)} \longleftrightarrow \frac{1}{\pi} e^{-\alpha t} e^{j\omega_0 t}
$$

Along the $j\omega$ axis, the transform becomes

$$
\frac{1}{\pi[\alpha + j(\omega - \omega_0)]} = \frac{\alpha}{\pi[\alpha^2 + (\omega - \omega_0)^2]} - j \frac{\omega - \omega_0}{\pi[\alpha^2 + (\omega - \omega_0)^2]}
$$

As α is allowed to approach zero, the real part, $\alpha/\{\pi[\alpha^2 + (\omega - \omega_0)^2]\}$, tends to zero everywhere except at $\omega = \omega_0$, where the function approaches infinity. If the real part is integrated from $\omega = -\infty$ to $\omega = +\infty$,

$$
\int_{-\infty}^{\infty} \frac{\alpha}{\pi[\alpha^2 + (\omega - \omega_0)^2]} \, d\omega = 1
$$

Hence, as α tends to zero, the transform becomes

$$
u_0(\omega - \omega_0) - j \frac{1}{\pi(\omega - \omega_0)}
$$

and

$$
u_0(\omega - \omega_0) - j \frac{1}{\pi(\omega - \omega_0)} \longleftrightarrow \frac{1}{\pi} e^{j\omega_0 t}
$$

Equation (6.122) follows directly from this transform pair.

Figure 6.52 illustrates the use of Guillemin's impulse method for determining the time function from a given real part of the transform. The various parts of the figure are derived as follows:

(1)   In part (a), $G_1(\omega)$ is plotted versus ω.

(2)   The real part is differentiated once to obtain the curve of (b).

(3)   A broken-line approximation is obtained for $G_1^{(1)}(\omega)$. The approximant $G_1^{*(1)}(\omega)$ is shown in (c).

(4)   The integral of $G_1^{*(1)}(\omega)$ is compared with the desired $G_1(\omega)$. In other words, part (d) shows the parabolic approximation used for the original real part. This curve is plotted only to indicate the accuracy of the approximation.

(5) $G_1^{*(1)}(\omega)$ is differentiated to obtain the set of step functions shown in (e).

(6)   Another differentiation yields the impulses of (f).

(7) · The time function is now written from Eq. (6.122), with $\nu = 3$ (three differentiations in all) and a_k and ω_k read from (f).

$$g(t) = \frac{2}{\pi t^3} (2.112 \sin 0.57t - 0.4925 \sin 2.4t - 0.01193 \sin 4.5t$$

$$+ 0.00241 \sin 12.8t) \qquad (6.123)$$

(8)   Part (g) of the figure indicates the accuracy of the method. The actual time function in this example is the inverse transform of $3/[(s+1)(s+3)]$, the transform used for the determination of the original real part.

Figure 6.52(g) demonstrates that the accuracy is poor for small values of t. Working from Eqs. (1.175) and (1.176), Guillemin describes a method of modifying the procedure in order to guarantee the appropriate asymptotic behavior of $g^*(t)$ for small values of t. This modification is a refinement ordinarily unwarranted by the accuracy desired by the designer of feedback control systems. In this example, the accuracy can be improved if the imaginary part, rather than the real part, is used as the starting point. In addition, the accuracy can be considerably improved if the real part is differentiated again before the broken-line approximation is made, but the actual procedure described by the figure demonstrates the method. For control-system engineers, the primary usefulness of the method is in problems where a simple correlation is desired between time and frequency domains.

Determination of $G(s)$. The preceding parts of this section have considered methods for determining the behavior of the transform *along the jω axis* from the time function. If the root-locus method or Guillemin's procedure is used for system design, the transfer function must be evaluated as a function of the complex frequency s. It is possible to determine $G(s)$ by first finding the magnitude and angle of $G(j\omega)$ from a Fourier transformation of the system input and response and then approximating the gain and phase by a rational algebraic function of $j\omega$ or s, as outlined in Secs. 6.4 and 6.5. Since such a procedure requires a two-stage approximation, the analysis is extensive and difficulties arise because of the two separate sources of error. For example, the error introduced in passing from the time domain to the $j\omega$ axis may be magnified unduly in the transition from the $j\omega$ axis to the s plane.

Unfortunately, there is no straightforward general procedure for

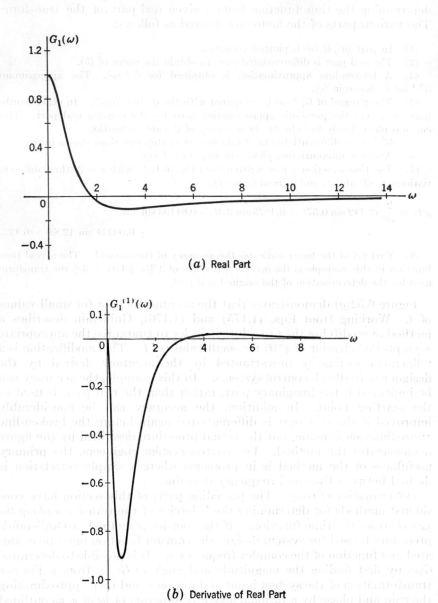

(a) Real Part

(b) Derivative of Real Part

Fig. 6.52. Approximate evaluation of time function from real part of $j\omega$ transform.

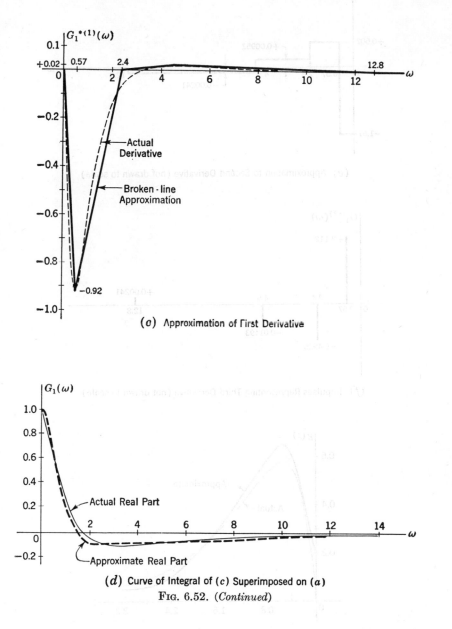

(c) Approximation of First Derivative

(d) Curve of Integral of (c) Superimposed on (a)

FIG. 6.52. (*Continued*)

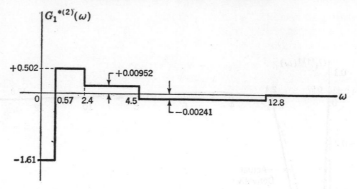

(e) Approximation to Second Derivative (not drawn to scale)

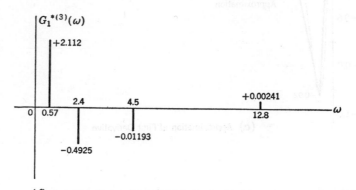

(f) Impulses Representing Third Derivative (not drawn to scale)

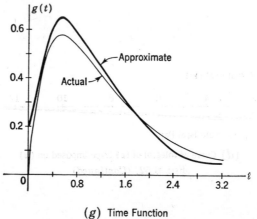

(g) Time Function

FIG. 6.52. (Continued)

determining a rational algebraic transfer function $G(s)$ from the corresponding response and input in the time domain. If the response is the impulse response and if the system function contains only a few critical frequencies, the poles and residues of $G(s)$ can often be determined directly from the time function. For example, complex poles of $G(s)$ generate a term in $g(t)$, the impulse response, of the form

$$Ae^{-\zeta\omega_n t} \sin (\omega_n \sqrt{1 - \zeta^2} \, t + \theta)$$

Here ζ and ω_n describe the poles, and A and θ are determined by the magnitude and angle, respectively, of the corresponding residues in the partial-fraction expansion of $G(s)$. If one pair of complex poles of $G(s)$ is much closer to the $j\omega$ axis than any other poles, an expression of the above form describes $g(t)$ after sufficient time has elapsed to allow all other terms to die out. In such a case, ζ, ω_n, A, and θ can be found from $g(t)$, and the above term can then be subtracted from the total $g(t)$ to give a simpler time function for consideration. This same simplification is useful even if $G(j\omega)$ rather than $G(s)$ is desired, since the approximate transformations described previously require an excessive number of samples if $g(t)$ contains a lightly damped term.

The actual determination of the parameters ζ, ω_n, A, and θ is effected as follows. The time function is considered after sufficient time has elapsed to guarantee that the waveform represents a damped sinusoid. The relative damping ratio is evaluated from the rate of decay of the damped oscillations. The ratio of the magnitudes of successive extremes is given by the expression $e^{-\pi\zeta/\sqrt{1-\zeta^2}}$. Once ζ is determined, ω_n can be found from the time between zero crossings. Successive zero crossings occur at an interval of $\pi/(\omega_n \sqrt{1 - \zeta^2})$ sec. With ω_n and ζ known, θ can be found by considering the instant of one of the zero crossings, which must occur when

$$\omega_n \sqrt{1 - \zeta^2} \, t + \theta = k\pi \qquad k = 1, 2, \ldots \qquad (6.124)$$

The amplitude of the damped exponential can be evaluated by considering any specific value of $g(t)$.

If $G(s)$ contains a simple real pole very close to the $j\omega$ axis, $g(t)$ contains a long tail, decaying exponentially. If $G(s)$ has both a simple real pole near the axis and a lightly damped pair of complex poles at about the same distance from the $j\omega$ axis, the oscillatory term considered above is superimposed on an exponential tail. If only a few long-duration low-time-constant components are included in $g(t)$, these can be determined and the corresponding terms evaluated in the partial-fraction expansion of $G(s)$. Once these long-duration terms are subtracted from $g(t)$, the remaining time function is analyzed for a determination of the short-duration components. In this way, the partial-fraction expansion of $G(s)$, and hence the complete function, can be determined in a wide variety of cases.

If $G(s)$ contains a large number of poles close together, the above procedure is blocked because of the difficulty associated with separating components corresponding to nearly the same complex frequency. In the present state of the art, the engineer then has no recourse but to return to a Fourier transformation, followed by an approximation in the frequency domain.

6.7. Design of A-C Systems. Because of the possibilities afforded for low weight requirements, ease of amplifier construction, and simplicity of

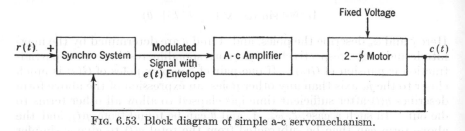

FIG. 6.53. Block diagram of simple a-c servomechanism.

components, a large percentage of the servomechanisms used in instrumentation and computers are a-c or carrier systems. The conventional a-c system is characterized by the transmission of the data as the envelope of a modulated signal. Although any type of modulation might be employed, the convenience of effecting the modulation in a synchro or a chopper circuit and the demodulation in a two-phase motor has resulted in the nearly exclusive use of suppressed-carrier amplitude modulation.

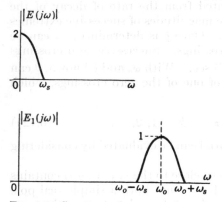

FIG. 6.54. Spectrum of suppressed-carrier amplitude modulation. (Shown for positive frequencies only.)

The block diagram of a common a-c system is shown in Fig. 6.53. A servomechanism controlling output-shaft position is shown, with the actuating signal measured by a synchro system. The output of the synchro-control transformer is a sine wave modulated by the information $e(t)$. An a-c amplifier is used to drive one phase of the two-phase motor, with the other phase excited by a fixed voltage at the carrier frequency. From the output of the synchro system to the motor, the information appears only as the envelope of the modulated signal.

The characteristics of the suppressed-carrier amplitude-modulated signal are described in elementary texts on communication engineering. If $e(t)$ is the modulating signal and $\cos \omega_0 t$ the carrier, the modulated wave $e_1(t)$ is described by the equation

$$e_1(t) = e(t) \cos \omega_0 t \tag{6.125}$$

The frequency spectrum of $e_1(t)$ consists of the upper and lower sidebands, shown in Fig. 6.54. If $e(t)$ is a simple sinusoidal signal, the waveform of $e_1(t)$ is as sketched in Fig. 6.55(a); the waveform is somewhat similar to that for 100-per cent amplitude modulation except that a phase reversal occurs at the instant the amplitude goes to zero. Because of this reversal, the envelope is as shown in Fig. 6.55(b), rather than part (c) of the figure.

Clearly, a wide variety of modifications are possible in the system shown in Fig. 6.53. For example, the comparison of $c(t)$ and $r(t)$ can be accomplished with potentiometers and an electrical subtracting circuit. Alternatively, $e(t)$ might be generated as a d-c signal and the modulation accomplished by a chopper or vibrator. Likewise, the two-phase motor can be replaced by a demodulator and a d-c motor, by an electric-hydraulic system, etc. Figure 6.53 suffices, however, as a basis for the brief discussion of this section.

The problems associated with the design of carrier systems are clarified by a consideration of the block diagram of Fig. 6.53. Two assumptions are made in the following discussion:

(1) The signal $e_1(t)$ represents perfect suppressed-carrier amplitude modulation of a sinusoidal carrier by the actuating signal $e(t)$. If synchros are used, voltage induced by rotation is neglected† and the output is assumed noise-free. Likewise, if potentiometers or choppers are used, no noise or corrupting signal is present in the output.

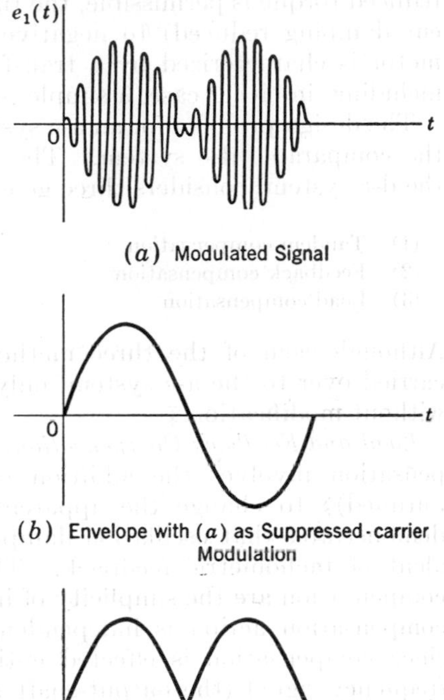

(a) Modulated Signal

(b) Envelope with (a) as Suppressed-carrier Modulation

(c) Envelope of (a) if (a) were Amplitude Modulation

FIG. 6.55. Modulation by a sinusoidal signal.

(2) The motor (with load) acts as a demodulator, with a known transfer function relating the output-shaft position to the *envelope* of the signal applied to the control phase.

Although neither of these assumptions is strictly valid, the failure to satisfy (2) is ordinarily the more troublesome. In spite of the considerable volume of work published on the characteristics of two-phase

† There is the possibility of utilizing the tachometric or rotationally induced voltage of a synchro for compensation of an a-c system. Such a design is practical only if the amplifier has a high gain and the carrier frequency is low. *Cf.* D. Morris, A Theoretical and Experimental Method of Modulation Analysis for the Design of AC Servo Systems, "Automatic and Manual Control," Proceedings of Cranfield Conference 1951, edited by A. Tustin, pp. 521–538, Butterworths Scientific Publications, London, 1952.

motors,† there still appears to be no completely adequate, simple description. Difficulties arise because of the dependence of motor characteristics on the input signal. For example, the apparent time constant of the response of the motor plus driving amplifier can be controlled over a wide range by variation of the amplifier output impedance; indeed, if reduced torque is permissible, the time constant can be decreased (apparent damping reduced) to negative values. In the usual analysis, the motor is characterized by a transfer function with two or three poles, including, in either case, a simple pole at the origin.

The design problem for an a-c system is most readily stated in terms of the comparable d-c system. The designer, attempting to compensate the d-c system, considers three general techniques:

(1) Tandem compensation
(2) Feedback compensation
(3) Load compensation

Although each of the three methods, illustrated in Fig. 6.56, can be carried over to the a-c system, only the last two are directly applicable without modification.‡

Load and Feedback Compensation. The commonest form of load compensation involves the addition of an oscillation damper (tuned or untuned)§ to change the apparent characteristics of the load. Hall demonstrates that oscillation dampers can be used to obtain the equivalent of tachometric feedback. The primary advantages of the load compensation are the simplicity of instrumentation and the fact that the compensation action is independent of drift of the carrier frequency, since compensation is effected entirely mechanically and on the low-frequency signal (the output-shaft rotation), rather than on the modulated signal.

Feedback compensation is ordinarily effected by a tachometric minor loop around the motor to change the apparent characteristics of the motor. Any compensation action which can be effected by tandem networks can also be accomplished by appropriately selected feedback networks driven by the tachometer, but in an a-c system (using an a-c tachometer) the networks driven by the tachometer are limited in the same manner as the tandem compensation networks described below. Feedback compensation, using just the differentiating action of the

† *Cf.* for example L. Brown, Transfer Function for a 2-Phase Induction Servo Motor, *Trans. AIEE*, Vol. 70, Part. II, pp. 1890–1893, 1951; A. Hopkin, Transient Response of Small Two Phase Induction Motors, *Trans. AIEE*, Vol. 70, Part I, pp. 881–886, 1951; and M. Steinhacker and W. Meserve, 2-phase A-C Servo Motor Operation for Varying Phase Angle of the Control Winding Applied Voltage, *Trans. AIEE*, Vol. 70, Part II, pp. 1987–1993, 1951.

‡ H. E. Blanton, Carrier Compensation for Servomechanisms, *J. Franklin Inst.*, Vol. 250, No. 5, pp. 391–407, and No. 6, pp. 525–542, November and December, 1950. This article contains a brief general survey of compensation techniques for a-c systems.

§ A. C. Hall, Damper Stabilized Instrument Servomechanisms, *Trans. AIEE*, Vol. 68, Part I, pp. 299–306, 1949.

tachometer, is advantageous in a-c systems, since the tachometer is driven by the output-shaft position and, consequently, the compensation is effective even if the carrier frequency changes. Thus, both load and feedback compensation can be used with a-c or d-c systems, although the permissible types of feedback compensation are limited in a-c systems. The design of oscillation dampers or the minor-loop feedback elements can be accomplished by use of the root-locus method or Guillemin's procedure, just as in the design of a d-c system.

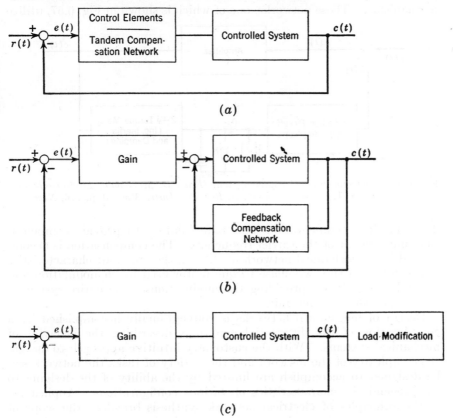

FIG. 6.56. Simple schemes for compensation.

Mechanical Networks. The oscillation dampers are basically mechanical networks to modify the dynamic characteristics of the load. The concept of mechanical compensation can be extended to the design of mechanical networks comparable to the conventional *RLC* electrical networks. Such mechanical networks have a number of important applications in feedback control systems. For example, in an airborne fire-control system the information may appear electrically only as the envelope of a suppressed-carrier amplitude-modulated wave in a three-phase synchro system. Electrical compensation, even with an a-c compensation network, requires conversion of the three-phase signal to single-phase, then back to three-phase for further transmission. A mechanical network can be used at the antenna to filter the signal representing antenna position before it is converted to an electrical signal. Mechanical networks find other applications as filters or compensation devices in servomechanisms which are entirely mechanical and hydraulic (*e.g.*, in the elevator-control system of certain aircraft). A final, specific example of the application of mechanical networks is provided by compensation systems suggested by McDonald† for use with a-c servomechanisms. These networks, one of which is shown in Fig. 6.57, utilize

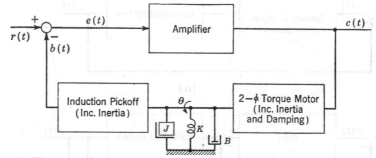

Fɪɢ. 6.57. Electromechanical compensation. (*From D. McDonald, Electromechanical Lead Networks for A. C. Servomechanisms, Rev. Sci. Instr., Vol. 20, p. 776, November, 1949.*)

demodulation, compensation, and remodulation to provide compensation independent of the carrier frequency. The compensation is accomplished by a mechanical network modifying the apparent characteristics of the rotors of the two-phase torque motor used for demodulation and the induction pickoff providing the modulation. The entire system is encased as one compact unit.

Design of mechanical networks is conventionally accomplished by a consideration of the differential equations describing the behavior of mechanical systems. With the customary intuitive approach to design, the complexity of the network and the variety of tasks the network can be designed to accomplish are limited by the ability of the designer to comprehend the characteristics of various configurations. Application of the principles of electrical network synthesis broadens the scope of usefulness of mechanical networks. The basic concepts described in Chap. 3 are all directly applicable to mechanical systems, as a result of the familiar analogies between electrical and mechanical systems. Table 6.2 lists the two analogies most often used. In these terms, the electrical *RC* network, for example, is similar to either a *BK* or a *BM* network in mechanical systems—*i.e.*, to a network consisting of dampers and either springs or masses.

Synthesis of a mechanical network proceeds in exactly the same manner as that of an electrical system. If a network is desired to realize a prescribed transfer function (*e.g.*, the ratio of translational velocities), appro-

† D. McDonald, Electromechanical Lead Networks for A. C. Servomechanisms, *Rev. Sci. Instr.*, Vol. 20, p. 775, November, 1949.

priate driving-point and transfer impedances or mobilities are selected, and the network is realized by reducing the driving-point function step by step, in such a way as to realize the proper zeros of the transfer function (Sec. 3.6). Dasher's procedure and other more complex synthesis tech-

TABLE 6.2

MECHANICAL-ELECTRICAL ANALOGIES

Mechanical quantity	Electrical quantity	
	Analogy I	Analogy II
Force,† F (or torque, T)	Voltage, E	Current, I
Velocity, V (or angular velocity, Ω)	Current, I	Voltage, E
Mass, M (or inertia, J)	Inductance, L	Capacitance, C
Viscous damping, B	Resistance, R	Conductance, $G = \dfrac{1}{R}$
Spring constant, K	Inverse capacitance, $\dfrac{1}{C} = S$	Inverse inductance, $\dfrac{1}{L} = \Gamma$
Displacement, X (or angular displacement, Θ)	Charge, Q	Integral of voltage
Mechanical impedance‡ (at sinusoidal angular frequency ω) $\dfrac{F}{X}(j\omega)$	$\dfrac{\text{Voltage}}{\text{Charge}}, \dfrac{E}{Q}(j\omega)$ or $\dfrac{j\omega E}{I}$ (or inverse capacitance)	$\dfrac{\text{Current}}{\text{(Integral of voltage)}}, \dfrac{j\omega I}{E}$ (or inverse inductance)
$\dfrac{F}{V}(j\omega)$	Electrical impedance, $\dfrac{E}{I}(j\omega)$	Electrical admittance, $\dfrac{I}{E}(j\omega)$
$\dfrac{V}{F}(j\omega)$	Electrical admittance, $\dfrac{I}{E}(j\omega)$	Electrical impedance, $\dfrac{E}{I}(j\omega)$

† The variables are denoted throughout this table by capital letters, indicating the amplitude of a sinusoidal signal. The analogies, of course, basically relate instantaneous values, and the notation e, i, f, v, etc., can be used equally well.

‡ There seems to be no standard definition for the term "mechanical impedance." Perhaps the commonest usage is to define impedance as $\dfrac{F}{X}(j\omega)$; in this case, the term "mobility" is often used for $\dfrac{V}{F}(j\omega)$.

niques can be adapted in the same way to the design of mechanical networks. Once the network configuration is determined, the physical construction of a *simple, compact* network depends upon the ingenuity of the mechanical engineer. Figure 6.58 shows one example, a mechanical twin-T network, with the electrical network shown in part (a), the mechanical system in part (b), and a sketch of the basic components of the physical unit in part (c) (supply lines, etc., are not indicated). The network shown is for a translational system; it is also possible to design rotational systems with exactly the same procedure.

There are three significant ways in which mechanical networks are less flexible than the electrical counterparts:

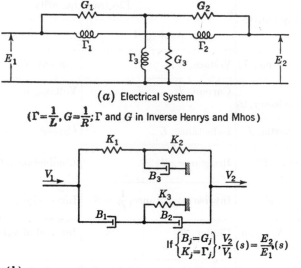

(a) Electrical System

$(\Gamma = \dfrac{1}{L}, G = \dfrac{1}{R}; \Gamma$ and G in Inverse Henrys and Mhos$)$

If $\begin{cases} B_j = G_j \\ K_j = \Gamma_j \end{cases}, \dfrac{V_2}{V_1}(s) = \dfrac{E_2}{E_1}(s)$

(b) Analogous Mechanical System (Translational Motion Only)

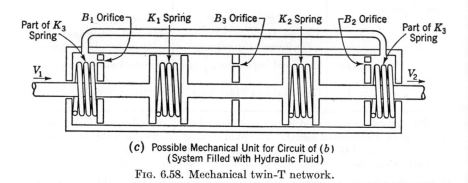

(c) Possible Mechanical Unit for Circuit of (b)
(System Filled with Hydraulic Fluid)

FIG. 6.58. Mechanical twin-T network.

(1) The mechanical realization of mutual mass is frequently troublesome. In Analogy I of Table 6.1, an inductance common to two loops or in Analogy II, a capacitance between two independent nodes corresponds in the mechanical system to a mass which moves with respect to a non-fixed point. Any physical mass, however, always moves with reference to ground: ma is the force to accelerate with reference to ground. The effect of mutual mass can be achieved by a variety of special schemes

(*e.g.*, a differential gear or a fixed bar†), but it is ordinarily desirable to avoid this difficulty if possible.

(2) A centering problem exists in the practical use of dampers. All dampers which do not go to ground must be centered by a spring or a combination of springs. If only a series damper connects points with motions x_1 and x_2, noise or disturbance variation of x_2 while x_1 is zero may cause the damper to move against one of the stops. A subsequent motion of x_1 may then be transmitted through the direct link to x_2 rather than through the damper. A spring across the damper gives an integrating action which prevents short-term disturbances on the x_2 shaft from destroying the centering.

(3) The dampers are actually characterized by more nearly a square law than a linear relation between force and velocity. In other words, if f is the force across the damper, v the relative velocity of the two sides, and k a constant of proportionality,

$$f \cong kv^2 \tag{6.126}$$

In practice, a linear relationship can be used to characterize the dampers over a limited range of amplitude and frequency. Although a variety of special techniques exist for extending the linear range of operation, it appears that the nonlinearity of the dampers is a basic limitation in the application of mechanical networks.

For the most part the mechanical engineer, although historically the first to develop techniques for circuit analysis, has fallen behind the electrical engineer's rapid development of network synthesis. Almost all mechanical networks used at the present time are simple configurations. The vibration dampers and the mechanical oscillation dampers used by the aeronautical engineer as pitch or yaw dampers are two common examples of simple mechanical networks. The very pronounced advantages the mechanical system so often has over the comparable electrical system (advantages such as the low loss, or high Q, obtainable at very low frequencies, the greater dependability, and the possibilities of lighter weight and smaller size when considered with the associated equipment) indicate that mechanical networks should find increasing application, not only in the compensation of a-c servomechanisms, but in a wide variety of other uses.

Tandem Compensation. In contrast to load and simple feedback compensation, where the same principles apply for a-c and d-c systems, attempts to introduce tandem compensation in an a-c system generate very real difficulties. In both load and simple feedback compensation, the compensating device is operating on the output $c(t)$, which is not a modulated signal. In tandem compensation, however, the compensation network, as shown in Fig. 6.59, is to operate on the envelope of a modulated signal. Specifically, the network g_1 must modify the envelope of e_1 in the same way that the corresponding d-c network would operate on

† M. F. Gardner and J. L. Barnes, "Transients in Linear Systems," pp. 69–81, John Wiley & Sons, Inc., New York, 1942.

the actuating signal. Clearly, one method of accomplishing this is to include in the block g_1 a demodulator, a d-c compensation network, and a modulator. Alternatively, if the lags of demodulation and modulation are to be avoided, g_1 can include a minor loop, with the forward path simply an amplifier, and the demodulation, compensation, and remodulation accomplished in the feedback path. Although such schemes of converting to d-c signals before compensating have been used extensively, the amount of equipment involved is excessive for many applications.

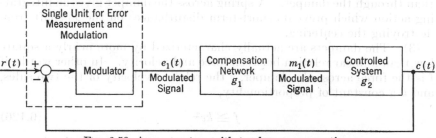

FIG. 6.59. An a-c system with tandem compensation.

It is impossible to obtain a network modifying the envelope of the modulated signal in *exactly* the same way that a d-c compensation network operates. Fortunately, however, adequate approximations can be obtained in a wide variety of cases. The notch, or twin-T, filter is the most familiar example of such an approximation. In the following discussion, the basic problems associated with tandem compensation are considered and various approximate solutions are suggested.

Ideal Tandem Compensation. Figure 6.60 shows both d-c and a-c tandem networks. For the d-c network, the input is denoted $e(t)$, the

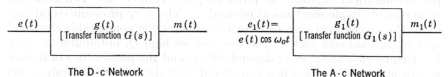

The D-c Network   The A-c Network

FIG. 6.60. Corresponding d-c and a-c networks.

output $m(t)$, and the transfer function $G(s)$, where

$$M(s) = G(s)E(s) \tag{6.127}$$

For the a-c network, the input is the modulated wave with envelope $e(t)$ and carrier angular frequency ω_o:

$$e_1(t) = e(t) \cos \omega_o t \tag{6.128}$$

If the network g_1 is to operate on the envelope of $e_1(t)$ just as g operates on $e(t)$, the desired output of the a-c network is

$$m_1(t) = m(t) \cos \omega_o t \tag{6.129}†$$

† More generally, an output $m(t) \cos (\omega_o t + \phi)$ is acceptable if ϕ is a constant, independent of $e(t)$, since a constant carrier phase shift is permissible. (The phase

The required transfer function for g_1 is the ratio of the Laplace transforms of $m_1(t)$ and $e_1(t)$. If the transform of $e(t)$ is $E(s)$, the transform of $e_1(t)$ can be found by writing the cosine wave as the sum of exponentials, with the result

$$E_1(s) = \frac{E(s - j\omega_o) + E(s + j\omega_o)}{2} \tag{6.130}$$

Likewise,

$$M_1(s) = \frac{M(s - j\omega_o) + M(s + j\omega_o)}{2} \tag{6.131}$$

Substituting Eq. (6.127) in (6.131) and forming the ratio $M_1(s)/E_1(s)$ yield the ideal transfer function of the a-c compensation network,

$$G_1(s) = \frac{G(s - j\omega_o)E(s - j\omega_o) + G(s + j\omega_o)E(s + j\omega_o)}{E(s - j\omega_o) + E(s + j\omega_o)} \tag{6.132}\star$$

This $G_1(s)$ is not physically realizable by an RLC network, since the transfer function depends on the input signal. Thus, it is not possible to determine the required $G_1(s)$ directly from $G(s)$ and proceed with the synthesis of the compensation network in the usual way. The design of the tandem a-c system is more complicated than the design of the d-c counterpart.

The conventional method for circumventing the difficulties imposed by Eq. (6.132) is to consider the required behavior of the transfer function along the $j\omega$ axis; in particular, the gain and phase of $G_1(j\omega)$ are investigated. If s is replaced by $j\omega$, the desired transfer function becomes

$$G_1(j\omega) = \frac{G[j(\omega - \omega_o)]E[j(\omega - \omega_o)] + G[j(\omega + \omega_o)]E[j(\omega + \omega_o)]}{E[j(\omega - \omega_o)] + E[j(\omega + \omega_o)]} \tag{6.133}$$

$G_1(j\omega)$ still depends on the input spectrum, but this difficulty disappears in a practical problem in which the modulating signal (or the reference input of the servomechanism) has no significant energy at frequencies larger than the carrier. In such a case,

$$\begin{aligned} E[j(\omega + \omega_o)] = 0 & \quad \text{for } \omega > 0 \\ E[j(\omega - \omega_o)] = 0 & \quad \text{for } \omega < 0 \end{aligned} \tag{6.134}$$

Substitution of Eq. (6.134) in (6.133) yields

$$G_1(j\omega) = \begin{cases} G[j(\omega - \omega_o)] & \omega > 0 \\ G[j(\omega + \omega_o)] & \omega < 0 \end{cases} \tag{6.135}$$

Although direct synthesis is still impossible since $G_1(j\omega)$ is not represented by a rational algebraic function of $j\omega$ with real coefficients, at least the

---

of the fixed voltage of the motor, for example, can be adjusted to compensate for ϕ.) Inclusion of the angle ϕ does not alter the results of the argument, although it does lead to complication of Eq. (6.132).

desired frequency characteristics for the ideal compensation network are independent of the input signal. Thus, even though the $G_1(j\omega)$ of Eq. (6.135) is not physically realizable, it is possible to find an *RLC* network with a transfer function approximating this $G_1(j\omega)$ within any specified accuracy over any desired finite band of frequencies.

The significance of Eq. (6.135) has been considered in detail by a number of authors, and this equation is the usual starting point in the design of a-c networks. Briefly, the equation states that the ideal $G_1(j\omega)$ is simply the corresponding d-c characteristic shifted an amount ω_o in both directions along the frequency axis. For example, Fig. 6.61(a) shows the gain and phase characteristics for a typical passive lead network

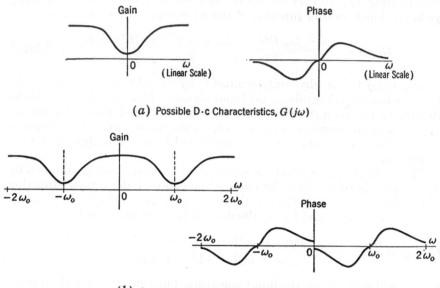

(a) Possible D-c Characteristics, $G(j\omega)$

(b) Corresponding A-c Characteristics, $G_1(j\omega)$

Fig. 6.61. Desired $G_1(j\omega)$.

in a d-c system; part (b) of the figure shows the gain and phase characteristics of an ideal a-c network accomplishing the same compensation. Since the input envelope $e(t)$ is assumed to have no energy at frequencies beyond ω_o, the shape of $G_1(j\omega)$ is immaterial for $\omega > 2\omega_o$ or $\omega < -2\omega_o$. The spectra of Fig. 6.61 are drawn for both positive and negative values of ω. Like the transfer function of any passive linear network, the $G_1(j\omega)$ of Eq. (6.135) possesses a gain characteristic which is an even function of frequency and a phase characteristic which is an odd function of ω. Accordingly, it is sufficient to plot the gain and phase for positive values of ω only, and the approximation of $G_1(j\omega)$ by a physically realizable function can be developed from the behavior along the positive $j\omega$ axis.

Narrow-band Systems. In the vast majority of a-c systems the bandwidth of the information (*i.e.*, of the reference input) is much less than the carrier frequency. Typically, for example, a carrier frequency of

400 cycles/sec might be used when the principal part of the energy of the reference input is concentrated at frequencies below 20 cycles/sec. The spectrum of the modulated wave is then concentrated in the immediate vicinity of the carrier frequency. If $e(t)$ possesses energy from 0 to ω_1 rad/sec, the angular bandwidth of the modulated signal is $2\omega_1$ rad/sec about the carrier frequency. The problem of design is concerned with control over the characteristics of the magnitude and angle of $G_1(j\omega)$ in this narrow band around the carrier frequency (cf. Fig. 6.62).

With this narrow-band operation, design of the a-c compensation network is simplified because the desired characteristics of Eq. (6.135) can

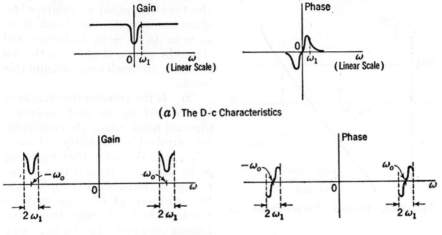

(*a*) The D-c Characteristics

(*b*) Corresponding A-c Characteristics

Fig. 6.62. Desired $G_1(j\omega)$ when $e(t)$ has no significant energy beyond ω_1.

be easily approximated with a $G_1(j\omega)$ which is physically realizable. There are two standard techniques for this approximation: the low-pass band-pass transformation, which can be used regardless of the form of $G(s)$, the transfer function of the equivalent d-c network; and the approximation by a transfer function with poles on the negative real axis in order that the network may be RC (for example, the twin-T or notch filter), an approximation which is widely used only when $G(s)$ describes a simple lead network.

Frequency Transformations.† The problem of synthesis of an a-c compensation network can be stated as follows: given the appropriate d-c characteristic [*e.g.*, part (*a*) of Fig. 6.62] and the corresponding d-c network, a network is to be determined with gain and phase characteristics which are as shown in part (*b*) of the figure. Although the network determined cannot realize exactly the desired gain and phase, since $G_1(j\omega)$ of Eq. (6.135) is not physically realizable, an accurate approximation is desired.

Clearly, one possible solution is a transformation of the frequency

† The discussion of frequency transformations follows that used by Dr. E. A. Guillemin in his network-synthesis course at MIT.

variable. If the $G(j\omega)$ of the d-c network is considered, the appropriate result can be achieved exactly (as long as the maximum signal frequency is less than the carrier frequency) if $j\omega$ is replaced by a function of frequency $p(j\omega)$ such that two conditions are satisfied:

(1) $p(j\omega)$ must be a linear function of frequency in the region from $\omega_o - \omega_1$ to $\omega_o + \omega_1$ and must take on the values $-j\omega_1$ and $+j\omega_1$ at the two end points.† If this condition is satisfied, $p(j\omega)$ takes the form shown in Fig. 6.63 for positive frequencies. $G[p(j\omega)]$ is then simply the desired $G_1(j\omega)$, since at any frequency $\omega_o + \omega_a$, $p(j\omega)$ has the value $j\omega_a$ and $G[p(j\omega)]$ is equal to $G(j\omega_a)$. The transformation $j\omega \rightarrow p(j\omega)$ results in the desired translation of gain and phase characteristics. The behavior of the function $p(j\omega)$ at positive frequencies outside the band from $\omega_o - \omega_1$ to $\omega_o + \omega_1$ is immaterial since the gain and phase of the a-c network are irrelevant outside this band.

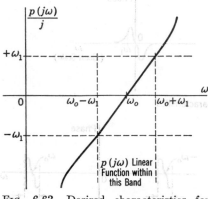

FIG. 6.63. Desired characteristics for $p(j\omega)$.

(2) If the transfer function is to be realized by an RLC network, $G[p(j\omega)]$ must satisfy the conditions for physical realizability. Practically, it is desirable that replacing $j\omega$ by $p(j\omega)$ correspond to a simple change in the network, in order that the synthesis of $G[p(j\omega)]$ may be accomplished directly from the known network for $G(j\omega)$. One possibility for satisfying this condition is to use a $p(j\omega)$ which is a physically realizable driving-point impedance. Replacing $j\omega$ by $p(j\omega)$ then corresponds, in the network, to replacing every inductance L by a network with impedance $Lp(j\omega)$, every capacitance C by a network with admittance $Cp(j\omega)$. The entire synthesis of the a-c network then resolves to determination of a network with the driving-point impedance $p(j\omega)$. Once this network is found, the impedance $Lp(j\omega)$ is realized by a simple multiplication of the impedance level by L, the admittance $Cp(j\omega)$ by determining the dual network and adjustment of the admittance level. Thus, the requirement that $p(j\omega)$ be a realizable driving-point impedance is not necessary but does result in a very desirable simplification of the synthesis.

Unfortunately, conditions (1) and (2) are not compatible. Exact satisfaction of one can be accomplished solely by functions which meet the other condition only approximately. The usual procedure is to select a simple $p(j\omega)$ which satisfies the physical realizability condition (2) and, at the same time, is approximately linear in the band from $\omega_o - \omega_1$ to $\omega_o + \omega_1$. If the bandwidth $2\omega_1$ is much less than ω_o, a reactance function suffices for $p(j\omega)$:

---

† In this discussion attention is focused on positive frequencies only.

$$p(j\omega) = j\omega K \left(1 - \frac{\omega_o^2}{\omega^2}\right) \tag{6.136}$$

This $p(j\omega)$, the impedance of the simple series resonant circuit of Fig. 6.64, varies with frequency as shown in Fig. 6.65. The curve of $p(j\omega)/j$ versus ω is actually geometrically antisymmetrical† about the frequency ω_o, but in a narrow band around ω_o this geometric antisymmetry is equivalent to the desired arithmetic antisymmetry described by Eq. (6.135).

The $p(j\omega)$ described by Eq. (6.136) has the appropriate center frequency

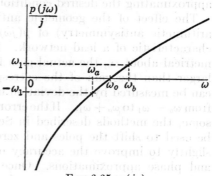

FIG. 6.65. $p(j\omega)$.

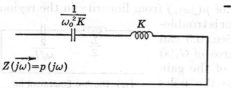

$Z(\overrightarrow{j\omega}) = p(j\omega)$

FIG. 6.64. Circuit with impedance equal to $p(j\omega)$.

ω_o, at which $p(j\omega) = 0$. The bandwidth fixes the value of K. Specifically, in the problem considered here, K is determined by the condition

$$\omega_b - \omega_a = 2\omega_1 \tag{6.137}$$

where ω_a is defined by

$$p(j\omega_a) = -j\omega_1 \tag{6.138}$$

and ω_b is defined by

$$p(j\omega_b) = j\omega_1 \tag{6.139}$$

In other words, ω_b and ω_a are, respectively, the upper and lower ends of the band. Substitution of Eq. (6.136) in (6.138) and (6.139) gives

$$j\omega_b K - j\frac{\omega_o^2 K}{\omega_b} = j\omega_1 \tag{6.140}$$

$$j\omega_a K - j\frac{\omega_o^2 K}{\omega_a} = -j\omega_1 \tag{6.141}$$

Subtraction of (6.141) from (6.140) yields

$$K(\omega_b - \omega_a)\left(1 + \frac{\omega_o^2}{\omega_a\omega_b}\right) = 2\omega_1 \tag{6.142}$$

Since ω_a and ω_b are geometrically symmetrical about ω_o, $\omega_a\omega_b = \omega_o^2$. Hence, substitution of Eq. (6.137) in (6.142) gives

$$K = \tfrac{1}{2} \tag{6.143}$$

† Geometric antisymmetry implies that $p(j\omega_a) = -p(j\omega_b)$ if $\omega_a/\omega_o = \omega_o/\omega_b$, or $\omega_o^2 = \omega_a\omega_b$. Arithmetic antisymmetry means that $p(j\omega_a) = -p(j\omega_b)$ if

$$\omega_o - \omega_a = \omega_b - \omega_o$$

Thus, the a-c compensation network is designed on the basis of the frequency transformation

$$p(j\omega) = j\omega \frac{1}{2}\left(1 - \frac{\omega_o^2}{\omega^2}\right) \tag{6.144}$$

Here ω_o is the carrier frequency. If $2\omega_1$, the bandwidth of the modulated signal, is much less than ω_o, Eq. (6.144) results in a network very closely approximating the desired conditions [Eq. (6.135)].

The effect of the geometric antisymmetry (rather than the desired arithmetic antisymmetry) of $p(j\omega)$ is shown in Fig. 6.66 for the gain characteristic of a lead network. Since the gain is geometrically symmetrical about ω_o, the actual gain for a given lower sideband is slightly larger than the gain of the corresponding upper sideband. The error can be measured by the deviation of $p(j\omega)/j$ from linearity in the region from $\omega_o - \omega_1$ to $\omega_o + \omega_1$. If the error is troublesome, the methods described in Sec. 6.5 can be used to shift the poles and zeros of $G_1(s)$ slightly to improve the accuracy of the gain and phase approximations. Once the poles and zeros are shifted, the second part of the

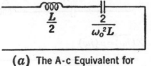
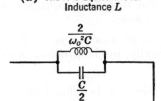

(a) The A-c Equivalent for Inductance L

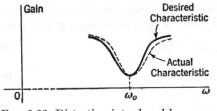

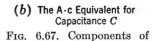

(b) The A-c Equivalent for Capacitance C

FIG. 6.66. Distortion introduced by geometric symmetry.

FIG. 6.67. Components of a-c network.

design, the synthesis of the compensation network, becomes more difficult: the a-c network is no longer the d-c network with each L replaced by a network with the impedance $Lp(j\omega)$ and each C replaced by a network with admittance $Cp(j\omega)$. Instead, the a-c network must be synthesized directly from the transfer function $G_1(s)$.

If the frequency transformation of Eq. (6.144) is used, the a-c network can be found, as mentioned above, directly from the d-c prototype. An inductance L in the d-c network is replaced by the network shown in Fig. 6.67(a) with the impedance

$$Lp(j\omega) = j\omega \frac{L}{2} + \frac{\omega_o^2 L}{j\omega 2} \tag{6.145}$$

Likewise, a capacitance C is replaced by the network of Fig. 6.67(b), with an admittance equal to

$$Cp(j\omega) = j\omega \frac{C}{2} + \frac{\omega_o^2 C}{j\omega 2} \tag{6.146}$$

The resistances remain unchanged.

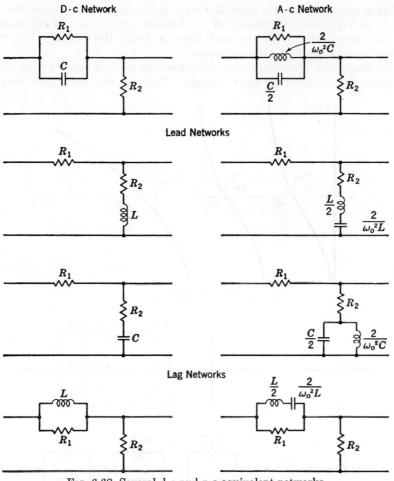

FIG. 6.68. Several d-c and a-c equivalent networks.

Equations (6.145) and (6.146) represent one possible procedure for the design of a-c compensation networks for feedback control systems. The a-c network is found by:

(1)   Dividing each L by 2
(2)   Adding in series with each inductance a capacitance to resonate at ω_o
(3)   Dividing by 2 each C of the original network
(4)   Adding in parallel with each $C/2$ an inductance to resonate at ω_o

The division by 2 is an expression of the principle termed by Bode[†] the "conservation of bandwidth." The bandwidth of the a-c network is twice that of the d-c network, since if the gain and phase in the d-c case are controlled from 0 to $+\omega_1$, they are controlled in the a-c network from approximately $\omega_o - \omega_1$ to $\omega_o + \omega_1$.

† H. W. Bode, "Network Analysis and Feedback Amplifier Design," pp. 211–214, D. Van Nostrand Company, Inc., New York, 1945.

The a-c equivalents for several simple d-c compensation networks are shown in Fig. 6.68. A variety of equivalent structures can be found if the a-c networks are synthesized directly from the transfer function, rather than through the d-c networks.

The frequency transformation described above is a special case of the transformations used in filter design. Clearly, the principles can be

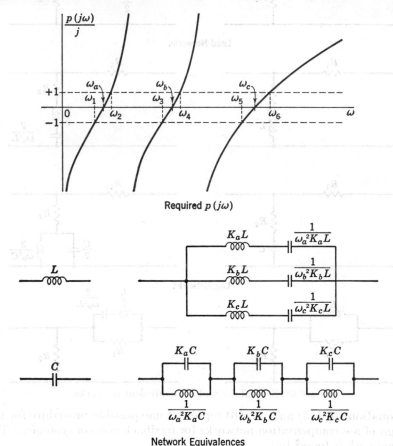

Required $p(j\omega)$

Network Equivalences

FIG. 6.69. Frequency transformation with three pass bands.

extended to obtain transformations going from a low-pass filter to a high-pass filter or from the low-frequency characteristics to band-pass characteristics with any desired number of pass bands. The only change required in the above development is a modification of the $p(j\omega)$ selected. For example, if a low-pass filter with a pass band from 0 to 1 rad/sec is to be used as a basis for the design of a band-pass filter with pass bands from ω_1 to ω_2, ω_3 to ω_4, and ω_5 to ω_6, the $p(j\omega)$ required has the form shown in Fig. 6.69. In the desired pass bands, $p(j\omega)$ must lie between $-j1$ and $+j1$. The corresponding changes in the network are also shown in the figure.

Other Approximations. Thus, a frequency transformation can be used to synthesize the a-c compensation network if the bandwidth is small compared to the carrier frequency. The resulting network always contains inductances, which are often undesirable, particularly if the carrier frequency is low enough that the inductors required are large and heavy. In addition, the fact that the dissipation ratio R/L of an inductor varies with frequency makes it difficult to predict network performance. Thus, in a number of applications, it is desirable to accomplish the a-c compensation with an RC network.

If a given transfer function is to be realizable by an RC network, all poles must be simple and lie on the negative real axis. But it is readily demonstrated that the transformation of Eq. (6.144) can never lead to real poles for $G_1(s)$. If a pole of $G(s)$, the transfer function of the d-c compensation network, lies at $-a$, the corresponding poles of $G_1(s)$ are given by the relation

$$s\frac{1}{2}\left(1 + \frac{\omega_o^2}{s^2}\right) - -a \qquad (6.147)$$

Solution for s gives

$$s = -a \pm j \sqrt{\omega_o^2 - a^2} \qquad (6.148)$$

The poles are real only if a is larger than ω_o, but, if the information bandwidth is much less than ω_o, the value of a must be much less than ω_o also, since if the pole at $-a$ is to have any effect on the signal the corresponding break frequency (at $\omega = a$) must lie inside the band from 0 to ω_1 or at least close to ω_1. Hence, the poles of $G_1(s)$, derived by the frequency transformation, occur in conjugate complex pairs, as indicated in Fig. 6.70 for the lead transfer function.

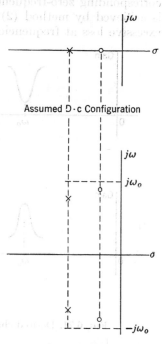

Assumed D-c Configuration

Corresponding A-c Configuration
FIG. 6.70. Pole-zero configuration in low-pass band-pass transformation.

Consequently, an RC network to accomplish a-c compensation cannot be derived from a frequency transformation, but must be synthesized by a return to the basic approximation problem. The desired gain and phase characteristics are plotted versus ω, as indicated in Fig. 6.71 for simple passive lead and lag compensation. An approximating transfer function is sought which has poles restricted to the negative real axis. Clearly, the lead characteristic is not difficult to obtain, since complex zeros very close to the $j\omega$ axis can be used to realize the sharp null in the gain characteristic.

The integral or lag characteristic, in contrast, is very difficult to achieve with a passive RC network, because of the problems associated with realizing the sharp peak appearing in the gain curve at ω_o. If the transfer function is to have only real poles, the large positive slope must be realized by a *very large* number of zeros, with the corresponding break frequencies below ω_o. The rapid decrease in gain with frequency can be achieved in two ways: (1) zeros can be inserted near the $j\omega$ axis; or (2) a large number of poles can be used with the associated break frequencies just above ω_o. In method (1), the poles which must be used with the desired zeros are placed with break frequencies well beyond ω_o, and the corresponding zero-frequency gain is very low. If the decrease in gain is achieved by method (2) (using real poles), these poles introduce an excessive loss at frequencies lower than those exhibiting a high rate of

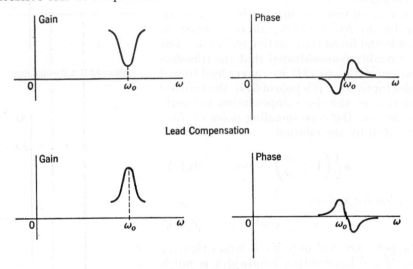

FIG. 6.71. Desired characteristics for a-c compensation networks.

cutoff. All these factors tend to cause an excessive flat loss through the network. Thus, the only practical a-c compensation with *RC* networks is the lead type.

The simplest lead compensation is realized by the twin-T network. Design of the network for a given carrier frequency, notch width, and attenuation at ω_o is described in detail in the literature.† Alternatively, the desired characteristic can be realized by selection of an appropriate transfer function (as outlined in Secs. 6.4 and 6.5), and synthesis of this function can be carried out on the basis of the procedures described in Chap. 3. If this more fundamental approach is used, the network can be more general than the six-element twin T described in the references, and it is possible to relax the conventional restrictions on the lags associated with the compensation, the phase shift at the carrier frequency, the absence of any attenuation of noise introduced well outside the narrow

† For example *cf.* H. M. James, N. B. Nichols, and R. S. Phillips, "Theory of Servomechanisms," MIT Radiation Laboratory Series, Vol. 25, pp. 117–124, McGraw-Hill Book Company, Inc., 1947.

band of interest, and the narrowness of the allowable bandwidth. For most purposes, however, the conventional twin-T network is adequate.

Relation to s-plane Design. The very brief description of a-c systems presented in this section entirely omits consideration of a number of problems of essential importance in design. For example, the characteristics of various components are omitted. The discussion is intended to indicate merely those theoretical design problems unique in a-c systems. From the viewpoint of design, the significant difference between a-c and d-c systems lies in the problems associated with the realization of appropriate a-c compensation networks designed to operate on the envelope of a modulated signal.

If load compensation is used or if demodulation, compensation, and remodulation are employed, the design of a-c systems is no different than that of the corresponding d-c systems; the root-locus method and Guillemin's procedure are directly applicable. If feedback compensation through an a-c tachometer and network is used or if tandem compensation is employed, the s-plane methods of design are applicable if the frequency transformation can be used to determine an appropriate compensation network or if the desired characteristics can be adequately approximated by a realizable transfer function with appropriate properties (*e.g.*, simple poles on the negative real axis).

The application of the more refined methods to the design of a-c systems has lagged behind similar applications to d-c systems. The vast majority of a-c systems have employed twin-T or tachometric compensation. It can be anticipated that, as the performance specifications become more stringent and the ratio of the required bandwidth to the carrier frequency increases, the root-locus method and similar techniques will be used with increasing advantage.

CHAPTER 7

PRINCIPLES OF STATISTICAL DESIGN

Conventional design procedures for networks are characterized by one artificiality, whether design is accomplished in the frequency or time domains or an attempt is made, through the consideration of the positions of the significant poles and zeros, to correlate the two domains. In every case, the system is designed to yield a satisfactory response to signals fabricated by the designer. Ordinarily, the typical inputs considered are either sinusoidal signals or particularly simple aperiodic signals, such as step functions or impulses. Indeed, it is true that any given input signal can be characterized by either a sum of sinusoids or a sum of step functions or impulses, but it is commonly impossible for the designer to visualize the manner in which the individual responses add up in the output. Thus, the conventional synthesis procedures essentially involve the initial and very basic assumption that the specifications on performance can be accurately interpreted in terms of the characteristics of the sinusoidal or the step-function response.

There are of course a number of problems in which the response of the system to the actual input signals can be readily interpreted in terms of the sinusoidal or step-function response. For example, in a number of systems the input is changing sufficiently slowly to permit an adequate description by a polynomial of second degree. The response of the system to an aperiodic input of the form $a + bt + ct^2$ completely describes the salient characteristics of system performance. In other systems, the actual input may be very closely approximated by a series of step functions spaced so far apart that the response to any one step function has almost settled down to a steady-state value before the next step function arrives. For the design of systems of this type, ordinary synthesis procedures are entirely adequate.

Statistical design theory is an attempt to broaden the design to include the consideration of general types of signal inputs. Evidently any general characterization of the signals entering a system must be statistical, based on the characteristics of the signals averaged over all time. Statistical design, as originally presented by Wiener† in connection with the antiaircraft-fire-control problem, involves the following factors:

(1)   Determination of the average characteristics of the signals.

(2)   Selection of an error criterion by which the quality of a system may be evaluated.

(3)   Design of the optimum system on the basis of factors (1) and (2).

† N. Wiener, "The Extrapolation, Interpolation, and Smoothing of Stationary Time Series," John Wiley & Sons, Inc., New York, 1948.

410

Statistical design theory has a number of applications of far-reaching significance to the servo engineer. It is the purpose of this chapter to summarize the basic points of the mathematical background for this theory and to indicate some of the most important applications. Chapter 8 is devoted to the detailed discussion of certain aspects of the statistical design of servomechanisms. The first two sections of this chapter are largely a collection of mathematical ideas concerning points (1) and (2) above. Sections 7.3 to 7.5 present some of the mathematical concepts essential to the explanation of the theory and applications. It is unfortunately true that the mathematics involved is somewhat unfamiliar to the average engineer. An attempt has been made to clarify certain of the important points without placing undue emphasis on mathematical rigor.

7.1. Typical Signals. The signals with which statistical theory is concerned are random time functions. Evidently periodic signals and aperiodic signals (the ordinary transients such as the step function) can represent but a small amount of information, since only a short interval of time elapses before the receiver is aware of the complete signal, both that which has been received and that yet to be received. Any signal carrying information must be generated by a series of selections: *e.g.*, the choice at given instants of time of one amplitude of voltage from a large number of possible amplitudes.

The various signals entering a servo system from time to time are not, however, entirely random and unrelated. On the average, these signals possess certain common characteristics such as the part of the frequency spectrum in which the major portion of the energy is concentrated. For example, in an instrumentation servo for a particular piece of measuring equipment, general characteristics of the input signals can frequently be defined in terms of the anticipated range and rate of variation of the quantity to be measured.

This concept of random functions must be made specific if the class of functions with which statistical theory deals is to be clearly defined. Statistical theory deals only with those random functions which belong to a random process. A random process consists of an ensemble of time functions, where the ensemble or set of functions can be described by certain probability distributions.

What is meant by the phrase "description by certain probability distributions"? If $f_1(t)$, $f_2(t)$, . . . are the functions comprising the ensemble, the values of these functions at time t_1 [that is, $f_1(t_1)$, $f_2(t_1)$, . . .] must obey a certain probability distribution. In other words, at any given time t_1, there must be a definite probability of any given member function lying between specified values. Likewise, the second probability distribution function refers to the probability of a member function lying in a specified incremental interval at time t_1 and also lying in another specified incremental interval at time t_2. This second probability distribution function, as well as all higher-order probability distribution functions, must exist if the ensemble of functions is to constitute a random process. In other words, if statistical design theory is to apply, it must be possible to describe statistically the ensemble of possible servo input functions.

Principle concern of servo theory is with a particular class of random processes, the stationary random processes. When the statistics of the signal (or the probability distribution functions) do not change with time, the random process is termed stationary. Thermal noise generated by the random motion of the conduction electrons in a resistor is a stationary random function; that is, a thermal-noise voltage function is a member of a stationary random process, for if the temperature is constant the statistics of the noise are independent of the choice of an origin in time. On the other hand, if the temperature of the resistor changes with time, the rms value, and also the statistics, of the thermal-noise voltage changes. This noise voltage would then no longer be a member of a stationary random process. A more striking example of a nonstationary random process is the signal from a radar used for both searching and tracking. The statistics of the radar input with the system searching may differ radically from the statistics with the system tracking. Considering only the searching time, however, the radar signal is ordinarily a member function of a stationary random process.

Ergodicity is the property of stationary random processes which is particularly important in the development of the statistical design theory. The ergodic property (or ergodic hypothesis) involves the assumption that the time average over one member function of a random process which is stationary is equivalent to an average over the ensemble of functions. Essentially ergodicity implies that after a sufficient length of time the effect of initial conditions is negligible. In other words, if one function of the ensemble is inspected over a sufficiently long period of time, all salient characteristics of the ensemble of functions will be observed. Any one function then can be used to represent the ensemble.

The ergodic property is readily interpreted in terms of the probability distribution functions. If $f_1(t)$, $f_2(t)$, . . . are the member functions of the ensemble, then by definition the first probability distribution function $p(y)$ describes the probability that *at any given time* t_1, any function $f_j(t)$ lies between y and $y + dy$. The ergodic property states that $p(y)$ also describes the probability that any given function $f_1(t)$ lies between y and $y + dy$ *at any time*. As a result of this ergodic property, the statistical characteristics of an ensemble can be determined by consideration of any one function. Furthermore, since the process is stationary, it is only necessary to consider a sample of this one function, if the sample is sufficiently long to exhibit the statistics of the entire function.

In summary of the above definitions, statistical design theory treats only random processes, or processes which can be described statistically (in terms of probability distributions). Principal concern is with stationary random processes which possess the ergodic property. The great majority of servo input functions satisfy these restrictions.

7.2. Mean-square Error. The previous section pointed out that statistical design theory is solely concerned with input signals which can be characterized statistically. Before considering further the method of characterization, it is desirable to consider the measure of error to be used in statistical design, for the choice of an error measure determines which statistical characteristics of the signals are of importance.

The error measure chosen by Wiener is the mean-square error. In other words, the average value of the square of the difference between the actual system output and the desired system output is considered to be the important characteristic measuring the quality of the system. With reference to Fig. 7.1, $f_i(t)$ is used

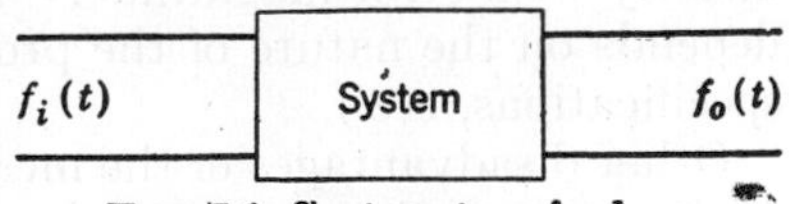

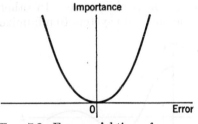

FIG. 7.1. System terminology.

to denote the input to the system, and $f_o(t)$ the resulting output.† If $f_d(t)$ is the desired output, the mean-square error, regardless of the nature of the system, is defined as

$$\overline{e^2} = \lim_{T \to \infty} \frac{1}{2T} \int_{-T}^{T} [f_o(t) - f_d(t)]^2 \, dt \qquad (7.1)$$

Statistical theory is concerned with the design of the system to minimize this mean-square error. In Sec. 7.6 the method is presented by which this analytic expression for the mean-square error leads to a knowledge of those statistical characteristics of the signal which are required for a design.

Certain results of the choice of this mean-square-error criterion should be pointed out at this time. The mean-square error is certainly only one of many possible error measures. It would appear, for example, that a much more significant indication of error might be the mean magnitude of the error. If the system is designed to minimize the mean-square error, it essentially means that emphasis is placed on the errors according to the square of the error magnitude. In other words, the system resulting from a minimization of the mean-square error attempts to cut down the large errors at the cost of many small errors. Plotting relative importance attached to the error versus error yields a curve of the form shown in Fig. 7.2. In the light of the fact that the mean-square error is chosen at least in part on the basis of mathematical expediency, it is of value to consider carefully the merit of such a design criterion.

It is very definitely true that there exists a large class of feedback con-

FIG. 7.2. Error weighting of mean-square-error criterion.

---

† Instead of $c(t)$ and $r(t)$, $f_i(t)$ and $f_o(t)$ are used in this chapter to denote the input and output signals, respectively, for two reasons: (1) the input and output terminals may refer to part or all of the feedback control system; (2) this notation follows more closely the majority of the literature in the statistical design field.

trol systems for which minimization of the mean-square error certainly is not the ideal design criterion. In a great many systems, intuitive reasoning indicates that the importance-versus-error curve should have the form of Fig. 7.3. For all errors larger in magnitude than A, full output-motor torque should be applied; for error magnitudes less than A but larger than a specified small error, the importance should increase linearly with error magnitude. The appropriate error measure certainly depends on the nature of the problem (the type of system involved, the specifications, etc.).

Other disadvantages of the mean-square-error criterion are apparent in feedback-control work. Emphasis on the large errors results in a system

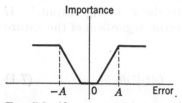

Fig. 7.3. Alternate weighting of the error.

with undesirably low stability in many cases. Figure 7.4 indicates a typical feedback-control-system response to a step function. Just after the application of the step function the error is large because of inertia on the output shaft. The mean-square-error criterion, emphasizing this large error, attempts to increase the output rapidly. The result is a system with large overshoot, or low damping. If the system were always linear, this low damping in itself would not necessarily be a serious detriment to system quality, but, if any parameters change in the direction of instability, the system may come intolerably close to absolute instability.

With these questionable characteristics of the mean-square-error theory, it is significant to ask whether the application of this design criterion ordinarily results in improved system performance. In other words, if statistical design indicates that the optimum system to minimize

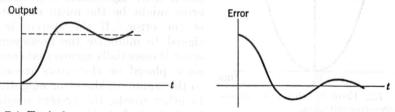

Fig. 7.4. Typical response of a feedback control system to a step-function input and the resulting error.

the mean-square error has a relative damping ratio of 0.4, is the performance of such a system noticeably better than one designed by conventional methods, with perhaps a relative damping ratio of 0.6? In the majority of systems, it appears that the mean-square error is relatively insensitive to changes in system parameters. In this sense, statistical design theory is a corroboration of the common sense of the design engineer, an indication that the human mind in a great many cases essentially comes close to minimizing the mean-square error and in addition considers the possible effects of nonlinearity.

This discussion should not be construed to mean that statistical design theory is of little value. On the contrary, the theory serves a number of very important functions:

(1) It fills an important gap in the general theory of feedback control systems by providing a straightforward design procedure which considers the actual input functions.

(2) It confirms the validity of other design procedures.

(3) It affords the only satisfactory solution to a number of design problems.

(4) The development of the theory indicates methods for measuring the characteristics of noise, corrupting signals, and input signals.

(5) The concepts involved in the theory have led to new methods for designing very-narrow-band filters, measuring the transfer function of a physical system, and determining and controlling the effect of saturation.

(6) As a result of this theory, work has been done on the description, analysis, and synthesis of nonlinear systems.

(7) The theory is closely tied in with information theory and the field of cybernetics.

7.3. Probability Theory. It does not seem necessary to consider in detail many aspects of probability theory. There are several excellent fundamental texts on probability which are considerably more rigorous and treat the subject in considerably more detail than is possible or desirable here.† Although a knowledge of probability theory is perhaps not essential to the applications of the theories discussed in this chapter, some familiarity with the theory of probability is a prerequisite for any extension of these methods, because the functions which statistical design theory considers are essentially characterized by probability distributions. The problem of prediction, for example, is essentially the problem of selecting the most probable future value of a function, where the selection, in a physical system, is to be made only on the basis of past values and the criterion for judging the quality of the approximation is to be the average of the squared error.

A brief summary of those aspects of probability theory which are essential to the statistical design method seems most simply to start with a series of definitions. These definitions should not be considered to constitute a logical development of probability theory, but rather should be viewed as a collection of certain facts of importance.

Sample space: The sample space is defined as the aggregate of all possible outcomes of a random experiment. If one die is thrown, the sample space consists of six points, each point corresponding to one possible face of the die. If the random variable is the thermal-noise voltage across a resistor, the sample space consists of an infinite number of points—all possible values of this voltage.

Probability: With each point in the sample space there is associated a probability, a real nonnegative number less than or equal to unity, such that these numbers summed over all points add up to unity. If a very large number of random trials of the same nature are made, the per-

---

† William Feller, "An Introduction to Probability Theory and Its Applications," John Wiley & Sons, Inc., New York, 1950; and James V. Uspensky, "Introduction to Mathematical Probability," McGraw-Hill Book Company, Inc., New York, 1937.

centage of the time that the outcome is the value of one point in the sample space is the probability associated with that point.   For example, if a die is tossed again and again, the number 5 will appear about one-sixth of the time if the average is taken over a sufficiently large number of trials.   Thus, the probability of a 5 is one-sixth, which is written as

$$P(5) = \tfrac{1}{6} \tag{7.2}$$

Random variable: It is convenient to consider a variable which takes on values corresponding to the various points in the sample space.   If this random variable is denoted as y, Eq. (7.2), describing the die-throwing experiment, can be written as

$$P(y = 5) = \tfrac{1}{6} \tag{7.3}$$

Probability distribution function: If the sample space consists of a continuous set of values, the probability of any one value is ordinarily zero. Thus, the probability that the instantaneous noise voltage across a 1-megohm resistor equals exactly 1 microvolt at any given time is zero.   In this example, every point probability is zero, although the sum of the probabilities over all points in the sample space equals unity.   In such a case, it is convenient to define a probability distribution function, also termed a density function or a frequency function. $p(x)$ is defined by the relation

$$P(x < y < x + dx) = p(x)\, dx \tag{7.4}$$

The probability that the random variable y lies between x and $x + dx$ is equal to $p(x)\, dx$, where $p(x)$ is the probability distribution function. Evidently, $p(x)$ must satisfy two conditions:

$$p(x) \geq 0 \tag{7.5}$$
$$\textstyle\int p(x)\, dx = 1 \tag{7.6}$$

In Eq. (7.6) the integral is taken over all possible values of x.

Gaussian distribution: A particularly useful probability distribution function is the Gaussian, or normal, distribution, for which

$$p(x) = \frac{1}{\sqrt{2\pi}\,\sigma}\, e^{-\frac{1}{2}(x-\mu)^2/\sigma^2} \tag{7.7}$$

where μ = average or expected value of the random variable y

   σ = standard deviation.   The square of the standard deviation is the variance, which is the expected or average value of $(y - \mu)^2$.   The standard deviation is a measure of the dispersion

The significance of the variance is clarified by consideration of the Gaussian distribution curve.   If the mean value μ is assumed to be zero (no d-c component existing in the random function), the $p(x)$ curve is symmetrical about the $x = 0$ axis. $p(x)$ is the bell-shaped curve indicated in Fig. 7.5. σ is a measure of the rapidity with which the curve drops off.   Both curves of Fig. 7.6 are for a Gaussian distribution, but with different standard deviations.   Figure 7.7 indicates the nature of the $p(x)$ curve if the expected value is not zero.

Thermal noise from a resistor is the best known random function exhibiting a Gaussian distribution. In this case, the probability distribution for the voltage across the resistor, if the resistor is unconnected electrically, is simply

$$p(x) = \frac{1}{\sqrt{2\pi}\,\sigma}\, e^{-\frac{1}{2}x^2/\sigma^2} \tag{7.8}$$

The average value of the voltage is zero. The standard deviation σ is simply the square root of the average of the square of the voltage, or the

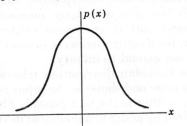

FIG. 7.5. Gaussian distribution function.

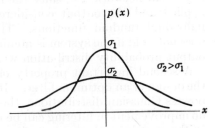

FIG. 7.6. Two Gaussian distribution functions with different standard deviations.

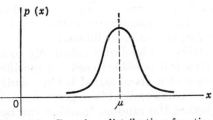

FIG. 7.7. Gaussian distribution function with nonzero expected value.

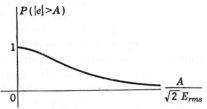

FIG. 7.8. The co-error function.

rms value. The probability that the magnitude of the voltage across the resistor exceeds A volts is given by

$$P(|e| > A) = 2 \int_A^\infty p(x)\, dx \tag{7.9}$$

$$P(|e| > A) = 2 \int_A^\infty \frac{1}{\sqrt{2\pi}\,E_{rms}}\, e^{-\frac{1}{2}x^2/E_{rms}^2}\, dx \tag{7.10}$$

If the substitution $u = x/(\sqrt{2}\,E_{rms})$ is made, Eq. (7.10) can be written

$$P(|e| > A) = \frac{2}{\sqrt{\pi}} \int_{A/\sqrt{2}E_{rms}}^\infty e^{-u^2}\, du \tag{7.11}$$

This function, the complementary error function, is tabulated extensively in the mathematical and engineering literature,† and a sketch of the function is shown in Fig. 7.8.

† Eugene Jahnke and Fritz Emde, "Tables of Functions," 4th ed., p. 24, Dover Publications, New York, 1945.

The Gaussian distribution possesses certain very unique and useful characteristics. The Gaussian distribution arises, in general terms, whenever the random function is essentially the sum of a very large number of independent random functions with any probability distribution. For example, in the case of thermal noise, the voltage is the sum of contributions due to a large number of conduction electrons. From this concept it is evident that a signal which possesses a Gaussian distribution function still has this type of distribution after passing through any linear network, for, since the network is linear, superposition can be applied and the output considered as the sum of a large number of individual random functions. The same sort of statement evidently does not hold if the system is nonlinear, for if saturation were present the output probability distribution would not extend to infinity.

A second important property of the Gaussian distribution relates to the design of an optimum filter. If the noise and signal at the input both possess Gaussian distributions, the linear filter is the best possible filter; no improvement in filtering can be realized by going to a nonlinear device. With general signals the same situation certainly does not exist. A linear system can filter only on the basis of differences in the frequency spectra of the signal and noise. If the amplitude or power spectra of the signal and noise are identical, the optimum linear system is simply a straight-through connection. In many cases, the mean-square error can be further reduced, however, by the addition of nonlinear filters.†

These properties of the Gaussian distribution lead quite naturally to a question of fundamental importance: How is it possible to tell in a specific case whether the probability distribution of a given signal is Gaussian? More generally, how can the distribution be determined for a given signal? It certainly is not usually obvious whether the random function can be considered as the sum of a very large number of independent random functions. Only in very special cases, such as thermal noise, shot noise, or noise from a gas tube such as the 884, is it apparent that the distribution is Gaussian.

An example of some practical importance of a function which is not obviously Gaussian is the force exerted on an airplane surface during flight as a result of wind gusts. A considerable amount of experimental data is available in this example,‡ and it is possible to analyze this data either experimentally or analytically to determine the probability distribution. These methods of measurement can, of course, be used to determine the probability distribution regardless of its nature.

The simplest experimental setup with sufficient accuracy to indicate the type of distribution involved is similar to that described by Knudtzon.§ The noise or signal is amplified, if necessary, and fed into a slicer which

† H. E. Singleton, Theory of Nonlinear Transducers, *MIT Research Laboratory of Electronics Tech. Rept.* 160, August 12, 1950.

‡ Philip Donely, Summary of Information Relating to Gust Loads on Airplanes, *NACA TN* 1976, 1949.

§ Nic Knudtzon, Experimental Study of Statistical Characteristics of Filtered Random Noise, *MIT Research Laboratory of Electronics Tech. Rept.* 115, July 15, 1949.

passes only peaks larger than a fixed level adjustable by the operator. The percentage of the time the voltage exceeds this slicing level is then determined electronically, by amplification, limiting, and averaging. The result is the probability that the input voltage exceeds the magnitude determined by the slicer-level adjustment. This measurement then yields the integral of the probability distribution function from the slicer level to infinity, from which the probability distribution function can be determined by differentiation.

In many cases it is necessary to determine the probability distribution from a graphical record of the function. For example, in the specific case mentioned above (wind gusts on airplane structures), the measurements are made and recorded in flight. It is desirable to determine the probability distribution at a later time. The science of mathematical statistics suggests a number of procedures for this. The simplest procedure theoretically, although tedious computationally, simply involves a measurement from recorded data of the percentage of the time the signal exceeds a definite level—essentially the manual equiv-

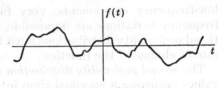

Fig. 7.9. Random function.

alent of the electronic technique described in the preceding paragraph—or the fraction of the time the signal lies within specified intervals.

These fundamental concepts (sample space, probability, random variables, and probability distribution functions) suffice to give an elementary background for the development of statistical design theory. Some familiarity with the concept of probability distribution functions is essential to a clear understanding of the type of time functions to which statistical design theory is applicable, for, as pointed out in Sec. 7.1, the fundamental criterion the signals must satisfy is describability by these probability distribution functions. The method of this description is discussed in the remainder of this section.

A stationary random process gives rise to a function which might be of the form shown in Fig. 7.9. The position of the axis representing $t = 0$ is arbitrary. As a result of the Strong law of large numbers if a sufficiently large section of this wave is considered, the statistical characteristics of the entire function can be measured by determination of the characteristics of this section. This is obviously necessary if the theory is to have any practical significance, since no physical measurement can take an infinite length of time.

An ensemble of these random functions is considered (where an ensemble is simply interpreted as a large number, theoretically an infinite number). The ensemble may be made up of either a large number of functions of the form of Fig. 7.9 and similar statistical characteristics or a large number of samples taken from one function.

The probability distribution functions describing the statistical characteristics of the stationary time series are most easily described in terms of this ensemble of functions. At a given time each member of the ensemble has a certain amplitude. The *first probability distribution* function $p(x)$ describes the distribution of these amplitudes. Specifically, the probability that the amplitude of any given member function lies between x and $x + dx$ is given by the equation

$$P(x < A_j < x + dx) = p(x)\,dx \qquad (7.12)$$

Here A_j is the particular amplitude under investigation. Since the process is stationary, $p(x)\,dx$ is also equal to the probability that A_j lies between x and $x + dx$ at *any* time.

For a general signal, the first probability distribution does not describe completely the statistical characteristics, for in a large number of practical cases the value of the signal at any time exerts a strong influence on the value a short time later. For example, if the signal contains only low-frequency components, very fast changes corresponding to high-frequency variations are impossible. Consequently, some sort of conditional probability distributions must be defined to describe the anticipated rate of change of the function.

The *second probability distribution* determines the likelihood of pairs of values occurring a specified time interval apart. More specifically, the probability that at time t_1, A_j lies between x_1 and $x_1 + dx$ and that τ sec later A_j lies between x_2 and $x_2 + dx$ is given by

$$P[x_1 < A_j(t_1) < x_1 + dx, x_2 < A_j(t_1 + \tau) < x_2 + dx]$$
$$= p_\tau(x_1, x_2)\,dx_1\,dx_2 \qquad (7.13)$$

$p_\tau(x_1, x_2)$, a function of τ, x_1, and x_2, is the second probability distribution function.

In a similar manner the higher-order distribution functions can be defined. The entire infinite set of distribution functions describes completely the statistical characteristics of the stationary time series. In only very special cases can the various distributions be calculated, but fortunately the only information required for design on the basis of the mean-square-error criterion is a knowledge of certain characteristics of the second probability distribution. This is discussed in more detail in Sec. 7.6.

7.4. The Two-sided Laplace Transform. During the past 15 years, the Laplace transformation has proven one of the most powerful analytical tools of the servomechanism engineer. Traditionally, transient problems have been treated in servomechanism texts by means of the one-sided Laplace transform. In other words, the time function is considered only for $t > 0$; the nature of the time function for negative values of time is irrelevant. The Laplace transform is given by

$$F(s) = \int_0^\infty f(t)e^{-st}\,dt \qquad (7.14)\dagger$$

† Strictly, the transform is

$$F(s) = \lim_{\substack{a \to 0 \\ T \to \infty}} \int_a^T f(t)e^{-st}\,dt \qquad (7.14a)$$

For example, the transform of the time function $\sin t$ is $1/(s^2 + 1)$. The time function is made aperiodic by throwing away all information concerning the value for $t < 0$.

This is ordinarily a satisfactory procedure since in transient problems the usual concern is with the behavior of the system after some sort of driving function is applied. The application of this drive is usually considered to begin at zero time. Difficulty does arise in certain cases with initial conditions, particularly when impulses are involved and it becomes difficult to decide what the initial conditions really are. For this reason, a number of engineers with particular interest in network theory have advocated the use of the Fourier-integral approach to transient problems rather than working through the Laplace transform.

The development of the statistical design theory requires consideration of the transform of functions which exist over all time, from $t = -\infty$ to $t = +\infty$. The familiar one-sided Laplace transform is then an unsatisfactory analysis tool since this transform cannot place in evidence the nature of the function for negative time. In the original development of the theory and in most of the later articles which have appeared in the literature, the Fourier transform has been used. In the discussion of the following sections, it seems desirable to modify this approach slightly in order that the transforms involved may be more familiar to the electrical engineer who already possesses a working knowledge of the usual Laplace-transform theory. Consequently, the Laplace transform is employed throughout the development, but, in order to characterize the function for negative as well as positive time, the two-sided Laplace transform is used.†

From the viewpoint of the engineer, there is essentially little difference between the two-sided Laplace transform as used in the following discussion and the usual Fourier integral. One difference is that the variable used in the following is the complex frequency $s = \sigma + j\omega$, whereas the Fourier integral is ordinarily written in terms of the variable ω. The use of the two-sided Laplace transform permits the retention of the complex-frequency plane in its usual form. The other differences essentially involve the possibility of using convergence factors in the Laplace transform as a result of the nonzero value of σ.

What are the characteristics of the two-sided Laplace transform? The transform is defined by the integral

$$F(s) = \int_{-\infty}^{\infty} f(t)e^{-st}\, dt \qquad \alpha < \operatorname{Re} s < \beta \qquad (7.15)$$

$$f(t) = \frac{1}{2\pi j} \int_{c-j\infty}^{c+j\infty} F(s)e^{ts}\, ds \qquad \alpha < c < \beta \qquad (7.16)$$

---

† Van der Pol, Balth., and H. Bremmer, "Operational Calculus Based on the Two-sided Laplace Integral," Cambridge University Press, London, 1950. This is an excellent discussion of the Laplace transform (both the two-sided and the one-sided transforms). The text is unusual in that it is readable by engineers and contains a large number of interesting examples.

There is no necessity here to discuss in detail the above definition integral (7.15) and the inverse transform. Only certain characteristics of this transform need be mentioned.

(1) If $f(t) = 0$ for $t < 0$, the transform reduces to the usual one-sided Laplace transform.

(2) If $f(t) = 0$ for $t > 0$, the definition integral (7.15) becomes

$$F(s) = \int_{-\infty}^{0} f(t)e^{-st}\,dt \tag{7.17}$$

If t is replaced by $-u$, this becomes

$$F(s) = \int_{\infty}^{0} f(-u)e^{su}\,(-du) \tag{7.18}$$

$$F(s) = \int_{0}^{\infty} f(-u)e^{-(-s)u}\,du \tag{7.19}$$

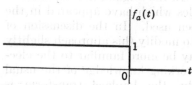

In other words, the transform of a function which is zero for positive time can be determined by finding the usual one-sided transform of the same function reflected about the $t = 0$ axis and then replacing s by $-s$. Two examples illustrate the procedure:

FIG. 7.10. Waveform for first example.

(a) $f_a(t) = u(-t)$ (Fig. 7.10)   (7.20)

Reflection about the $t = 0$ axis results in the unit step function. The transform of this reflected function is $1/s$, valid for all s such that $\sigma > 0$. Then

$$F_a(s) = -\frac{1}{s} \tag{7.21}$$

This transform is valid for all s such that $\sigma < 0$.

(b) $f_b(t) = \begin{cases} e^{at} & t < 0 \\ 0 & t > 0 \end{cases}$ [Fig. 7.11(a)]   (7.22)

Reflection yields the function shown in Fig. 7.11(b). The ordinary transform of this

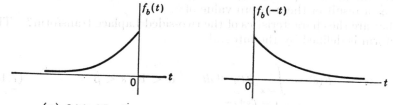

(a) Original Function   (b) Reflected Function

FIG. 7.11. Time function of second example.

function is $1/(s + a)$, valid for $\sigma > -a$. The desired transform is then

$$F_b(s) = \frac{1}{a - s} \tag{7.23}$$

The transform here is valid for all $\sigma < +a$.

(3)   Time functions which are zero for positive time (hereafter called negative-time functions) and which tend to zero as t tends to $-\infty$ give rise to transforms with poles in the right-half plane. The transform exists in the complex plane to the left of all poles. Ordinary transform theory indicates that positive-time functions which tend to zero as t tends to $+\infty$ give rise to transforms with poles in the left-half plane (*i.e.*, stable system functions). The transform exists in the complex plane to the right of all poles.

(4)   Since the transform of the sum of two functions is the sum of the transforms, any time function can be considered as a negative-time func-

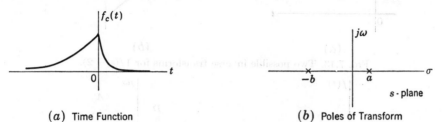

(*a*) Time Function   (*b*) Poles of Transform

FIG. 7.12. Time function and pole configuration for third example.

tion plus a positive-time function. The use of this additive property is illustrated by example (*c*).

(*c*)
$$f_o(t) = \begin{cases} e^{at} & t < 0 \\ e^{-t} & t > 0 \end{cases} \tag{7.24}$$

Then

$$F_c(s) = \frac{1}{a - s} + \frac{1}{s + b} \tag{7.25}$$

$F_c(s)$ has two poles, one at $-b$ with a residue of $+1$, the other at $+a$ with a residue of -1, as in Fig. 7.12. The transform $F_c(s)$ is defined in the region between $\sigma = +a$ and $\sigma = -b$.

(5)   Poles in the right-half plane correspond to either a nonzero value for the time function for negative time or a growing exponential for positive time. For example, the inverse transform of $1/(s - 2)$ is either of the two functions indicated below and shown in Fig. 7.13.

$$f_d(t) = \begin{cases} 0 & t < 0 \\ e^{2t} & t > 0 \end{cases} \tag{7.26}$$

$$f_d(t) = \begin{cases} -e^{2t} & t < 0 \\ 0 & t > 0 \end{cases} \tag{7.27}$$

The decision as to which time function is represented by the transform depends upon the region in the s plane in which the transform is defined. If this region is to the left of the pole, the negative-time function is indicated; if the region lies to the right of the pole, the growing-exponential positive-time function is the solution.

If the region of interest is along the $j\omega$ axis, as in the Fourier transform, the transform must always be defined to the left of right-half-plane poles.

Thus, right-half-plane poles represent negative-time functions. Therefore in Fig. 7.14, poles A, B, and C describe the function for $t < 0$, or in
region 2 in the time domain, while poles D, E, and F describe the function
for positive time. If $F(s)$ can be written as $F_+(s) + F_-(s)$, where $F_+(s)$
has poles only in the left-half plane and $F_-(s)$ only in the right-half plane,

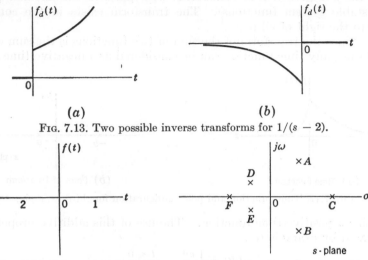

FIG. 7.13. Two possible inverse transforms for $1/(s - 2)$.

FIG. 7.14. Pole-zero configuration and corresponding time-domain regions.

$f(t)$ is readily found by taking the two inverse transforms and adding the
resulting time functions.

Therefore, the two-sided Laplace transform is a rather natural extension of the ordinary one-sided transform. For the purposes of the following discussion, poles in the right-half plane are simply interpreted as
representing a time function for negative time.

7.5. Physical Realizability of Linear Networks. Development of statistical design theory depends upon a knowledge of the available techniques for characterizing a transducer.

FIG. 7.15. Two-terminal-pair network.

In particular, the design theory in its
basic form involves the determination
of the physically realizable network
which minimizes the mean-square
error. Imposition of the constraint that the network be physically
realizable requires a concise definition of realizability.

The general linear two-terminal-pair network takes the form shown in
Fig. 7.15. The transfer properties of the network with given termina-
tions can be described by a system function $G(s)$ relating the output and
input in the following manner:†

$$G(s) = \frac{E_{\text{out}}(s)}{E_{\text{in}}(s)} \tag{7.28}$$

† In a specific case the input might be a current, voltage, velocity, etc. The notation $E_{\text{in}}(s)$ is used to denote the transform of the general input signal.

In the special case when the input is a sine wave of frequency ω_1, the output is also a sine wave of the same frequency, with the input and output waves related by

$$|E_{\text{out}}| = |G(j\omega_1)| \, |E_{\text{in}}| \tag{7.29}$$

$$\underline{/E_{\text{out}}} = \underline{/E_{\text{in}}} + \underline{/G(j\omega_1)} \tag{7.30}$$

That is, in passage of the signal through the network, the amplitude is multiplied by $|G(j\omega_1)|$ and the phase is advanced by the angle of $G(j\omega_1)$.

The criteria of physical realizability are simply expressed in terms of the characteristics of $G(s)$. Regardless of the nature of the input and output signals, physical realizability of the network requires that $G(s)$ be analytic in the right half of the s plane. In other words, if $G(s)$ is the ratio of polynomials (if the network consists only of lumped parameters), all poles of $G(s)$ must lie in the left-half plane.

If $|G(j\omega)|$ drops off as ω^{-n}, where n is an integer and $G(s)$ is the ratio of polynomials, analyticity in the right-half plane is the necessary and sufficient condition for physical realizability. More generally, the Paley-Wiener criterion[†] furnishes the rigorous necessary and sufficient condition for physical realizability in terms of the behavior of $|G(j\omega)|$ along the $j\omega$ axis. Specifically, the condition is that

$$\int_0^\infty \frac{|\log |G(j\omega)| \,|}{1 + \omega^2} \, d\omega$$

have a finite value.

The case of special interest is that in which $G(s)$ is the ratio of polynomials. Physical realizability requires that the poles lie in the left-half plane, but the zeros in general can lie anywhere in the plane, as long as any complex zeros occur only in conjugate pairs.[‡] In particular, there is the possibility of zeros lying in either the right-half plane or the left-half plane. If the zeros are all reflected about the $j\omega$ axis, there is no change in the attenuation of the network. Figure 7.16 indicates the result of this reflection, if the original function, $G_2(s)$, possesses only zeros in the right-half plane. With reference to Fig. 7.16, $|G_1(j\omega)| = |G_2(j\omega)|$ at all frequencies, since the only difference between $G_1(j\omega)$ and $G_2(j\omega)$ is that the numerators are conjugates. Consequently, the only difference between the networks of $G_1(s)$ and $G_2(s)$ lies in the phase characteristics.

If the phase characteristics of the two system functions are compared, it can be readily shown that the net phase displacement between zero and infinite frequency is less for $G_1(s)$. As a result, the transfer function with zeros entirely in the left-half plane (including infinity) is termed a minimum-phase transfer function. Reflection of any zero or pair of zeros into the right-half plane results in a nonminimum-phase transfer function.

[†] George E. Valley, Jr., and Henry Wallman, "Vacuum Tube Amplifiers," MIT Radiation Laboratory Series, Vol. 18, pp. 721–727, McGraw-Hill Book Company, Inc., New York, 1948.

[‡] In any physical circuit there is at least one zero at infinity, since in any practical circuit, the gain always falls off to zero as the frequency is increased indefinitely.

Minimum-phase networks are particularly important because the inverse network [with a transfer function $1/G(s)$] is physically realizable. For example, again with reference to Fig. 7.16, $1/G_1(s)$ is a physically realizable transfer function:

$$\frac{1}{G_1(s)} = \frac{(s^2 + 2s + 2)(s + 3)(s + 4)}{(s + 2)(s^2 + 4s + 8)} \tag{7.31}$$

The pole at infinity may cause difficulty, but the function can be realized, at least theoretically, within any desired accuracy by considering it to be

$$\frac{1}{G_1(s)} = \frac{(s^2 + 2s + 2)(s + 3)(s + 4)}{(s + 2)(s^2 + 4s + 8)(\alpha s + 1)} \tag{7.32}$$

Here α is chosen to be a very small number. This transfer function does not possess a pole at infinity and is essentially equal to $1/G_1(s)$ over the important part of the frequency spectrum if α is sufficiently small.

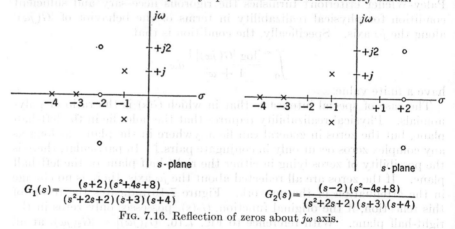

$$G_1(s) = \frac{(s+2)(s^2+4s+8)}{(s^2+2s+2)(s+3)(s+4)} \qquad\qquad G_2(s) = \frac{(s-2)(s^2-4s+8)}{(s^2+2s+2)(s+3)(s+4)}$$

Fig. 7.16. Reflection of zeros about $j\omega$ axis.

Although the transfer characteristics of a transducer have classically been described in terms of the real-frequency transfer function $G(j\omega)$ or the more general complex-frequency function $G(s)$, description in terms of the transient response of the network is a method not only equally valid but also particularly useful in the development of the statistical design theory. The network transfer characteristics are completely described by the response of the system to any specified transient function. Of particular interest is the unit-impulse response $g(t)$, which is simply the inverse Laplace transform of the system function.

The condition for physical realizability in terms of the impulse response is simply stated. *The impulse response must be zero for all negative time.* In other words, there must be no output before the excitation is applied. As indicated in the preceding section, this condition is a direct consequence of the condition that the system function have no poles in the right-half plane. The question of the allowable behavior of the time function as t tends to infinity depends on the exact definition of physical realizability being used. In a practical system, poles cannot exist on the $j\omega$ axis, with the result that the transient response is also required to approach zero as $t \to \infty$. Theoretically, if pure inductances and capacitances and ideal current or voltage sources are allowed, poles on the $j\omega$ axis can under certain restrictions be realized in the transfer function. In this hypothetical situation, the impulse response might oscillate indefinitely at a constant amplitude.

Whether the physical-realizability condition is described in the time or frequency domains, there is also a condition in general on the multiplying constant that can be realized. The condition depends upon whether the transfer function is to be realized as a voltage ratio, a transfer impedance, etc. This difficulty disappears, however, if ideal amplifiers are permitted.

Thus, the physical-realizability conditions can be summarized as follows:

(1) $|G(j\omega)|$ is the gain function of a physically realizable network if the Paley-Wiener criterion is satisfied.

(2) $g(t)$ is realizable if $g(t) = 0$ for $t < 0$ and $g(t) \to 0$ as $t \to \infty$.

(3) If $G(s)$ is given as the ratio of polynomials with real coefficients, it is realizable if all poles lie in the left-half plane excluding infinity and the $j\omega$ axis. If there is a pole at infinity, $G(s)$ can be realized within any desired accuracy over any finite portion of the frequency spectrum.

7.6. Correlation Functions.

The core of statistical design theory is the mean-square-error criterion, the philosophy that the synthesis should aim toward the minimization of the mean-square error between the actual output and the desired output. In this theory the input is considered as a stationary time series existing over all time. The first step in the development of a synthesis procedure evidently involves a characterization of the input. Those particular characteristics of the input which are of importance to this theory are specified by the type of error to be minimized. If the concern is with the mean-square error, for example, only certain aspects of the input signal are of importance.

The essential signal characteristics are determined by a consideration of the mathematical form for the mean-square error. The basic definition of the mean-square error $\overline{e^2}$ is given by Eq. (7.1):

$$\overline{e^2} = \lim_{T \to \infty} \frac{1}{2T} \int_{-T}^{T} [f_o(t) - f_d(t)]^2 \, dt \qquad (7.33)$$

In order to express this mean-square error in terms of the system characteristic and the input signal, it is convenient to replace $f_o(t)$ by an expression involving $f_i(t)$, the input, and $g(t)$, the unit-impulse response of the system. The superposition integral states that

$$f_o(t) = \int_{-\infty}^{\infty} g(\tau) f_i(t - \tau) \, d\tau \qquad (7.34)$$

Substitution of Eq. (7.34) into Eq. (7.33) yields an alternate expression for the mean-square error.

$$\overline{e^2} = \lim_{T \to \infty} \frac{1}{2T} \int_{-T}^{T} dt \left[\int_{-\infty}^{\infty} g(\tau)f_i(t - \tau)\, d\tau - f_d(t) \right]^2 \tag{7.35}$$

The next step involves an expansion of the squared sum:

$$\overline{e^2} = \lim_{T \to \infty} \frac{1}{2T} \int_{-T}^{T} dt \left[\int_{-\infty}^{\infty} g(\tau)f_i(t - \tau)\, d\tau \int_{-\infty}^{\infty} g(\sigma)f_i(t - \sigma)\, d\sigma \right.$$
$$\left. - 2f_d(t) \int_{-\infty}^{\infty} g(\tau)f_i(t - \tau)\, d\tau + f_d^2(t) \right] \tag{7.36}$$

The variable σ is used in the second integrand of the first term of the expansion simply to denote that a variable of integration other than τ is used. The mean-square error can, therefore, be written as the sum of three terms:

$$\overline{e^2} = \lim_{T \to \infty} \frac{1}{2T} \int_{-T}^{T} dt \int_{-\infty}^{\infty} g(\tau)f_i(t - \tau)\, d\tau \int_{-\infty}^{\infty} g(\sigma)f_i(t - \sigma)\, d\sigma$$
$$- 2 \lim_{T \to \infty} \frac{1}{2T} \int_{-T}^{T} dt\, f_d(t) \int_{-\infty}^{\infty} g(\tau)f_i(t - \tau)\, d\tau$$
$$+ \lim_{T \to \infty} \frac{1}{2T} \int_{-T}^{T} f_d^2(t)\, dt \tag{7.37}$$

If the order of integration and the processes of integrating and taking the limit are interchanged in the first two terms (a step which can be rigorously justified mathematically), the expression for $\overline{e^2}$ can be written

$$\overline{e^2} = \int_{-\infty}^{\infty} g(\tau)\, d\tau \int_{-\infty}^{\infty} g(\sigma)\, d\sigma \lim_{T \to \infty} \frac{1}{2T} \int_{-T}^{T} f_i(t - \tau)f_i(t - \sigma)\, dt$$
$$- 2 \int_{-\infty}^{\infty} g(\tau)\, d\tau \lim_{T \to \infty} \frac{1}{2T} \int_{-T}^{T} f_i(t - \tau)f_d(t)\, dt$$
$$+ \lim_{T \to \infty} \frac{1}{2T} \int_{-T}^{T} f_d^2(t)\, dt \tag{7.38}$$

Inspection of the rather formidable equation (7.38) reveals the significant fact that the input signal function $f_i(t)$ and the desired output function $f_d(t)$ enter the mean-square-error expression only in the form of an averaging of the product of two time functions. The significance of this is clearer if a function $\phi_{ab}(\tau)$ is defined

$$\phi_{ab}(\tau) = \lim_{T \to \infty} \frac{1}{2T} \int_{-T}^{T} f_a(t)f_b(t + \tau)\, dt \tag{7.39}$$

If the mean-square error is rewritten in terms of the ϕ function, Eq.

(7.38) becomes

$$\overline{e^2} = \int_{-\infty}^{\infty} g(\tau) \, d\tau \int_{-\infty}^{\infty} g(\sigma) \, d\sigma \, \phi_{ii}(\tau - \sigma) - 2 \int_{-\infty}^{\infty} g(\tau) \, d\tau \, \phi_{id}(\tau) \\ + \phi_{dd}(0) \quad (7.40)$$

This function, $\phi(\tau)$, is the correlation function of statistics. $\phi_{ii}(\tau)$ is the *autocorrelation* function of the input signal $f_i(t)$, $\phi_{dd}(\tau)$ the autocorrelation function of the desired output, and $\phi_{id}(\tau)$ the *crosscorrelation* function between the input signal and the desired output. Consequently, Eq. (7.40) demonstrates that the mean-square error can be determined entirely by the system characteristics, described by the unit-impulse response $g(t)$, and by the correlation functions of the input and the desired output. The basic statement can be made:

If the minimization of the mean-square error is adopted as the design criterion, the signals are adequately described by the correlation functions.

It is the purpose of this section to point out the significance of this statement by considering certain characteristics of autocorrelation and crosscorrelation functions.

It should be emphasized at this point that the first clause of the above statement is of fundamental importance. If alternate error measures or design criteria were adopted, e.g., the minimization of the average magnitude of the error, the correlation functions would not be sufficient to describe the signals.

The autocorrelation function of a simple signal $f_1(t)$ is given by either of two expressions:

$$\phi_{11}(\tau) = \lim_{T \to \infty} \frac{1}{2T} \int_{-T}^{T} f_1(t) f_1(t + \tau) \, dt \quad (7.41)$$

$$\phi_{11}(\tau) = \lim_{T \to \infty} \frac{1}{2T} \int_{-T}^{T} f_1(t - \tau) f_1(t) \, dt \quad (7.42)$$

It makes no difference whether the function is shifted ahead τ sec and multiplied by $f_1(t)$ or shifted back before multiplication and averaging. Figure 7.17 indicates one rather pedagogical method for measuring the autocorrelation function. The signal $f_1(t)$ is assumed available as a voltage. This voltage is applied directly to the voltage coil of a wattmeter. In addition, the voltage is transmitted through a delay line with a delay of τ sec. The output voltage is used to drive a voltage-to-current converter giving an output current equal to $f_1(t - \tau)$. If this current is passed through the current coil of the wattmeter, the meter will read the autocorrelation function for one particular value of τ, since the wattmeter performs the multiplication and averaging. If a plot of $\phi_{11}(\tau)$ is desired, the delay of the line can be varied and a number of discrete readings taken. The experiment would demand, of course, that the wattmeter average over a much longer time than any value of τ desired and that this averaging period be much longer than the period during which the statistics of the signals vary. These restrictions on the length of the averaging period are discussed in detail later; this example is designed only to illustrate the basic physical significance of the autocorrelation function.

The autocorrelation function is qualitatively a measure of the regularity of the function. If the value τ sec from now is closely dependent upon the present value, $\phi_{11}(\tau)$ will in general be large. This is not a rigorous rule since the value τ sec from now may be completely determined by the present value with ϕ still equal to zero. This phenomenon is demonstrated in the case of the autocorrelation function of a periodic wave, considered in the examples given later. It can be definitely stated, however, that, if there is no d-c component in the signal, the autocorrelation function will be small if the argument τ is taken larger

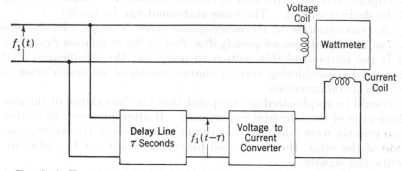

Fig. 7.17. Experimental setup for measuring the autocorrelation function.

than the interval over which values of the function are strongly dependent.

This argument is clarified by the relationship between the autocorrelation function and the probability distributions. The autocorrelation function for any argument τ is simply the average of the product of e_1 and e_2, values of the function τ sec apart. This average is given by

$$\phi_{11}(\tau) = \int\!\!\!\int_{-\infty}^{\infty} e_1 e_2 p_\tau(e_1, e_2)\, de_1\, de_2 \qquad (7.43)$$

The product is given by $e_1 e_2$. The probability of any given product having the first term between e_1 and $e_1 + de_1$ and the second term between e_2 and $e_2 + de_2$ is given by

$$p_\tau(e_1, e_2)\, de_1\, de_2$$

The expected or average value is simply the summation, or integration, of all products multiplied by the respective probabilities. As a result of the ergodic property assumed for the stationary time series, this average can be either an ensemble average—taken at a fixed time for a large number of member functions of the ensemble—or a time average—taken with a large number of widely separated choices of initial time and using only one function of the ensemble.

Thus, the autocorrelation function can be considered either in the light of the shifting, multiplying, and averaging processes or from the viewpoint of the probability distributions describing the stationary time series, in particular the second probability distribution. For experimental measurement of the autocorrelation function, the former viewpoint is ordinarily strongly preferable; for analysis, both viewpoints are essential.

7.7. Properties of Autocorrelation Functions. Certain properties of the autocorrelation function are readily deduced from the preceding discussion and the definition

$$\phi_{11}(\tau) = \lim_{T \to \infty} \frac{1}{2T} \int_{-T}^{T} f_1(t)f_1(t + \tau) \, dt \tag{7.44}$$

(1) The autocorrelation function is an even function of τ; that is, $\phi_{11}(\tau) = \phi_{11}(-\tau)$. $\phi_{11}(\tau)$ is measured by shifting the function τ sec ahead and averaging the product of the original and shifted functions; $\phi_{11}(-\tau)$ is measured by shifting the function backward by τ sec and averaging in the same way. Since the functions are averaged over a doubly infinite interval, the time origin is inconsequential and the averaged product is independent of the direction of the shift.

(2) The autocorrelation function of zero argument, $\phi_{11}(0)$, is the average power of the time function, since $\phi_{11}(0)$ is simply the average value of $f_1(t)$ multiplied by itself. The interpretation of this mean-square value as power assumes that the function $f_1(t)$ represents the voltage across a 1-ohm resistor or the current through a similar resistance.

(3) The value of the autocorrelation function never exceeds the value for zero argument; that is, $|\phi_{11}(\tau)| \le \phi_{11}(0)$. Again, this characteristic is apparent from the definition of autocorrelation since the maximum value inevitably occurs when the function is multiplied by itself without shifting. A mathematical proof is also straightforward.

$$\pm f_1(t)f_1(t + \tau) = +\tfrac{1}{2}\{[f_1(t) \pm f_1(t + \tau)]^2 - f_1^2(t) - f_1^2(t + \tau)\} \tag{7.45}$$

If an average is taken on both sides of Eq. (7.45), the result is

$$\pm \phi_{11}(\tau) = \tfrac{1}{2}\{\overline{[f_1(t) \pm f_1(t + \tau)]^2} - \phi_{11}(0) - \phi_{11}(0)\} \tag{7.46}$$

$$\pm \phi_{11}(\tau) = \tfrac{1}{2}\overline{[f_1(t) \pm f_1(t + \tau)]^2} - \phi_{11}(0) \tag{7.47}$$

A change of signs on both sides of the equation yields

$$\mp \phi_{11}(\tau) = \phi_{11}(0) - \tfrac{1}{2}\overline{\{f_1(t) \pm f_1(t + \tau)\}^2} \tag{7.48}$$

Equation (7.48) leads directly to the inequality desired,

$$|\phi_{11}(\tau)| \le \phi_{11}(0) \tag{7.49}$$

(4) If the signal contains periodic components (or a d-c value), the autocorrelation function contains components of the same periods (or a d-c component). This property follows directly from the definition since a periodic wave shifted by one period is indistinguishable from the unshifted wave. Similarly, if there is a d-c component in $f_1(t)$, there will be a component of $\phi_{11}(\tau)$ independent of the shift τ. One significant fact

concerning periodic components should be noted: since the time origin is irrelevant, the autocorrelation function contains no information concerning the phase of the periodic component of $f_1(t)$.

(5)   If the input signal contains only random components (no periodic components), the autocorrelation function tends to zero as τ tends to infinity, for as the shift of the time function becomes very large, the two functions $f_1(t)$ and $f_1(t + \tau)$ become essentially independent. Since neither contains a d-c component, the average value of the product must be zero.   Consequently, the behavior of the autocorrelation function for large τ determines the fundamental nature of the time function, *i.e.*, whether the time function contains d-c, periodic, or only random components.

(6)   The autocorrelation function is equal to the sum of the autocorrelation functions of the individual frequency components, since the multiplication of components of different frequencies results in a zero average value.   This is simply a form of the familiar electrical-network theorem that a voltage and a current of different frequencies result in zero average power.

(7)   A given autocorrelation function may correspond to an infinite number of different time functions.   (Any given time function has, of course, only one autocorrelation function.)   This absence of a 1:1 correspondence is clearly illustrated by the autocorrelation function of a sinusoidal signal, for $\phi_{11}(\tau)$ is independent of the phase of the signal (*cf.* Example 1 of Sec. 7.8).   Correspondingly in the case of random waves, $\phi_{11}(\tau)$, since it contains no phase information, may correspond to a large number of different time functions.   Since the mean-square error depends only on the correlation functions, it evidently is irrelevant which of the equivalent time functions is considered to be the input.   By "equivalent time functions" here is meant those functions yielding identical correlation functions.

(8)   The autocorrelation function of the derivative of $f_1(t)$ can be simply expressed in terms of the autocorrelation function of $f_1(t)$.   By definition, $\phi(\tau)$, the autocorrelation function of $f_1'(t)$, is given by

$$\phi(\tau) = \lim_{T \to \infty} \frac{1}{2T} \int_{-T}^{T} f_1'(t)f_1'(t + \tau)\, dt \tag{7.50}$$

Integration by parts yields

$$\phi(\tau) = \lim_{T \to \infty} \frac{1}{2T} \left\{ [f_1(t)f_1'(t + \tau)]_{-T}^{T} - \int_{-T}^{T} f_1(t) \frac{d^2}{dt^2} [f_1(t + \tau)]\, dt \right\} \tag{7.51}$$

Since τ and t occur only in the form $\tau + t$, the second derivative under the integral can be considered to be a differentiation with respect to τ. Interchange of the order of integration and differentiation yields

$$\phi(\tau) = -\frac{d^2}{d\tau^2} \left\{ \lim_{T \to \infty} \frac{1}{2T} \int_{-T}^{T} f_1(t)f_1(t + \tau)\, dt \right\} \tag{7.52}$$

$$\phi(\tau) = -\phi_{11}''(\tau) \tag{7.53}$$

In an analogous manner the autocorrelation functions of the integrals and higher-order derivatives of $f_1(t)$ can be found.

7.8. Examples of Autocorrelation Functions.   The characteristics of autocorrelation functions are illustrated by two very simple examples.

Example 1.   *A Sine Wave.*

$$f_1(t) = E \sin (\omega_o t + \psi) \tag{7.54}$$

The basic definition of the autocorrelation function is given in Eq. (7.44).

$$\phi_{11}(\tau) = \lim_{T \to \infty} \frac{1}{2T} \int_{-T}^{T} E \sin (\omega_o t + \psi) E \sin [\omega_o(t + \tau) + \psi] \, dt \tag{7.55}$$

Since the integrand is periodic, the integral and limiting step can be

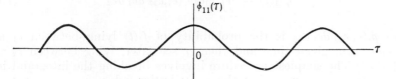

Fig. 7.18. Autocorrelation function of a sinusoidal signal.

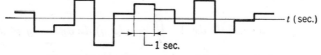

FIG. 7.19. Random wave used in Example 2.

replaced by the integral over one period and division by the period.

$$\phi_{11}(\tau) = \frac{\omega_o}{2\pi} E^2 \int_0^{2\pi/\omega_0} \sin (\omega_o t + \psi) \sin (\omega_o t + \psi + \omega_o \tau) \, dt \tag{7.56}$$

The integration is simplified by the change of variable

$$\omega_o t + \psi = u \tag{7.57}$$

After substitution of (7.57), Eq. (7.56) becomes

$$\phi_{11}(\tau) = \frac{E^2}{2\pi} \int_{\psi}^{\psi+2\pi} \sin u \sin (u + \omega_o \tau) \, du \tag{7.58}$$

The integral can be evaluated by expansion of the integrand, with the final result

$$\phi_{11}(\tau) = \frac{E^2}{2} \cos \omega_o \tau \tag{7.59}$$

The form of $\phi_{11}(\tau)$ is shown in Fig. 7.18.

Example 2.   *A Random Wave.*   As a second example, the wave shown in Fig. 7.19 is considered.   The signal is constant for a time interval of one sec and then jumps discontinuously.   Values in successive intervals are independent and have equal probability of being positive or negative. The magnitudes obey a Poisson distribution.   If A_n is the magnitude of

$f_1(t)$ from $t = n$ to $t = n + 1$, the probability that A_n lies between x and $x + dx$ is given by

$$P(x < A_n < x + dx) = p(x)\, dx = \frac{\lambda^x}{x!} e^{-\lambda}\, dx \qquad (7.60)$$

Here λ is the expected value of A_n, or the first moment of the probability distribution.

The autocorrelation function can be computed in a straightforward manner from its basic definition as the average value of $f_1(t)f_1(t + \tau)$ or from the formula [Eq. (7.43)] in terms of probability distributions. If the latter method is chosen for illustrative purposes,

$$\phi_{11}(\tau) = \iint\limits_{-\infty}^{\infty} e_1 e_2 p_\tau(e_1, e_2)\, de_1\, de_2 \qquad (7.61)$$

Here $p_\tau(e_1, e_2)\, de_1\, de_2$ is the probability of $f_1(t)$ lying between e_1 and $e_1 + de_1$ at a given time and then, τ sec later, lying between e_2 and $e_2 + de_2$. The simplest procedure involves breaking the integrand into two parts, one representing the contribution when $e_1 = e_2$ (or t and $t + \tau$ lie in the same interval) and the other when t and $t + \tau$ lie in different intervals.

$$\phi_{11}(\tau) = \iint\limits_{-\infty}^{\infty} xx p_\tau(x,x)\, dx\, dx + \iint\limits_{-\infty}^{\infty} xy p_\tau(x,y)\, dx\, dy \qquad y \neq x \quad (7.62)$$

The probability that e_1 lies between x and $x + dx$ is $(\lambda^x/x!)e^{-\lambda}\, dx$, as given in Eq. (7.60). The probability that e_2 has the same value is simply the probability that t and $t + \tau$ lie in the same interval, which is evidently $1 - |\tau|$ if $|\tau| < 1$ and zero if $|\tau| > 1$. The limits of integration are changed from $-\infty$ and $+\infty$ to 0 and $+\infty$ because Eq. (7.60) refers to the magnitude without question of sign.

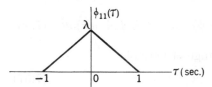

FIG. 7.20. Autocorrelation function for second example.

$$\phi_{11}(\tau) = \begin{cases} \displaystyle\int_0^\infty x^2 \frac{\lambda^x}{x!} e^{-\lambda}(1 - |\tau|)\, dx & |\tau| < 1 \\ 0 & |\tau| > 1 \end{cases} \qquad (7.63)$$

The second term in Eq. (7.62) vanishes identically since the values of A_k in any two different intervals are independent and each has an average value of zero.

The integration required by Eq. (7.63) can be performed by reference to standard tables, with the final result

$$\phi_{11}(\tau) = \begin{cases} \lambda(1 - |\tau|) & |\tau| < 1 \\ 0 & |\tau| > 1 \end{cases} \qquad (7.64)$$

The autocorrelation function is shown in Fig. 7.20. It is noteworthy here that the final result is actually independent of the amplitude distribution initially assumed (a Poisson distribution, above). Integration of Eq. (7.63) yields $(1 - |\tau|)$ multiplied by the variance of the assumed distribution function.

7.9. Autocorrelation Function of Signals with Two Components. Since in a wide variety of design problems the input signal is made up of two components, the message and the noise, significance must be attached to the autocorrelation function of the sum of two functions in terms of the individual correlation functions. The appropriate expression is derived directly from the definition of autocorrelation functions given by Eq. (7.41). If $f_1(t) = f_a(t) + f_b(t)$, the shifting, multiplying, and averaging involved in the determination of the autocorrelation function are given by

$$\phi_{11}(\tau) = \lim_{T \to \infty} \frac{1}{2T} \int_{-T}^{T} [f_a(t) + f_b(t)][f_a(t + \tau) + f_b(t + \tau)]\, dt \quad (7.65)$$

The integrand can be expanded:

$$\phi_{11}(\tau) = \lim_{T \to \infty} \frac{1}{2T} \int_{-T}^{T} f_a(t)f_a(t + \tau)\, dt + \lim_{T \to \infty} \frac{1}{2T} \int_{-T}^{T} f_a(t)f_b(t + \tau)\, dt$$
$$+ \lim_{T \to \infty} \frac{1}{2T} \int_{-T}^{T} f_b(t)f_a(t + \tau)\, dt + \lim_{T \to \infty} \frac{1}{2T} \int_{-T}^{T} f_b(t)f_b(t + \tau)\, dt \quad (7.66)$$

The first and fourth terms are immediately recognizable as autocorrelation functions. The second and third terms are crosscorrelation functions. Thus, the expression for $\phi_{11}(\tau)$ can be condensed using symbolic notation:

$$\phi_{11}(\tau) = \phi_{aa}(\tau) + \phi_{ab}(\tau) + \phi_{ba}(\tau) + \phi_{bb}(\tau) \quad (7.67)$$

The crosscorrelation function is defined by the equation

$$\phi_{ab}(\tau) = \lim_{T \to \infty} \frac{1}{2T} \int_{-T}^{T} f_a(t)f_b(t + \tau)\, dt \quad (7.68)$$

$f_b(t)$ is advanced in time by τ sec and then multiplied by $f_a(t)$. The crosscorrelation function is the average of this product over all time.

Certain significant properties of the crosscorrelation function follow at once from this definition:

(1) The crosscorrelation function $\phi_{ab}(\tau)$ is not an even function. In general, shifting $f_b(t)$ ahead by τ sec yields a different result than a retardation. This is simply demonstrated by a consideration of the two aperiodic waves shown in Fig. 7.21. $f_b(t + \tau)$ represents a shift to the left of the $f_b(t)$ function. Clearly any positive τ yields a $\phi_{ab}(\tau)$ which is zero, while a negative τ yields a nonzero value.

(2) $\phi_{ab}(\tau) = \phi_{ba}(-\tau)$. A shift in $f_b(t)$ must yield the same result as a shift of $f_a(t)$ the same amount in the opposite direction.

(3) $\phi_{ab}(\tau)$ does not necessarily possess a maximum at $\tau = 0$. The example of Fig. 7.21 demonstrates this.

$\phi_{ab}(\tau)$ is in a very special way a measure of the interdependence of $f_a(t)$ and $f_b(t)$. Evidently, if both time functions are random waves with no d-c components and are derived from independent sources (*e.g.*, one from thermal noise in a resistor, the other from fading of a radar echo), the crosscorrelation function is identically zero, for the average value (over all time) of the product of the two functions must be zero. In such a case, the two time functions are termed *uncorrelated*. The term "incoherent" is also used in the literature, but there exists a certain ambiguity concerning the rigorous definition of incoherency. Several authors, for example, have used the term "coherent" to describe two functions which are rigidly related; *e.g.*, two signals from the same source with a knowledge of one determining the other completely. Such a definition of coherence does not imply, however, that the two signals are

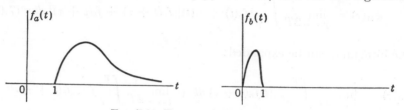

FIG. 7.21. Two aperiodic functions.

correlated. A simple example of coherent, but uncorrelated, signals is the side bands in the spectrum of an amplitude-modulated wave with the modulating signal sinusoidal. The crosscorrelation of two sinusoidal signals of different frequencies is identically zero since the average power is involved. Because of this ambiguity, the term "uncorrelated" is used throughout these chapters to describe two signals which have zero crosscorrelation.

In the field of feedback control the majority of synthesis problems involve the consideration of two signals which are uncorrelated. Typically, the designer is concerned with an input signal and a corrupting signal. The input is the control signal; the corruption may take the form of noise riding in with the control signal, noise generated in the amplifier, or noise entering the system at points other than the input, such as load-torque disturbances entering the system on the output shaft. In all these cases, there are many instances when the corruption is essentially uncorrelated with the control signal. Under these conditions, Eq. (7.67) indicates that the autocorrelation function of the sum of two signals is simply the sum of the individual autocorrelation functions.

This superposition property of autocorrelation is the theoretical basis for the fact that correlation techniques make possible tremendous improvements in the signal-noise ratio when the signal is periodic. For example, if the autocorrelation function is found for a sinusoidal signal in the presence of noise, the result, as shown in Fig. 7.22, consists of two components: a periodic component and a component (due to the noise) which tends to zero for large τ. Consequently, even if the noise level far exceeds the amplitude of the input sinusoid, the autocorrelation function for large argument places in evidence the presence of the sinusoidal component of the input.   The quantitative improvement in signal-noise ratio depends on the length of time permitted for observation.†

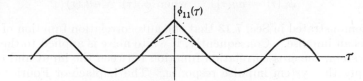

FIG. 7.22. Autocorrelation function of sinusoid plus random noise.

7.10. System Functions Measured by Correlation.   There is another very useful relationship which follows directly from this discussion of crosscorrelation functions.   In many cases, correlation affords a particularly simple method for the experimental measurement of the transfer function of a given linear system.   The theory underlying the measurement technique is based upon a consideration of the crosscorrelation between the input and the output of a system.   If $f_o(t)$ is the output resulting from the input $f_i(t)$, the crosscorrelation function is given by

$$\phi_{io}(\tau) = \lim_{T \to \infty} \frac{1}{2T} \int_{-T}^{T} f_i(t - \tau) f_o(t) \, dt \tag{7.69}$$

The output is related to the input by the superposition integral, involving the system impulse response $g(t)$.

$$f_o(t) = \int_{-\infty}^{\infty} g(x) f_i(t - x) \, dx \tag{7.70}$$

Substitution of Eq. (7.70) into (7.69) yields

$$\phi_{io}(\tau) = \lim_{T \to \infty} \frac{1}{2T} \int_{-T}^{T} f_i(t - \tau) \, dt \int_{-\infty}^{\infty} g(x) f_i(t - x) \, dx \tag{7.71}$$

After interchange of the order of integration and averaging, the expression for the crosscorrelation function becomes

$$\phi_{io}(\tau) = \int_{-\infty}^{\infty} g(x) \, dx \left[\lim_{T \to \infty} \frac{1}{2T} \int_{-T}^{T} f_i(t - \tau) f_i(t - x) \, dt \right] \tag{7.72}$$

The bracketed expression is the autocorrelation function with argument $\tau - x$.

$$\phi_{io}(\tau) = \int_{-\infty}^{\infty} g(x) \phi_{ii}(\tau - x) \, dx \tag{7.73}$$

The significant feature of Eq. (7.73) is the resemblance to Eq. (7.70). Comparison of the two relations indicates that $\phi_{io}(\tau)$ would be the

† It is possible to increase the improvement of signal-noise ratio by the use of crosscorrelation if the fundamental frequency of the periodic component of the input is known. *Cf.* Y. W. Lee, Application of Statistical Methods to Communications Problems, *MIT Research Laboratory of Electronics Tech. Rept.* 181, pp. 28–38, September 1, 1950.

response of the system if the input were $\phi_{ii}(\tau)$. If $\phi_{ii}(\tau)$ is an impulse function, $\phi_{io}(\tau)$ is equal to the impulse response of the system: *i.e.,*

$$\phi_{io}(\tau) = ag(\tau) \qquad \text{when } \phi_{ii}(\tau) = au_0(\tau) \qquad (7.74)$$

It is demonstrated in Sec. 7.13 that the autocorrelation function of white noise is an impulse. Consequently, if white noise is applied to the input of a system, the crosscorrelation function between the input and output is simply the system impulse response. The Laplace or Fourier transform of this $g(\tau)$ is the system function.†

These concepts provide a convenient method for measuring the impulse response $g(t)$ or the system function $G(j\omega)$ of a system. The experimental setup is shown in Fig. 7.23. $n_i(t)$, the output from a white-noise generator [giving noise with a spectrum which is flat over appreciably more than the frequency range covered by $G(j\omega)$], is superimposed on

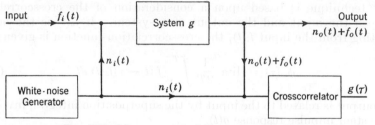

FIG. 7.23. Measurement of the system function.

the normal system input $f_i(t)$. Inputs to the crosscorrelator are the white noise $n_i(t)$ and the system output $f_o(t) + n_o(t)$. These two output components are the output due to the normal input and the output due to the white noise. Since only the latter component, $n_o(t)$, is correlated with the white noise, the output of the crosscorrelator is the system impulse response. A rather unique advantage of this method for measuring system functions is that neither external disturbances nor noise generated within the system has any appreciable effect on the results because of the action of the crosscorrelator in rejecting all signals not correlated with the output of the white-noise generator. A second advantage, stemming from this same filtering action of the crosscorrelator, is the possibility of measuring the transfer characteristic of the system without stopping normal operation.

7.11. Power-density Spectra. In the preceding sections it was demonstrated that, if the input is a stationary time series and the minimization of the mean-square error is used as a design criterion, the signals are adequately described by correlation functions. In other words, the correlation functions are sufficient data for the synthesis of a minimum-mean-square-error system.

In essence, correlation functions describe the signals in terms of time-domain characteristics. For many purposes it is convenient, on the other

† Y. W. Lee, Application of Statistical Methods to Communication Problems, *MIT Research Laboratory of Electronics Tech. Rept.* 181, pp. 25–28, September 1, 1950.

hand, to describe the input signal in terms of frequency-domain characteristics. If the autocorrelation function defines the input adequately,
what corresponding description of the input can be made in the frequency
domain? Evidently, the frequency-domain function must carry exactly
the information contained in the autocorrelation function. A function
satisfying such requirements is the Laplace transform of the autocorrelation function, which is denoted as $\Phi_{11}(s)$.

$$\Phi_{11}(s) = \int_{-\infty}^{\infty} \phi_{11}(\tau)e^{-s\tau}\,d\tau \tag{7.75}$$

Before the properties of $\Phi_{11}(s)$ are investigated, it is advantageous to
determine exactly what characteristics of the random input signal are
measured by this frequency function. The investigation is most readily
introduced by a consideration of the significance of the Laplace transforms of the more usual classes of functions. Most basic is the transform
of periodic waves. If $f_p(t)$ is periodic, then the associated Fourier series
places in evidence the amplitude and phase of the sinusoidal components.
The relationship between $f_p(t)$ and its sinusoidal components is given by
the familiar formula

$$f_p(t) = \sum_{n=-\infty}^{\infty} a_n e^{jn\omega t} \tag{7.76}$$

Here ω is the fundamental frequency (equal to $2\pi/T$, where T is the
fundamental period), and a_n are the coefficients evaluated from the
formulas

$$a_0 = \frac{1}{T}\int_{t_0}^{t_0+T} f_p(t)\,dt \tag{7.77}$$

$$a_n = \frac{1}{T}\int_{t_0}^{t_0+T} f_p(t)e^{-jn\omega t}\,dt \tag{7.78}$$

A plot of the amplitude spectrum of this wave involves a plot of the magnitude of a_n as a function of n and is of the form shown in Fig. 7.24. The
corresponding phase spectrum is of
a similar nature. The spectra of a
periodic wave are line spectra—i.e.,
the energy in the signal is concentrated at isolated frequencies. The
height of the spectral lines in the
amplitude spectrum indicates the
actual amplitude of the signal component at the corresponding frequency. More specifically, if the

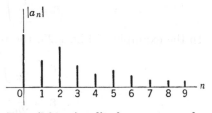

FIG. 7.24. Amplitude spectrum for
periodic wave.

signal is a voltage, the ordinates of the amplitude spectrum are measured
directly in volts.

The situation changes somewhat in the consideration of aperiodic, or
transient, signals. The conversion from the Fourier series to the Fourier-
or Laplace-integral transformation involves a limiting process, and the

spectrum of an aperiodic signal is no longer an amplitude spectrum in the ordinary sense, but rather an amplitude-density spectrum.

A specific example illustrates the significance of the above observations. The time function and the corresponding Laplace transform are shown in Fig. 7.25. Part (b) of the figure is a plot of the magnitude of $F_1(j\omega)$, the amplitude density. Although there is only an incremental voltage amplitude at any one frequency, there does exist a relative distribution of amplitudes. In the plot of the magnitude of $F_1(j\omega)$, the square of any ordinate at a frequency ω is a measure of the relative amount of energy in the vicinity of that frequency.

Actually, more direct significance is associated with the square of this amplitude-density spectrum, although the squared curve is not ordinarily

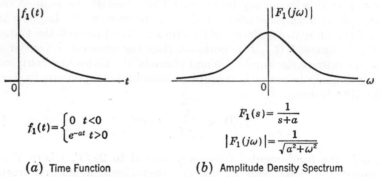

$$f_1(t) = \begin{cases} 0 & t<0 \\ e^{-at} & t>0 \end{cases}$$

$$F_1(s) = \frac{1}{s+a}$$

$$|F_1(j\omega)| = \frac{1}{\sqrt{a^2+\omega^2}}$$

(a) Time Function   (b) Amplitude Density Spectrum

Fig. 7.25. Transform of an aperiodic function.

plotted. If $f_1(t)$ is considered to be the voltage across a 1-ohm resistor, the squared spectrum [a plot of $|F_1(j\omega)|^2$ versus ω] is the energy-density spectrum, a direct indication of the energy dissipated in the 1-ohm resistor as a function of frequency. The area under the curve between ω_1 and ω_2 is proportional to the total energy at all frequencies within these limits. Likewise, the total energy is proportional to the area under the entire curve:

$$\mathcal{E} = \frac{1}{2\pi} \int_{-\infty}^{\infty} |F_1(j\omega)|^2 \, d\omega \tag{7.79}$$

In the example of Fig. 7.25, the total energy is

$$\mathcal{E} = \frac{1}{2\pi} \int_{-\infty}^{\infty} \frac{1}{a^2 + \omega^2} \, d\omega \tag{7.80}$$

$$\mathcal{E} = \frac{1}{2a} \tag{7.81}$$

Thus, the spectrum of a periodic wave is an amplitude spectrum. Aperiodic waves are characterized by amplitude-density spectra. Random time functions, in contrast, are characterized by the $\Phi_{11}(s)$ function, originally defined in Eq. (7.75), repeated below:

$$\Phi_{11}(s) = \int_{-\infty}^{\infty} \phi_{11}(\tau)e^{-s\tau} \, d\tau \tag{7.82}$$

The first step in the determination of the significance of this $\Phi_{11}(s)$ function involves a replacement of the autocorrelation function by the corresponding expression in terms of the signal $f_1(t)$.

$$\Phi_{11}(s) = \int_{-\infty}^{\infty} e^{-s\tau} d\tau \lim_{T \to \infty} \frac{1}{2T} \int_{-T}^{T} f_1(t)f_1(t+\tau) dt \qquad (7.83)$$

If the limiting process and the integration with respect to τ are interchanged, Eq. (7.83) becomes

$$\Phi_{11}(s) = \lim_{T \to \infty} \frac{1}{2T} \int_{-\infty}^{\infty} e^{-s\tau} d\tau \int_{-T}^{T} f_1(t)f_1(t+\tau) dt \qquad (7.84)$$

It would now be desirable to interchange the order of integration, but since $f_1(t)$ is a stationary random process, the associated Laplace integral does not converge. This difficulty can be circumvented if the infinite limits are replaced by finite limits. In other words, instead of considering a function $f_1(t)$ which exists over all time from $-\infty$ to $+\infty$, a signal $f_{11}(t)$ is considered, where $f_{11}(t)$ is equal to $f_1(t)$ over the time interval from $-T$ to $+T$ but is zero elsewhere. With this signal, Eq. (7.84) becomes

$$\Phi_{11}(s) = \lim_{T \to \infty} \frac{1}{2T} \int_{-T}^{T} e^{-s\tau} d\tau \int_{-T}^{T} f_{11}(t)f_{11}(t+\tau) dt \qquad (7.85)$$

With this restriction, the Laplace transform of $f_{11}(t)$ exists, and the order of integration can be interchanged.

$$\Phi_{11}(s) = \lim_{T \to \infty} \frac{1}{2T} \int_{-T}^{T} f_{11}(t) dt \int_{-T}^{T} f_{11}(t+\tau)e^{-s\tau} d\tau \qquad (7.86)$$

The equation is now simplified if a change of variable is made, $t + \tau = x$, and T is considered so large that $\tau - T$ and $\tau + T$, as limits, are equivalent to $-T$ and $+T$, respectively.

$$\Phi_{11}(s) = \lim_{T \to \infty} \frac{1}{2T} \int_{-T}^{T} f_{11}(t) dt \int_{-T}^{T} f_{11}(x)e^{-s(x-t)} dx \qquad (7.87)$$

$$\Phi_{11}(s) = \lim_{T \to \infty} \frac{1}{2T} \int_{-T}^{T} f_{11}(t)e^{st} dt \int_{-T}^{T} f_{11}(x)e^{-sx} dx \qquad (7.88)$$

The two integrals of Eq. (7.88) are separate, conjugate expressions. Thus, $\Phi_{11}(s)$ can be written as

$$\Phi_{11}(s) = \lim_{T \to \infty} \frac{1}{2T} \left| \int_{-T}^{T} f_{11}(t)e^{-st} dt \right|^2 \qquad (7.89)$$

Now consideration is reverted to the original function, $f_1(t)$ which is equal to $f_{11}(t)$ in the interval $-T \le t \le T$, an interval which is allowed to become infinite after the integral of Eq. (7.89) is evaluated.

What is the significance of the step above, in which the infinite limits were replaced by finite limits, the integration performed, and then the

limits allowed to become infinitely large?   Since the random time function involves infinite energy, it has been necessary to convert, by the
averaging process with respect to time, to a consideration of power.
$\Phi_{11}(j\omega)$ is the *power-density spectrum*.

The significance of $\Phi_{11}(j\omega)$ is now clear.   The power between the fre-
quencies ω_1 and ω_2 is simply $1/2\pi$ times the integral of $\Phi_{11}(j\omega)$ from ω_1 to
ω_2; that is, if the signal is considered as the voltage across a 1-ohm
resistor, this integral yields the power dissipated in the resistor by all
signal components with frequencies lying within the range ω_1 to ω_2.   As
a special case, the total average power dissipated in the resistor is

$$P_{\text{total}} = \frac{1}{2\pi} \int_{-\infty}^{\infty} \Phi_{11}(j\omega) \, d\omega \tag{7.90}$$

Equation (7.90) agrees with the previous interpretation of $\phi_{11}(0)$ as the
total power, since the inverse transformation

$$\phi_{11}(\tau) = \frac{1}{2\pi} \int_{-\infty}^{\infty} \Phi_{11}(j\omega) e^{j\omega\tau} \, d\omega \tag{7.91}$$

yields, with $\tau = 0$,

$$\phi_{11}(0) = \frac{1}{2\pi} \int_{-\infty}^{\infty} \Phi_{11}(j\omega) \, d\omega \tag{7.92}$$

The significance of the power-density spectrum is more clearly represented by a direct electrical interpretation, based on hypothetical
measurements.   As indicated in Fig. 7.26, $f_1(t)$ is considered an electrical

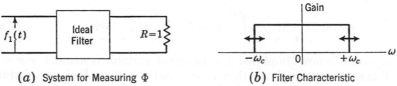

(a) System for Measuring Φ (b) Filter Characteristic
FIG. 7.26. Significance of the power-density spectrum.

voltage, which is passed through an ideal low-pass filter with adjustable
cutoff frequency.   A wattmeter measures the power dissipated in the
1-ohm resistor.   The filter output voltage across the resistor contains all
frequencies of $f_1(t)$ below the cutoff ω_c, with no distortion introduced, but
none of the frequencies above ω_c.   The wattmeter reads the power dissipated in the resistor by all frequency components of $f_1(t)$ from $-\omega_c$
to $+\omega_c$.

$$\text{Wattmeter reading} = \frac{1}{2\pi} \int_{-\omega_c}^{\omega_c} \Phi_{11}(j\omega) \, d\omega \tag{7.93}$$

7.12. Characteristics of Power-density Spectra.   Power-density-spec-
tra functions, $\Phi_{11}(j\omega)$, possess the following important characteristics:

(1) $\Phi_{11}(j\omega)$ measures the power-density spectrum rather than the
amplitude or phase spectra of the signal.   Consequently, the relative
phase of the various frequency components is lost when the signal is
described by means of a power-density spectrum.

(2) As a result of this discarding of the phase information, a given power-density spectrum may correspond to a large number of different time functions.

(3) $\Phi_{11}(j\omega)$ is purely real. This statement follows directly from the fact that time-average power dissipated in a pure resistance is being measured.

(4) $\Phi_{11}(j\omega)$ is an even function of frequency,

$$\Phi_{11}(j\omega) = \Phi_{11}(-j\omega) \tag{7.94}$$

This characteristic follows directly from the original definition of $\Phi_{11}(s)$ as the Laplace transform of $\phi_{11}(\tau)$ and the fact that $\phi_{11}(\tau)$ is an even function of τ. The defining integral for $\Phi_{11}(j\omega)$ is repeated below:

$$\Phi_{11}(j\omega) = \int_{-\infty}^{\infty} \phi_{11}(\tau)e^{-j\omega\tau}\,d\tau \tag{7.95}$$

The exponential can be replaced by the trigonometric form:

$$\Phi_{11}(j\omega) = \int_{-\infty}^{\infty} \phi_{11}(\tau)\cos\omega\tau\,d\tau - j\int_{-\infty}^{\infty} \phi_{11}(\tau)\sin\omega\tau\,d\tau \tag{7.96}$$

Since the second integrand is an odd function of τ, the integral is zero and (7.96) reduces to

$$\Phi_{11}(j\omega) = \int_{-\infty}^{\infty} \phi_{11}(\tau)\cos\omega\tau\,d\tau \tag{7.97}$$

The right-hand side of Eq. (7.97) is an even function of ω.

(5) $\Phi_{11}(j\omega)$ is nonnegative at all frequencies. A negative $\Phi_{11}(j\omega)$ in any frequency band would indicate power being taken from the passive 1-ohm resistor.

(6) If the input signal contains a periodic component such that the Fourier series for this component contains terms representing frequencies $\omega_1, \omega_2, \ldots, \omega_n$, $\Phi_{11}(j\omega)$ contains impulses at $\omega_1, -\omega_1, \omega_2, -\omega_2, \ldots, \omega_n$, and $-\omega_n$. This characteristic of the power-density spectrum is apparent from Eq. (7.97). If $f_1(t)$ contains a periodic component of frequency ω_1, $\phi_{11}(\tau)$ will contain a term of the form $a_1\cos\omega_1\tau$. The corresponding part of $\Phi_{11}(j\omega)$ is

$$\Phi_{11}(j\omega) = a_1\int_{-\infty}^{\infty}\cos\omega_1\tau\cos\omega\tau\,d\tau \tag{7.98}$$

The right-hand side of (7.98) is zero for all ω other than ω_1 or $-\omega_1$ and is infinite at these two frequencies. The area under $\Phi_{11}(j\omega)$, however, is finite and equal to the power contained in the sinusoidal component. This infinite spike of finite area is just the definition of an impulse.

7.13. Examples of Power-density Spectra. A few simple examples illustrate the nature of the power-density spectrum.

White Noise. White noise is ordinarily defined as noise which possesses a flat frequency spectrum. In other words, by definition white noise possesses a power-density spectrum which is a constant. Evidently, if the power-density spectrum at all frequencies has a constant value, the total power represented by the noise voltage wave is infinite, since this total power is simply given by the integral of the power-density spectrum from minus infinity to plus infinity. This difficulty is ordinarily circumvented by defining white noise as a signal possessing a flat frequency distribution over considerably more of the frequency spectrum than is of importance for the system under investigation. In other words, for a feedback control system in which the signals are concentrated in the band from 0 to 10 cycles/sec, any noise voltage which possesses a flat frequency distribution from zero frequency to well above 10 cycles/sec is considered essentially equivalent to white noise.

It is of interest at this point to determine the autocorrelation function of white noise. If white noise is defined as possessing a flat frequency

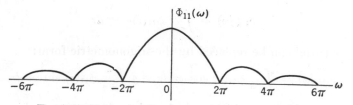

FIG. 7.27. Power-density spectrum for second example.

spectrum over *all* frequencies, the autocorrelation function is an impulse at $\tau = 0$. If the power-density spectrum of the noise is assumed flat over a frequency band wide compared with the input signals, the corresponding autocorrelation function is a pulse at $\tau = 0$ and is of short duration compared to the time constants of the system, with the result that the pulse behaves effectively as an impulse.

Second Example. As a second example, the power-density spectrum is computed for the wave for which the autocorrelation function was derived in Sec. 7.8. The autocorrelation function was there found to be

$$\phi_{11}(\tau) = \begin{cases} \lambda(1 - |\tau|) & |\tau| < 1 \\ 0 & |\tau| > 1 \end{cases} \tag{7.99}$$

Substitution of Eq. (7.99) into the Fourier integral [Eq. (7.97)] for the power-density spectrum yields

$$\Phi_{11}(j\omega) = 2 \int_0^1 \lambda(1 - |\tau|) \cos \omega\tau \, d\tau \tag{7.100}$$

$$\Phi_{11}(j\omega) = \lambda \left(\frac{\sin \omega/2}{\omega/2}\right)^2 \tag{7.101}$$

This function is sketched in Fig. 7.27.

7.14. Experimental Techniques for Measuring Statistical Characteristics. As indicated in the introduction to this chapter, one of the most important applications of statistical design theory has been the insight the theory has given into techniques for the measurement of the important characteristics of both signals and noise. The popularization of the concepts of correlation and power-density spectra has led to refined measurement techniques. Indeed, in the majority of cases, the design of systems has proceeded in the following manner: the characteristics of signals and disturbances have been determined in statistical terms and reinterpreted in the more familiar frequency domain, after which design has been accomplished using well-known methods in the domains of real or complex frequencies.

Statistical theory indicates appropriate methods for the description of stationary random series. For the purposes of linear design on the basis of the mean-square-error criterion, the time function can be adequately described in a number of ways:

(1) By the autocorrelation function
(2) By the power-density spectrum
(3) By an appropriate function of the second probability distribution

The three methods are equivalent since the autocorrelation function and power-density spectrum constitute a Laplace-transform pair and the required function of the second probability distribution is equivalent to the autocorrelation function as a result of the ergodic property of the time functions. Techniques for measuring these statistical characteristics fall into two general categories: measurements can be made in the time domain to determine the correlation functions, or measurements can be made in the frequency domain (ordinarily yielding the power-density spectrum directly).

Although the following discussion considers the two distinct measurement problems, it should be borne in mind that it is of course possible to measure any one of the three describing functions by first determining one of the others and then performing the appropriate calculations. For example, the power-density spectrum can be determined by measurement of the autocorrelation function followed by a direct Laplace transformation. In certain cases, this indirect technique may be simpler than a direct measurement of the power-density spectrum.

The measurement problems here are no different from those in any other field in the sense that the choice of a particular procedure depends upon many factors which are difficult to express analytically, or even qualitatively.† In the last analysis, the engineer must depend to a great extent on ingenuity and experience to select that procedure which is optimum for the given specifications on accuracy, cost, measuring speed, frequencies contained in the signals, etc.

Measurement of Correlation Functions. Techniques for the measurement of correlation functions are based upon the definition given in

† Two general papers on the errors arising in measurements of the statistical characteristics of random signals are: W. B. Davenport, Jr., R. A. Johnson, and D. Middleton, Statistical Errors in Measurements on Random Time Functions, *J. Appl. Phys.*, Vol. 23, No. 4, pp. 377–388, April, 1952; and J. W. Tukey, The Sampling Theory of Power Spectrum Estimates, *Symposium on Applications of Autocorrelation Analysis to Physical Problems*, pp. 47–67, Publication of ONR, Department of Navy, Washington, 1949.

Eq. (7.41),

$$\phi_{11}(\tau) = \lim_{T \to \infty} \frac{1}{2T} \int_{-T}^{T} f_1(t)f_1(t + \tau)\, dt \qquad (7.102)$$

Here $\phi_{11}(\tau)$ is the autocorrelation function of the time function $f_1(t)$. The procedures described below could equally well be applied to the determination of crosscorrelation functions.

The definition above indicates that determination of $\phi_{11}(\tau)$ requires three distinct operations:

(1)   Shifting the time axis to generate $f_1(t + \tau)$
(2)   Multiplying
(3)   Averaging

The most difficult of these three operations is ordinarily the second, the multiplication of $f_1(t)$ by $f_1(t + \tau)$. A number of schemes are available; a few of the simpler methods are described below. The averaging

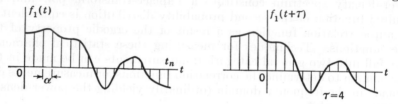

FIG. 7.28. Sampled section of input time function.

process introduces the principal time lag involved in correlation, since in most correlators the curve is determined point by point and for each point the product of the two time functions must be averaged over a time interval sufficiently long to make sure the time functions exhibit average characteristics in this interval.

The discussion of the following pages describes briefly three general methods of calculating correlation functions. This discussion is specifically concerned with three methods which constitute only a sampling of the wide variety of ways in which the time shifting, multiplication, and averaging may be performed.

Method I.   *Manual Calculation.* With a graphical sample of the input signal, the autocorrelation function can be determined by a brute-force analytical method. A possible section of the time function is shown in Fig. 7.28. The function is sampled every α sec, at $t_1, t_2, \ldots, t_n$. The function is then shifted τ sec, where τ is chosen to be an integral multiple of α in order that samples of the shifted function may coincide with samples of the original $f_1(t)$. The autocorrelation function is given by the average of the products of the samples occurring at the same time. In the case shown in Fig. 7.28, this would involve the average over all samples from 0 to $t_n - \tau$. Thus,

$$\phi_{11}(\tau) = \frac{1}{n - \tau/\alpha + 1} \int_{j=0}^{n - \tau/\alpha} f_1(t_j)f_1(t_j + \tau) \qquad (7.103)$$

The computation involved in the determination of $\phi_{11}(\tau)$ for a large number of values of τ is obviously tremendous.

An attempt to carry out the above procedure immediately raises certain specific questions:

(1) How long a sample of the original time function is required? With reference to Fig. 7.28, how large must t_n be? Certainly the sample must be sufficiently long to indicate the lowest frequency components of importance in the signal. In view of the fact that somewhat less than the entire t_n interval is used when τ is other than zero, it appears that the sample should be approximately 10 times the period of the lowest important frequency components of the signal. It is impossible to make any definite statement of significance here, however, since the power-density spectrum of the signal in general does not cut off sharply at low frequencies, with the result that in a practical case it is difficult to decide, even if the power-density spectrum is known approximately, what constitutes significance. Indeed, the importance of this criterion, based on the lowest frequency content of the input, is even more meaningless when it is considered that in a practical case all the information given is the curve of the signal sample. If the power-density spectrum were known, there would be no point in calculating the autocorrelation function. Consequently, this concept of a sample length 10 times the largest period of the signal components can only serve as a rough guide toward making an intelligent initial guess.

Once this initial estimate has been made, however, there is a fairly straightforward test to determine whether the sample length is sufficiently long. If the time series is known to possess the property of ergodicity, a number of different samples of duration T are analyzed. If the average over the duration of any one sample is identical with the average taken over all samples, a sufficient time interval has been used. Alternately, the time interval is sufficient if each of the samples yields essentially the same autocorrelation function.

There are alternate schemes for determining the required sample length. For example, if the sample length is increased appreciably and the autocorrelation function is unchanged, the original sample length is probably adequate. In addition, there are standard statistical procedures for determining the required sample duration.[†] It is certainly true, in general, that a sample can be used which is not sufficiently long, for the short-term and long-term autocorrelation functions may differ radically.[‡]

(2) Is the sample length unnecessarily long? Here again, there unfortunately appears to be no simple way to decide whether the sample length is unnecessarily long until the correlation function has been determined. However, even this postevaluation is helpful if a number of

† H. B. Brainerd, pp. 144–176, in "Instrument Engineering," Vol. I, by C. S. Draper, W. McKay, and S. Lees, McGraw-Hill Book Company, Inc., New York, 1952.

‡ Such a radical difference is exhibited by experimental results on the autocorrelation functions of speech, as obtained by Fano and his students. *Cf.* "Quarterly Progress Report," Research Laboratory of Electronics, MIT, Cambridge, Mass., October 15, 1950, pp. 45–48.

samples of the same general type are to be analyzed. In general, the sample length need not be much more than 10 times the value of τ at which $\phi_{11}(\tau)$ becomes essentially zero. For example, if $\phi_{11}(\tau)$ is in the neighborhood of zero for all τ greater than 1 sec, a 10-sec sample should be sufficient. Two values of the function more than 1 sec apart are essentially independent.

(3) How small must α, the spacing between samples, be made to obtain reasonable accuracy? It can certainly be stated that the samples should be taken sufficiently close together to ensure that the function does not change a significant amount within the sampling interval. This follows directly from the fact that a time function can be represented by periodic samples taken at a frequency equal to twice the highest significant frequency present in the signal. Here again, there is a great deal of vagueness in such a criterion, and the final decision as to the sampling intervals is necessarily a compromise between the desire for accuracy and the desire to keep the ennui of the calculations to a minimum. If the signal is the input to a physical system, the sampling interval is satisfactory if it is much less than the lowest significant time constant of the system, if this can be determined. It is certainly true, however, that once α is chosen no frequency components are measured higher than $1/2\alpha$ cycles/sec. (Actually, as the discussion of Sec. 9.1 indicates, the properly measured frequency components do not extend this high if there are signal components above $1/2\alpha$ cycles/sec.)

Method II. *Machine Calculation.* The tediousness of the calculations involved in the manual calculation of correlation functions early led engineers to investigate methods by which machine operations could be substituted for these manual tasks. Evidently there exist two possible approaches to the problem of mechanizing the calculations. On the one hand, general-purpose computers may be adapted to the calculation of correlation functions: on the other hand, computers may be built specifically for the purposes of correlation. The selection of the approach to be followed in a specific case evidently depends on the availability of a suitable general-purpose computer and the number of correlations required. Both approaches have been used extensively.

A number of general-purpose computers can be modified to perform the shifting, multiplying, and averaging required in the calculation of correlation functions. For example, recent models of the IBM punched-card calculating machines can be used to perform all three operations. If the signals are available in graphical records, it is necessary to punch the sample amplitudes into the cards. As in many computer applications, this data-input operation is the most time-consuming part of the entire calculation. If a large amount of correlation is to be performed, it is economical to add automatic data input effected by a curve follower, sampling circuits, and automatic card punching. The time-shifting operation is performed very simply by removing from the stack of cards the number corresponding to the number of samples in the desired shift τ. Multiplying and averaging are straightforward operations of the machine. With the process completely mechanized, high accuracy can be attained at a speed that is high compared with manual calculations, although still much slower than electronic correlation, described below. An added advantage of this method is that the transform of the correlation function can also be found automatically, with the computer output yielding the power-density spectrum.

The application of general-purpose computers to the computation of correlation functions is ordinarily uneconomical if a large number of correlations are to be performed. Computers constructed specifically for the purpose of correlation are usually simpler and more economical for specified speed, accuracy, and types of input signals. There are a number of methods of correlation. Perhaps the simplest, particularly for feedback-control applications in which the energy of the signals is concentrated at low frequencies, is a mechanical correlator.

One typical form for a mechanical correlator employs the basic components of the MIT differential analyzer.† The multiplication and integration can be performed as two successive integrations on the basis of the relation

$$\int f_1(t)f_2(t) \, dt = \int f_1(t) \, d[\int f_2(t) \, dt] \tag{7.104}$$

Integration can be accomplished mechanically by a screw, disk, and wheel combination. Simple correlators can be constructed using these general principles, particularly if the accuracy requirements are not high.

Greater accuracy and more flexibility are realizable if an electronic correlator is constructed, involving the use of pulse-circuit techniques to accomplish the required multiplication and averaging.‡ The theory of this method is based on the ergodic property of the time functions to be studied and the fact that the time functions of interest are stationary: the statistics do not change with time. The time function is sampled at time $t_1, t_2, \ldots, t_n$, leading to a set of pulses $p_1, p_2, \ldots, p_n$. The height of the pulses represents the magnitude of the function at the sampling times. The signal is in each case again sampled τ sec later (at $u_1, u_2, \ldots, u_n$), leading to another set of pulse-amplitude-modulation pulses $q_1, q_2, \ldots, q_n$. If the number of samples n is made sufficiently large, the autocorrelation function is given by

$$\phi_{11}(\tau) \cong \frac{1}{n} \sum_{i=1}^{n} p_i q_i \tag{7.105}$$

† E. C. Berkeley, "Giant Brains or Machines that Think," pp. 65–88, John Wiley & Sons, Inc., New York, 1949; and V. Bush and S. H. Caldwell, A New Type of Differential Analyzer, *J. Franklin Inst.*, Vol. 240, No. 4, pp. 255–326, 1945.

‡ Two correlators operating on the principles described here have been constructed at MIT. The earlier system, based on digital-computer techniques, is described in the report by H. E. Singleton, A Digital Electronic Correlator, *MIT Research Laboratory of Electronics Tech. Rept.* 152, February 21, 1950. The later system, based on analog-computer techniques, is described in the paper by J. Francis Reintjes, An Analogue Electronic Correlator, *Proc. Natl. Electronics Conf.* 1951, Vol. 7, pp. 390–400, 1952. Both correlators have considerably more flexibility than is required for applications in feedback-control-system engineering and also operate over a higher frequency range, necessitating a speeding up of the input data.

The problem of correlation has been reduced to the multiplication of two quantities given by pulse amplitudes. This process is illustrated by Fig. 7.29.

Certain questions immediately arise concerning the validity of this technique:

(1) How far apart must the samples at t_1 and t_2, t_2 and t_3, and so on, be for Eq. (7.105) to be valid? Evidently if t_2 occurs sufficiently soon after t_1, the value of p_2 will be strongly dependent on p_1. Two distinct conditions may exist. If $t_2 - t_1$ is so large that p_2 is essentially independent of p_1, the signal from t_1 onward to t_2 may be considered as one function of an ensemble, that from t_2 to t_3 another member function, etc. In this case, the average of Eq. (7.105) is essentially an ensemble average. If, on the other hand, t_2 is so close to t_1 that t_1, t_2, . . . , t_n are sufficient sampling points to describe the time function completely, Eq. (7.105) represents a

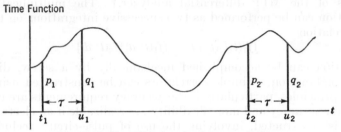

Fig. 7.29. Sampling involved in correlation.

time average for this one function, or the basic definition of the auto-correlation function. For values of $t_2 - t_1$ lying between these two extremes, a sufficient number of samples still leads to the correlation function.

(2) How many samples must be taken for the result to be the auto-correlation function? In other words, how many samples are required to describe the long-term statistical characteristics of the signal? The answer to this question depends on the characteristics of the input signal. If the sampling intervals are so close together that p_1, p_2, . . . , p_n suffice to describe completely all significant variations in the signal, the required number of samples n is determined by the sample length required for the section of the time function, as described in the discussion of Method I. With a general sampling interval $t_2 - t_1$, at least this many samples are required. Ordinarily a very large number of samples is used in this form of correlator to increase accuracy, but if it is desired to approach the minimum required number, this minimum can be determined fairly simply experimentally. Since the output of the correlator for any given τ is the integrated product of the samples, sufficient samples have been taken when this output reaches a steady value.

(3) What is the effect of periodic components in the signal? Evidently, if the sampling frequency is synchronized with the frequency of the periodic component of the signal, this periodic component appears as a d-c component to the correlator, since at every sampling time the

periodic component has the same value. This is not ordinarily an insurmountable difficulty, however, since in practice the sampling frequency drifts during operation. Unless this drift is significant, a large number of samples is required before the true nature of the periodic component is apparent.

The details of the operation of multiplication and averaging can be accomplished in a number of ways. In Singleton's equipment, the amplitudes of the two pulses to be multiplied are converted to a binary system and the multiplication is performed using basically the ordinary methods of a digital computer. Integration likewise is accomplished by a cascade arrangement of scale-of-two circuits. An alternate procedure involves converting the p_j set of pulses to a group of pulses of duration larger than any τ to be used in the correlation and of height proportional to the amplitude of the signal at the sampling time. The information contained in the second sampling (at u_1, u_2, . . . , u_n) is converted to constant-amplitude pulses of duration proportional to the amplitude of the signal at this second sampling time. The two sets of pulses are applied to a gating circuit yielding a set of output pulses with the area under the pulse proportional to the product $p_j q_j$. Integration then simply involves determination of the total area under all these pulses corresponding to a given τ.

The principal disadvantages of this electronic method for the determination of the correlation functions are the amount of equipment required and the time required for determination of a complete curve of $\phi_{11}(\tau)$. The amount of equipment becomes particularly impressive if digital methods are used for multiplying and integrating. Furthermore, the amount of equipment is increased if the signals are available only in recorded form, since a reading system to convert the signals to voltages is then required. The time involved may not be a serious handicap if the energy of the signal is concentrated at high frequencies—in the audio band, for example—but if, as commonly occurs in servo work, the principal frequencies of interest in typical signals are in the vicinity of a few cycles/sec, the time required for the determination of a correlation curve with reasonable accuracy becomes excessive. An attempt has been made to overcome this disadvantage of excessive time lag by the design of a correlator which computes five points on the correlation curve simultaneously.† The outstanding advantage of the equipment is, of course, the accuracy that can be realized. If the multiplication and integration are performed with binary digits representing the numbers, the only limit on accuracy occurs in the circuits for sampling the signal and converting these sample amplitudes to binary numbers.

Method III. *Space Integration.* As described on the preceding pages, correlation can be performed by manual calculation or by straightforward machine computation. In addition, certain schemes have been used for specific problems and special types of signals. For example, if the signal frequencies are very low, a decrease in the excessive time required for

† J. J. Levin and J. F. Reintjes, A Five-channel Electronic Analog Correlator, *Proc. Natl. Electronics Conf.*, Vol. 8, pp. 647–656, 1953.

correlation is the principal advantage of the method originated by the group at Ohio State University working on the response of human beings. In this procedure, the averaging with respect to time is replaced by an averaging with respect to space, with the result that the averaging can be performed in a short interval of time.   The basic elements of the procedure are as follows:

A sample of the time function to be autocorrelated is recorded on photographic film.   The recording is similar to a variable-density record, but is actually accomplished by first converting the signal to pulse-frequency modulation, with the number of pulses between sampling points proportional to the amplitude of the signal at the earlier sampling point.   Each pulse results in a line on the record, with the result that

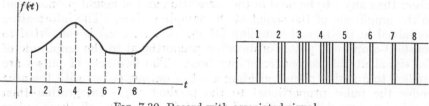

FIG. 7.30. Record with associated signal.

the record for a typical signal has the form shown in Fig. 7.30.   It is usually convenient to add a d-c voltage to the time function in order to make the minimum value at least zero during the observation time.

With the time function in this form, multiplication is readily accomplished.   Two similar records are superimposed, one displaced an amount τ from the other.   Light from a fixed source is passed through these two records, collected by an integrating sphere, and measured electronically. The amount of light passing through the two records is a measure of the autocorrelation function for the particular value of τ used as the relative displacement of the records.   The result is not directly the autocorrelation function, but includes also the d-c component resulting from the average product of the d-c components added to the two time functions to make the minimum values zero.   This d-c component is readily removed, however, by subtraction of the d-c component from the output and only introduces difficulties if the original time function possesses a d-c component.

The principal disadvantage of this scheme is the relatively low accuracy attainable as a result of inaccuracy in the measurement of the total quantity of light passing through the film and the difficulty of making a variable-density record of the time functions.   In addition, there is the associated problem of realizing a uniform amount of light incident along the length of the record.   For many applications, these disadvantages are offset by the simplicity of the equipment (compared to other methods) and the speed of measurements.   The high speed of correlation realized by this method is particularly important in cases in which the frequency content of the signals is concentrated in the lower portion of the frequency spectrum (*e.g.*, in the vicinity of 1 cycle/sec or lower).   In such a case, any completely electronic method would require a prohibitive amount of time for the determination of a complete autocorrelation function as a result of the duration of the sample of the signal and the time required by the averaging process.

Measurement of Power-density Spectra.   It was pointed out that perhaps the most important application of the statistical design methods during these first few years has been the insight gained by engineers into methods for characterizing signals and noise.   The concept of correlation functions has been particularly important, for it is commonly simpler to determine the characteristics of noise or signals by correlation than by direct attempts to measure the power-density spectra.   In design, however, it is usually simpler, and certainly more in line with traditional design methods, to use the power-density spectra.

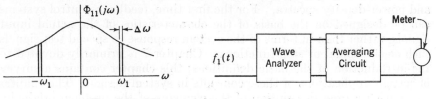

FIG. 7.31. Measurement of power-density spectra.

The power-density spectrum $\Phi_{11}(j\omega)$ can be determined through the correlation function and the Laplace transform, or it can be measured directly on the basis of the definition.   Direct measurements depend on the fact that $\Phi_{11}(j\omega_1)$ is a measure of the power between ω_1 and $\omega_1 + d\omega$. An approximate determination of $\Phi_{11}(j\omega_1)$ can be made using a narrowband wave analyzer with an averaging circuit.   The wave analyzer is tuned to the frequency ω_1.   If the bandwidth of the wave analyzer is $\Delta\omega$, and $\Delta\omega$ is sufficiently small to ensure that in this interval around ω_1 the power-density spectrum does not change significantly, the output meter of Fig. 7.31 reads approximately $\Phi_{11}(j\omega_1)\,\Delta\omega$.   The averaging circuit is required since the narrow band of the analyzer results in a fluctuating output reading except in the unusual situation when the short-time statistics of the signal are the same as the long-term statistics.

This method of measurement is satisfactory for signals with a power-density spectrum covering a portion of the frequency spectrum considerably larger than the bandwidth of the wave analyzer.   However, for the measurement of many servo signals it is impracticable to build a variable filter with a band much narrower than the low-frequency band occupied by the signal energy.   Under these conditions, correlation seems a much more satisfactory method of analysis.

CHAPTER 8

APPLICATION OF STATISTICAL
DESIGN PRINCIPLES

The basic concepts of statistical design are described in the preceding chapter. The work of Wiener and the men who followed him has introduced to control-system engineers the concepts of correlation functions and power-density spectra. For the first time, feedback control systems can be designed on the basis of the characteristics of the actual input signals, rather than in terms of the system response to special test signals such as sinusoidal or step functions. Chapter 7 is primarily devoted to the introduction of the basic definitions; this chapter contains a survey of certain applications of these concepts in system design. The chapter starts with a brief description of the elements of the problem originally considered by Wiener—the design of a linear system which minimizes the mean-square error between the actual output and the desired output when the input is a stationary time series. Sections 8.5 and 8.6 summarize modifications particularly useful in the analysis and design of feedback control systems. The chapter concludes with a brief survey of the work

FIG. 8.1. Notation.

which has been done in the consideration of nonlinear systems and in the design of systems for which the input time series is not stationary.

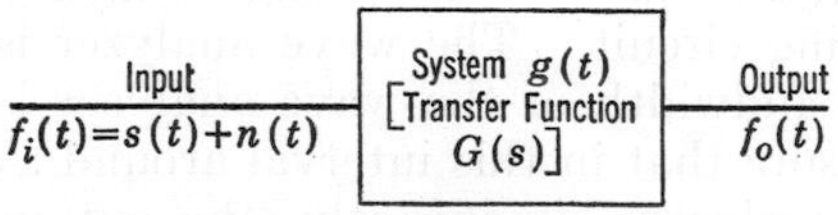

8.1. Power-density Spectrum of System Output. The fundamental design problem is illustrated in Fig. 8.1. The specifications describe the characteristics of the input $f_i(t)$,† consisting of the signal $s(t)$ and noise $n(t)$. The desired output $f_d(t)$ is also known. In the pure filtering problem, the desired output is $s(t)$, the signal component of the input, and the system ideally eliminates all noise. In general, the desired output may be any linear functional of $s(t)$: e.g., the derivative or integral or a prediction or a delay of $s(t)$. The design problem is the determination of a physically realizable *linear* system, described by the impulse response $g(t)$, such that the mean-square error between $f_d(t)$ and the actual output $f_o(t)$ is minimized.

The determination of the $g(t)$ or the transfer function $G(s)$ which

† Throughout this chapter the notation follows that of Fig. 8.1, which is common in the literature on statistical design. Only when the discussion is concerned directly with feedback control systems (as in Secs. 8.5 and 8.6) is the notation of $c(t)$ as the output, $r(t)$ as the input, and $e(t)$ as the actuating signal introduced.

results in minimization of the mean-square error clearly requires the evaluation of this error. As described in Eq. (7.40), the mean-square error depends only on the correlation functions:

$$\overline{e^2} = \int_{-\infty}^{\infty} g(\tau)\, d\tau \int_{-\infty}^{\infty} g(\sigma)\, d\sigma\ \phi_{ii}(\tau - \sigma) - 2 \int_{-\infty}^{\infty} g(\tau)\, d\tau\ \phi_{id}(\tau) + \phi_{dd}(0)$$

(8.1)

where $\phi_{ii}(\tau)$ = autocorrelation function of total input $s(t) + n(t)$

$\phi_{id}(\tau)$ = crosscorrelation function of total input with desired output

$\phi_{dd}(\tau)$ = autocorrelation function of desired output

With a given impulse response, input, and desired output, the mean-square error can be calculated from Eq. (8.1). It is considerably simpler, however, to perform the calculations in terms of the frequency-domain functions (the transfer function and the power-density spectra).

The mean-square error is the sum of two components: the error arising from the transmission of noise through the system and the error resulting from the difference between the desired output and the actual output component caused by the signal $s(t)$. Because only linear systems are considered, the two components of error can be evaluated separately. If the signal and noise components of the input are uncorrelated, the mean-square value of the error is simply the sum of the mean-square values of these two components.†

The Noise Output. If the input is exclusively noise $n(t)$, the resulting output, denoted $f_{on}(t)$, is entirely error in the usual problem. The corresponding autocorrelation functions and power-density spectra are denoted as shown in Fig. 8.2, where $\phi_{nn}(\tau)$ and $\Phi_{nn}(s)$ describe the input, $\phi_{on-on}(\tau)$ and $\Phi_{on-on}(s)$ the output. The power-density spectrum is proportional to the power per radian per second if the signal represents the voltage across a 1-ohm resistor. The mean-square value of the output (*i.e.*, the total power represented by the output signal) is given by the integral

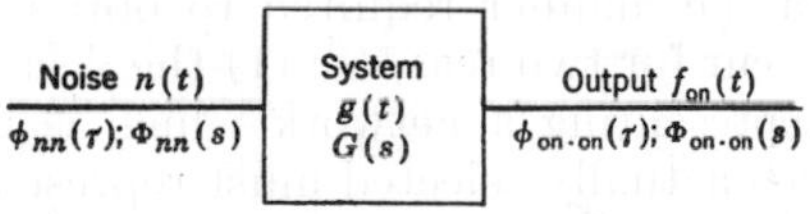

FIG. 8.2. Noise as only input.

$$\overline{e_n^2} = \frac{1}{2\pi} \int_{-\infty}^{\infty} \Phi_{on-on}(j\omega)\, d\omega$$

(8.2)

But the power-density spectrum of the output of a linear system is related to the power-density spectrum of the input by the equation

$$\Phi_{on-on}(j\omega) = |G(j\omega)|^2 \Phi_{nn}(j\omega)$$

(8.3)

† Throughout this chapter it is assumed that signal and noise arise from essentially independent sources and are, consequently, uncorrelated. In unusual cases in which correlation does exist between signal and noise, calculation of the mean-square error requires determination of the crosscorrelation between noise input and desired output, as indicated in Eq. (8.1). Only slight modifications are required in the various analyses of this chapter when this crosscorrelation exists.

Equation (8.3) follows directly from the definition of the power-density spectrum and the fact that the output power in an incremental frequency band of width $d\omega$ around ω_1 depends on $|G(j\omega_1)|^2$ and is independent of the phase angle of the system function. The equation can also be derived from the convolution integral relating $f_{on}(t)$ to $n(t)$, the defining equations for the autocorrelation functions, and the Fourier transform relating $\Phi(j\omega)$ to $\phi(\tau)$.

The mean-square value of the noise output is given by the combination of Eqs. (8.2) and (8.3):

$$\overline{e_n^2} = \frac{1}{2\pi} \int_{-\infty}^{\infty} |G(j\omega)|^2 \Phi_{nn}(j\omega) \, d\omega \qquad (8.4)$$

The Signal Component of Error. The signal component of error arises because the linear system does not operate on the signal part of the input

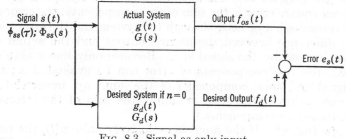

Fig. 8.3. Signal as only input.

in the manner required to obtain the desired output. The error may occur for two reasons: (1) the desired operation may correspond to a $g(t)$ representing a network which is not physically realizable, and (2) the $g(t)$ actually selected must represent a compromise between the desire to operate on $s(t)$ properly and the desire to filter the noise as completely as possible. In the problem of pure prediction in the absence of noise [where $n(t) = 0$, and $f_d(t)$ is simply $s(t + \alpha)$, with α the prediction time], the signal component of error (in this case, the total error) arises because the $g(t)$ required to give the perfect advance or lead of α sec is not physically realizable: a network cannot respond before it is excited. In the case of pure filtering of the signal from noise, a system function $G(s) = 1$ would result in no signal component of error, but, in the general case when the noise error is considered, a $G(s)$ other than unity results in a smaller total error.

The instantaneous value of the signal component of error is given by the relation

$$e_s(t) = f_d(t) - f_{os}(t) \qquad (8.5)$$

where $f_{os}(t)$ denotes the output component resulting from $s(t)$. Figure 8.3 illustrates the notation and the significance of Eq. (8.5). $s(t)$ is considered the only input to the system g. The desired and actual outputs are compared in a subtracting circuit, which itself yields an output equal to the signal component of error. The entire system is equivalent to one with the single transfer function $G_d(j\omega) - G(j\omega)$, where $G_d(j\omega)$ represents the transfer function relating $s(t)$ to $f_d(t)$. Hence, if $\Phi_{ss}(j\omega)$ is the power-density spectrum of the signal component of the input, an equation similar to (8.4) can be written:

$$\overline{e_s^2} = \frac{1}{2\pi} \int_{-\infty}^{\infty} |G_d(j\omega) - G(j\omega)|^2 \Phi_{ss}(j\omega)\, d\omega \qquad (8.6)$$

Total Mean-square Error. The total mean-square error for the system of Fig. 8.1 is found by summing the components given by Eqs. (8.4) and (8.6):

$$\overline{e^2} = \frac{1}{2\pi} \int_{-\infty}^{\infty} [|G(j\omega)|^2 \Phi_{nn}(j\omega) + |G_d(j\omega) - G(j\omega)|^2 \Phi_{ss}(j\omega)]\, d\omega \qquad (8.7)$$

Equation (8.7) is the frequency-domain form of Eq. (8.1). As considered in detail in Sec. 8.2, the design of the optimum system is the determination of a physically realizable $G(j\omega)$ which minimizes $\overline{e^2}$ with the given values for $G_d(j\omega)$, $\Phi_{nn}(j\omega)$, and $\Phi_{ss}(j\omega)$.

Computation of the Noise Error. Even if the over-all system design is effected without the use of the statistical methods, the relation between

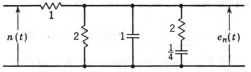

FIG. 8.4. Circuit excited by noise.

the mean-square noise error and the power-density spectrum is useful in analysis. Equation (8.4) states that the mean-square noise output can be determined from the magnitude of the transfer function and the power-density spectrum of the input noise. The method of calculation can be illustrated by a determination of the mean-square noise output for the circuit of Fig. 8.4. The input is assumed to be white noise with a power-density spectrum equal to a constant (assumed 4) over a band-width much greater than the frequency band of interest in the problem. Thus,

$$\Phi_{nn}(j\omega) = 4 \qquad (8.8)$$

The transfer function of the network shown is

$$G(j\omega) = \frac{(j\omega + 2)}{(j\omega + 1)(j\omega + 3)} \qquad (8.9)$$

The mean-square value of the output resulting from the noise input is given by Eq. (8.4), which becomes

$$\overline{e_n^2} = \frac{1}{2\pi} \int_{-\infty}^{\infty} \left| \frac{(j\omega + 2)}{(j\omega + 1)(j\omega + 3)} \right|^2 4\, d\omega \qquad (8.10)$$

The integral can be evaluated in several ways:

(1)   Standard tables can be consulted.† These tables give the value of the integral in terms of the coefficients of the numerator and denominator polynomials of the integrand and, hence, are particularly useful if the denominator is not known in factored form [as when the integrand corresponds to $\left|\dfrac{C}{R}(j\omega)\right|^2$ in a feedback-control problem and only the open-loop transfer function has been factored].

(2)   The integration can be performed graphically. The product of $|G(j\omega)|^2$ and $\Phi_{nn}(j\omega)$ is plotted, and the integral of Eq. (8.10) is evaluated with a planimeter or any of the common numerical methods. Both $|G(j\omega)|^2$ and $\Phi_{nn}(j\omega)$ can be plotted readily if the familiar asymptotic methods are utilized. On the logarithmic scale, the multiplication becomes addition. The only tedious step is the replotting of $|G(j\omega)|^2\Phi_{nn}(j\omega)$ on linear scales in order to permit graphical integration. Such a graphical approach is particularly useful if the transfer function is known only graphically, a situation which occurs frequently in the design of feedback control systems.

(3)   The integration of Eq. (8.10) can be carried out analytically on the basis of residue theory. If the integrand is considered a function of the complex variable s, the path of integration is along the imaginary axis, and Eq. (8.4) becomes

$$\overline{e_n^2} = \frac{1}{2\pi j}\int_{-j\infty}^{j\infty} G(s)G(-s)\Phi_{nn}(s)\,ds \tag{8.11}$$

In the rewriting of Eq. (8.4) in terms of s, $|G(j\omega)|^2$ is replaced by $G(s)G(-s)$, since‡

$$|G(j\omega)|^2 = G(j\omega)\bar{G}(j\omega) = G(j\omega)G(-j\omega) = [G(s)G(-s)]_{s=j\omega}$$

$\bar{G}(j\omega)$ is equal to $G(\overline{j\omega})$, or $G(-j\omega)$, as a result of the fact that $G(j\omega)$ is a physically realizable transfer function, and, consequently, $\operatorname{Re} G(j\omega)$ and $\operatorname{Im} G(j\omega)$ are, respectively, even and odd functions of ω.

The example considered in Fig. 8.4 and Eq. (8.10) is readily completed with an analytical evaluation of the integral. In the complex plane, the integral of Eq. (8.10) becomes

$$\overline{e_n^2} = \frac{1}{2\pi j}\int_{-j\infty}^{j\infty} \frac{(s+2)}{(s+1)(s+3)}\frac{(-s+2)}{(-s+1)(-s+3)}\,4\,ds \tag{8.12}$$

The path of integration is shown in Fig. 8.5. Since the integrand behaves as $-4/s^2$ as s tends to infinity, the value of the integral is unaltered if the path of integration is closed by a large semicircle in either the right- or left-half plane. Thus,

$$\overline{e_n^2} = \sum_{\nu} k_\nu \tag{8.13}$$

---

† H. M. James, N. B. Nichols, and R. S. Phillips, "Theory of Servomechanisms," MIT Radiation Laboratory Series, Vol. 25, pp. 369–370, McGraw-Hill Book Company, Inc., New York, 1947.

‡ The bar over G indicates the conjugate.

where k_{ν} are residues of $\dfrac{4(s+2)(-s+2)}{(s+1)(s+3)(-s+1)(-s+3)}$ in the poles in

the left-half plane. In this example there are only two poles, at -1 and -3. The corresponding residues are

$$k_{-1} = \frac{4(1)(3)}{(2)(2)(4)} = \tfrac{3}{4}$$

$$k_{-3} = \frac{4(-1)(5)}{(-2)(4)(6)} = \tfrac{5}{12} \quad (8.14)$$

The mean-square noise output is

$$\overline{e_n^2} = \tfrac{3}{4} + \tfrac{5}{12} = \tfrac{7}{6} \quad (8.15)$$

The output power-density spectrum is simply $|G(j\omega)|^2 \Phi_{nn}(j\omega)$, or

$$\Phi_{on-on}(j\omega) = \frac{4(4+\omega^2)}{(1+\omega^2)(9+\omega^2)}$$
$$(8.16)$$

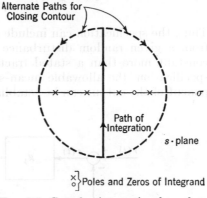

FIG. 8.5. Complex integration for calculation of mean-square output.

Application to Control Problem. The calculation of mean-square noise output is an important aspect of a variety of design problems. Unfortunately, in spite of the rather impressive theories available, many complex feedback control systems are of necessity designed to a large extent by a trial-and-error procedure. The evaluation of a specific configuration frequently requires the determination of the effect of noise present with the input signal—*e.g.*, the thermal, glint, propeller, and other noise superimposed on the radar signal in an air-to-air fire-control system. Even though the characteristics of the noise are not known accurately, an intelligent estimate of the power-density spectrum (or autocorrelation function) can often be made on the basis of relatively meager data.

A second example of the application of Eq. (8.4) is provided by the design of a feedback control system subject to disturbances entering the system at points other than the input. As pointed out in Sec. 6.1 in connection with the discussion of load-torque disturbances, the effects of such unwanted signals are in many cases most easily considered in terms of the statistics of the resultant output, in particular the mean-square value of the disturbance output. In this problem, the mean-square output is calculated from the power-density spectrum of the disturbance and the magnitude of the transfer function $\dfrac{C}{U}(j\omega)$, in Fig. 8.6.

If the first probability distribution function of the output is known, the mean-square value permits determination of the probability that the output exceeds any specified level (*i.e.*, the fraction of the total time the output exceeds this level). Ordinarily, the probability distribution of the disturbance is measured; if this distribution is Gaussian, the distribution of the disturbance output is also Gaussian, since the network from disturbance input to output is linear. Hence, the probability that the magnitude of the output exceeds the value A is given by the co-error function [Eq. (7.11)]

$$P(|c| > A) = \frac{2}{\sqrt{\pi}} \int_{A/\sqrt{2}C_{\text{rms}}}^{\infty} e^{-u^2} \, du \tag{8.17}$$

Thus, the specification can include a statement that the output resulting from a given random disturbance input should not exceed a specified constant more than a stated fraction of the time. From this type of specification, the allowable mean-square value of the disturbance component of the output can be established and the appropriateness of given

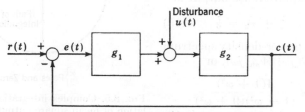

FIG. 8.6. System subject to multiple inputs.

$\dfrac{C}{U}$ (s) functions determined. A slight modification of this approach to design is presented in detail in Sec. 8.6, describing techniques for the control of the probability of saturation at various points throughout the system.

8.2. Minimization of the Mean-square Error.† Equation (8.7), expressing the mean-square value of the error between desired and actual outputs, is the starting point for the determination of the *optimum linear system*—that linear system which minimizes this measure of error. Before the minimization is considered, it is appropriate to review the assumptions underlying Eq. (8.7), repeated here:

$$\overline{e^2} = \frac{1}{2\pi} \int_{-\infty}^{\infty} [|G(j\omega)|^2 \Phi_{nn}(j\omega) + |G_d(j\omega) - G(j\omega)|^2 \Phi_{ss}(j\omega)] \, d\omega \tag{8.18}$$

The relation has been derived under two important assumptions:

(1)   The system is linear.
(2)   The time series are stationary.

If significance is to be associated with the $G(j\omega)$ resulting from consideration of Eq. (8.18), one additional assumption is obviously implied:

(3)   The mean-square error is the appropriate measure of system error.

Solution Neglecting Physical Realizability. The work of Wiener is fundamentally concerned with the derivation of the optimum *physically*

† The discussion of this section follows closely the presentation given by H. W. Bode and C. E. Shannon, A Simplified Derivation of Linear Least Square Smoothing and Prediction Theory, *Proc. IRE*, Vol. 38, pp. 417–425, April, 1950.

realizable system.   As described in Sec. 7.5, the constraint of realizability can be imposed in either the time or frequency domains.   In this section, realizability is interpreted as the time-domain restriction that the impulse response of the system must be zero for t negative (*i.e.*, the system cannot respond until excited).   In the optimization procedure, it is convenient to neglect this constraint initially and determine first the optimum linear system without regard to realizability.

With the notation described in Fig. 8.7, the mean-square error is given by Eq. (8.18).   The analysis is simplified if the transfer functions $G(j\omega)$

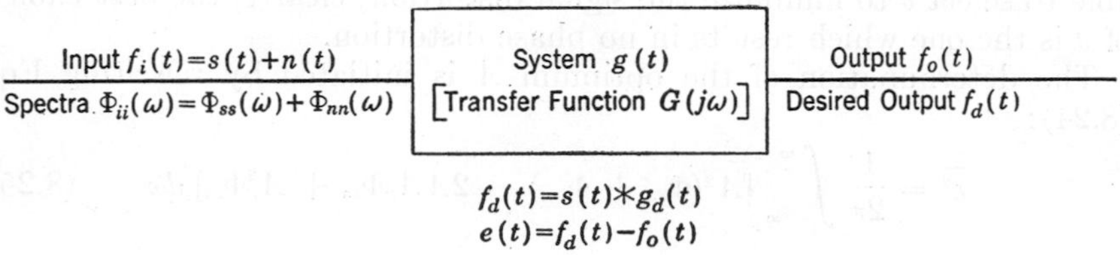

Input $f_i(t)=s(t)+n(t)$	System $g(t)$	Output $f_o(t)$
Spectra $\Phi_{ii}(\omega)=\Phi_{ss}(\omega)+\Phi_{nn}(\omega)$	[Transfer Function $G(j\omega)$]	Desired Output $f_d(t)$

$$f_d(t)=s(t)*g_d(t)$$
$$e(t)=f_d(t)-f_o(t)$$

FIG. 8.7. Notation.

and $G_d(j\omega)$ are written in terms of magnitude and phase,

$$G(j\omega) = A(\omega)e^{j\theta(\omega)}$$
$$G_d(j\omega) = A_d(\omega)e^{j\theta_d(\omega)} \tag{8.19}$$

Here both $A(\omega)$ and $\theta(\omega)$ are assumed real functions of the real variable ω. Substitution of Eq. (8.19) in (8.18) yields

$$\overline{e^2} = \frac{1}{2\pi} \int_{-\infty}^{\infty} [A^2(\omega)\Phi_{nn}(j\omega) + |A_d(\omega)e^{j\theta_d(\omega)} - A(\omega)e^{j\theta(\omega)}|^2\Phi_{ss}(j\omega)]\,d\omega \tag{8.20}$$

The exponentials are written in rectangular form, and for simplicity the arguments ω and $j\omega$ are omitted when the various functions are written:

$$\overline{e^2} = \frac{1}{2\pi} \int_{-\infty}^{\infty} [A^2\Phi_{nn} + |A_d \cos\theta_d + jA_d \sin\theta_d - A\cos\theta - jA\sin\theta|^2\Phi_{ss}]\,d\omega \tag{8.21}$$

The expression within the magnitude signs is written as the sum of the squares of real and imaginary parts and simplified with the use of trigonometric identities:

$$\overline{e^2} = \frac{1}{2\pi} \int_{-\infty}^{\infty} \{A^2\Phi_{nn} + [A_d^2 + A^2 - 2AA_d \cos(\theta - \theta_d)]\Phi_{ss}\}\,d\omega \tag{8.22}$$

Equation (8.22) indicates at once the optimum choice of θ (if physical-realizability conditions are neglected).   Since A, A_d, Φ_{nn}, and Φ_{ss} are all nonnegative for all values of ω, the minimum value of the integral (as a function of θ) occurs when the term $2AA_d \cos(\theta - \theta_d)$ is a maximum, or when

$$\theta = \theta_d \tag{8.23}$$

The resulting mean-square error is

$$\overline{e^2} = \frac{1}{2\pi} \int_{-\infty}^{\infty} [A^2\Phi_{nn} + (A_d^2 + A^2 - 2AA_d)\Phi_{ss}] \, d\omega \qquad (8.24)$$

The minimization is resolved to a determination of the optimum A. It should be noted here that Eq. (8.23) might have been written at once from purely physical reasoning. Since the choice of θ has no effect on the mean-square value of the noise component of the output, it is reasonable to select θ to minimize the signal distortion; clearly, the best choice of θ is the one which results in no phase distortion.

The determination of the optimum A is initiated by rewriting Eq. (8.24):

$$\overline{e^2} = \frac{1}{2\pi} \int_{-\infty}^{\infty} [A^2(\Phi_{ss} + \Phi_{nn}) - 2AA_d\Phi_{ss} + A_d^2\Phi_{ss}] \, d\omega \qquad (8.25)$$

The term $A_d^2\Phi_{ss}^2/(\Phi_{ss} + \Phi_{nn})$ is added and subtracted to complete the square.

$$\overline{e^2} = \frac{1}{2\pi} \int_{-\infty}^{\infty} \left[\left(A\sqrt{\Phi_{ss} + \Phi_{nn}} - \frac{A_d\Phi_{ss}}{\sqrt{\Phi_{ss} + \Phi_{nn}}} \right)^2 + A_d^2\Phi_{ss} - \frac{A_d^2\Phi_{ss}^2}{\Phi_{ss} + \Phi_{nn}} \right] d\omega \qquad (8.26)$$

Equation (8.26) can be written

$$\overline{e^2} = \frac{1}{2\pi} \int_{-\infty}^{\infty} \left[\left(A\sqrt{\Phi_{ss} + \Phi_{nn}} - \frac{A_d\Phi_{ss}}{\sqrt{\Phi_{ss} + \Phi_{nn}}} \right)^2 + \frac{A_d^2\Phi_{ss}\Phi_{nn}}{\Phi_{ss} + \Phi_{nn}} \right] d\omega \qquad (8.27)$$

Neither the squared term nor the last term in the integrand of Eq. (8.27) can be negative for any ω, but the variable A appears only in the squared term. Accordingly, the minimum value of $\overline{e^2}$ occurs when the squared term is zero, or

$$A = A_d \frac{\Phi_{ss}}{\Phi_{ss} + \Phi_{nn}} \qquad (8.28)$$

Thus, the optimum transfer function, without regard to physical realizability, is given by Eqs. (8.28) and (8.23):

$$G_{opt}(j\omega) = \frac{\Phi_{ss}(j\omega)}{\Phi_{ss}(j\omega) + \Phi_{nn}(j\omega)} G_d(j\omega) \qquad (8.29)\star\dagger$$

The corresponding mean-square error is expressed by Eq. (8.27), with the squared term equated to zero:

$$\overline{e^2}_{\min opt} = \frac{1}{2\pi} \int_{-\infty}^{\infty} \frac{\Phi_{ss}\Phi_{nn}}{\Phi_{ss} + \Phi_{nn}} A_d^2 \, d\omega \qquad (8.30)\star$$

† The subscript *opt* is used throughout this chapter to indicate the optimum without regard to realizability.

Interpretation. Equation (8.29) describes the result of minimization of the mean-square error. The significance of this particular error measure is indicated in part by a simple example illustrating the nature of the optimum system function. A filtering problem is considered, with

$$\Phi_{ss}(j\omega) = \frac{36}{\omega^2 + 36} \tag{8.31}$$

$$\Phi_{nn}(j\omega) = a^2 \tag{8.32}$$

The desired output is the signal component of the input, although a time delay T is permitted; hence,

$$G_d(j\omega) = e^{-i\omega T} \tag{8.33}$$

Substitution of the given data in Eq. (8.29) yields the optimum transfer function

$$G_{opt}(j\omega) = \frac{36/a^2}{\omega^2 + 36(1 + a^2)/a^2} e^{-i\omega T} \tag{8.34}$$

The minimum error is determined from Eq. (8.30):

$$\overline{e_{min}^2} = \frac{1}{2\pi} \int_{-\infty}^{\infty} \frac{36}{\omega^2 + 36(1 + a^2)/a^2} \, d\omega \tag{8.35}$$

$$\overline{e_{min}^2} = \frac{3a}{\sqrt{1 + a^2}} \tag{8.36}$$

It is of interest to compare this optimum filter with a filter which might be designed on the basis of classical theory. The filtering problem is illustrated in Fig. 8.8, showing the nature of the power-density

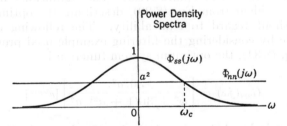

FIG. 8.8. Power-density spectra for filtering example.

spectra of signal and noise. Classical design might use an "ideal" low-pass filter, with the cutoff placed at the frequency at which the noise and signal power-density spectra are equal; *i.e.*, at the value of ω at which

$$\frac{36}{\omega^2 + 36} = a^2 \qquad \text{or} \qquad \omega_c = \frac{6}{a} \sqrt{1 - a^2} \tag{8.37}$$

The corresponding mean-square error can be calculated as the sum of noise and signal components. The noise component is

$$\overline{e_n^2} = \frac{1}{2\pi} a^2 \frac{12}{a} \sqrt{1 - a^2} = \frac{6a}{\pi} \sqrt{1 - a^2} \tag{8.38}$$

The signal component is given by the integral:

$$\overline{e_s^2} = \frac{1}{\pi} \int_{\omega_c}^{\infty} \frac{36}{\omega^2 + 36} \, d\omega = 3 - \frac{6}{\pi} \arctan \frac{\omega_c}{6} \tag{8.39}$$

The total mean-square error is then

$$\overline{e^2} = \frac{6a}{\pi} \sqrt{1 - a^2} + 3 - \frac{6}{\pi} \arctan \frac{\omega_c}{6} \tag{8.40}$$

where $\omega_c = (6/a) \sqrt{1 - a^2}$. When $a^2 = 0.5$, the mean-square error of the classical filter is 2.45, while that of the Wiener filter is only 1.73. The classical filter yields a mean-square error about 42 per cent greater than the filter designed by minimizing the mean-square error.

The statement is often made that the improved performance of the Wiener filter is a result of the consideration of phase, where the classical filter neglects the phase entirely. Such an argument is valid in a restricted sense. The Wiener filter does not exhibit a sharp cutoff because of the possibility that the high-frequency components of the signal may add in just the correct phase to yield a very rapid change of signal waveform. The actual phase spectrum of a portion of the input signal does not influence the optimum filter characteristics. Indeed, exactly the same optimum filter is realized with all possible input waveforms yielding the same autocorrelation function.

Physical Realizability. Introduction of the additional constraint that the transfer function should describe a physically realizable system ordinarily increases the mean-square error. The significance of this added constraint is evident from Eq. (8.29), describing the optimum transfer function without regard to realizability. The following discussion is made specific by considering the filtering example used previously. As shown in Eq. (8.34), the optimum system function is

$$G_{opt}(j\omega) = \left[\frac{36/a^2}{\omega^2 + 36(1 + a^2)/a^2} \right] [e^{-i\omega T}] \tag{8.41}$$

The first term in brackets arises from $\Phi_{ss}/(\Phi_{ss} + \Phi_{nn})$ in Eq. (8.29); the second term in brackets is $G_d(j\omega)$, the desired transfer function in the absence of noise. $G_{opt}(s)$ can be found by replacing $j\omega$ by s in Eq. (8.41):

$$G_{opt}(s) = \left[\frac{36/a^2}{-s^2 + 36(1 + a^2)/a^2} \right] [e^{-sT}] \tag{8.42}$$

As written above, $G_{opt}(s)$ possesses two poles, at $\pm 6 \sqrt{1 + a^2}/a$, one pole in each half plane. The inverse transform of the first term in brackets of Eq. (8.42) is sketched in Fig. 8.9(a); the impulse response corresponding to the total $G_{opt}(s)$ is the above response delayed by T sec, as shown in Fig. 8.9(b).

Figure 8.9 demonstrates that, regardless of the allowable delay, the optimum system is never exactly physically realizable; the optimum impulse response is never zero for all negative time even though the response for negative time can be made as small (and insignificant) as desired if sufficiently great delay is admitted. The difficulty arises, regardless of $G_d(j\omega)$, because $\Phi_{ss}/(\Phi_{ss} + \Phi_{nn})$ is always a function of ω^2 (or $-s^2$) and hence always possesses poles in both the left- and right-half planes. The right-half-plane poles call for an impulse response which is nonzero for $t < 0$. Consequently, the only situation in which the optimum system function is realizable is the trivial case in which there is no noise and $G_d(j\omega)$ is itself realizable. Under any other conditions, a physically realizable $G(j\omega)$ must be chosen to approximate the $G_{opt}(j\omega)$ of Eq. (8.29). The remainder of this section is concerned primarily with the method of approximation which leads to a minimum mean-square error.

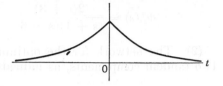

(a) Inverse Transform of First Term of (8.42)

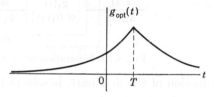

(b) Optimum Response with Delay T

Fig. 8.9. Optimum impulse response without regard to realizability

Noise-free Systems. The simplest nontrivial problem occurs when there is no noise present, in which case Eq. (8.29) yields

$$G_{opt}(j\omega) = G_d(j\omega) \tag{8.43}$$

As stated above, if $G_d(j\omega)$ satisfies the realizability condition, the desired $G(j\omega)$ is determined. If $G_d(j\omega)$ corresponds to a nonrealizable network, the corresponding inverse transform, the desired impulse response, is not zero for $t < 0$.† The simplest example of this problem arises in the design of a predictor, where the desired output is a prediction of the input: *i.e.*,

$$f_d(t) = s(t + \alpha) \tag{8.44}$$

where α, the prediction time, is positive. The corresponding $G_{opt}(j\omega)$, or $G_d(j\omega)$, is

$$G_{opt}(j\omega) = e^{j\omega\alpha} \tag{8.45}$$

The associated unit-impulse response is a unit impulse at $t = \alpha$.

The problem of how best to approximate this $G_{opt}(j\omega)$ by a realizable $G(j\omega)$ is solved by Bode and Shannon with the following artifice. The design is divided into the following steps:

(1) Φ_{ss}, the power-density spectrum of the signal input, is factored

---

† $g_d(t)$ might also violate physical-realizability conditions because of the behavior as $t \rightarrow \infty$.

into two components, $\Phi_{ss}^+(s)$ with poles and zeros in the left-half plane only and $\Phi_{ss}^-(s)$ with all critical frequencies in the right-half plane:[†]

$$\Phi_{ss}(s) = \Phi_{ss}^+(s)\Phi_{ss}^-(s) \tag{8.46}$$

For example,
$$\Phi_{ss}(s) = \frac{-4(s^2 - 9)}{(s^2 - 1)(s^2 - 36)}$$

$$\Phi_{ss}^+(s) = \frac{2(s + 3)}{(s + 1)(s + 6)} \qquad \Phi_{ss}^-(s) = \frac{-2(s - 3)}{(s - 1)(s - 6)} \tag{8.47}$$

(2) The network for the optimum realizable system is broken into two tandem components, as indicated in Fig. 8.10. $G_1(s)$, the transfer

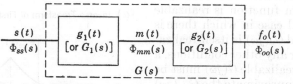

FIG. 8.10. Separation of system into two tandem sections.

function of the first part, is selected as

$$G_1(s) = \frac{1}{\Phi_{ss}^+(s)} \tag{8.48}$$

As a consequence of this choice, $\Phi_{mm}(s)$, the power-density spectrum of $m(t)$ (the output of the g_1 block), is simply unity, since

$$\Phi_{mm}(j\omega) = \Phi_{ss}(j\omega)|G_1(j\omega)|^2 = \Phi_{ss}(j\omega)[G_1(s)G_1(-s)]_{s=j\omega}$$

$$= \Phi_{ss}(j\omega)\left[\frac{1}{\Phi_{ss}^+(s)}\frac{1}{\Phi_{ss}^-(s)}\right]_{s=j\omega} \tag{8.49}$$

Hence, $m(t)$ is white noise. The waveform of $m(t)$ in a particular example depends on the waveform of $f_i(t)$ [or $s(t)$ in the present analysis], but the optimum filter is independent of this waveform and depends only on the power-density spectrum (or the autocorrelation function). Accordingly, it is permissible to consider $m(t)$ as a train of closely spaced, narrow, random, and statistically independent pulses. The design of the optimum predictor is now resolved to the problem of selecting the transfer function $G_2(s)$ to operate on these pulses to give the best prediction of the original input signal $s(t)$.

(3) Each of these pulses produces an output proportional to the impulse response $g_2(t)$; the total output $f_0(t)$ is the sum of the individual responses, as shown in Fig. 8.11. The desired output (i.e., the input advanced by α sec) would be realized if $g_2(t)$ were the inverse transform of $\Phi_{ss}^+(s)$, but advanced α sec in time (i.e., starting at $-\alpha$). Hence, at any given instant, the desired output depends on the pulses of $m(t)$ which have occurred and those which will occur during the next α sec. Thus,

[†] The plus superscript is used in $\Phi_{ss}^+(s)$ to indicate that the corresponding inverse transform, denoted $g_{ss}(t)$ below, is nonzero for positive time, zero for negative time.

the optimum output at any time consists of two *statistically independent* components:

(a) The sum of the tails of all pulse responses for pulses of $m(t)$ which have occurred. This component is completely predictable and can be realized if $g_2(t)$ is that part of the inverse transform of $\Phi_{ss}^+(s)e^{\alpha s}$ which occurs for $t > 0$.

(b) The sum of all contributions from $m(t)$ pulses which have not yet occurred. This component is completely unpredictable, but has a mean value which is zero because future pulses of $m(t)$ are equally likely positive or negative. Since the arithmetic mean is the point about which the mean-square value is minimum, the best realizable output for this component is zero. The minimum mean-square error is realized if the output of the g_2 network is simply the correct value on the basis of all present and past pulses of $m(t)$ and neglects completely future pulses.

(4) Accordingly, the appropriate impulse response for the second section of the predictor is

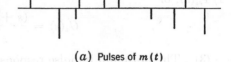

(a) Pulses of $m(t)$

$$g_2(t) = \begin{cases} 0 & t < 0 \\ g_{ss}(t + \alpha) & t > 0 \end{cases}$$

(8.50)

where $g_{ss}(t)$ is the inverse transform of $\Phi_{ss}^+(s)$.

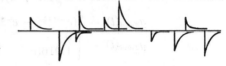

(b) Components of $f_o(t)$

Fig. 8.11. Components of output.

(5) The mean-square error of the prediction is the error introduced by neglecting the pulses of $m(t)$ from $t = 0$ to $t = \alpha$ if the output at $t = 0$ is considered. Each of these independent pulses contributes to the mean-square error according to the corresponding value of $g_{ss}(\alpha - l)$. Hence, the mean-square error of prediction is

$$\overline{e^2} = \int_0^\alpha g_{ss}^2(\alpha - l) \, dl = \int_0^\alpha g_{ss}^2(t) \, dt$$

(8.51)

The mean-square value of the optimum output is simply the mean-square value of the input, or

$$\overline{f_d^2} = \int_0^\infty g_{ss}^2(t) \, dt$$

(8.52)

The relative error introduced by the prediction is measured by the ratio,

$$\frac{\overline{e^2}}{\overline{f_d^2}} = \frac{\int_0^\alpha g_{ss}^2(t) \, dt}{\int_0^\infty g_{ss}^2(t) \, dt}$$

(8.53)

A simple example illustrates the procedure described above and indicates the significance of the various equations. The assumed power-density spectrum of the signal input is

$$\Phi_{ss}(s) = \frac{36}{(s^2 - 1)(s^2 - 36)}$$

(8.54)

The desired prediction time is $\frac{1}{6}$ sec. The predicting network is determined as follows:

(1) $\Phi_{ss}(s)$ is factored to yield

$$\Phi_{ss}^+(s) = \frac{6}{(s+1)(s+6)} \qquad \Phi_{ss}^-(s) = \frac{6}{(s-1)(s-6)} \tag{8.55}$$

$g_{ss}(t)$ is the inverse transform of $\Phi_{ss}^+(s)$, or

$$g_{ss}(t) = \begin{cases} 0 & t < 0 \\ \frac{6}{5}(e^{-t} - e^{-6t}) & t > 0 \end{cases} \tag{8.56}$$

(2)   The transfer function of the first section of the predictor is simply $1/\Phi_{ss}^+(s)$, or

$$G_1(s) = \frac{(s+1)(s+6)}{6} \tag{8.57}$$

(3)   The optimum impulse response for the g_2 block, if physical realizability is not considered, is $g_{ss}(t + \frac{1}{6})$, or

$$g_{2,opt}(t) = \frac{6}{5}(e^{-(t+\frac{1}{6})} - e^{-6(t+\frac{1}{6})}) \qquad t > -\frac{1}{6} \tag{8.58}$$

$$g_{2,opt}(t) = \begin{cases} 0 & t < -\frac{1}{6} \\ 1.016(e^{-t} - 0.435e^{-6t}) & t > -\frac{1}{6} \end{cases} \tag{8.59}$$

(4)   Physical realizability requires that $g_2(t)$ be zero for $t < 0$.   Hence,

$$g_2(t) = \begin{cases} 0 & t < 0 \\ 1.016(e^{-t} - 0.435e^{-6t}) & t > 0 \end{cases} \tag{8.60}$$

The waveforms of the various time functions are sketched in Fig. 8.12.
(5)   The corresponding $G_2(s)$ is found by transformation of Eq. (8.60):

$$G_2(s) = 1.016\left(\frac{1}{s+1} - \frac{0.435}{s+6}\right) \tag{8.61}$$

$$G_2(s) = 5.65\frac{0.1015s + 1}{(s+1)(s+6)} \tag{8.62}$$

(6)   The over-all transfer function for the optimum physically realizable predictor is the product of $G_1(s)$ and $G_2(s)$, or

$$G(s) = 0.942(1 + 0.1015s) \tag{8.63}$$

The optimum prediction is a combination of simple gain and differentiation.
(7)   The mean-square error of prediction is evaluated from Eq. (8.53) and $g_{ss}(t)$ as given by (8.56).   Both integrals take the form

$$\int g_{ss}^2(t)\, dt = \tfrac{36}{25} \int (e^{-2t} - 2e^{-7t} + e^{-12t})\, dt = -\frac{3}{7}\frac{42e^{-2t} - 24e^{-7t} + 7e^{-12t}}{25} \tag{8.64}$$

Substitution of appropriate limits yields

$$\frac{\overline{e^2}}{\overline{f_d^2}} \cong 0.05 \qquad (8.65)$$

[The mean-square error is not the difference between the mean-square values of the input (or desired output) and the actual output because of the crosscorrelation between desired output and actual output.]

The small prediction error is indicated by inspection of Fig. 8.12. The difference between $g_2(t)$ and $g_{2,opt}(t)$ is slight; in other words, the principal part of $g_{ss}(t)$ occurs after $t = \frac{1}{6}$, the desired prediction time. The significance of the low value of the ratio $\overline{e^2}/\overline{f_d^2}$ is clarified if the random nature of the time functions is considered. If the ratio is 0.05, as above, the mean-square value of $e(t)$ is 5 per cent of the mean-square value of the input or desired output. A knowledge of the distributions of the signal and error permits evaluation of the percentage of the time (or the probability) that the error exceeds any specified magnitude.

Noise Included with Input. If the input includes both signal and noise components, the design pro-

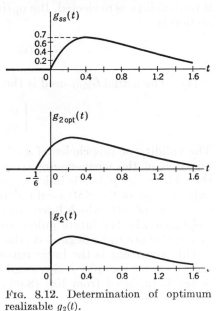

FIG. 8.12. Determination of optimum realizable $g_2(t)$.

cedure is modified slightly. Equation (8.29) states that the optimum system function without regard for physical realizability is

$$G_{opt}(s) = \frac{\Phi_{ss}(s)}{\Phi_{ii}(s)} G_d(s) \qquad (8.66)$$

where $\Phi_{ii}(s) = \Phi_{ss}(s) + \Phi_{nn}(s)$, the input power-density spectrum (under the assumption that the signal and noise are uncorrelated), and $G_d(s)$ describes the desired operation on the signal component of the input. $G_{opt}(s)$ does not satisfy the conditions for physical realizability, however, because $g_{opt}(t)$, the inverse transform, is not zero for $t < 0$.

This difficulty can be circumvented if the artifice suggested by Bode and Shannon is again introduced: *i.e.*, the input is first converted to white noise, which is then considered as a sequence of statistically independent, short-duration pulses. The complete design involves the following steps:

(1) $\Phi_{ii}(s)$ is factored:

$$\Phi_{ii}(s) = \Phi_{ii}^+(s)\Phi_{ii}^-(s) \qquad (8.67)$$

Again, $\Phi_{ii}^+(s)$ contains all critical frequencies in the left-half plane.

(2)   The input is passed through a system with the transfer function

$$G_1(s) = \frac{1}{\Phi_{ii}^{+}(s)} \tag{8.68}$$

The output $m(t)$ has a power-density spectrum of unity and can be considered as the sequence of pulses.

(3)   Since $1/\Phi_{ii}^{+}(s)$ is already instrumented, Eq. (8.66) indicates that, if realizability is neglected, the optimum transfer function for the second section is

$$G_{2,opt}(s) = \frac{\Phi_{ss}(s)}{\Phi_{ii}^{-}(s)} G_d(s) \tag{8.69}$$

(4)   The actual $G_2(s)$ used is the "realizable part" of $G_{2,opt}(s)$; that is,

$$g_2(t) = \begin{cases} 0 & t < 0 \\ g_{2,opt}(t) & t > 0 \end{cases} \tag{8.70}$$

The validity of this choice of $g_2(t)$ follows from the fact that, for minimization of the mean-square error, the optimum operation on each of the white-noise pulses is independent of the other pulses.[†]   This is true only because of the statistical independence of the pulses.   Accordingly, the pulses of $m(t)$ which have already occurred must be given the *same* weighting whether future pulses are to be considered (the nonrealizable system) or are to be neglected (the realizable system).

This argument is the basic reason for converting the signal to white noise before the physical-realizability conditions are introduced.   If design is initiated from Eq. (8.66), the first inclination is to use a $g(t)$ given by the equation

$$g(t) = \begin{cases} 0 & t < 0 \\ g_{opt}(t) & t > 0 \end{cases} \tag{8.71}$$

The incorrectness of this equation arises from the fact that when the network is designed to operate on the actual input, which possesses an autocorrelation function other than zero for $\tau \neq 0$, future values of the input are in part determined by the present and past values.   The proper operation on these present values depends on the weighting given to future values.

The procedure is illustrated by the design of a system for prediction in the presence of noise:

$$\Phi_{ss}(s) = \frac{36}{(s^2 - 1)(s^2 - 36)}$$
$$\Phi_{nn}(s) = 0.5 \tag{8.72}$$
$$G_d(s) = e^{0.1s}$$

[†] *Cf.* H. W. Bode and C. E. Shannon, A Simplified Derivation of Linear Least Square Smoothing and Prediction Theory, *Proc. IRE*, Vol. 38, pp. 423–424, April, 1950.

The design is carried out in the following steps:

(1) $\Phi_{ii}(s)$ is formed:

$$\Phi_{ii}(s) = \frac{36}{(s^2 - 1)(s^2 - 36)} + 0.5$$

$$= \frac{(s - 1.79)(s + 1.79)(s - 5.82)(s + 5.82)}{2(s - 1)(s + 1)(s - 6)(s + 6)} \tag{8.73}$$

(2) $\Phi_{ii}(s)$ is factored:

$$\Phi_{ii}^{+}(s) = \frac{1}{\sqrt{2}} \frac{(s + 1.79)(s + 5.82)}{(s + 1)(s + 6)} \tag{8.74}$$

(3)   The input is converted to white noise by passage through a network with the transfer function

$$G_1(s) = \sqrt{2} \frac{(s + 1)(s + 6)}{(s + 1.79)(s + 5.82)} \tag{8.75}$$

(4)   The optimum $G_2(s)$ without regard to realizability is given by Eq. (8.69):

$$G_{2,opt}(s) = \frac{36\sqrt{2}}{(s + 1)(s + 6)(s - 1.79)(s - 5.82)} e^{0.1s} \tag{8.76}$$

The impulse response $g_{2,opt}(t)$ is not realizable because of the right-half-plane poles of $G_{2,opt}(s)$ and because of the lead indicated by the factor $e^{0.1s}$ in Eq. (8.76).   The mean-square error is minimized if $g_2(t)$ is made equal to $g_{2,opt}(t)$ for t positive.

(5) $g_{2,opt}(t)$ for $t > 0$ is determined by the inverse transformation of $G_{2,opt}(s)$.   For the first term of Eq. (8.76), the residues are

$$k_{-1} = \frac{36\sqrt{2}}{(5)(2.79)(6.82)} = 0.536$$

$$k_{-6} = -\frac{36\sqrt{2}}{(5)(7.79)(11.82)} = -0.111 \tag{8.77}$$

Hence,

$$g_2(t) = \begin{cases} 0 & t < 0 \\ 0.536e^{-(t+0.1)} - 0.111e^{-6(t+0.1)} & t > 0 \end{cases} \tag{8.78}$$

(6)   Direct transformation of Eq. (8.78) gives

$$G_2(s) = \frac{0.485}{s + 1} - \frac{0.0607}{s + 6} = 0.424 \frac{s + 6.72}{(s + 1)(s + 6)} \tag{8.79}$$

(7)   The optimum over-all system function is the product of $G_1(s)$ [Eq. (8.75)] and $G_2(s)$:

$$G(s) = 0.60 \frac{s + 6.72}{(s + 1.79)(s + 5.82)} \tag{8.80}$$

Discussion.   Bode and Shannon discuss at some length the significance of the assumptions underlying the design described in this section.   The three basic assumptions are:

(1)   The mean-square error is the significant error measure.
(2)   Both signal and noise are stationary time series.
(3)   A linear system is desired.

The first assumption has been considered briefly in Sec. 7.2 and is discussed again in Sec. 8.7.

The validity of the assumption that the time series are stationary can in many cases be determined by the experimental measurements of the statistics of the input signal and noise.   The primary difficulty with this assumption arises because economic factors all too frequently limit severely the quantity of available samples of input signal and noise. Further difficulty is experienced in problems (*e.g.*, certain fire-control problems) in which it is known that the time series are not exactly stationary.   In such cases, what significance can be attached to a design based on average statistical characteristics?   The discussion of Sec. 8.8 considers briefly some of the work which has been done in the design of systems with nonstationary inputs.

The final assumption of linearity certainly does not result in the optimum system except in the very special case in which both signal and noise are characterized by Gaussian distributions.   Section 8.7 surveys certain aspects of the design of nonlinear systems.

8.3. Minimization with One Variable Parameter.   The preceding section presents the basic elements of the statistical design theory as presented by Wiener.   Attempts to apply this philosophy to the design of feedback control systems encounter certain difficulties.   For example, the first problem the designer faces is usually the lack of sufficient information concerning both signals and noise.   In many situations, it is difficult to obtain adequate samples of the noise-free signal.   Even if adequate information is available and the correlation functions of signal and noise are known, the designer must decide whether the mean-square-error criterion is logical for the particular problem and whether a linear system offers the possibility of a satisfactory solution to the design problem.   In practice, of course, the design of any complex system is never carried out in terms of a single method.   The ultimate system is the result of a theoretical study of performance characteristics from several different viewpoints, as well as an experimental evaluation and adjustment.   The principal advantage of the statistical design lies in the different basis presented for evaluating system performance.

Thus, in the design of many feedback control systems, it is desirable to consider the straightforward optimization described in the preceding section.   The resulting transfer function represents the optimum performance of the over-all, closed-loop system.   Actual realization of the optimum realizable transfer function can be carried out with Guillemin's procedure as described in Chap. 5.   If the configuration of Fig. 8.13 is desired, for example, the optimization procedure yields the required $\frac{C}{R}$ (s).

The forward transfer function $\frac{C}{E}$ (s) is determined as indicated in Sec. 5.3,

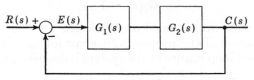

FIG. 8.13. Closed-loop system.

and, if $G_2(s)$ is specified, the compensation transfer function $G_1(s)$ is given by the equation

$$G_1(s) = \frac{C}{E} (s) \frac{1}{G_2(s)} \tag{8.81}$$

Certain modifications are required in the procedure under the following circumstances:

(1) If a delay is permitted in the optimization, $\frac{C}{R}$ (s) may contain a factor of the form e^{-Ts}. Realization of the optimum transfer function with the use of lumped elements only (R, L, and C in electric systems) then requires the approximation of e^{-Ts} by a rational algebraic function of s. A few approximations are listed in Sec. 9.8.

(2) The $G_1(s)$ given by Eq. (8.81) may possess more finite zeros than poles; i.e., the degree of the numerator may exceed that of the denominator. Since poles can be added with break frequencies well above the system cutoff frequency, $G_1(j\omega)$ may be realized within any desired accuracy over the frequency band of interest.

The straightforward optimization procedure is most useful for evaluating systems designed by more conventional methods. The value of the minimum mean-square error serves as a basis for the quantitative measure of system quality.

The difficulty associated with realizing the optimum transfer function suggests the possibility of constraining the form of the system function at the outset. A very simple example is illustrated in Fig.

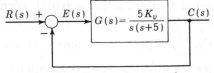

FIG. 8.14. System for example.

8.14. At the very beginning of the design, the form of the forward transfer function is fixed as

$$\frac{C}{E} (s) = \frac{5K_v}{s(s + 5)} \tag{8.82}$$

The K_v is to be selected to minimize the mean-square error with the input described by the relations

Power-density spectrum of derivative of signal component of input
$$\Phi_{s's'}(s) = \frac{-1000}{s^2 - 0.01}$$

Power-density spectrum of noise component of input
$$\Phi_{nn}(s) = 1$$

$$G_d(s) = 1 \qquad\qquad (8.83)\dagger$$

The signal and noise are assumed uncorrelated.

The determination of the mean-square error follows directly from Eq. (8.7). The closed-loop nature of the system is described by the equations

$$\frac{E}{R}(s) = \frac{1}{1 + \dfrac{C}{E}(s)} = \frac{s(s+5)}{s^2 + 5s + 5K_v} \qquad (8.84)$$

$$\frac{C}{R}(s) = \frac{\dfrac{C}{E}(s)}{1 + \dfrac{C}{E}(s)} = \frac{5K_v}{s^2 + 5s + 5K_v} \qquad (8.85)$$

The noise error is $c_n(t)$, the output resulting from the noise input; the signal error is $e_s(t)$, the actuating signal when the signal component only is applied as the input. Hence, the total mean-square error is

$$\overline{e^2} = \frac{1}{2\pi} \int_{-\infty}^{\infty} \left[\underbrace{\left| \frac{C}{R}(j\omega) \right|^2 \Phi_{nn}(j\omega)}_{\text{Noise error}} + \underbrace{\left| \frac{1}{j\omega} \frac{E}{R}(j\omega) \right|^2 \Phi_{s's'}(j\omega)}_{\text{Signal error}} \right] d\omega \qquad (8.86)$$

Since $\Phi_{s's'}(j\omega)$ is the spectrum for the derivative of the input, the appropriate transfer function in Eq. (8.86) is $\dfrac{1}{j\omega} \dfrac{E}{R}(j\omega)$, rather than $\dfrac{E}{R}(j\omega)$. In general, differentiation of the time function corresponds to multiplication of the power-density spectrum by $(j\omega)(-j\omega) = \omega^2$, or $-s^2$; integration is represented by multiplication of the spectrum function by $1/\omega^2$, or $-1/s^2$. In this example, however, this relation yields a $\Phi_{ss}(j\omega)$ equal to $1000/[\omega^2(\omega^2 + 0.01)]$, corresponding to an unbounded average power. If the signal error is written as in Eq. (8.86), the requirement that $\dfrac{E}{R}(j\omega)$ possess a zero at the origin is apparent. If $\dfrac{E}{R}(j\omega)$ does not possess this zero, the mean-square error is infinite and the minimization

† This particular example is taken from "Theory of Servomechanisms" by H. M. James, N. B. Nichols, and R. S. Phillips, MIT Radiation Laboratory Series, Vol. 25, pp. 340–345, McGraw-Hill Book Company, Inc., New York, 1947. In the reference, the problem is described in more general terms; in the discussion here, a specific value of the time constant ($\frac{1}{5}$ sec) is used for $\dfrac{C}{E}(s)$ in order to simplify the presentation.

$\Phi_{s's'}(s)$ corresponds to a simple rational algebraic approximation of the actual power-density spectrum for the *derivative* of the signal input of an automatic-tracking radar system for antiaircraft fire control with low-speed targets.

meaningless, even though the equations may yield an optimum system function.

Evaluation of the integral [Eq. (8.86)] yields the results

$$\text{Noise error} = \overline{c_n^2} = \frac{K_v}{2} \tag{8.87}$$

$$\text{Signal error} = \frac{1000}{K_v} \frac{25.5 + 0.1K_v}{5K_v + 0.51} \tag{8.88}$$

The value of K_v for a minimum mean-square error is found by differentiating the expression for $\overline{c_n^2} + \overline{e_s^2}$. The optimum K_v is approximately 27, with the corresponding mean-square errors

$$\overline{c_n^2} = 13.5 \qquad \overline{e_s^2} = 7.7$$
$$\overline{e_s^2} + \overline{c_n^2} = 21.2 \tag{8.89}$$

The characteristics of the system with K_v adjusted for minimum mean-square error can be observed from the closed-loop transfer function, which becomes

$$\frac{C}{R}(s) = \frac{135}{s^2 + 5s + 135} \tag{8.90}$$

The second-order system is described by

$$\omega_n = 11.62$$
$$\zeta = 0.215 \tag{8.91}$$

The step-function response exhibits an overshoot of 50 per cent (cf. Fig. 1.18) and relatively poor settling time. The conventional design criteria indicate that the relative stability of the system is unsatisfactory.

The oscillatory nature of the system response is a consequence of the use of the mean-square-error criterion, with the attendant heavy weighting of the large errors. The great importance of the large error just after the application of a step function results in a very rapid response and the accompanying large overshoot. The relatively small value of the noise power-density spectrum permits this low ζ. The mean-square error, given by the sum of Eqs. (8.87) and (8.88), can be expressed approximately by the relation

$$\overline{c_n^2} + \overline{e_s^2} \cong \frac{K_v}{2} + \frac{5100}{K_v^2} \tag{8.92}$$

The minimum of this expression occurs for a K_v such that the noise error is twice the signal error. Accordingly, the larger the value of noise input power, the smaller the K_v. Specifically, K_v is proportional to $A^{-\frac{1}{3}}$, where A is a multiplying factor of $\Phi_{nn}(s)$. With the low noise level of the above example, a pronounced peak is permissible in the gain-frequency characteristic of the closed-loop system.

The poor relative stability of the optimum system indicates the difficulty to be anticipated when minimization of the mean-square error is used as a criterion for adjustment of system parameters. Aside from the intuitive disadvantages associated with such poor relative stability, there are two additional disadvantages in many servo applications:

(1) Commonly, the system is used in applications where transient performance is of importance. Although the quality of the system depends primarily on the response to a random input, the system is also required to settle down in a reasonable time interval after sudden application of an aperiodic signal. For example, in the design of a fire-control system emphasis is placed on tracking performance, but the effect of the initial transient (which may include a large step function if the gun is initially far from the selected target) must have died out by the time the target is within firing range.

(2) A system designed with poor relative stability is undesirably sensitive to changes in system parameters. In the above example, a 20 per cent decrease in the ζ (from 0.215 to 0.172) with no change in ω_n results in an increase in the overshoot from 50 to almost 60 per cent. The nearer the closed-loop poles to the $j\omega$ axis, the more troublesome are the effects of parameter changes.

Fortunately, the mean-square error is not particularly sensitive to changes in K_v. A K_v of 15 corresponds to a mean-square error of about 30, and the ζ is increased from 0.215 to 0.288. Thus, an increase in the *root*-mean-square error of only 20 per cent decreases the overshoot from 50 to 40 per cent. In more complex systems, it is not uncommon to find the mean-square error even less sensitive to changes in overshoot or relative stability.

It is of interest to conclude this example by comparing the system designed above with the absolutely optimum system. If a long delay is permitted, the minimum error is given by Eq. (8.30):

$$\overline{e^2_{\min opt}} = \frac{1}{2\pi} \int_{-\infty}^{\infty} \frac{\Phi_{ss}\Phi_{nn}}{\Phi_{ss} + \Phi_{nn}} \, d\omega \tag{8.93}$$

Substitution of the values for the power-density spectra [Eq. (8.83)]† yields

$$\overline{e^2_{\min opt}} = 2 \tag{8.94}$$

Thus, the mean-square error of the system realized by optimizing K_v is considerably greater than the absolute optimum without regard to realizability (or delay). The lag required in the realization of the error of Eq. (8.94) is not tolerable in many servo applications.

A fairer evaluation is based on comparison of the mean-square error resulting from optimization of K_v with the minimum mean-square error for a physically realizable system without lag. On the basis of the methods described in Sec. 8.2, the optimum realizable transfer function can be shown to be

$$\frac{C}{R}(s) = 7.9 \frac{s + 4}{s^2 + 7.99s + 31.6} \tag{8.95}$$

The corresponding mean-square error is 6.8. If the rms errors are compared, the system resulting from optimization of K_v yields an error 78

† It can be shown that correct results are obtained if Eq. (8.93) is used with Φ_{ss} replaced by $\Phi_{s's'}/\omega^2$.

per cent greater than the optimum realizable system without delay. The large error associated with the $\dfrac{C}{R}$ (s) of Eq. (8.90) is a result of the sharp cutoff in the vicinity of 12 rad/sec. Although the signal power-density spectrum exceeds the noise spectrum at all frequencies below 31.6 rad/sec, the $\dfrac{C}{R}$ (s) of Eq. (8.90) cannot have a bandwidth approaching 30 rad/sec or a gradual cutoff because the factor 5 in the denominator is fixed. If ω_n^2 (now 135) is increased, the ζ of the transfer function becomes undesirably small. Thus, the mean-square error resulting from optimization of K_v could be decreased if the time constant of the open-loop system were decreased.

8.4. Optimum System Described in Time Domain. The discussion of Sec. 8.2 described the determination of $G(s)$ to minimize the mean-square error. In that section, the minimization is carried through in terms of the frequency-domain functions: the mean-square error is expressed in terms of $G(j\omega)$, $G_d(j\omega)$, and the various power-density spectra. After the optimum $G(j\omega)$ without regard to physical realizability is determined by inspection of the error expression, the condition of realizability is imposed by introduction of the Bode-Shannon technique involving conversion of the input signal to white noise before the optimum realizable network is determined.

The same results can be obtained with little additional effort by working in terms of the autocorrelation functions and the network impulse response $g(t)$. This "time-domain" approach is presented in this section. The apparent redundancy of this derivation and that of Sec. 8.2 is justifiable on at least three grounds:

(1) A large percentage of the applications described in current journals are based upon such a time-domain optimization.

(2) As indicated in the following two sections, several modifications of the basic optimization are more readily formulated in terms of the time-domain analysis.

(3) The time-domain operation can be simplified in terms of impulse-train approximations for the various autocorrelation functions.†

Minimization of the Mean-square Error. The expression for the mean-square error is given in terms of the autocorrelation functions and impulse responses by Eq. (8.1), repeated here:

$$\overline{e^2} = \int_{-\infty}^{\infty} g(\tau) \, d\tau \int_{-\infty}^{\infty} g(\sigma) \, d\sigma \; \phi_{ii}(\tau - \sigma) - 2 \int_{-\infty}^{\infty} g(\tau) \, d\tau \; \phi_{id}(\tau) + \phi_{dd}(0)$$

$$(8.96)$$

---

† The analysis, similar to that of Sec. 1.6, is described in detail in the reference by N. Levinson, The Wiener RMS (root-mean-square) Error Criterion in Filter Design and Prediction, Appendix B of N. Wiener, "The Extrapolation, Interpolation, and Smoothing of Stationary Time Series," pp. 129–148, The Technology Press, Cambridge, Mass., and John Wiley & Sons, Inc., New York, 1949. Essentially the same material with an illustrative example is presented by F. W. Bubb, "Linear Noise Smoothing and Predicting Filters," *Air Force Tech. Rept.* 6586, WADC, May, 1951.

Equation (8.96) is to be used to determine that $g(t)$ satisfying physical-realizability conditions ($g = 0$ for t negative) and at the same time minimizing the value of $\overline{e^2}$.

The general procedure for considering problems of this type is described in detail in texts on advanced calculus† or the calculus of variations. If $g(t)$ is an optimum, $\overline{e^2}$ must increase when $g(t)$ is replaced by $g(t) + \epsilon\eta(t)$, where ϵ is a parameter and $\eta(t)$ is an arbitrary function of the form of $g(t)$.‡ After substitution of $g(t) + \epsilon\eta(t)$, $\overline{e^2} + \Delta\overline{e^2}$ is evaluated, where $\Delta\overline{e^2}$ is the change in $\overline{e^2}$. A necessary condition that $\overline{e^2}$ have an extremum for the assumed $g(t)$ is that $\Delta\overline{e^2}$ must have an extremum (as a function of ϵ) when $\epsilon = 0$: that is,

$$\left[\frac{\partial(\Delta\overline{e^2})}{\partial\epsilon}\right]_{\epsilon=0} = 0 \tag{8.97}$$

Whether this extremum is a minimum or maximum can be determined from the sign of the second derivative of $\Delta\overline{e^2}$ with respect to ϵ when $\epsilon = 0$ (a positive sign indicating a minimum).§

Thus, the determination of $g(t)$ from Eq. (8.96) is initiated by replacing $g(t)$ by $g(t) + \epsilon\eta(t)$:

$$\overline{e^2} + \Delta\overline{e^2} = \int_{-\infty}^{\infty} [g(\tau) + \epsilon\eta(\tau)]\,d\tau \int_{-\infty}^{\infty} [g(\sigma) + \epsilon\eta(\sigma)]\,d\sigma\,\phi_{ii}(\tau - \sigma)$$
$$- 2\int_{-\infty}^{\infty} [g(\tau) + \epsilon\eta(\tau)]\,d\tau\,\phi_{id}(\tau) + \phi_{dd}(0) \tag{8.98}$$

Expansion yields

$$\overline{e^2} + \Delta\overline{e^2} = \int_{-\infty}^{\infty} g(\tau)\,d\tau \int_{-\infty}^{\infty} g(\sigma)\,d\sigma\,\phi_{ii}(\tau - \sigma)$$
$$+ \epsilon\left[\int_{-\infty}^{\infty} \eta(\tau)\,d\tau \int_{-\infty}^{\infty} g(\sigma)\,d\sigma\,\phi_{ii}(\tau - \sigma)\right]$$
$$+ \epsilon\left[\int_{-\infty}^{\infty} g(\tau)\,d\tau \int_{-\infty}^{\infty} \eta(\sigma)\,d\sigma\,\phi_{ii}(\tau - \sigma)\right]$$
$$+ \epsilon^2\int_{-\infty}^{\infty} \eta(\tau)\,d\tau \int_{-\infty}^{\infty} \eta(\sigma)\,d\sigma\,\phi_{ii}(\tau - \sigma) - 2\int_{-\infty}^{\infty} g(\tau)\,d\tau\,\phi_{id}(\tau)$$
$$- 2\epsilon\int_{-\infty}^{\infty} \eta(\tau)\,d\tau\,\phi_{id}(\tau) + \phi_{dd}(0) \tag{8.99}$$

The terms shown in brackets are essentially the same except for an interchange of the order of integration (since the autocorrelation function is even). Hence, inspection of Eq. (8.96) demonstrates that (8.99) can be

† For example, cf. R. Courant, "Differential and Integral Calculus," Vol. II, pp. 491–497, Blackie & Son, Ltd., Glasgow, 1936.

‡ Specifically, $\eta(t)$ is zero for t negative, $\eta(0)$ and $\eta(\infty)$ are zero, and $\eta(t)$ possesses continuous first and second derivatives from zero to infinity. $\epsilon\eta(t)$ is termed the variation of the function $g(t)$.

§ Exactly the same variational technique can be used to determine the optimum $G(s)$ when $\overline{e^2}$ is written in terms of the frequency function, as in Sec. 8.2. $G(s)$ is replaced by $G(s) + \epsilon\,\delta G(s)$, where $\delta G(s)$ satisfies the realizability condition.

rewritten

$$\Delta \overline{e^2} = 2\epsilon \left[\int_{-\infty}^{\infty} \eta(\tau)\, d\tau \int_{-\infty}^{\infty} g(\sigma)\, d\sigma\, \phi_{ii}(\tau - \sigma) - \int_{-\infty}^{\infty} \eta(\tau)\, d\tau\, \phi_{id}(\tau) \right]$$
$$+ \epsilon^2 \int_{-\infty}^{\infty} \eta(\tau)\, d\tau \int_{-\infty}^{\infty} \eta(\sigma)\, d\sigma\, \phi_{ii}(\tau - \sigma) \quad (8.100)$$

Differentiation with respect to ϵ yields

$$\frac{\partial (\Delta \overline{e^2})}{\partial \epsilon} = 2 \int_{-\infty}^{\infty} \eta(\tau)\, d\tau \left[\int_{-\infty}^{\infty} g(\sigma)\, d\sigma\, \phi_{ii}(\tau - \sigma) - \phi_{id}(\tau) \right]$$
$$+ 2\epsilon \int_{-\infty}^{\infty} \eta(\tau)\, d\tau \int_{-\infty}^{\infty} \eta(\sigma)\, d\sigma\, \phi_{ii}(\tau - \sigma) \quad (8.101)$$

With $\epsilon = 0$, the second term above drops out, and Eq. (8.97) gives

$$2 \int_{-\infty}^{\infty} \eta(\tau)\, d\tau \left[\int_{-\infty}^{\infty} g(\sigma)\, d\sigma\, \phi_{ii}(\tau - \sigma) - \phi_{id}(\tau) \right] = 0 \quad (8.102)$$

This relation must be satisfied for any $\eta(\tau)$. Since $\eta(\tau)$ is identically zero for τ negative, the bracketed term need be zero only for $\tau > 0$. Hence, the $g(t)$ for minimum mean-square error is given by the equation

$$\int_{-\infty}^{\infty} g(\sigma)\, d\sigma\, \phi_{ii}(\tau - \sigma) - \phi_{id}(\tau) = 0 \qquad \text{for } \tau > 0 \quad (8.103)^{*}\dagger$$

Equation (8.103) is a basic relation in the design of optimum linear filters on a mean-square-error basis. Although the four or five equations used as intermediate steps in the derivation are lengthy, the analysis is straightforward throughout. It should be noted that Eq. (8.103) is general in the sense that no assumption has been made that the signal and noise are uncorrelated.

Solution of the Integral Equation for $g(t)$. Equation (8.103) is an integral equation for the optimum impulse response $g(t)$. The solution, as indicated by Wiener, is initiated by the Laplace transformation of the expression

$$\left[\int_{-\infty}^{\infty} g(\sigma)\, d\sigma\, \phi_{ii}(\tau - \sigma) \right] - [\phi_{id}(\tau)]$$

The first term in brackets is the convolution integral yielding the output of the network when excited by $\phi_{ii}(\tau)$, the autocorrelation function of the

---

† Strictly, the sufficiency of this condition for a minimum must be established; the above derivation proves only the *necessity*. The sufficiency can be shown if (8.103) is substituted back in (8.100) to yield

$$\Delta \overline{e^2} = \epsilon^2 \int_{-\infty}^{\infty} \eta(\tau)\, d\tau \int_{-\infty}^{\infty} \eta(\sigma)\, d\sigma\, \phi_{ii}(\tau - \sigma)$$

If $\phi_{ii}(\tau - \sigma)$ is replaced by the definition in terms of $f_i(t)$ (the actual input for the design problem), the expression on the right side above is equal to the zero-argument value of the autocorrelation function of the output of the network with an impulse response $\epsilon \eta(t)$ and an input equal to $f_i(t)$. Thus, $\Delta \overline{e^2}$, the variation of $\overline{e^2}$, is positive, and $\overline{e^2} + \Delta \overline{e^2}$ approaches a minimum as ϵ approaches zero.

input; the second term in brackets is the crosscorrelation function between input and desired output. If the transform of the entire expression is denoted $A(s)$,

$$A(s) = G(s)\Phi_{ii}(s) - \Phi_{id}(s) \qquad (8.104)$$

Equation (8.103) states that $a(\tau)$ must be zero for τ positive; in other words, $A(s)$ must be analytic (or have no poles, in the usual case) in the left-half plane. This fact alone suffices to determine $G(s)$.†

If $\Phi_{ii}(s)$ is factored in the usual way, $A(s)$ can be written

$$A(s) = \Phi_{ii}^-(s) \left[G(s)\Phi_{ii}^+(s) - \frac{\Phi_{id}(s)}{\Phi_{ii}^-(s)} \right] \qquad (8.105)$$

where $\Phi_{ii}^+(s)$ includes all critical frequencies in the left-half plane. The function $A(s)/\Phi_{ii}^-(s)$ can have poles only in the right-half plane, since both the poles of $A(s)$ and the zeros of $\Phi_{ii}^-(s)$ are restricted to this region. Hence,

$$G(s)\Phi_{ii}^+(s) - \frac{\Phi_{id}(s)}{\Phi_{ii}^-(s)}$$

has no left-half-plane poles. But $G(s)\Phi_{ii}^+(s)$ contains poles in the left-half plane only [if $G(s)$ describes a realizable network]. Thus, in the partial-fraction expansion of $\Phi_{id}(s)/\Phi_{ii}^-(s)$, the terms representing left-half-plane poles must equal $G(s)\Phi_{ii}^+(s)$. $G(s)$ is then

$$G(s) = \frac{1}{\Phi_{ii}^+(s)} \left[\text{partial-fraction-expansion terms for} \right.$$
$$\left. \text{left-half-plane poles of } \frac{\Phi_{id}(s)}{\Phi_{ii}^-(s)} \right] \qquad (8.106)$$

If the inverse Laplace transform of $\Phi_{id}(s)/\Phi_{ii}^-(s)$ is denoted $g_{2,opt}(t)$, the bracketed term above is the transform of the time function which is zero for t negative and $g_{2,opt}(t)$ for t positive:

$$G(s) = \frac{1}{\Phi_{ii}^+(s)} \int_0^\infty g_{2,opt}(t)e^{-st}\, dt \qquad (8.107)\star$$

Equation (8.107) is identical with the result derived in Sec. 8.2 [Eqs. (8.66) to (8.70)]. The first term, $1/\Phi_{ii}^+(s)$, represents the part of the network converting the input to white noise. The second factor, $\int_0^\infty g_{2,opt}(t)e^{-st}\, dt$, is the physically realizable part of the impulse response $g_{2,opt}(t)$, which is the inverse transform of $\Phi_{id}(s)/\Phi_{ii}^-(s)$. If signal and noise are uncorrelated, the discussion of Sec. 7.10 indicates that

$$\Phi_{id}(s) = G_d(s)\Phi_{ss}(s) \qquad (8.108)$$

Thus, in this case, $g_{2,opt}(t)$ is the inverse transform of $\Phi_{ss}(s)G_d(s)/\Phi_{ii}^-(s)$, as given in Eq. (8.69).

† Note that $\int_{-\infty}^\infty g(\sigma)\, d\sigma\; \phi_{ii}(\tau - \sigma) - \phi_{id}(\tau)$ need not be zero for τ negative; hence $A(s)$ is not zero, but may have poles in the right-half plane.

8.5. Modifications of Minimization Procedure for Certain Servo Problems. Attempts to apply the statistical theory to the design of feedback control systems generate objections immediately because of the difficulty of phrasing the optimization in practical terms. In many problems minimization of the mean-square error is not an adequate design criterion. For example, a basic servo-design problem may include only two specifications: the characteristics of the controlled system (motor, gear train, and load) and the statistics of the input signal. If no noise is present, the optimum over-all system function is unity; the optimum physically realizable tandem compensation network is one with essentially infinite gain over the frequency band of interest. The addition of noise results in an optimum system function $\frac{C}{R}(s)$ which differs from unity, but no consideration is given to the closed-loop nature of the system or the characteristics of the fixed components. If the mean-square value of the noise is small, the optimum system exhibits nearly perfect following; the compensation is designed to extend the bandwidth of the fixed components, and the possibility of motor saturation, power saturation, etc., is not involved.

If statistical methods are to be useful in the design of feedback control systems, it is clear that it is not sufficient to consider only the filtering or smoothing problem. It must be possible to determine the optimum system function, not in the class of all physically realizable system functions, but rather in the class of all *practical* functions. Such an optimization requires an explicit definition of the term "practical functions."

The approach described in Sec. 8.3, where the form of the transfer function is selected at the outset and the optimum values of one or more parameters are determined, is one method of introducing the constraint of practicality. Such an approach comes very close, however, to discarding completely the statistical methods. The question naturally arises: Is there no intermediate approach, representing an acceptance of reality, but still leading to an optimum form for the system function? The problem of introducing reality into the analytical statement of the problem has been treated in several ways:

(1) The technique used in Guillemin's procedure (Chap. 5) can be adopted. The allowable behavior of the closed-loop system function as $s \to \infty$ is determined from the transfer function of the controlled system.[†] In spite of this restriction, however, the absence of noise results in an optimum $\frac{C}{R}(s)$ which represents a bandwidth very much larger than the frequency band of significance for the signal. The optimum system is still in many cases idealistic and unrealizable because of high amplifier gain, high motor rating, etc.

(2) Newton[‡] has suggested controlling the rms value of the signal at various

[†] M. J. Pelegrin, A Statistical Approach to Servomechanisms and Regulators, *ASME Paper* 53-A-20, Frequency Response Symposium, December 1-2, 1953.

[‡] G. C. Newton, Jr., Compensation of Feedback Control Systems subject to Saturation, *J. Franklin Inst.*, Vol. 254, pp. 281–296, October, 1952, and pp. 391–413, November, 1952.

points throughout the system. The basic characteristics of Newton's approach are described briefly in the next section.

(3) A special case of Newton's general theory involves a convenient constraint based on the power rating of the output motor. In other words, the average power dissipated by the output motor and load is limited to a specified value. The optimum system is that one which minimizes the mean-square error while simultaneously requiring only the specified average power.

If either the probability of saturation or the average power is limited, the optimum system represents a compromise and in general is no longer described by a $\frac{C}{R}(s)$ of unity, even if no noise is present.

There are a number of other problems in which it is desirable to introduce constraints limiting system performance characteristics. For example, if the system must be designed to handle not only random inputs but also polynomial functions of time, it is desirable to specify certain of the generalized error coefficients.[†] In other cases, certain characteristics of the response to particular aperiodic signals must be controlled.

All these considerations fall into the general category of constraints on the optimum transfer function $G(s)$. The variation $\epsilon\,\delta G(s)$ cannot be arbitrarily selected but must satisfy the constraints. In the usual case of interest here, the mean-square error is given by a complex integral involving $G(s)$ or a real, definite integral involving $g(t)$. If the constraints can be phrased in terms of the requirement that integrals of the same form assume a specified value, the minimization can be considered using Lagrange multipliers.[‡]

Basic Method. A simple example[§] illustrates the basic method of introducing constraints. The block diagram of the system is shown in Fig. 8.15(a). The controlled system includes an armature-controlled motor, gear train, and load, with the equivalent electric circuit shown in Fig. 8.15(b), where R represents the viscous damping of motor and load referred to the motor shaft, r_a the armature resistance, and C the inertia of motor rotor, gears, and reflected load. Armature inductance is assumed negligible. In the equivalent circuit, the voltage e_b, representing the back emf, is proportional to the output velocity, with the constant K_e including the gear ratio from motor shaft to load. The problem is described by the following specifications:

Parameters in the equivalent circuit:

$$R = 250 \text{ ohms} \qquad C = \tfrac{1}{250} \text{ farad}$$
$$r_a = 100 \text{ ohms} \qquad K_e = 1000 \text{ volts}/(\text{rad/sec}) \tag{8.109}$$

† L. A. Zadeh, and J. R. Ragazzini, An Extension of Wiener's Theory of Prediction, *J. Appl. Phys.*, Vol. 21, pp. 645–655, July, 1950.

‡ F. B. Hildebrand, "Methods of Applied Mathematics," pp. 141–144, Prentice-Hall, Inc., New York, 1952. Chapter II of this text contains a readable exposition of the basic methods of the calculus of variations. Emphasis is directed toward engineering applications. A specific description of the admissible classes of constraints is included.

§ J. H. Westcott, Synthesis of Optimum Feedback Systems Satisfying a Power Limitation, *ASME Paper* 53-A-17, Frequency Response Symposium, December 1–2, 1953.

with the result

$$G(s) = \frac{C(s)}{M(s)} = \frac{1}{400s(s + 3.5)} \tag{8.110}$$

Input: $r(t)$ contains signal, but no noise. The power-density spectrum of the input velocity is

$$\Phi_{r'r'}(s) = \frac{-0.08}{16s^2 - 1} \tag{8.111}$$

The average power P drawn by the motor (*i.e.*, power dissipation in r_a and R) is to be less than 150 watts.

The problem can be divided conveniently into two parts. In the first stage, an equivalent tandem open-loop system is considered, as drawn in

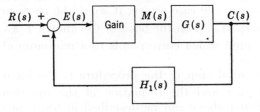

(*a*). System Block Diagram

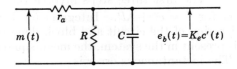

(*b*) Equivalent Circuit of Armature-controlled Motor

$$R(s) \quad \boxed{T(s)} \quad M(s) \quad \boxed{G(s)} \quad C(s)$$

(*c*) Equivalent System for Analysis

FIG. 8.15. Example.

Fig. 8.15(*c*). The optimum $T(s)$ is determined to minimize $\overline{e^2}$, the mean-square error, under the condition that the average power should not exceed 150 watts. Once $T(s)$ is known, the second part of the design involves determination of an appropriate $H_1(s)$ [Fig. 8.15(*a*)]. Since this part is a straightforward problem in closed-loop design as described in Chap. 5, it is not considered here.

Evaluation of the optimum $T(s)$ is effected in the following steps:

(1) The mean-square error $\overline{e^2}$ is written as a function of $T(s)$ and the known $\Phi_{r'r'}(s)$ and $G(s)$.

(2) The power P is derived in the form of a similar integral.

(3) A new function is formed:

$$I = \overline{e^2} + \lambda P \tag{8.112}$$

I is an integral involving $T(s)$.

(4)   That $T(s,\lambda)$ is determined which minimizes I. $T(s,\lambda)$ is written rather than $T(s)$ because it is a function of not only s, but also the Lagrange multiplier λ, as yet unknown.

(5) $P(\lambda)$ is evaluated from the equation for P in terms of $T(s)$, and λ is selected to correspond to a P of 150 watts.   (In the absence of noise, the maximum power clearly corresponds to a minimum mean-square error.)

(6)   With the value of λ known, the optimum $T(s)$ is also known and $\overline{e^2}$ can be evaluated.

The above six steps comprise a widely applicable method for the introduction of constraints.   In this particular example, the desired P is known from physical reasoning to be 150 watts.   In the more general case, a value of the constrained quantity less than the maximum (or greater than the minimum) allowed value may correspond to minimum mean-square error.   If such were the case above, it would be necessary to plot both P and $\overline{e^2}$ as functions of λ on the basis of the known $T(s,\lambda)$.   That value of λ is then selected which corresponds to a minimum $\overline{e^2}$ with P within the allowed range.†

Thus, the essential step in the procedure is the introduction of the Lagrange multiplier and the formation of the function $I = \overline{e^2} + \lambda P$. The six steps listed above can be described in terms of the example of Fig. 8.15, with the specifications listed previously.

Formulation of I.   The first three steps involve the derivation of the integral expression for $I = \overline{e^2} + \lambda P$.   Integrals for both $\overline{e^2}$ and P are written by consideration of the circuit and block diagram.

Since no noise is present in the system, the mean-square error is entirely following error.   The instantaneous error is

$$e(t) = r(t) - c(t) \tag{8.113}$$

The transfer function relating $c(t)$ to $r(t)$ is $T(s)G(s)$.   Hence, the error is related to the derivative of the input by the transfer function $[1 - T(s)G(s)]/s$.   Thus,

$$\overline{e^2} = \frac{1}{2\pi j} \int_{-j\infty}^{j\infty} \frac{1 - T(s)G(s)}{s} \frac{1 - T(-s)G(-s)}{-s} \Phi_{r'r'}(s) \, ds \tag{8.114}$$

The total power P is that dissipated in R and r_a.   The power dissipated in R is proportional to the mean-square value of output velocity, or

$$P_R = \frac{1}{R} \frac{1}{2\pi j} \int_{-j\infty}^{j\infty} K_e^2 \Phi_{c'c'}(s) \, ds \tag{8.115}$$

But $c'(t)$ is related to $r'(t)$ by the transfer function $T(s)G(s)$; the power-density spectra are related by the function $T(s)G(s)T(-s)G(-s)$:

$$P_R = \frac{K_e^2}{R} \frac{1}{2\pi j} \int_{-j\infty}^{j\infty} T(s)G(s)T(-s)G(-s)\Phi_{r'r'}(s) \, ds \tag{8.116}$$

† It is also necessary to establish the sufficiency of the condition for a minimum $\overline{e^2}$. In the above example, the sufficiency is obvious from physical reasoning, since the more power drawn, the better the following and the less the error.

Likewise, the armature dissipation can be expressed in terms of the power-density spectrum of the output velocity and the impedance of R and C in parallel:

$$P_{r_a} = r_a \frac{1}{2\pi j} \int_{-j\infty}^{j\infty} \frac{K_e^2 \Phi_{c'c'}(s)}{Z_{RC}(s)Z_{RC}(-s)} \, ds \tag{8.117}$$

Combination of Eqs. (8.116) and (8.117) and substitution of the parameter values of (8.109) yield

$$P = \frac{1600}{2\pi j} \int_{-j\infty}^{j\infty} (3.5 - s^2)T(s)G(s)T(-s)G(-s)\Phi_{r'r'}(s) \, ds \tag{8.118}$$

The function I is formed, and for simplicity $\bar{G}$ is written for $G(-s)$, G for $G(s)$, $\bar{T}$ for $T(-s)$, and T for $T(s)$:

$$I = \frac{1}{2\pi j} \int_{-j\infty}^{j\infty} \Phi_{r'r'}(s) \left[\frac{1 - TG}{s} \frac{1 - \bar{T}\bar{G}}{-s} + 1600\lambda(3.5 - s^2)T\bar{T}G\bar{G} \right] ds \tag{8.119}$$

Minimization. In order to determine that T yielding a minimum I, the variation $\epsilon \, \delta T$ is introduced by replacing T by $T + \epsilon \, \delta T$, $\bar{T}$ by $\bar{T} + \epsilon \, \overline{\delta T}$. Differentiation of the corresponding change in I with respect to ϵ, setting $\epsilon = 0$, and equating the derivative to zero correspond to equating to zero the coefficient of ϵ in the expression for $I + \Delta I$.

The solution is simplified if the equation is written by collecting separately all coefficients of δT and $\overline{\delta T}$:

$$\frac{1}{2\pi j} \int_{-j\infty}^{j\infty} \delta T \, F \, ds + \frac{1}{2\pi j} \int_{-j\infty}^{j\infty} \overline{\delta T} \, \bar{F} \, ds = 0 \tag{8.120}$$

where

$$F = \Phi_{r'r'}(s) \left[\frac{G - G\bar{G}\bar{T}}{s^2} + 1600\lambda(3.5 - s^2)G\bar{G}\bar{T} \right]$$

$F(s)$ and $F(-s)$, or $\bar{F}$, are complicated algebraic functions of $\Phi_{r'r'}(s)$, $G(s)$, and $T(s)$. An $F(s)$ must be found which satisfies Eq. (8.120) regardless of the function δT, as long as δT satisfies the physical-realizability conditions. In other words, the only thing known about δT is that the function has no poles in the right-half plane.

The value of each of the two integrals above can be made zero if two conditions are satisfied:

(1) The integrand $\delta T \, F$ and hence also $\overline{\delta T} \, \bar{F}$ approach zero at least as fast as $1/s^2$ as $s \to \infty$.

(2) F has no poles in the right-half plane.

If the former condition is met, the path of integration can be closed by a large semicircle in either half plane without changing the value of the integral. But if condition (2) is satisfied, the integrand $\delta T \, F$ has no poles in the right-half plane, and closing the path in this half plane must result in a zero value for the integral. Likewise, the second integral is zero since no poles are encircled if the path is closed in the left-half plane. Hence, Eq. (8.120) is satisfied if $F(s)$ *has no poles in the left-half plane.* This condition alone suffices to determine T.

The following discussion is simplified if $\bar{F}$ is considered. $\Phi_{r'r'}(s)$ is factored in the usual manner, with $\Phi_{r'r'}^{+}(s)$ including poles and zeros in the left-half plane and $\Phi_{r'r'}^{-}(s)$ the critical frequencies in the right-half plane. Clearly, $\bar{G}$ can be factored from the bracketed expression for $\bar{F}$, and both $\bar{G}$ and $\Phi_{r'r'}^{-}(s)$, containing right-half-plane poles only, can be neglected. The condition then becomes: $F_1(s)$ *has no left-half-plane poles,* where

$$F_1(s) = \Phi_{r'r'}^{+}(s) \left[\frac{-1 + GT}{(s)(-s)} + 1600\lambda(3.5 - s^2)GT \right] \quad (8.121)$$

The significance of this condition is clarified if the terms multiplying T are collected:

$$F_1(s) = \Phi_{r'r'}^{+}(s) \frac{1}{(s)(-s)} \{-1 + [1 - 1600\lambda s^2(3.5 - s^2)]GT\} \quad (8.122)$$

Left-half-plane poles of $F_1(s)$ might arise for three reasons:

(1) GT has poles in the left-half plane.

(2) The factor $1/s$ multiplying the braced expression in Eq. (8.122) must be considered a left-half-plane pole. (The factor $-s$ represents an admissible pole, since it is assumed in the right-half plane.)

(3) $\Phi_{r'r'}^{+}(s)$ has poles in the left-half plane.

There is only one $T(s)$ function which avoids poles from these three sources and also satisfies realizability conditions.

(1) If condition (1) above is not to result in left-half-plane poles for $F_1(s)$, any poles of GT in the left-half plane must be canceled by the zeros of $1 - 1600\lambda s^2(3.5 - s^2)$. Hence, the denominator of GT is selected as

$$1 + \sqrt{5600 + 80 \sqrt{\lambda}} \, s + 40 \sqrt{\lambda} \, s^2$$

(2) The factor $1/s$ is canceled if the braced expression in Eq. (8.122) has a zero at the origin. Hence GT must be unity at zero frequency.

(3) The braced expression must have left-half-plane zeros coinciding with the poles of $\Phi_{r'r'}^{+}(s)$, in this example at $s = -\frac{1}{4}$. Thus,

$$-1 + [1 - 1600\lambda s^2(3.5 - s^2)]GT = 0 \quad \text{when } s = -\tfrac{1}{4} \quad (8.123)$$

or
$$(GT)_{s=-\frac{1}{4}} = \frac{1}{1 - 344\lambda} \quad (8.124)$$

As a result of these restrictions, GT must have the form

$$GT = \frac{k_1 s + 1}{40 \sqrt{\lambda} \, s^2 + \sqrt{5600 + 80 \sqrt{\lambda}} \, s + 1} \quad (8.125)$$

where k_1 is chosen to satisfy Eq. (8.124). The numerator of GT is selected of first degree only in order that the mean-square error may be finite. The optimum $T(s)$ is found by substituting $G(s)$ from Eq. (8.110):

$$T(s,\lambda) = \frac{400s(s + 3.5)(k_1 s + 1)}{40 \sqrt{\lambda}\, s^2 + \sqrt{5600 + 80 \sqrt{\lambda}}\, s + 1} \qquad (8.126)$$

where k_1 is a known function of λ. This $T(s,\lambda)$ is the function which minimizes the quantity I.

Evaluation of the Lagrange Multiplier. If the allowable average power P is specified, the corresponding value of λ can be determined. $T(s,\lambda)$ is substituted for $T(s)$ in Eq. (8.118), and P is evaluated as a function of λ. In certain simple examples, it is possible to solve directly for λ in terms of P. In this problem, such an explicit solution is impractical, and the simplest approach involves a trial-and-error solution or a plot of P as a function of λ. A somewhat lengthy calculation of the integral of Eq. (8.118) results in a value of λ equal to $\frac{13}{160}$. The associated $T(s)$ is

$$T(s) = \frac{400s(s + 3.5)(0.121s + 1)}{\frac{1}{130}s^2 + \frac{16}{130}s + 1} \qquad (8.127)$$

If desired, the corresponding mean-square error can be evaluated from Eq. (8.114). With λ selected to yield the specified average power, minimization of I corresponds to the minimization of the mean-square error.

Modification of the Procedure. The procedure for considering constraints has been illustrated in this section by a typical example. The minimization has been carried throughout in terms of the frequency-domain characterizations of signals and physical systems. Exactly the same methods can be used if the descriptions are made in the time domain, in terms of autocorrelation functions and impulse responses rather than power-density spectra and transfer functions. In the example used above, where the average power is constrained, there is little choice between the two descriptions.

In general, any constraints can be considered which can be described in terms of definite integrals similar to the integral expression for the mean-square error. For example, a variety of design problems demand control over the generalized error coefficients K_v, K_a, etc. As indicated in Sec. 1.8, the error coefficients are defined in terms of the derivatives of the over-all system function at $s = 0$ or, alternatively, in terms of the moments of the impulse response. For example, K_v and K_a are given by the equations

$$\frac{1}{K_v} = \int_0^\infty t c_0(t)\, dt$$

$$\qquad (8.128)$$

$$\frac{2}{K_a} = -\int_0^\infty t^2 c_0(t)\, dt$$

where $c_0(t)$ is the unit-impulse response of the over-all system. If the frequency-domain characterization is preferred, the velocity constant can also be written in terms of a complex definite integral of $\dfrac{C}{R}(s)$ and $\dfrac{C}{R}(-s)$.

8.6. Control of Saturation. Newton† has suggested using the procedure described in the preceding section as a first approach to the problem of considering the effects of system nonlinearities. As indicated in Sec. 8.2, one of the basic assumptions underlying the entire statistical design theory as presented in the preceding sections of this chapter is the restriction to linear systems. Evaluation of the significance of this restriction has two facets. First, is it economical or practicable to construct a system which operates in a linear mode at essentially all times? Second, is a linear system actually desired, or is the improvement obtainable with a simple nonlinearity sufficiently great to make a linear system a poor engineering design?

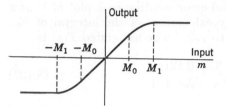

FIG. 8.16. Typical input-output characteristic.

Newton treats only the former question and further restricts consideration to only a single type of nonlinearity: saturation. Any physical device eventually becomes nonlinear as the signal amplitude is increased. A typical operating characteristic for physical equipment takes the form shown in Fig. 8.16. When the excitation exceeds the value M_0, the gain starts to decrease, and, for $|m|$ greater than M_1, the output is essentially constant.

When the signals applied to the system are random in nature and possess, for example, a Gaussian distribution of amplitude, which admits a nonzero probability that the signal will exceed any specified level, a certain amount of saturation is obviously unavoidable. With a normal amplitude distribution, a signal exceeds twice the rms value about 5 per cent of the time and exceeds three times the rms value about 0.3 per cent of the time. The realization of the optimum linear system requires unnecessarily large motors and amplifiers with unreasonable linear ranges if saturation is allowed to occur only an insignificant fraction of the time.

In order to allow specification of a reasonable motor at the outset of the design and at the same time retain the simplicity of the design techniques associated with linear systems, Newton suggests that the optimum system be designed under the constraint that the probability of saturation at various points throughout the system must also be controlled. In other words, a very simple design problem might be phrased as follows: a certain motor with a known transfer function $G(s)$ is to be used in a servo system. The motor saturates when the output velocity exceeds a specified value. The optimum system (to minimize the mean-square error) is to be determined from the class of all over-all system

† G. C. Newton, Jr., Compensation of Feedback Control Systems Subject to Saturation, *J. Franklin Inst.*, Vol. 254, pp. 281–296, October, 1952, and pp. 391–413, November, 1952.

functions which result in velocity saturation less than a given percentage of the time.

Since the details of Newton's method follow closely the procedure outlined in the preceding section, it suffices here to indicate the general steps in the approach by means of the simple servo example illustrated in Fig. 8.17. $G(s)$, the transfer function of the controlled elements, is given. In addition, the specifications describe two possible sources of saturation: torque and velocity saturation. Again the over-all design is broken into

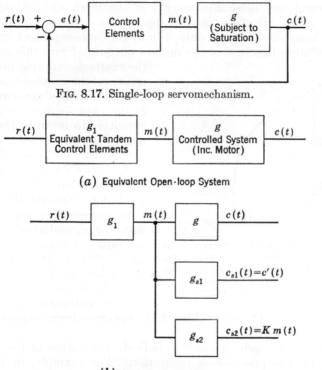

FIG. 8.17. Single-loop servomechanism.

(a) Equivalent Open-loop System

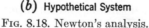

(b) Hypothetical System

FIG. 8.18. Newton's analysis.

two parts, with the system realization following conventional lines after the optimum closed-loop system function is evaluated. Thus, the system desired initially is that shown in Fig. 8.18(a).

A hypothetical system [Fig. 8.18(b)] is visualized, with three outputs, the actual output as well as the two saturation signals $c_{s1}(t)$ and $c_{s2}(t)$. These two outputs are related to $m(t)$, the input to the controlled elements, by the transfer functions $G_{s1}(s)$ and $G_{s2}(s)$. In this particular example, with $c_{s1}(t)$ simply the output velocity and $c_{s2}(t)$ the torque,

$$G_{s1}(s) = sG(s) \qquad (8.129)$$
$$G_{s2}(s) = K \qquad (8.130)$$

The specifications must further include information permitting the selection of σ_{sm1}^2 and σ_{sm2}^2, the allowed maxima for the mean-square values of $c_{s1}(t)$ and $c_{s2}(t)$. For example, if velocity saturation is to occur less than 0.3 per cent of the time and the amplitude distribution is normal, the rms value of the output velocity must be less than $\frac{1}{3}$ the saturation level. Thus, optimization is the problem of determining that $G(s)$ which minimizes the mean-square error and simultaneously holds the mean-square values of $c_{s1}(t)$ and $c_{s2}(t)$ below σ_{sm1}^2 and σ_{sm2}^2.

Finally, the specifications must include the autocorrelation functions of the signal and noise components of the input or, equivalently, the autocorrelation function of the input, the crosscorrelation function between input and desired output, and the zero-argument value of the autocorrelation function of the desired output. From this information, the expressions for the mean-square error and the mean-square values of the saturation signals are written. I, the expression to be minimized, is written in terms of the Lagrange multipliers:

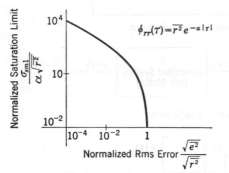

$$I = \overline{e^2} + \lambda_1\sigma_{s1}^2 + \lambda_2\sigma_{s2}^2 \quad (8.131)$$

The minimization of I yields $g_1(t,\lambda_1,\lambda_2)$. Substitution of this impulse response in the two expressions for σ_{s1}^2 and σ_{s2}^2 gives appropriate values of λ_1 and λ_2 to control the probability of saturation, although in any but the simplest cases λ_1 and λ_2 can be determined only by extensive calculations or a graphical solution. Once λ_1 and λ_2 are evaluated, the optimum impulse response $g_1(t)$ is fixed.

FIG. 8.19. Variation of saturation limit with error. (*From G. C. Newton, Jr., Compensation of Feedback Control Systems Subject to Saturation, J. Franklin Inst., Vol. 254, p. 398, November, 1952.*)

The results of such an analysis indicate the nature of the limitations imposed by the presence of saturation. For example, in the case of velocity saturation only, no noise, and an input signal described by the autocorrelation function $\overline{r^2}e^{-\alpha|\tau|}$ the variation of the rms error can be plotted as a function of the allowable rms velocity (Fig. 8.19). The curve indicates that the rms error is not increased markedly by the admission of a significant amount of saturation. In other words, it is possible to trade mean-square error for a lower saturation limit.

The limitations of Newton's analysis arise primarily from the fact that only the linear system is studied. The mean-square error plotted in Fig. 8.19 is the error of a linear system *without saturation* and does not include any measure of the error introduced by the actual saturation present. If the probability of saturation is small, this omission is clearly not serious. Thus, curves such as Fig. 8.19 are valid only when the saturation level is significantly larger than the mean-square value of the actual signal subject to saturation. The significance of Newton's work is twofold: the analysis represents a technique for introducing practical constraints into the optimization procedure; and the work represents one approach to the analysis and design of nonlinear systems, an approach in which the effects of the nonlinearity are maintained small.

8.7. Nonlinear Systems. The linear system is truly an optimum only when both signal and noise possess normal distributions. In a wide variety of practical problems, the signal definitely does not possess a normal distribution, and marked improvement can be realized if the linear filter is replaced by even a simple nonlinear system. The reception of pulse signals in the presence of random noise is perhaps the most important example in which nonlinear characteristics can be used to advantage,† although whenever the input signal is aperiodic rather than a stochastic process, an improvement should be possible.

The limited efficiency of the optimum linear system arises because the optimization utilizes only the autocorrelation function (or the second probability distribution) of the input. In general, an efficient system must consider the higher-order distribution functions in the formulation of the best estimate of the desired output. In other terms, the validity of superposition indicates that the linear system can only separate two signals on the basis of differences in the power-density or energy-density spectra; a nonlinear system, in contrast, may be able to effect a certain amount of filtering even if signal and noise possess proportional spectra.

A simple example‡ illustrates the improvement obtainable with a nonlinear filter. Both signal and noise are assumed to be sampled time functions, with the samples spaced uniformly in time. The signal pulses have only three possible values: $+1$, 0, and -1, with the values equally probable. The noise pulses have the amplitudes $+2$, 0, and -2. For this example, the probabilities, adjusted to make the two autocorrelation functions identical, are

$$P(+2) = P(-2) = \tfrac{1}{12} \qquad P(0) = \tfrac{5}{6} \qquad (8.132)$$

The optimum linear filter has a transfer function equal to the constant $\tfrac{1}{2}$ [cf. Eq. (8.29) with Φ_{ss} and Φ_{nn} equal] and the minimum mean-square error is one half the mean-square value of the input signal.

A nonlinear filter can be designed which yields an output depending on the probable signal when the total input is known. For example, the first two columns of Table 8.1 indicate the various values of the total input and the associated probability of occurrence. The third and fourth columns give the signal and noise combinations which might generate the input. Clearly, only when the input is $+1$ or -1 is there

---

† The Van Vleck-Middleton criterion establishes the nature of the optimum linear system (cf. S. Goldman, "Information Theory," 230–235, Prentice-Hall, Inc., New York, 1953). The improvement obtainable with nonlinear systems is indicated by W. D. White, The Role of Nonlinear Filters in Electronic Systems, *Proc. Natl. Electronic Conf.* 1953, Vol. 9, 1954.

‡ H. E. Singleton, Theory of Nonlinear Transducers, *MIT Research Laboratory of Electronics Tech. Rept.* 160, pp. 22–24, August 12, 1950.

any reason for the filter to yield an incorrect output. An input of $+1$ may represent either a signal of $+1$ and a noise of 0 or a signal of -1 and a noise of $+2$. If the output is x when the input is $+1$ (and $-x$ with an input of -1), the error is $1 - x$ for $\frac{20}{36}$ of the time, $1 + x$ for $\frac{2}{36}$ of the time, and zero at all other times. Thus, the mean-square error is proportional to

$$(1 - x)^2 \tfrac{20}{36} + (1 + x)^2 \tfrac{2}{36}$$

Minimization gives the value of $\frac{9}{11}$ for x and a mean-square error $\frac{20}{33}$ of that with the optimum linear system. Clearly, in a problem this simple,

TABLE 8.1
EXAMPLE†

Input signal	Probability		Signal	Noise
$+3$	$\frac{1}{36}$		$+1$	$+2$
$+2$	$\frac{1}{36}$		0	$+2$
$+1$	$\frac{11}{36}$	$\frac{10}{36}$	$+1$	0
		$\frac{1}{36}$	-1	$+2$
0	$\frac{10}{36}$		0	0
-1	$\frac{11}{36}$	$\frac{1}{36}$	$+1$	-2
		$\frac{10}{36}$	-1	0
-2	$\frac{1}{36}$		0	-2
-3	$\frac{1}{36}$		-1	-2

† Taken from Singleton, *op. cit.*, p. 23.

the nonlinear system (and also the linear system) might be designed to optimize on the basis of other error criteria: *e.g.*, to minimize the probability of error or the probable error. In any case, the nonlinear system is in general better than the linear system.

Derivation of a logical design procedure becomes an incomparably more difficult problem when nonlinear elements are admitted. Perhaps the primary source of difficulty arises in the classification of nonlinearities. Zadeh† has suggested a classification based on an integral representation in which Class I includes the linear system as a special case and each class embraces the lower-ordered classes, but the significance of the classification in terms of design is not clear at the present time. The widely different types of systems within the meaning of the term "nonlinear systems" make a logical general attack difficult.

† L. A. Zadeh, A Contribution to the Theory of Nonlinear Systems, *J. Franklin Inst.*, Vol. 255, pp. 387–408, May, 1953.

Singleton's work presents the general solution for the optimum design of a nonlinear system. If the input is in sampled and quantized form with a finite number of possible signals,[†] the optimum transducer can be determined in a form in which there is a single output associated with each of the possible inputs. Clearly, if the memory of the system must extend over a large number of input samples and the number of quantization levels is large, the instrumentation of the system is completely impracticable. Singleton demonstrates that the optimum system can also be realized in terms of a series expansion in the higher-order correlation functions (measuring higher-order probability distributions). Again, however, the optimum system for a problem of any scope is impractically complex, and design involves the calculation of an excessive number of correlation functions.

The primary significance of Singleton's approach lies in the design philosophy: the attitude that the nonlinear system should be forced to yield the desired results. In this respect, Singleton's work stands in direct contrast to a large body of the previous work,[‡] concerned with the analysis of the response of particular nonlinear systems to stationary time series. A very great gap still exists between these analytic investigations and the idealistic, synthesis approach of Singleton, designing the optimum system without regard to practical considerations. The bridging of the gap seems to call for two attacks:

(1) The extension of Singleton's philosophy to the optimization within classes of nonlinearities or at least an optimization which restricts the complexity of the system. It is in this connection that the work of Zadeh is of interest.

(2) The extension of the analysis techniques to the point where design becomes practical: i.e., where the effects of varying nonlinear characteristics can be estimated simply. Boonton[§] suggests one promising approach in this direction. In the study of feedback control systems with saturation, Boonton considers the case in which the input to the nonlinear device has a normal distribution. The nonlinear element is replaced by a quasi-linear element—an attenuator in which the attenuation varies with the input signal. The attenuation for any given input is calculated by minimization of the mean-square error between the actual output and the hypothetical output resulting from the quasi linearization. The method is very similar to the describing-function analysis for nonlinear systems excited by sinusoidal signals (cf. Chap. 10). As reported by Boonton, the correlation between analytical and experimental results

[†] The same methods can be used if the input is continuous, but with a limited frequency bandwidth in order that the signal can be represented by periodic samples.

[‡] L. Weinberg and L. G. Kraft, Measurements of Detector Output Spectra by Correlation Methods, *Proc. IRE*, Vol. 41, pp. 1157–1166, September, 1953. S. O. Rice, Statistical Properties of a Sine Wave Plus Random Noise, *Bell System Tech. J.*, Vol. 27, pp. 109–157, 1948. D. Middleton, Some General Results in the Theory of Noise Through Nonlinear Devices, *Quart. Appl. Math.*, Vol. 5, pp. 445–498, 1948.

[§] R. C. Boonton, Jr., "Nonlinear Control Systems With Statistical Inputs," *MIT Dynamic Analysis and Control Laboratory Rept.* 61, March 1, 1952.

for a saturation type of nonlinearity is well within the accuracy desired for any ordinary engineering analysis.

8.8. Nonstationary Time Series.　A wide variety of practical problems are not satisfactorily considered by the Wiener theory.　In many cases the short-term correlation functions differ radically from the long-term functions, yet a system is desired which predicts or filters accurately on a short-term basis.　For example, in the fire-control problem the signal component of the input may be accurately describable by a polynomial of known degree over the time interval of interest.　In the simplest application of the Wiener analysis, the optimum prediction in any one interval is based on the characteristics of all intervals.　In other words, the input signal is not a stationary random process, but rather an aperiodic signal, perhaps of the form at, with the value of a known only in terms of a probability distribution.

Furthermore, the statistics of the signal may vary markedly during a single interval.　If the fire-control problem is used again as an example, the mean-square value of the noise is a function of the range.　The system designed on the basis of average statistics is necessarily not utilizing the available information.

In a problem in which the signal component of the input can be described by a polynomial or simple analytic function, while the noise is a random process, the optimum filter is generally a nonlinear system. Effective utilization of the available information about the probability distributions of the signal can only be accomplished with the use of a nonlinear computer.　The difficulty of analyzing and synthesizing nonlinear systems and the awesome complexity of most nonlinear systems designed (on paper) by a logical procedure have resulted in numerous attempts to extend the Wiener theory to the consideration of the smoothing and prediction of signals which are not stationary random processes. In the present state of the art, there appears to be no completely satisfactory solution for any but the simplest cases.　The remainder of this section is devoted to a brief description of several of these extensions.

The earliest significant work is that of Zadeh and Ragazzini,[†] who considered the synthesis of the optimum system under the following conditions: the input includes both random noise and a signal consisting of a random component and a polynomial of known degree.　In other words, the mean value of the signal component is restricted to a polynomial in time.　Furthermore, two restrictions are imposed on the impulse response: (1) the steady-state error with a polynomial input must be zero; and (2) the steady-state must be attained in a finite time interval T.

Condition (1) means that in the steady state the network must yield an output that is exactly the desired linear functional of the polynomial input.　If the system is a differentiator, the condition requires that, if the polynomial is of a degree no greater than n, the first $n + 1$ terms of the Maclaurin expansion of $G(s)$ must be simply s, or alternatively the

† L. A. Zadeh and J. R. Ragazzini, An Extension of Wiener's Theory of Prediction, *J. Appl. Phys.*, Vol. 21, pp. 645–655, July, 1950.

first $n + 1$ moments of $g(t)$ must satisfy the equations

$$\mu_0 = 0 \qquad \mu_1 = -1 \qquad \mu_2 = \cdot \cdot \cdot = \mu_n = 0 \qquad (8.133)\dagger$$

where $\qquad \mu_j = \int_0^\infty t^j g(t)\, dt$

Condition (1) is essential since the error is evaluated as an average over all time. Any steady-state error from the polynomial input is itself a polynomial and hence unbounded.

Condition (2) states that the system has a memory of only T sec; the output at any time depends on the input during the last T sec only. This condition is necessary if the results of the design are to be applicable to the case in which the only signal input is the polynomial. In this situation, the optimum filter, in the absence of condition (2), would have a very narrow bandwidth about zero frequency and would require an excessively long interval for the transient to subside.

A problem of this type arises frequently in the design of aircraft fire-control systems, in which the total duration of the target run is limited and to a first approximation a typical signal can be described by a poly-nomial. Actually, condition (1) is not quite compatible with the usual fire-control problem, since the time T must be selected considerably less than the total duration of the run be-cause the system requires T sec for settling; it is only after T sec that the transient has died out and the

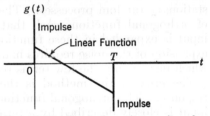

FIG. 8.20. Typical optimum impulse response ($n = 1$).

network is actually performing the desired operation on the polynomial input. If T is much less than the target run, during the later stages of the run the system is using only a small fraction of the available input as a basis for making the best estimate of the desired output. Thus, the restrictions described above represent a compromise between a desire for mathematical expediency and the intuitively desirable formulation of the problem.

The analysis, straightforward once the problem is formulated, is carried out in the usual way. The quantity I is formed from $\overline{e^2}$, the constrained moments, and the Lagrange multipliers. The calculus of variations is used to generate the integral equation to be satisfied by the optimum $g(t)$. This equation is in this case most readily solved by writing the form of $g(t)$ (that is, the sum of impulses and polynomials in the interval from 0 to T) and evaluating the unknown coefficients from the optimizing integral equation and the moment conditions. The form of the opti-mum $g(t)$ is sketched in Fig. 8.20 for the case when the input polynomial is of degree unity and prediction is desired.

The usefulness of the procedure is limited by several factors, in addi-tion to the difficulty discussed at the beginning of the section. With

† The relation between the moments of $g(t)$ and the Maclaurin expansion of $G(s)$ is shown in Sec. 1.8.

only the polynomial component present in the signal, the entire error is the result of noise. By averaging the error over all time, the analysis assumes that the transient error, of duration T sec, is insignificant. In practice, the duration of the total run is finite, and the interval T may be a significant part of the total period over which the system performance is of interest. Again here, if T can be selected sufficiently small (without the noise error becoming excessive), the analysis is valuable.

The application of this theory parallels that of the Wiener theory. The result is primarily useful as a basis for the evaluation of filters and systems designed by more conventional methods. The realization of an impulse response of the form shown in Fig. 8.20 requires the use of delay lines and integrators. Essentially the same performance can be obtained in many cases with passive RC networks, designed as indicated in Chap. 3 and with the transfer function selected by trial and error.

The significant departure of the above analysis from that of Wiener lies in the admission of polynomial input functions. Pike[†] proposes a somewhat different technique for the separation of signals which are not stationary random processes. The basic approach is to determine a set of orthogonal functions such that, when the signal component of the input is expanded in these functions, only a few terms are needed, but expansion of the noise requires many terms. A filter is then constructed which passes only the few terms required in the signal expansion.

The crux of the method is the determination of the filter impulse response. The orthogonal functions $\phi_j(t)$ are chosen such that the signal input is closely described by n terms, with n as small as possible.

$$s(t) = \sum_{j=1}^{n} a_j \phi_j(t) \tag{8.134}$$

where
$$a_j = \frac{1}{I_j} \int_0^R w(x) s(x) \phi_j(x) \, dx$$

Here I_j is the normalization constant, $w(x)$ is the weighting function associated with the set of orthogonal functions, and R is the interval over which the functions are orthogonal with respect to $w(x)$. Expansion of the total input $f_i(t) = s(t) + n(t)$ gives

$$f_i(t) = \sum_{j=1}^{\infty} b_j \phi_j(t) \tag{8.135}$$

The coefficients b_j are the sum of the coefficients of the signal and noise expansions. The first n of these coefficients are primarily the result of the signal component, the remainder primarily the result of the noise. Hence, an approximation to $s(t)$ is realized by the function

$$f_{in}(t) = \sum_{j=1}^{n} b_j \phi_j(t) \tag{8.136}$$

[†] E. W. Pike, A New Approach to Optimum Filtering, *Proc. Natl. Electronics Conf.* 1952, Vol. 8, pp. 407–418. 1953.

The system impulse response depends on the desired operation on the signal. If a predictor is sought, with prediction time α, the output desired is approximated by

$$f_{in}(t + \alpha) = \sum_{j=1}^{n} b_j \phi_j(t + \alpha) \qquad (8.137)$$

Substitution of the value of b_j and interchange of the order of integration and summation yield

$$f_{in}(t + \alpha) = \int_R \left[w(x) \sum_{j=1}^{n} \phi_j(t + \alpha) \frac{1}{I_j} \phi_j(x) \right] f_i(x) \, dx \qquad (8.138)$$

Comparison of the integral of Eq. (8.138) with the convolution integral indicates that $f_{in}(t + \alpha)$ is the output of a network with the input $f_i(t)$ and the impulse response

$$g(x) = \begin{cases} 0 & x < 0, x > t \\ w(t - x) \sum_{j=1}^{n} \phi_j (t + \alpha) \frac{1}{I_j} \phi_j(t - x) & 0 < x \le t \end{cases} \qquad (8.139)$$

The basic elements of Pike's method are simple, and the result is a physically realizable impulse response. The primary difficulty arises in the selection of the set of orthogonal functions. There is very little beyond intuition and experience to guide the designer, yet the success of the method depends almost exclusively on this selection. In certain cases, as when the signal is clearly very nearly a low-degree polynomial and the noise is oscillatory, a desirable set of functions is apparent (in this case, the Laguerre polynomials if the interval is to be infinite). In such an example, a filter designed along conventional lines might also be expected to accomplish considerable filtering. In many cases, however, the difference between the noise and signal is more subtle; typical waveforms of the two components do not indicate at once an appropriate set of orthogonal functions. For example, in the extreme case in which signal and noise possess proportional expansions, Pike's approach results simply in the prediction of signal plus noise, whereas a smaller mean-square error is obtained if the predicted value is a constant fraction of the predicted value of signal plus noise.

Pike's solution does not represent an optimum in any mathematical sense, but rather an intuitive design which can be readily visualized and synthesized. Davis[†] presents the derivation of the optimum system minimizing the mean-square error of prediction when the input is known over a finite time interval T. In Davis's approach, the input $f_i(t) = s(t) + n(t)$ is expanded in a set of orthogonal functions $\phi(t)$,

† R. C. Davis, On the Theory of Prediction of Nonstationary Stochastic Processes, *J. Appl. Phys.*, Vol. 23, No. 9, pp. 1047–1053, September, 1952.

which are the eigenfunctions of the integral equation

$$\phi(u) = \lambda \int_0^T R_{sn}(u,t)\phi(t) \, dt \qquad (8.140)$$

Here λ_j are the eigenvalues, and $\phi_j(t)$ the corresponding eigenfunctions. $R_{sn}(u,t)$ is the autocorrelation function, the expected value of the product of $f_i(u)$ and $f_i(t)$.

In an actual system, the eigenfunctions and eigenvalues are known from the autocorrelation function of the input. The signal is observed during the interval of T sec, and the coefficients of the expansion are evaluated from the integral

$$x_j = \int_0^T [s(t) + n(t)]\phi_j(t) \, dt \qquad (8.141)$$

x_j is the coefficient of $\phi_j(t)$ in the expansion of $s(t) + n(t)$. The best estimate of $s(T + \alpha)$ is then

$$s^*(T + \alpha) = \sum_{j=1}^{\infty} a_j x_j \qquad (8.142)$$

The constants a_j are known before the arrival of the signal and noise and are given by the expansion

$$a_j = \lambda_j \int_0^T R_{ss}(T + \alpha, t)\phi_j(t) \, dt \qquad (8.143)$$

where R_{ss} is the autocorrelation function of the signal alone.

Thus, the optimum linear system requires knowledge of only the correlation functions of the input.   (If signal and noise are correlated, R_{ss} is replaced by the crosscorrelation function between signal and input.) Implementation of the optimum system requires a computer to determine the coefficients x_j from the input and a system to generate the series of Eq. (8.142).   The procedure is very similar to Pike's method, with the advantage here that the orthogonal functions are automatically selected.   Pike's use of only a finite number of terms in the expansion is also accomplished here if the signal and noise are markedly different, since the a_j's tend rapidly to zero if the signal possesses an autocorrelation function which would yield only a few eigenfunctions if substituted in Eq. (8.140): in other words, if $R_{ss}(T + \alpha, t)$ is orthogonal, or nearly orthogonal, to the higher-order eigenfunctions.

The complexity of Davis's analysis and the difficulty of system synthesis are the penalties for an optimum linear system.   Davis's work represents the optimization at a point only; practically most systems require a continuous prediction of the signal.   The extension to this case is straightforward.   In addition, Davis's analysis can be extended to the consideration of nonstationary inputs, with the correlation functions changing with time.   The selected eigenfunctions must change with the correlation functions, but if all functions are continuous with time it should be possible to design a time-varying system or computer to modify the prediction continuously.

8.9. Concluding Comments. During the last decade tremendous research effort has been expended in attempts to augment, modify, and extend Wiener's design theories. Wiener's greatest contribution is unquestionably the philosophy of design: the emphasis on the statistical nature of the signals and on the need for examining the basic objectives of system design. Closely allied with the investigations described briefly in this chapter has been the development of the broader aspects of information theory, in which the performance of a system is evaluated in terms of the handling of information. There is every indication that further refinements of the design techniques will be accompanied by increased emphasis on evaluation and design on the basis of information theory. As feedback control systems become more complex, the over-all system design will lean more heavily on the basic concepts associated with the control and flow of information.

CHAPTER 9

SAMPLED-DATA CONTROL SYSTEMS

The preceding chapters consider various theories appropriate for the design of linear feedback systems operating on continuous signals. There is an entirely distinct class of servomechanisms which operate on sampled data: *i.e.*, systems for which the input (or the actuating signal) is represented by samples at regular intervals of time, with the information ordinarily carried in the amplitudes of the samples.

The basic elements of the simplest sampled-data system are shown in Fig. 9.1. The output $c(t)$ is compared to the input $r(t)$ at the summing

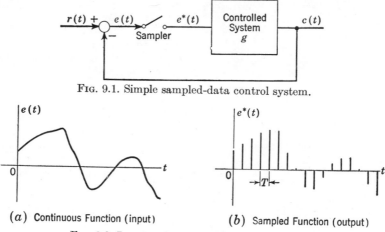

FIG. 9.1. Simple sampled-data control system.

(*a*) Continuous Function (input)   (*b*) Sampled Function (output)

FIG. 9.2. Input and output signals of a sampler.

point (*i.e.*, in the error-measuring device), with the difference denoted $e(t)$. This actuating signal is a continuous function of time, with a possible waveform shown in Fig. 9.2(*a*). At regular intervals, every T sec, the signal $e(t)$ is measured by the sampler, as shown in Fig. 9.2(*b*). The sampler output, consisting of a train of pulses of varying amplitudes, is denoted $e^*(t)$ (the starred notation indicating that the signal is in sampled form†). The pulse train is then used to control the output through a system with the transfer function $G(s)$. The output $c(t)$ is a continuous function as a result of the smoothing properties of the g network.

---

† The notation used here is that of J. R. Ragazzini and L. A. Zadeh, The Analysis of Sampled-data Systems, *Trans. AIEE*, Vol. 71, Part II, *Applications and Industry*, pp. 225–232, 1952.

This sampled-data operation is characteristic of an increasingly large number of feedback control systems. In many instrumentation systems, for example, the power available from the sensitive element is extremely small. By the use of sampling, the sensitive element may be utilized to control large amounts of power without excessive power amplification and with the load on the sensitive instrument maintained extremely small. Sampled-data systems have been used extensively, particularly in temperature measurements but also in the control of pressure, flow, and other physical quantities.

In addition, the increasingly extensive application of digital computers in control problems (*e.g.*, in fire-control systems) places more and more importance on the development of techniques for the analysis and design of sampled-data systems,† for a digital computer works on samples of the input time function and yields a sampled output. Other applications of sampled-data servos arise in connection with radar tracking systems (in which the scanning operation results in sampling of both azimuth and elevation information), with pulsed detectors in amplitude-modulation systems, and with phase-modulation systems.

The analysis of sampled-data systems presents several features quite different from those found in continuous systems. In many respects the sampled-data system is close to the characteristics of a human in a control system; in both the sampled-data system and the system including a human operator, there is action only at discrete instants of time. The error (or actuating signal) is measured, the correction applied, and then the system passes through a waiting period before the error is again determined. The most obvious result of this waiting interval is the generally greater tendency for the sampled-data closed-loop system to oscillate, as a result of the desire to overcorrect the errors which accumulate during the interval between samples.

The discussion of this chapter attempts to clarify some of these basic concepts concerning the fundamental characteristics of sampled-data systems and at the same time to indicate the general techniques for the analysis and design of such systems. The distinctive component of the sampled-data system is, of course, the sampler, for it is here that the continuous signals are converted to pulse trains. Once the characteristics of the sampler are determined, the remainder of the system can be described and analyzed in the usual manner. The analysis of the sampler as a component of the over-all system is considerably simplified if certain mathematical tools are introduced, particularly the z transform and the associated theory.

9.1. Analysis of the Sampler. The sampler, or chopper bar, converts the continuous signal to a train of regularly spaced pulses, with the height (or area) of any pulse representing the value of the time function at the associated sampling instant. If the sampling time (the duration of the sample pulse) is small compared to the significant time constants of the system, the output of the sampler can be considered a train of

† W. K. Linvill and J. M. Salzer, Analysis of Control Systems Involving Digital Computers, *Proc. IRE*, Vol. 41, pp. 901–906, July, 1953.

impulses with the impulse dimension representing the value of the continuous time function. This assumption permits the description of sampler operation in terms of the usual Laplace-transform theory.

The sampler is shown schematically in Fig. 9.3, with the input and output denoted as $e(t)$ and $e^*(t)$, respectively. The output can be written as

$$e^*(t) = e(t)i(t) \tag{9.1}$$

$e(t) \qquad e^*(t)$

FIG. 9.3. Schematic representation of a sampler.

Here $i(t)$ is a train of unit impulses occurring every T sec, where T is the sampling period. The impulse occurring at any given time is multiplied by the value of the input function at that time to obtain the size of the corresponding output impulse. The components of the process are shown in Fig. 9.4.

The Laplace-transform equivalent of Eq. (9.1) can be determined in two forms to obtain equivalent descriptions of the sampler in the frequency domain. If $i(t)$ is written as an infinite series, Eq. (9.1) becomes

$$e^*(t) = e(t) \sum_{n=0}^{\infty} u_0(t - nT) \tag{9.2}$$

where $u_0(t)$ is the unit impulse function occurring at $t = 0$, and T is the sampling interval or period.   It is assumed that the time functions are of interest only for positive values of time.

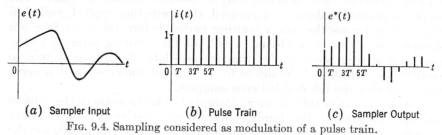

(a) Sampler Input   (b) Pulse Train   (c) Sampler Output

FIG. 9.4. Sampling considered as modulation of a pulse train.

As a result of the definition of the impulse function, Eq. (9.2) can be rewritten as

$$e^*(t) = \sum_{n=0}^{\infty} e(nT)u_0(t - nT) \tag{9.3}$$

Here $e(nT)$ is the value of the input time function when $t = nT$. The Laplace transformation of both sides of Eq. (9.3) yields

$$E^*(s) = \sum_{n=0}^{\infty} e(nT)e^{-nTs} \tag{9.4}$$

In Eq. (9.4), $E^*(s)$ represents the ordinary Laplace transform of the function $e^*(t)$. The above relationship, expressing the Laplace transform of the sampler output in terms of the values of the input function at the sampling times, is particularly useful in the analysis of the over-all system.

Although Eq. (9.4) serves as a useful tool in analysis, it fails to give a physical picture of the behavior of the sampler in the frequency domain. An equivalent relation can be derived by taking the Laplace transform of Eq. (9.1) directly,

$$E^*(s) = E(s) * I(s) \tag{9.5}$$

The symbol $*$ signifies convolution in the s domain. Equation (9.5) states that $E^*(s)$ is the complex convolution of $E(s)$ and $I(s)$, the ordinary Laplace transforms of the sampler input and the pulse train. The transform $I(s)$ is

$$I(s) = 1 + e^{-Ts} + e^{-2Ts} + \cdots \tag{9.6}$$

With the closed form for the series for $I(s)$, Eq. (9.5) becomes

$$E^*(s) = E(s) * \frac{1}{1 - e^{-sT}} \tag{9.7}$$

Although convolution in the s domain generally involves evaluation of a complicated integral expression, if one of the two transforms possesses only simple poles, the expression can be simplified.† In this case, $I(s)$ possesses simple poles at $s = jn\omega_s$, where ω_s is the angular sampling frequency $2\pi/T$, and n is any integer, positive, zero, or negative. The convolution is equivalent to

$$E(s) * I(s) = \sum_n k_I(s_n) E(s - s_n) \tag{9.8}$$

where s_n is a pole of $I(s)$, $k_I(s_n)$ is the residue of $I(s)$ in the pole at s_n, and the summation is taken over all the poles of $I(s)$. In the specific case of interest here, the poles are at $jn\omega_s$ and the residue of $I(s)$ at each pole is simply $1/T$, with the result that Eq. (9.7) becomes

$$E^*(s) = \frac{1}{T} \sum_{n=-\infty}^{\infty} E(s + jn\omega_s) \tag{9.9}‡$$

Equation (9.9) places in evidence the effects of the sampler in terms of the frequency spectrum of input and output. The most important char-

---

† M. F. Gardner and J. L. Barnes, "Transients in Linear Systems," Vol. I, pp. 277–278, John Wiley & Sons, Inc., New York, 1942.

‡ Equation (9.9) is in error if $e(t)$ possesses a nonzero value at $t = 0+$. The difficulty is associated with the convergence of the integral represented by Eq. (9.7), or, from a different viewpoint, the error arises because in Eq. (9.7) only one-half of the value of $e(0+)$ is sampled, whereas Eq. (9.3) implies a full sampling. Equation (9.9) strictly should be written

$$E^*(s) = \frac{1}{T} \sum_{n=-\infty}^{\infty} E(s + jn\omega_s) + \tfrac{1}{2} e(0+)$$

In the analysis of feedback control systems, $E(s)$ customarily tends to zero at least as fast as $1/s^2$ as s becomes large, and Eq. (9.9) is adequate.

acteristic of the sampler output is the periodicity. $E^*(s)$ is a simply periodic function with a period $j\omega_s$. In other words, for any value of s_1, $E^*(s_1 + j\omega_s)$ is equal to $E^*(s_1)$. In the s plane (Fig. 9.5), $E^*(s)$ takes on the same value at congruent points in the various period strips (*e.g.*, at the points a_0, a_1, a_{-1}, etc.).

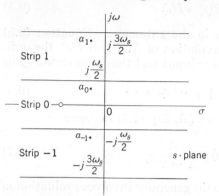

FIG. 9.5. Periodicity strips of $E^*(s)$.

The behavior of $E^*(s)$ along the $j\omega$ axis is of particular interest. If the amplitude spectrum of the input signal has the shape shown in Fig. 9.6(*a*), the amplitude spectrum of the sampler output is as shown in Fig. 9.6(*b*), with a primary component at the proper frequency plus complementary components at all frequencies separated by the fundamental sampling frequency ω_s. (The amplitude of each component of the output spectrum is $1/T$ times the corresponding input component.) One effect of the sampler is then the introduction of the high-frequency components. The band around zero frequency still carries essentially all the information contained in the input, but this same information appears also in regions all along the frequency axis. The

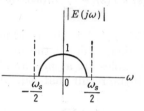

(*a*) Amplitude Spectrum of Sampler Input

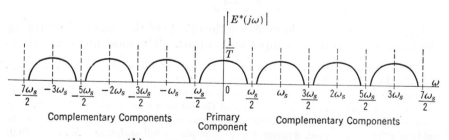

(*b*) Amplitude Spectrum of Sampler Output

FIG. 9.6. Sampler transfer characteristics in the frequency domain.

change in the part of the frequency spectrum carrying the information immediately suggests that the sampler can be considered a modulation device; indeed, sampling can be viewed as the amplitude modulation of the train of impulses by the input signal.

The significance of the sampling in terms of the frequency-domain characteristics of the signal is illustrated by Fig. 9.6. In addition, the view of sampling as a modulation process demonstrates the effect of variations in the sampling frequency. As the sampling frequency is increased, the regions of signal energy are spread out, as illustrated in Fig. 9.7 (a) and (b). If the sampling frequency is decreased, however, distortion starts to appear as soon as the sampling frequency is less than

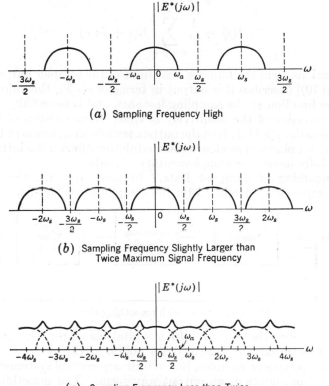

(a) Sampling Frequency High

(b) Sampling Frequency Slightly Larger than
Twice Maximum Signal Frequency

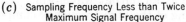

(c) Sampling Frequency Less than Twice
Maximum Signal Frequency

FIG. 9.7. Effect of sampling frequency on spectrum of sampler output.

twice the highest frequency present in the input signal. The signals at frequencies just below $\omega_s/2$ become an entangled combination of the components in the replica of the input around the origin and the lower side bands of the first higher group (the first of the complementary signals). If the information is to be recovered by a linear circuit, which can separate only on the basis of differences in the frequency spectrum, the sampling frequency must be at least twice the highest input frequency. If this condition is not satisfied, the information which can be recovered by linear filtering is that in a frequency band somewhat less than one half the sampling frequency. For example, in the case shown in Fig. 9.7(c), in which ω_s is about 1.3 times the highest input frequency

(ω_a), the bandwidth of the recoverable information extends to only $0.3\,\omega_a$ (not one half the sampling frequency, which is $0.65\,\omega_a$).

Thus, the analytical description of sampling can be effected in either of two ways, as demonstrated by Eqs. (9.4) and (9.9), repeated below:

$$E^*(s) = \sum_{n=0}^{\infty} e(nT)e^{-nTs} \qquad (9.10)^{\star}$$

$$E^*(s) = \frac{1}{T}\sum_{n=-\infty}^{\infty} E(s + jn\omega_s) \qquad (9.11)^{\star}$$

Both equations yield the Laplace transform of the sampler output. The former [(9.10)] describes this output in terms of $e(nT)$, the values of the input time function at the sampling instants, and is essentially a mathematical expression of the intuitively obvious characteristics of the sampler. The latter [(9.11)] gives the output transform in terms of the input transform and places in evidence the modulation effects: the introduction of the high-frequency, or complementary, signals.

9.2. Smoothing of Sampled Data. In most systems, the high-frequency components introduced by the sampler must be removed before

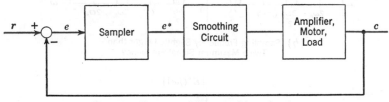

FIG. 9.8. System with smoothing circuit.

the signal reaches the output. In a digital computer, this smoothing might be unnecessary at intermediate points in the system since each component operates on samples, but in ordinary control systems the train of pulses is inadequate as an output waveform. The smoothing of the time function, or filtering of the high-frequency components of the signal, can be accomplished by a low-pass filter designed to pass the primary signal [shown in Fig. 9.6(b)] and block the complementary signals: i.e., to cut off in the vicinity of one half the sampling frequency.

In most sampled-data servo systems, a large portion of the required smoothing is accomplished by the components (motor, etc.) between the sampler and output. More complete smoothing can be accomplished by the introduction of additional circuits, as shown in the block diagram of Fig. 9.8. From a filtering standpoint, the optimum characteristic for the transfer function of the smoothing circuit and amplifier-motor combination would be that of an ideal low-pass filter cutting off in the vicinity of $\omega_s/2$. Any approximation of such a characteristic within close tolerances, however, introduces either undesirable system complexity or excessive phase lag at frequencies below $\omega_s/2$ (in the pass band of the system).

Severe closed-loop stability problems arise with the addition of such a lag. Ordinary attempts to stabilize the system, as lead or integral compensation, then either decrease the filtering action or decrease the frequency at which the open-loop system starts to cut off.

The design of the smoothing circuit thus represents a well-defined compromise between the desire for heavy filtering and the usual problem of stabilization of the over-all closed-loop system. The problems of compromise become more and more acute as the sampling frequency decreases, and the filtering requirements become more difficult to meet.

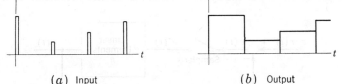

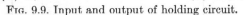

(a) Input   (b) Output

FIG. 9.9. Input and output of holding circuit.

Increasing the sampling frequency leads eventually to a continuous system, with no filtering problems of this type.

The selection of the compromise between filtering and stability is a major element in the design of the sampled-data control system. This compromise can be chosen using conventional servo-design techniques, as described in the following sections. Alternatively, the design of the optimum filter might be carried out on the basis of minimization of the mean-square error in the manner of Wiener and as described in Chap. 8, for here the statistics of the primary and complementary signals are known if the statistics of the input are available.

One particularly simple filter is the holding circuit or boxcar generator. In this circuit, the value of a sampling pulse is held until the arrival of the next pulse. Typical input and output waveforms for the circuit are shown in Fig. 9.9. The transfer function of such a network is determined readily from the impulse response, which is the combination of a positive step at zero time and a negative step at T sec, where T is the sampling period:

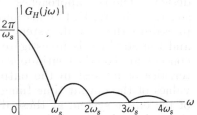

FIG. 9.10. Gain characteristic of holding circuit.

$$G_H(s) = \frac{1 - e^{-Ts}}{s} \qquad (9.12)$$

The gain-frequency characteristic, sketched in Fig. 9.10, is readily determined if the behavior of $G_H(s)$ along the $j\omega$ axis is considered:

$$|G_H(j\omega)| = \frac{2\pi}{\omega_s} \frac{|\sin (\pi\omega/\omega_s)|}{\pi\omega/\omega_s} \qquad (9.13)$$

The filter does not cut off sharply, the gain being down only 36 per cent at $\omega_s/2$, and the phase changes rather rapidly, but the circuit is simply constructed, ordinarily as part of the sampling equipment.

9.3. z-transform Theory. As indicated in the preceding sections, the sampled-data feedback control system ordinarily contains both a sampler and some combination of conventional linear elements, possibly including a holding circuit, but at least furnishing a certain amount of filtering or smoothing. The simplest system takes the form shown in Fig. 9.11, with the transfer function of the conventional elements denoted $G(s)$. The design of the over-all system resolves to the selection of a suitable

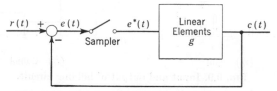

FIG. 9.11. Simple sampled-data control system.

transfer function $G(s)$, which, when inserted in tandem with the sampler, results in satisfactory system stability and dynamic performance.

The design problem differs from that of the conventional closed-loop system only by virtue of the sampler characteristics. At the output of the sampler, a signal exists only at the sampling instants. Although a number of techniques have been used to analyze such a system, there is at the present time no wholly satisfactory method for the complete design. The two approaches which offer the greatest promise are those suggested by W. K. Linvill† and by Ragazzini and Zadeh‡. In Linvill's procedure, the over-all system function is determined in the usual manner and the stability is investigated by a Nyquist diagram. Attention is concentrated on the continuous nature of the output. If the only characteristics of interest in the output are adequately determined from the values of the output time function at the sampling times, the behavior of the entire system at these discrete instants can be investigated and the various signals existing throughout the system at all other times disregarded. In this situation, the Ragazzini-Zadeh approach yields simple results rapidly. The differences in the two methods are more superficial than basic, however, and in the following discussion both are considered with the z transform as the starting point.

The analysis of a sampled-data system is complicated by the sampler characteristics. Equations (9.10) and (9.11) describe the operation of this part of the system:

† W. K. Linvill, Sampled-data Control Systems Studied through Comparison of Sampling with Amptitude Modulation, *Trans. AIEE*, Vol. 70, Part II, pp. 1779–1788, 1951.

‡ J. R. Ragazzini and L. A. Zadeh, The Analysis of Sampled-data Systems, *Trans. AIEE*, Vol. 71, Part II, *Applications and Industry*, pp. 225–232, 1952.

$$E^*(s) = \sum_{n=0}^{\infty} e(nT)e^{-nTs} \tag{9.14}$$

$$E^*(s) = \frac{1}{T} \sum_{n=-\infty}^{\infty} E(s + jn\omega_s) \tag{9.15}$$

where $e(t)$ and $E(s)$ refer to the input signal, $E^*(s)$ is the Laplace transform of the sampler output, T is the sampling period, and ω_s is the sampling angular frequency. Inspection of either equation reveals at once that the sampler cannot be described by an ordinary transfer function relating the transforms of input and output. The two equations also indicate, however, that the sampler is a linear device, with the result that the principle of superposition is applicable. As a result of this fortunate characteristic, analysis can be effected with only a slight modification in the usual approach.

The z Transform. The analysis of the over-all system is simplified if the z transform is introduced. The z transform of a signal $c(t)$ describes the behavior of the signal at the sampling instants. The z transform is derived in three steps:

(1) The values of the signal are determined at the sampling instants. These values form the starred time function $c^*(t)$.

(2) The Laplace transform of this succession of samples is taken, with the result $C^*(s)$.

(3) $C^*(s)$ involves s in the form e^{sT}. The z transform $C(z)$ is obtained by making the substitution†

$$z = e^{sT} \tag{9.16}$$

Thus, the z transform carries information about the corresponding time function at the sampling instants only. The z transform depends upon the original choice of sampling frequency, although not necessarily on the actual signal being in sampled form. Any continuous signal possessing a Laplace transform also has a z transform. As indicated by the discussion of sampling in Sec. 9.1, if it is known that the sampling frequency is at least twice the highest signal frequency, the z transform carries all the information contained in the Laplace transform. If, on the other hand, system design includes the problem of determining the minimum sampling frequency which results in suitable system performance, the z transform does not carry sufficient information. Calculation of the behavior of the output between sampling instants necessitates the

† The z transform $C(z)$ could also be written $C^*(z)$, the notation used by Raggazzini and Zadeh, but the addition of the asterisk seems superfluous, since the fact that z is the argument implies directly that the transform is associated with a time function defined only at the sampling instants.

Also, the terminology $C(z)$, or $C^*(z)$, is somewhat loose. $C(z)$ is neither $C(s)$ with s replaced by z nor $C^*(s)$ with s replaced by z, but rather it is $C^*(s)$ with e^{sT} replaced by z. Strictly, the notation should be $C^*\left(\frac{1}{T}\ln z\right)$.

use of the Laplace transform. These concepts are explained further in the following sections.

In terms of the variable z, the transform of the sampler output as given in Eq. (9.14) becomes a power series in $1/z$,

$$E(z) = \sum_{n=0}^{\infty} e(nT)z^{-n} \tag{9.17}$$

With the sample described in this way, the analysis of a closed-loop system (such as that of Fig. 9.11) is effected in three steps:

(1) The z transform corresponding to $G(s)$ is determined.
(2) The effect of closing the loop around the sampler and block g is evaluated.
(3) The relation between the z transforms of input and output signals is found.

The significance of the z transform is clarified by a simple example. If the input to the sampler is a simple exponential $e^{-\alpha t}$,† Eq. (9.14) gives the output as

$$E^*(s) = 1 + e^{-\alpha T}e^{-Ts} + e^{-2\alpha T}e^{-2Ts} + \cdots \tag{9.18}$$

The simple power series can be written in closed form:

$$E^*(s) = \frac{1}{1 - e^{-\alpha T}e^{-Ts}} \tag{9.19}$$

The corresponding z transform is

$$E(z) = \frac{z}{z - e^{-\alpha T}} \tag{9.20}$$

The z transform gives a complete description of the values of the time function at the sampling instants, but no indication of the behavior of the function between these times. The z transform is essentially the transform of the sampled function.

Useful z Transforms. A list of the z transforms of common functions can be constructed readily from the above definition and is shown in Table 9.1. As an example of the derivation of the entries in this table, the unit ramp function $r(t) = t$ is considered. The values of the function at the sampling instants are 0, T, $2T$, $3T$, etc. The ordinary Laplace transform of this series of samples is

$$R^*(s) = Te^{-Ts} + 2Te^{-2Ts} + 3Te^{-3Ts} + \cdots \tag{9.21}$$

The z transform is found by replacing e^{Ts} by z:

$$R(z) = \frac{T}{z} + \frac{2T}{z^2} + \frac{3T}{z^3} + \cdots \tag{9.22}$$

The expression for $R(z)$ can be put in closed form by summing the series.

† Only one-sided transforms are considered throughout this chapter; the assumption is made that the time functions are zero for negative time.

TABLE 9.1
LAPLACE AND z TRANSFORMS†

Row	Column 1 Laplace transform	Column 2 Time function	Column 3 z transform	Column 4 Description of time function
a	1	$u_0(t)$	1	Impulse function at $t = 0$
b	e^{-nTs}	$u_0(t - nT)$	$\dfrac{1}{z^n}$	Impulse function at $t = nT$
c	$\dfrac{1}{1 - e^{-Ts}}$	$i(t)$	$\dfrac{z}{z - 1}$	Train of impulses at sampling instants
d	$\dfrac{1}{s}$	$u(t)$	$\dfrac{z}{z - 1}$	Step function
e	$\dfrac{1}{s^2}$	t	$\dfrac{Tz}{(z - 1)^2}$	Ramp function
f	$\dfrac{1}{s^3}$	$\tfrac{1}{2}t^2$	$\tfrac{1}{2}T^2 \dfrac{z(z + 1)}{(z - 1)^3}$	Quadratic or acceleration function
g	$\dfrac{1}{s + a}$	e^{-at}	$\dfrac{z}{z - e^{-aT}}$	Exponential function
h	$\dfrac{a}{s^2 + a^2}$	$\sin at$	$\dfrac{z \sin aT}{z^2 - 2z \cos aT + 1}$	Sinusoidal function
i	$\dfrac{1}{s - (1/T) \ln a}$	$a^{t/T}$	$\dfrac{z}{z - a}$	Constant raised to power t
j	$\dfrac{b}{[s - (1/T) \ln a]^2 + b^2}$	$a^{t/T} \sin bt$	$\dfrac{za \sin bT}{z^2 - 2az \cos bT + a^2}$	Sine wave multiplied by $a^{t/T}$
k	$\dfrac{s - (1/T) \ln a}{[s - (1/T) \ln a]^2 + b^2}$	$a^{t/T} \cos bt$	$\dfrac{z(z - a \cos bT)}{z^2 - 2az \cos bT + a^2}$	Cosine wave multiplied by $a^{t/T}$
l	$F(s + a)$	$e^{-at}f(t)$	$F(e^{+aT}z)$	Effect of multiplication by e^{-at}

† This list of transforms was developed from a table in the article by W. M. Stone, A List of Generalized Laplace Transforms, *Iowa State Coll. J. Sci.*, Vol. 22, pp. 215–225, April, 1948. The table is similar, except for a few additional entries, to that appearing in the paper by Ragazzini and Zadeh, *op. cit.*

Equation (9.22) is first rewritten

$$\frac{R(z)}{zT} = \frac{1}{z^2} + \frac{2}{z^3} + \frac{3}{z^4} + \cdots \tag{9.23}$$

Multiplication of both sides of the above equation by dz and integration yield

$$\int \frac{R(z)}{zT}\, dz = -\frac{1}{z} - \frac{1}{z^2} - \frac{1}{z^3} - \cdots + K \tag{9.24}$$

where K is the constant of integration. The series on the right side of the equation can be written in closed form:

$$\int \frac{R(z)}{zT}\, dz = -\frac{1}{z-1} + K \tag{9.25}$$

Differentiation of Eq. (9.25) with respect to z gives

$$\frac{R(z)}{zT} = \frac{1}{(z-1)^2} \tag{9.26}$$

$$R(z) = \frac{Tz}{(z-1)^2} \tag{9.27}$$

Table 9.1 demonstrates one source of difficulty associated with use of the z transform. Rows c and d indicate that the z transform $z/(z-1)$ may correspond to either of two functions: a train of impulses of unit area and occurring at the sampling instants, or a unit step function. Likewise, the z transform 1 may refer either to a unit impulse at $t = 0$ or to a square pulse of amplitude unity and occurring when $t = 0$, but at no other sampling instants. This difficulty arises, of course, because multiplication of a unit impulse by either unity or another unit impulse yields again a unit impulse.

This ambiguity causes difficulty in the analysis when the z transform of the output signal contains terms of both types—some terms representing impulsive time functions, others derived from bounded functions. For example, the z transform $1/(z-1)$ can be written as $-1 + z/(z-1)$ or as $\frac{z}{z-1}\frac{1}{z}$. The former form leads naturally to the time function $-u_0(t) + u_{-1}(t)$, where $u_{-1}(t)$ denotes a unit step function at $t = 0$. The latter form may be interpreted as the z transform of $u_{-1}(t - T)$, with the multiplication by $1/z$ denoting a delay of one sampling interval. In system analysis with the z transform, there is no way of determining which of the quite different time functions is correct.

Fortunately, the difficulty is not serious in the study of most sampled-data feedback control systems, since the smoothing properties of $G(s)$ mean that the output can contain no impulses. (One of the two possible interpretations always implies impulses in the time function.) If the ordinary transfer function of the system following the sampler has more poles than zeros in the finite part of the s plane, impulses do not appear in the output of this network, and no ambiguity arises in the use of the z transform. Care must be exercised when an interpretation is desired of the z transform of the signal at the output of a compensation network following the sampler. The appropriate time function for the z transform can always be determined by consideration of the actual network.

Inverse z Transformation. The inverse z transformation can be effected in either of two ways:

(1) The z transform is manipulated into a partial-fraction type of expansion such that the inverse transform of each component term is recognizable from Table 9.1. In general, evaluation of the inverse transform of $G(z)$ requires an expansion in terms of the form $kz/(z - \alpha)$ for the real poles and the form

$$\frac{2k_1z(z - a) - 2bk_2z}{(z - a)^2 + b^2}$$

for the complex poles. Here k is the residue of $G(z)/z$ at $z = \alpha$, and $k_1 + jk_2$ is the residue of $G(z)/z$ at $z = a + jb$. Once the $G(z)$ function is written as the sum of terms of this type, rows i, j, and k of Table 9.1 allow immediate writing of $g(t)$.

(2) The alternative method of taking the inverse z transform involves a power-series expansion of $G(z)$ in powers of $1/z$. In the expansion, the coefficient of $1/z^n$ corresponds to the value of the time function at the nth sampling instant. In contrast to the partial-fraction method, in which the resultant $g^*(t)$ is given as a continuous function of time with correct values only at the sampling instants, this second method yields a sequence of discrete values for $g^*(nT)$, the time function at the sampling instants.

z Transform of a Network. The usefulness of the z-transform theory depends upon the availability of a relation between the z transforms of the input and output of a linear, continuously operating network. For example, the analysis of a system similar to that of Fig. 9.11 in terms of z transforms depends on a description of the way in which the section with the transfer function $G(s)$ determines the values of the output $c(t)$ at the sampling instants. In Fig. 9.11, the input to the g network is assumed to be a series of samples $e^*(t)$, with the Laplace transform $E^*(s)$. The output of the network is denoted $c(t)$, with the corresponding transform $C(s)$. The relation desired is $C(z)$ in terms of $E(z)$.

Clearly, the definition of $G(s)$ implies that

$$C(s) = G(s)E^*(s) \tag{9.28}$$

The values of $c(t)$ at the sampling instants are determined by $C^*(s)$, which is in turn given by Eq. (9.15):

$$C^*(s) = \frac{1}{T} \sum_{n=-\infty}^{\infty} G(s + jn\omega_s)E^*(s + jn\omega_s) \tag{9.29}$$

But $E^*(s)$ is a periodic function with period ω_s, since $e^*(t)$ is assumed to be the output of a sampler. Hence,

$$E^*(s + jn\omega_s) = E^*(s) \tag{9.30}$$

Substitution of Eq. (9.30) in (9.29) yields

$$C^*(s) = E^*(s)\frac{1}{T}\sum_{n=-\infty}^{\infty} G(s + jn\omega_s) \tag{9.31}$$

In terms of the z transform, Eq. (9.31) can be written

$$C(z) = E(z)G(z) \tag{9.32}$$

Here it is implied that $G(z)$ is given by

$$G(z) = \left[\frac{1}{T}\sum_{n=-\infty}^{\infty} G(s + jn\omega_s)\right]_{e^{sT}=z} \tag{9.33}$$

In other words, the z transform of the output of a network is simply the z transform of the input multiplied by the z transfer function, where

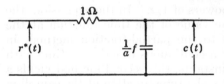

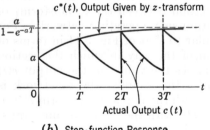

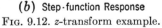

(a) Integrating Circuit

$c^*(t)$, Output Given by z-transform

Actual Output $c(t)$

(b) Step-function Response

Fig. 9.12. z-transform example.

this z transfer function is determined by *exactly the same rules as the z transform of any time function.* The z transfer function $G(z)$ can be determined either by a partial-fraction expansion of $G(s)$ and use of columns 1 and 3 of Table 9.1, or by a determination of $g(t)$, the impulse response of the network, and a subsequent use of columns 2 and 3 of the table or the basic definition of z transforms.

Example. An example of the application of the relations derived above is furnished by the integrating circuit of Fig. 9.12(a). If the input is a sampled unit step function, $R(z)$ is $z/(z-1)$. The transfer function $G(s)$ of the network is $a/(s+a)$. The corresponding z transfer function can be read directly from Table 9.1, columns 1 and 3 of row g:

$$G(z) = \frac{az}{z - e^{-aT}} \tag{9.34}$$

The z transform of the output is the product of $R(z)$ and $G(z)$. The inverse transform $c^*(t)$ can be found either by making the power-series expansion of $C(z)$ in inverse powers of z or by developing $C(z)/z$ in a partial-fraction expansion and multiplying throughout by z. The latter method gives

$$C(z) = \frac{az^2}{(z-1)(z-e^{-aT})} = \frac{(a/1-e^{-aT})z}{z-1} + \frac{[ae^{-aT}/(e^{-aT}-1)]z}{z-e^{-aT}} \quad (9.35)$$

Each term on the right side of Eq. (9.35) can be identified with the corresponding time function by reference to Table 9.1:

$$c^*(t) = \frac{a}{1-e^{-aT}}(1-e^{-aT}e^{-at}) \quad (9.36)$$

Equation (9.36), sketched in Fig. 9.12(b), gives the correct values of the output time function at the sampling instants but is incorrect at all other times. The values at the sampling instants can be written by substituting (nT) for t:

$$c^*(nT) = a\frac{1-e^{-a(n+1)T}}{1-e^{-aT}} \quad (9.37)$$

In this simple example, the actual output waveform can be determined by ordinary Laplace-transform methods and is shown in Fig. 9.12(b).†

Modification of z Transform to Determine Output between Sampling Instants. The z transform can be modified to give the output between sampling instants.‡ In the analysis of the integrating circuit of Fig. 9.12(a), Eq. (9.37) yields the values of the output at the sampling intervals. These values are the output of the network when the input is a train of impulses occurring every T sec, with the impulse areas representing the input at the sampling instants. The input is zero between sampling instants. Consequently, exactly the same output is obtained if the sampling frequency is multiplied by any integer and the continuous input is assumed zero at the newly introduced sampling times.

Thus, if the output of the system of Fig. 9.12(a) is to be evaluated halfway between sampling instants, the continuous input is assumed to possess the waveform shown in Fig. 9.13. This input is denoted $r_s(t)$,

† The instantaneous jump in the output from 0 to a volts frequently puzzles the engineer, since a step function applied to the network leads to an output which increases exponentially from zero toward unity. The jump in the output results from the impulse nature assumed for the sampling. The analysis of the sampler is based on the concept of the input $r(t)$ modulating a train of impulses. If $r(t)$ is a unit step function, $r^*(t)$ is a train of impulses, each of unit area. Since the impulse response of the network alone is ae^{-at}, the unit-step-function response of the integrating circuit behaves as ae^{-at} during the period from 0 to T sec.

If the sampling actually is the modulation of a train of pulses of finite amplitude and unit area, rather than unit impulses, the response does not jump to a, but changes from 0 to a during the sampling time (the time the sampler is turned on). As long as the duration of the pulse is short compared to the time constants of the system, the pulses of unit area can be considered as unit impulses. Thus, the jump in the response of Fig. 9.12(b) corresponds to the charge placed on the capacitor during the sampling time.

‡ The modification below was suggested to the author by G. V. Lago. The author is indebted to Professor Lago for his studied comments and constructive suggestions on this entire chapter.

where the subscript s denotes the synthetic nature of the signal. The z transform of $r_s(t)$ is determined from the original $R(z)$ by replacing z by z^2. This transformation is obvious from the expansions of $R(z)$ and $R_s(z)$ in inverse powers of z, since $r(nT)$ is simply $r_s(2nT_s)$, where T_s (the sampling period of the synthetic system) is $T/2$, and the other samples

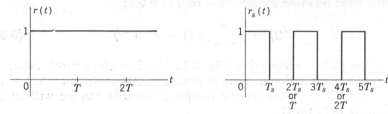

FIG. 9.13. Synthetic input. (Waveform between sampling times irrelevant.)

of $r_s(t)$, corresponding to an odd number of periods, are all zero. Hence, in this example,

$$R_s(z) = \frac{z^2}{z^2 - 1} \tag{9.38}$$

The z transfer function of the network is also modified as a result of the doubling of the sampling frequency. In the specific example considered here, $G_s(z)$, the transfer function for the synthetic sampling frequency, is

$$G_s(z) = \frac{az}{z - e^{-aT/2}} \tag{9.39}$$

In the above example, $G_s(z)$ is found directly from $G(z)$ in Eq. (9.34) by replacing T by $T/2$. In general, when $G(z)$ is the ratio of polynomials in z, $G_s(z)$ is determined from a partial-fraction expansion of $G(z)/z$. In this expansion, each denominator, of the form $z - \alpha$, is replaced by $z - \sqrt{\alpha}$ to obtain the partial-fraction expansion of $G_s(z)/z$.

For the system of Fig. 9.12(a), the output every half sampling period is then determined by multiplying $R_s(z)$ by $G_s(z)$. The product is expanded in inverse powers of z by repeated division of the denominator into the numerator. With the functions of Eqs. (9.38) and (9.39), the result of this division is

$$C_s(z) = a + ae^{-aT/2}\frac{1}{z} + a(1 + e^{-aT})\frac{1}{z^2} + ae^{-aT/2}(1 + e^{-aT})\frac{1}{z^3}$$
$$+ a(1 + e^{-aT} + e^{-2aT})\frac{1}{z^4} + \cdots \tag{9.40}$$

$$c_s(0) = a$$

$$c_s\left(T_s \text{ or } \frac{T}{2}\right) = ae^{-aT/2}$$

$$c_s(2T_s \text{ or } T) = a(1 + e^{-aT})$$

$$c_s\left(3T_s \text{ or } \frac{3T}{2}\right) = a(1 + e^{-aT})e^{-aT/2}$$

$$c_s(4T_s \text{ or } 2T) = a(1 + e^{-aT} + e^{-2aT})$$

The division is simple if numerical values are used for the parameters a and T. The values for $c_s(nT_s)$ agree with the values derived from the exact output shown in Fig. 9.12(b).

Thus, the z transform can be used to determine the values of the output between sampling instants. The synthetic sampling frequency used above can be chosen as any integral harmonic of the actual sampling frequency, and a simple division suffices to determine the output as accurately as desired. The method described here is identical with the impulse techniques described in Sec. 1.6 for evaluation of the convolution integral. In the case of sampled-data systems, the input is actually a train of impulses, and no approximation is involved in the determination of the output at periodic intervals. The determination becomes a multiplication (rather than the above division) if both $r_s(t)$ and $g_s(t)$ are described in terms of samples (*i.e.*, in terms of the power series for the two z transforms).

This flexibility in the use of the z transform removes the most serious objection to use of the z transform for analysis and design—the objection that use of the transform requires complete disregard for the output between sampling instants, with the result that the actual continuous output might oscillate wildly in this interval. Actually, in most cases this objection is not so serious as often believed, since in most systems designed using the z transform the output cannot have a frequency of oscillation larger than the sampling frequency because of the low-pass nature of the transfer functions used in the design of the system components.

9.4. Combinations of Networks. The discussion of the previous section established the usefulness of the z transform in the case when the system consists merely of a sampler followed by a linear network. In this special situation, the z transform of the output of the tandem combination is the product of the z transform of the input and the z transfer function of the network. The situation is completely analogous to the conventional theory in terms of Laplace transforms for continuous systems.

If the z-transform theory is to be used to analyze a feedback configuration, it is necessary to consider tandem combinations of networks. If two networks are separated by a sampler [Fig. 9.14(a)], the z transform of the output is, of course, nothing more than

$$C(z) = R(z)G_1(z)G_2(z) \tag{9.41}$$

In the more common situation depicted in Fig. 9.14(b), however, there is no sampler separating networks N_1 and N_2, and Eq. (9.41) is no longer valid since N_2 is driven not only by the values of $e(t)$, the output of N_1, at the sampling times, but also by $e(t)$ between sampling instants. In this case,

$$C(z) = G_1G_2(z)R(z) \tag{9.42}$$

Here $G_1G_2(z)$ is to be interpreted as the z transform of the tandem combination of N_1 and N_2, that is, the z transform corresponding to the ordinary transfer function $G_1(s)G_2(s)$.†

Example. A simple example illustrates the very significant (and troublesome) differences between Eqs. (9.41) and (9.42). $G_1(s)$ and $G_2(s)$ are both considered to be simple integrating transfer functions:

$$G_1(s) = \frac{1}{s+1} \qquad G_2(s) = \frac{1}{s+2} \tag{9.43}$$

The individual z transforms are found at once by inspection of Table 9.1:

$$G_1(z) = \frac{z}{z - e^{-T}} \qquad G_2(z) = \frac{z}{z - e^{-2T}} \tag{9.44}$$

The configuration of Fig. 9.14(a) yields the over-all z transfer function:

$$\frac{C(z)}{R(z)} = \frac{z^2}{(z - e^{-T})(z - e^{-2T})} \tag{9.45}$$

On the other hand, the z transfer function corresponding to the tandem connection of N_1 and N_2 [Fig. 9.14(b)] is found from a partial-fraction

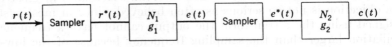

(*a*) Networks Separated by Sampler

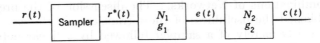

(*b*) Networks in Tandem
FIG. 9.14. Networks N_1 and N_2 interconnected.

expansion of $G_1(s)G_2(s)$:

$$G_1(s)G_2(s) = \frac{1}{(s+1)(s+2)} = \frac{1}{s+1} - \frac{1}{s+2} \tag{9.46}$$

$$G_1G_2(z) = \frac{z}{z - e^{-T}} - \frac{z}{z - e^{-2T}} \tag{9.47}$$

Collection of terms in Eq. (9.47) results in the over-all z transfer function, an expression markedly different from that of Eq. (9.45):

$$G_1G_2(z) = \frac{z(e^{-T} - e^{-2T})}{(z - e^{-T})(z - e^{-2T})} \tag{9.48}$$

Feedback Systems. Thus, the z transfer function must be determined for all networks from the output of a sampler to the input of the next

† Some care is required in interpretation of the notation here. Since $G_1G_2(z)$ is quite different from $G_1(z)G_2(z)$, the argument z cannot be omitted in writing equations for the analysis of complicated systems.

sampler in the system. In the case of a digital computer, in which information is carried throughout in terms of samples, the z transfer functions simply multiply in the usual way. In the conventional sampled-data feedback control system, however, there is only one sampler, as indicated in Fig. 9.15. The analysis of this simple system takes the following form.

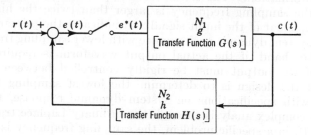

FIG. 9.15. Single-loop sampled-data system.

$E(s)$, the transform of the actuating signal, is given by

$$E(s) = R(s) - H(s)C(s) \qquad (9.49)$$

The output transform $C(s)$ is related to $E^*(s)$ by the transfer function $G(s)$:

$$E(s) = R(s) - H(s)G(s)E^*(s) \qquad (9.50)$$

The output of the sampler is $E(z)$ or $E^*(s)$. Since the sampler is a linear device in the sense that superposition is valid,

$$E^*(s) = R^*(s) - HG^*(s)E^*(s) \qquad (9.51)$$

Algebraic manipulation yields

$$E^*(s) = R^*(s)\,\frac{1}{1 + HG^*(s)} \qquad (9.52)$$

In terms of the z transforms,

$$E(z) = \frac{R(z)}{1 + HG(z)} \qquad (9.53)$$

The actual Laplace transform of the output is simply $G(s)E^*(s)$, since $e^*(t)$ is the signal driving the N_1 network.

$$C(s) = \frac{G(s)R^*(s)}{1 + HG^*(s)} \qquad (9.54)$$

The value of the output at the sampling instants is given by $C(z)$,

$$C(z) = \frac{R(z)G(z)}{1 + HG(z)} \qquad (9.55)$$

Equations (9.54) and (9.55) are the two relations placing in evidence the characteristics of the system. It is only at this point that Linvill's approach to design differs from that proposed by Ragazzini and Zadeh, for Linvill prefers to work in terms of $C(s)$ while Ragazzini and Zadeh choose to concentrate their attention on $C(z)$. The selection of the appropriate method depends primarily on the information desired and the motivations for the system analysis. If relative stability is of primary importance, the values of the output at the sampling instants carry sufficient information. The z-transform approach is completely satisfactory if the sampling frequency is larger than twice the highest frequency component of the input signal and indicates the primary characteristics of system dynamic performance with lower sampling frequencies. On the other hand, if the actual output waveform is required, if the behavior of the output must be rigidly controlled between sampling times, or if the design is to determine the lowest sampling frequency consistent with specifications on system dynamic response, the somewhat more complex analysis through the ordinary Laplace transform is required. If, in a specific problem, the sampling frequency is specified, as is ordinarily the case, some preliminary calculations using the Laplace transform are often desirable, even if only to verify the validity of the z-transform approach for the desired analysis.

If analysis is carried through with the z transform, the same procedure described at the end of the preceding section can be used to determine, for a closed-loop system, the output at regularly spaced points between the sampling intervals. The sampling frequency is doubled (or multiplied by any integer), and an $e_s(t)$ is hypothesized such that $e_s(t)$ is identical with $e(t)$ at the sampling instants and zero at those instants which are sampling times for $e_s(t)$ but not for $e(t)$. In the system of Fig. 9.15, $E(z)$, the z transform of the actuating signal, is given by the expression $R(z)/[1 + HG(z)]$. If $E_s(z)$ denotes the synthetic z transform of $e(t)$, under the assumption that the sampling frequency is doubled, $E_s(z)$ is simply $E(z^2)$. $C_s(z)$, the synthetic z transform of the output, is then $G_s(z)E_s(z)$, where $G_s(z)$ is found from $G(z)$ by writing a partial-fraction expansion for $G(z)/z$ and then replacing the pole at α by a pole at $\sqrt{\alpha}$ with the same residue. $C_s(z)$ gives the actual value of the output twice during every actual sampling period.

This procedure is straightforward, with the only complexity arising in the derivation of $G_s(z)$ from $G(z)$ when $G(s)$ is a function of high order. If the g block contains a holding circuit, the procedure must be modified slightly since the output of the holding circuit must be constant throughout an actual sampling period. In other words, each synthetic sample must be equal to the preceding sample.

The techniques of system analysis, as described above for the simple system of Fig. 9.15, can be applied without modification to the study of more complicated configurations. Results of the analysis of several configurations are shown in Table 9.2. In each case, the Laplace transform of the continuous output is given, as well as the z transform indicating only the values at the sampling times.

Inspection of the various z transforms of Table 9.2 indicates that in general there is no simple z transfer function any more than there is an s transfer function. The transform of the input signal does not always appear as a simple multiplicative factor in the numerator of the expression for $C(z)$. The input signal does always appear, however, only as a numerator factor, with the result that the principle of superposition is valid and system performance can be described by the response to certain typical test inputs. In the light of these comments, the sampled-data control system stands as an intermediate step between the linear,

TABLE 9.2
OUTPUT TRANSFORMS FOR BASIC SAMPLED-DATA SYSTEMS†

System	Laplace transform of output $C(s)$	z transform of output $C(z)$
1	$R^*(s)$	$R(z)$
2	$GR^*(s)$	$GR(z)$
3	$G(s)R^*(s)$	$G(z)R(z)$
4	$\dfrac{G(s)R^*(s)}{1 + HG^*(s)}$	$\dfrac{G(z)R(z)}{1 + HG(z)}$
5	$\dfrac{G^*(s)R^*(s)}{1 + H^*(s)G^*(s)}$	$\dfrac{G(z)R(z)}{1 + H(z)G(z)}$
6	$G(s)\left[R(s) - \dfrac{H(s)RG^*(s)}{1 + HG^*(s)}\right]$	$\dfrac{RG(z)}{1 + HG(z)}$
7	$\dfrac{G_2(s)RG_1^*(s)}{1 + HG_1G_2^*(s)}$	$\dfrac{G_2(z)RG_1(z)}{1 + HG_1G_2(z)}$

† This table is taken directly from the article by J. R. Ragazzini and L. A. Zadeh, The Analysis of Sampled-data Systems, *Trans. AIEE*, Vol. 71, Part II, *Applications and Industry*, p. 228, 1952.

continuous system and the vastly more complex nonlinear system, in which neither a transfer function exists nor the principle of superposition is valid.

9.5. Analytical Determination of Stability. The simplest design problem for linear feedback control systems involves the question of the maximum allowable gain if the system is to be absolutely stable. In continuous systems, the stability may be investigated by four well-known techniques:

(1)   The Routh test, a determination whether any poles of the closed-loop system function lie in the right-half plane.

(2)   The Nyquist diagram, an investigation of the encirclements of the -1 point by the plot of the open-loop transfer function at real frequencies.

(3)   The gain and phase plots versus frequency, a determination whether any real frequency exists at which the open-loop gain is larger than 0 db and the phase greater than 180°.

(4)   The root-locus method, a graphical procedure for determining the location of the poles of the closed-loop system function.

Each of these techniques can be applied to the analysis of sampled-data closed-loop systems.   In this and the following section, the four methods are discussed and an attempt is made to indicate the difficulties associated with each.

Only the simple single-loop system shown in Fig. 9.15 is considered in this section in order to illustrate the basic approach.   For this system, the Laplace and z transforms of the output are given by Eqs. (9.54) and (9.55), repeated below:

$$C(s) = \frac{G(s)R^*(s)}{1 + HG^*(s)} \tag{9.56}$$

$$C(z) = \frac{G(z)R(z)}{1 + HG(z)} \tag{9.57}$$

Either equation indicates that, if the assumption is made that $G(s)$ is stable, the stability of the closed-loop system depends exclusively on $1 + HG^*(s)$ or $1 + HG(z)$.   The discussion of the preceding section indicates that this denominator factor is a rational algebraic function of z or of the variable e^{sT}.   The stability depends on the location of the zeros of this denominator.   In particular, the system is stable if $1 + HG^*(s)$ possesses no zeros in the right half of the s plane.   The analytical determination (e.g., by Routh's criterion) of whether any zeros lie in the right-half plane meets immediate difficulties, however, because the function $1 + HG^*(s)$ is a transcendental function of s.

Analysis in the z Plane.   The analytical stability test is simplified if the z domain is considered.   In terms of the z function $1 + HG(z)$, the system is stable if there are no zeros outside the unit circle, since the transformation $z = e^{sT}$ maps the right half of the s plane into the exterior of the unit circle in the z plane.   Thus, stability can be determined by investigating the location of the zeros of $1 + HG(z)$, zeros determined by a polynomial in z.

A simple example illustrates the analytical determination of stability in the z domain.   The single-loop unity-feedback closed-loop system shown in Fig. 9.16 is to be analyzed, particularly to determine the gain K required to place the system on the dividing line between stability and instability.   The first step in the analysis involves a determination of the open-loop z transfer function, in this case simply $G(z)$. $G(z)$ can be found by a partial-fraction expansion of $G(s)$, conversion term by term to z transforms with the aid of Table 9.1, and, lastly, collection of these terms over a common denominator. These three steps take the form shown below:

$$G(s) = \frac{K}{s} - \frac{K}{s+1} \tag{9.58}$$

$$G(z) = \frac{Kz}{z-1} - \frac{Kz}{z-e^{-T}} \tag{9.59}$$

$$G(z) = \frac{Kz(1-e^{-T})}{(z-1)(z-e^{-T})} \tag{9.60}$$

For stability analysis, the polynomial of interest here is the numerator of $1 + G(z)$,

$$1 + G(z) = \frac{z^2 + [K(1-e^{-T}) - (1+e^{-T})]z + e^{-T}}{(z-1)(z-e^{-T})} \tag{9.61}$$

The closed-loop system is stable if the numerator possesses no zeros outside the unit circle in the z plane. In the general case, the determination

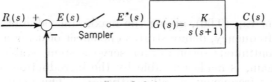

FIG. 9.16. Sampled-data system.

of whether there is a zero outside this circle can be effected in either of two ways:

(1) The nth-degree polynomial in z can be converted to the ratio of nth-degree polynomials in w by means of a bilinear transformation,

$$z = \frac{w+1}{w-1} \tag{9.62}$$

The exterior of the unit circle in the z domain is mapped 1:1 into the right half of the w plane. The condition for stability then becomes the absence of any right-half-plane zeros in the numerator polynomial of the w function.

(2) A somewhat more elegant approach is to test the polynomial in z directly. The analysis is based on the Schur-Cohn citerion.† The work involved does not, however, differ significantly in the two methods, at least for polynomials of the moderately low degrees ordinarily encountered in the study of feedback control systems.

In the particular example considered here, the polynomial is a quadratic and no elaborate tests are required. If the quadratic polynomial $p(z)$ has real coefficients and if the coefficient of z^2 is unity, the necessary and sufficient conditions for $p(z)$ to have no zeros outside the unit circle are

$$|p(0)| < 1 \qquad p(1) > 0 \qquad p(-1) > 0 \tag{9.63}‡$$

† M. Marden, "The Geometry of the Zeros of a Polynomial in a Complex Variable," p. 152, American Mathematical Society, New York, 1949.

‡ The criteria expressed in Eq. (9.63) can be established heuristically. Clearly, if both zeros are to lie within the unit circle, $|p(0)|$, the magnitude of the product of

In this example,

$$p(z) = z^2 + [K(1 - e^{-T}) - (1 + e^{-T})]z + e^{-T} \qquad (9.64)$$

The three conditions of Eq. (9.63) applied to this polynomial lead to the relations

$$\begin{aligned} |e^{-T}| &< 1 \\ K(1 - e^{-T}) &> 0 \\ 1 - K(1 - e^{-T}) + 1 + e^{-T} + e^{-T} &> 0 \end{aligned} \qquad (9.65)$$

The first and second conditions are satisfied for any positive K. The third condition places the bound on gain,

$$K < 2\,\frac{1 + e^{-T}}{1 - e^{-T}} \quad \text{or} \quad K < 2\coth\frac{\pi}{\omega_s} \qquad (9.66)$$

If the sampling frequency is four rad/sec, for example, Eq. (9.66) yields a limit on K:

$$K < 3.05 \qquad (9.67)$$

Inspection of Eq. (9.66), giving the maximum value of K in terms of the sampling frequency, demonstrates one effect of using a sampled-data system. A continuous second-order servo system, stable regardless of the value of gain, is made unstable by the introduction of the sampler if the sampling frequency is sufficiently low. The lower the sampling frequency, the more difficult the stabilization problem. This relationship is intuitively obvious without any derivation, for the lower the sampling frequency, the more stale the data fed to the output controller, and the greater the tendency for the output controller to be operating on the error in the past rather than on the present value. For example, if a step function is applied to the input, the sampler immediately transmits a large error, after which the system operates open-loop until the next sample. During this period of open-loop operation, high torque is initially applied to accelerate the output toward the desired position. If the gain is sufficiently high, the output approaches exponentially a value greater than the value specified by the input. If the integration gain is larger than 2 $(K > 2)$, the output approaches more than twice the desired value, the steady-state error in the absence of further error samples is larger than the initial error, and the system is unstable, even if the sampling frequency tends to zero. The larger the gain, the sooner another error sample must arrive to correct this tendency for the output to be driven far beyond the desired value.

---

the zeros, must be less than unity. If the two zeros comprise a conjugate complex pair, they are then automatically inside the unit circle. There still exists the possibility of two real zeros, one inside the circle, the other outside, and with the product less than unity. Since $p(z)$ is positive as z tends to either $+\infty$ or $-\infty$, however, the condition $p(1) > 0$ assures no single real zero on the positive real axis outside the unit circle, and $p(-1) > 0$ precludes the existence of one negative real zero of magnitude greater than unity.

Analysis in the s Plane. Although a graphical procedure is ordinarily preferable to analytical techniques in the stability analysis of sampled-data control systems, just as in the case of continuous systems, analytical techniques are possible. The simplest form of analytical test for stability, as indicated above, involves a determination of whether any roots of the z-domain characteristic equation lie outside the unit circle. It is also possible in many cases of practical interest to work directly with the Laplace transforms, although generally no significant saving in labor results. Equation (9.56) indicates, for example, that stability of the single-loop system requires that all zeros of $1 + HG^*(s)$ lie in the left half of the s plane. In the simple example considered above and shown in Fig. 9.16, this denominator rational algebraic function takes the form

$$1 + HG^*(s) = 1 + G^*(s) \qquad \text{where} \quad G(s) = \frac{K}{s(s+1)} \qquad (9.68)$$

$G^*(s)$ can be represented by an infinite sum of functions, as shown in Eq. (9.11),

$$G^*(s) = \frac{1}{T} \sum_{n=-\infty}^{\infty} G(s + jn\omega_s) \qquad (9.69)$$

As indicated previously, attempts to apply Routh's test directly to the transcendental function of Eq. (9.68) break down, but the function can be approximated by a rational algebraic function.

If a few terms of the infinite summation for $G(s)$ are written out, Eq. (9.69) becomes

$$G^*(s) = \frac{1}{T} [G(s) + G(s - j\omega_s) + G(s + j\omega_s) + G(s - j2\omega_s)$$
$$+ G(s + j2\omega_s) + \cdots] \qquad (9.70)$$

$G^*(s)$ is a periodic function with a period $j\omega_s$ and repeats in horizontal period strips in the s plane, as indicated in Fig. 9.5. Consequently, the absence of zeros of $1 + G^*(s)$ in the right-half plane in the period strip from $-j\omega_s/2$ to $+j\omega_s/2$ ensures the stability of the system. Since $1 + G^*(s)$ is a function with all real coefficients (if the conjugate terms in the series are combined), it is necessary to investigate only the half of the period strip from the σ axis to $j\omega_s/2$, or the function in the region shown shaded in Fig. 9.17.

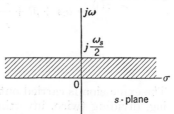

Fig. 9.17. s-plane strip for stability analysis.

Because, in the majority of feedback control systems, $|G(j\omega)|$ tends toward zero as the frequency tends to infinity, the terms representing the higher frequencies in the summation are not particularly important. Along the $j\omega$ axis, $1 + G^*(s)$ becomes

$$1 + G^*(j\omega) = 1 + \frac{K}{T}\left[\frac{1}{j\omega(j\omega + 1)} + \frac{1}{(j\omega - j\omega_s)(j\omega - j\omega_s + 1)}\right.$$

$$+ \frac{1}{(j\omega + j\omega_s)(j\omega + j\omega_s + 1)} + \frac{1}{(j\omega - j2\omega_s)(j\omega - j2\omega_s + 1)}$$

$$\left. + \frac{1}{(j\omega + j2\omega_s)(j\omega + j2\omega_s + 1)} + \cdots \right] \quad (9.71)$$

If ω is held within the limits $0 \le \omega \le \omega_s/2$, the first two terms clearly predominate in the above series. All other terms are equivalent to the original $G(s)$ function evaluated at frequencies larger than the sampling frequency. Only in the exceptional cases in which the cutoff frequency of the system exceeds the sampling frequency can these other terms contribute significantly to the summation. Thus, in the vast majority of practical cases, an approximate check on the system stability is available from a consideration of only two terms in the infinite series of Eq. (9.71).

$$1 + G^*(s) = 1 + \frac{K}{T}\left[\frac{1}{s(s + 1)} + \frac{1}{(s - j\omega_s)(s - j\omega_s + 1)}\right] \quad (9.72)$$

Collection of terms over a common denominator yields a fourth-degree numerator polynomial to which the Routh test can be applied, with a slight modification because of the complex coefficients.

Determination of whether the polynomial $p(s)$ has any zeros in the right-half plane is initiated by writing $p(s)$ in the form

$$p(s) = s^n + (a_1 + jb_1)s^{n-1} + (a_2 + jb_2)s^{n-2} + \cdots + (a_n + jb_n) \quad (9.73)$$

Two new polynomials are formed by taking alternatively the real and imaginary parts of the coefficients of $p(s)$:

$$q(s) = a_1 s^{n-1} + jb_2 s^{n-2} + a_3 s^{n-3} + \cdots \quad (9.74)$$
$$r(s) = p(s) - q(s) = s^n + jb_1 s^{n-1} + a_2 s^{n-2} + \cdots \quad (9.75)$$

The rational algebraic function $r(s)/q(s)$ is expanded in a continued fraction by removing the pole and constant value at infinity, inverting, repeating the removals, inverting, etc.

$$\frac{r(s)}{q(s)} = \alpha_1 s + \beta_1 + \cfrac{1}{\alpha_2 s + \beta_2 + \cfrac{1}{\alpha_3 s + \beta_3 + \cfrac{\cdot}{\cdot \cdot + \cfrac{1}{\alpha_n s + \beta_n}}}} \quad (9.76)$$

The expansion is carried out by dividing $q(s)$ into $r(s)$ twice, then inverting, dividing twice, inverting, and so on, until the remainder is a constant, β_n.† All zeros of $p(s)$ lie in the left-half plane if each α is real and positive and each β is purely imaginary.‡

† The procedure is analogous to that described in Sec. 3.3.
‡ H. S. Wall, "Analytic Theory of Continued Fractions," pp. 178–182, D. Van Nostrand Company, Inc., New York, 1948. A test of this type is also occasionally

The primary disadvantage of this method of attack on the stability problem lies in the high degrees of the polynomials involved. Consideration of two terms in the infinite series for $G^*(s)$ doubles the degree of the polynomial, in comparison with the continuous system with the same transfer function $G(s)$.

Thus, the analytical tests available for sampled-data feedback control systems take two forms, in each case involving a determination of the region within which the zeros of a polynomial lie. In the first approach, the z transfer function of the closed-loop system is determined and the absence of poles outside the unit circle checked. In the second method, an approximate analytical expression for the closed-loop system function is found as a function of the complex frequency s and the usual Routh test is applied. In both cases, the analysis suffers from the same difficulties experienced in applying Routh's test to continuous systems: the complexity of the analysis and the lack of any readily obtained information about the relative stability of the system or the effects on stability of varying system parameters.

9.6. Graphical Stability Analysis. Early in the history of servomechanism design, engineers turned to graphical procedures for the analysis of the relative stability of a closed-loop system. Most of these graphical techniques carry over directly to the analysis of sampled-data control systems. The work of Linvill, for example, is primarily concerned with the application of the Nyquist-diagram analysis to pulsed systems. The application of Bode's gain and phase plots is somewhat more difficult, but involves essentially identical principles. The adaptation of the root-locus methods of analysis and Guillemin's synthesis procedure to sampled-data feedback control systems is not as yet fully developed.

Nyquist-diagram Analysis from s Plane. Linvill's application of the Nyquist diagram to sampled-data systems is based on an approximation for the starred open-loop transfer function, an approximation of the same nature as that described in the preceding section in the derivation of Eq. (9.72). It is demonstrated in Sec. 9.5 that, along the $j\omega$ axis between zero frequency and one half the sampling frequency, the expression $1 + G^*(j\omega)$, or the equivalent expression for more

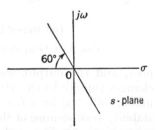

Fig. 9.18. Line in s plane corresponding to imaginary axis in w plane.

complicated systems, can be approximated by a very few terms in the infinite series for $G^*(j\omega)$. The validity of this approximation depends upon the low-pass characteristic of $G(j\omega)$ and the fact that the $G(s)$ part of the system cuts off at frequencies below the sampling frequency. (If the cutoff frequency is higher, the smoothing properties of the system are

___

useful to determine whether a polynomial has any zeros with a relative damping ratio larger than a specified value. If s is replaced by $we^{j\pi/6}$, for example, the imaginary axis in the w plane corresponds to the line shown in Fig. 9.18 in the s plane. Any right-half-plane zeros of the polynomial in w mean that the polynomial in s has zeros with a relative damping ratio less than 0.5 (or cos 60°).

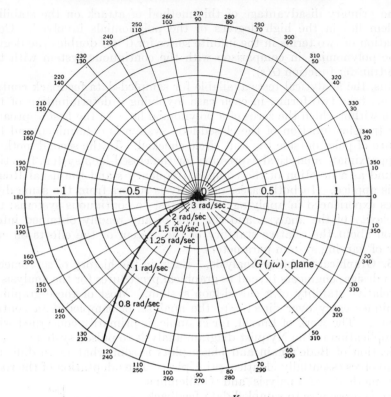

(a) Nyquist Diagram for $G(s) = \dfrac{K}{s(s+1)}$ Plotted for $K = 1$

FIG. 9.19. Graphical construction of Nyquist diagram for $G^*(s)$.

poor, and the output waveform is not a smooth function but instead changes rapidly in the vicinity of the sampling instants.) This approximation of $G^*(s)$ by a few terms is not particularly useful in an analytical stability test because of the complex nature of the transfer functions. In a graphical stability analysis, however, the few terms are easily handled.

What does this approximation mean if a Nyquist diagram of $G^*(j\omega)$ is to be constructed? If the example of the preceding section is again used,

$$G(s) = \frac{K}{s(s+1)} \tag{9.77}$$

The Nyquist diagram for $G(j\omega)$ alone is shown in Fig. 9.19(a). The Nyquist diagram for the corresponding $G^*(j\omega)$ can be found from the expression for $G^*(s)$ in terms of $G(s)$:

$$G^*(s) = \frac{1}{T} \sum_{n=-\infty}^{\infty} G(s + jn\omega_s) \tag{9.78}$$

In other words, $G^*(j\omega)$ is periodic, with a period $j\omega_s$. The value of

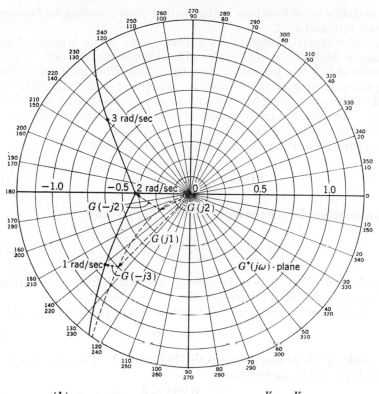

(b) Nyquist Diagram for $G^*(s)$ with $G(s) = \dfrac{K}{s(s+1)}$, $\dfrac{K}{T} - 1$, and $\omega_s = 4$ rad/sec (Constructed Using Two-term Approximation)

FIG. 9.19. (Continued)

$G^*(j1)$, for example, is the summation

$$G^*(j1) = \frac{1}{T}[G(j1) + G(j1 - j\omega_s) + G(j1 + j\omega_s) + \cdots] \quad (9.79)$$

If the sampling frequency is 4 rad/sec, Eq. (9.79) becomes

$$G^*(j1) = \frac{1}{T}[G(j1) + G(-j3) + G(j5) + G(-j7) + \cdots] \quad (9.80)$$

But it is clear from Fig. 9.19(a) that $G(j5)$, $G(-j7)$, and all later terms are very small. Thus, the value of $G^*(j1)$ is essentially just the sum of the vectors representing $G(j1)$ and $G(-j3)$. The construction is shown on Fig. 9.19(b).

The value of $G^*(j\omega_s/2)$ is purely real and is shown constructed in Fig. 9.19(b). At frequencies above $\omega_s/2$, the Nyquist diagram continues into the upper-half plane, as shown in the sketch, until it reaches infinity at the sampling frequency. Clearly, the only part of the diagram of interest from stability considerations is the section corresponding to frequencies between zero and $\omega_s/2$.

Nyquist-diagram Analysis from z Transforms. The Nyquist diagram can also be drawn by consideration of $G(z)$ rather than $G^*(s)$. The poles and zeros of $G(z)$ are located, and the gain and phase shift are evaluated along the unit circle in the z domain. Traversal of the unit circle corresponds to passing along the $j\omega$ axis in one of the period strips in the s plane. The finite number of critical frequencies for $G(z)$ permits simple graphical evaluation of the entire Nyquist diagram.

For example, in the problem previously considered,

$$G(z) = \frac{Kz(1 - e^{-T})}{(z - 1)(z - e^{-T})} \tag{9.81}$$

With a sampling frequency of 4 rad/sec, $G(z)$ becomes

$$G(z) = \frac{0.792\,Kz}{(z - 1)(z - 0.208)} \tag{9.82}$$

The gain and phase at any frequency are determined by locating the point on the unit circle corresponding to this angular frequency. For example, an angular frequency of 1 rad/sec corresponds to the value of z

$$z = e^{j1T} = 1\underline{/90°} \tag{9.83}$$

(The angle of z is proportional to the frequency.) The associated value of $G(z)$ is given by the equation

$$G(z) = \frac{0.792\,K\,\mathbf{A}}{\mathbf{B}\,\mathbf{C}} \tag{9.84}$$

$\mathbf{A}$ is the vector from the origin to $1\underline{/90°}$, $\mathbf{B}$ the vector from 1 to $1\underline{/90°}$, and $\mathbf{C}$ the vector from 0.208 to $1\underline{/90°}$. Graphical measurements, shown in Fig. 9.20, indicate that

$$G(j1) = \frac{0.792\,K(1\underline{/90°})}{(1.414\underline{/135°})(1.0216\underline{/101.8°})} \tag{9.85}$$

$$G(j1) = 0.86\,\frac{K}{T}\underline{/-146.8°} \tag{9.86}$$

Although slightly more difficult than the graphical summation of the series for $G^*(s)$, the construction of the Nyquist diagram from $G(z)$ has the very strong advantage of not involving any approximation. Even though the individual terms neglected in the series for $G^*(s)$ are small, the aggregate of all neglected terms may be significant. The designer is left with a disturbing uncertainty about the accuracy.

The interpretation of the Nyquist diagram, however it may be constructed, follows conventional lines. The diagram of Fig. 9.19(b) demonstrates that the general effect of the sampling in a system of the simple type considered here is to increase the phase lag for a given gain; in other words, to decrease the relative stability.† From the Nyquist diagram, the maximum gain for a stable system is read directly. In the example of Fig. 9.19(b), this gain is found by considering the value of $G^*(j2)$, which can be increased to unity before instability sets in. If only the two terms are used in the series expansion of $G^*(j\omega)$, the allowable K/T is found to be 2.5. With a sampling frequency of 4 rad/sec, K is 3.93, compared to the exact value of 3.05 found in the last section. (If the

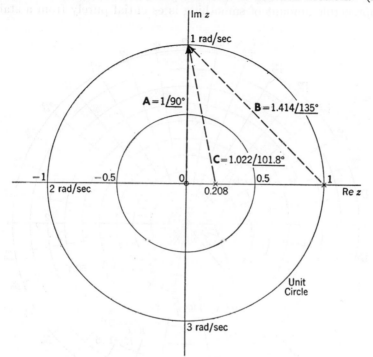

Fig. 9.20. Pole-zero configuration for $G(z)$, with vectors shown for calculation of Nyquist diagram at $\omega = 1$ rad/sec. $G(s) = \dfrac{K}{s(s+1)}$, and $\omega_s = 4$ rad/sec.

Nyquist diagram is drawn from $G(z)$, the value of gain is determined exactly, of course, since no approximations are involved in constructing the diagram.) Consideration of two additional terms in the series for $G^*(j\omega)$ results in a K of 3.46 for stability, and additional terms reduce the value toward 3.05.

The Nyquist diagram places in evidence not only the absolute stability but also the relative stability of the system, and it indicates, in addition, the manner in which the system can be compensated. An indication of the relative stability can be found in the customary manner by construction of the appropriate M_p circles.‡ As an example, the Nyquist

† In certain very special cases, the sampling may tend to stabilize the system, as pointed out in Sec. 9.9.

‡ G. S. Brown and D. P. Campbell, "Principles of Servomechanisms," pp. 185–188, John Wiley & Sons, Inc., New York, 1948.

diagram of $G^*(j\omega)$, shown in Fig. 9.19(b), is redrawn in Fig. 9.21, with the circle for an M_p of 1.3 also drawn.   The graphical construction yields an allowable K of $1.05T$, or 1.65.

The Nyquist diagram demonstrates the difficulty of compensating sampled-data systems with any sort of lead network.   Pushing up the bandwidth of the system tends to increase rapidly the contribution of the higher-order terms in the series expansion of $G^*(s)$.   In other words, an appreciable amount of smoothing is essential purely from a stability

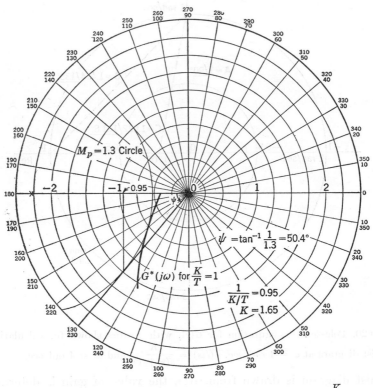

Fig. 9.21. Determination of K for $M_p = 1.3$ with $G(s) = \dfrac{K}{s(s+1)}$.

viewpoint, even if the effect of irregular output motion is not considered. Realization of high error coefficients by means of integral compensation, on the other hand, is perfectly satisfactory from the stability standpoint.

Gain and Phase Plots.   Clearly, exactly the same sort of analysis can be carried out in terms of the Bode diagrams, but with the disadvantage that the addition of the contributions from the various terms in the series for $G^*(s)$, an addition performed vectorially in the case of the Nyquist-diagram analysis, is not readily accomplished in terms of gain-frequency and phase-frequency plots.   The Bode diagrams are primarily useful when a transfer function is expressed as a product of simple factors; a transfer function written as a sum is ordinarily more readily handled by a vector diagram.

Root-locus Methods in s Plane. Just as the Nyquist-diagram and Bode-diagram methods of analysis are carried over to the design of sampled-data systems, it is reasonable to consider the possibility of modifying the root-locus techniques and Guillemin's procedure for the analysis and synthesis of pulsed systems. To the author's knowledge, no work has been done in this direction.

Several difficulties arise at once if such a transition is attempted. The stability depends on the zeros of $1 + G^*(s)$. If work is confined to the s domain, the poles of $G^*(s)$ are known from the outset, since they are just the poles of $G(s)$ repeated every $j\omega_s$ unit along lines parallel to the imaginary axis. The zeros of $G^*(s)$, also infinite in number, can be determined. For example, in the problem considered in this section, with $G(s)$ equal to $K/[s(s + 1)]$,

$$G^*(s) = \frac{Ke^{Ts}(1 - e^{-T})}{(e^{Ts} - 1)(e^{Ts} - e^{-T})} \quad (9.87)$$

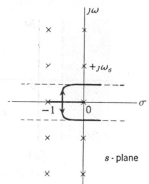

The zeros of $G^*(s)$ are located at the zeros of e^{Ts}, or entirely at infinity. Thus, the open-loop pole-zero configuration is as shown in Fig. 9.22.

As the gain is increased from zero, the various loci remain periodic, with period $j\omega_s$. Hence the shape of the loci in the period strip centered around the σ axis takes the general

Fig. 9.22. General shape of primary part of s-plane root locus.

form shown in Fig. 9.22 (a more accurate locus is derived in the following discussion). The value of K at which the crossing into the right-half plane occurs can be found approximately by consideration of only a few of the infinite number of poles. Clearly, the poles far from the σ axis have a negligible effect on the shape of the locus in this primary strip.

The situation is not, however, so clear-cut as indicated by the preceding paragraph. The difficulty is demonstrated by the fact that the net phase angle contributed by all the poles is 0° at the frequency $(\omega_s/2)$ at which the locus crosses the $j\omega$ axis. The zero factor e^{Ts} contributes the entire 180° phase shift. The construction of the locus requires the consideration of the effect of this multiplicative factor e^{Ts} at each point of the locus. Addition of the gain and phase contribution from this transcendental factor complicates the locus construction, already made more difficult than in the case of the continuous system by the large number of poles which must be considered (at least four in this example, even if the roughest sort of approximation is made). In addition, the complicated nature of the root-locus plot makes it more difficult to study the effects of added compensation, particularly since consideration of a compensation network, with a transfer function $G_1(s)$ and added in tandem with $G(s)$, requires determination of $GG_1^*(s)$, rather than the simple product of the starred transforms.

If $G^*(s)$ is approximated at the outset of the analysis by a few terms in the infinite series [e.g., the two-term approximation used in the construction of Fig. 9.19(b)], the root-locus plot is more readily drawn. The zeros are determined by collecting terms in the expression for $G^*(s)$ over a common denominator. In this method, again, the complexity introduced by both the number of poles and zeros and the complex nature of the coefficients in the numerator and denominator polynomials of the approximate $G^*(s)$ discourages application of the technique in any but the simplest problems.

Root-locus Methods in z Plane.   If the ideas of the root-locus method are applied in the z domain, the number of critical frequencies is reduced

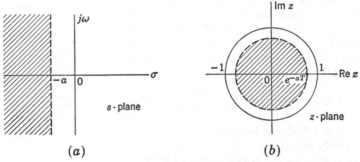

(a)   (b)

Fig. 9.23. Loci of constant time constant $1/a$.

to approximately the number involved in $G(s)$ alone. As pointed out in the preceding section, z and s are related by the transformation

$$z = e^{Ts} \qquad (9.88)$$

Absolute stability requires that all poles of the closed-loop z system function (or, if more general systems are considered, all poles of the z transform of the system output) lie inside the unit circle in the z plane.

Relative stability, also, can be studied in terms of the poles and zeros of the output z transform. The transformation [Eq. (9.88)] maps a line a units to the left of the $j\omega$ axis in the s plane into a circle of radius e^{-aT} in the z plane, as shown in Fig. 9.23. Design of a pulsed system with a certain minimum settling time then requires that all poles of the z transform of the output lie inside a specified circle.

If the realization of specified relative damping is of basic interest, the region shown shaded in Fig. 9.24(a) corresponds to the interior of the shaded region of Fig. 9.24(b), a region bounded by parts of logarithmic spirals. The line segment from 0 to s_a corresponds to the part of the spiral from 1 to z_a in the upper half of the z plane. The semi-infinite line from s_a to infinity is transformed into the segment of the negative real axis in the z plane from z_a to the origin.

Clearly, if the relative damping ratio is to be a specification in the design, only a limited number of the poles of the s transform of the output can be considered, since in any ordinary system, if poles far enough from the σ axis are included, the relative damping ratio can be made arbitrarily small.   In practice, the forward loop (represented by the numerator of the output s transform) introduces attenuation at high frequencies, with the result that the high-frequency poles are of no importance.   Figure 9.24 is drawn for a system in which only the poles in the primary period strip are considered important.   If the first period

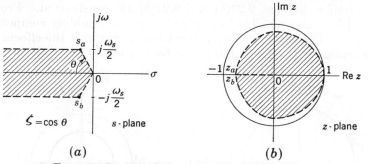

(a)   (b)

FIG. 9.24. Loci of constant relative damping ratio.

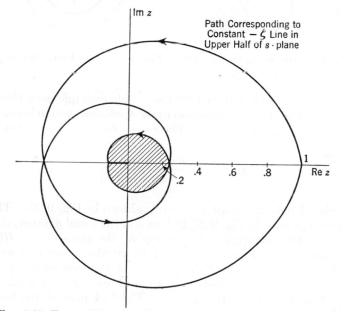

FIG. 9.25. Form of Fig. 9.24(b) if three s-plane strips are significant.

strip on either side of the primary strip were to be included, Fig. 9.24(b) would take the form shown in Fig. 9.25.   One and one-half revolutions of each of the two logarithmic spirals are involved since each half revolution corresponds to the passage of the sloped constant-damping-ratio lines in the s plane through a change in ordinate of $j\omega_s/2$.

The application of the root-locus method to the analysis is straightforward.   The poles of interest for relative stability are the zeros of

$1 + G(z)$ in the case of the simple single-loop system. The poles and zeros of $G(z)$ alone are determined from the open-loop z transfer function. The root loci are plotted in the usual fashion, the only difference in the analysis of pulsed and continuous systems arising from the difference in the allowable pole locations. The gain constant is readily chosen to give any desired settling time or relative damping ratio once families of curves similar to Figs. 9.23(b) and 9.24(b) are constructed. From the root loci it is also possible to study the effects of adding compensation networks. The only difficulty arises from interpreting the effects of the compensation networks on the z transfer function.

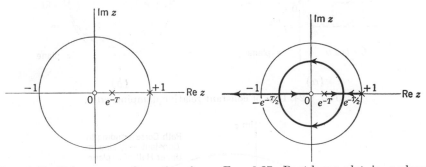

Fig. 9.26. Pole-zero configuration for $G(z)$.   Fig. 9.27. Root-locus plot in z plane

These concepts are illustrated by the simple example used throughout this section. The simple single-loop unity-feedback system is considered, with $G(s)$ given as $K/[s(s + 1)]$. The corresponding z transform is given by Eq. (9.60), repeated below:

$$G(z) = \frac{Kz(1 - e^{-T})}{(z - 1)(z - e^{-T})} \tag{9.89}$$

The associated pole-zero configuration is shown in Fig. 9.26. The root-locus diagram, shown in Fig. 9.27, is drawn in the usual manner, described in Chap. 4. As a function of increasing K, the zeros of $1 + G(z)$ start from the poles at $+1$ and $+e^{-T}$ and move along the real axis until they coalesce at $z = e^{-T/2}$. (The product of the two zeros has a value e^{-T}, independent of K.) Motion is then along the two semicircles to $z = -e^{-T/2}$ on the negative real axis. The last part of the locus consists of the paths to $z = -\infty$ and $z = 0$.

Several characteristics of the system are at once apparent:

(1) Instability occurs only when the locus crosses the -1 point, corresponding to real frequencies of $\omega_s/2$, $3\omega_s/2$, etc. At this time, the other zero is at $z = -e^{-T}$ (since the product of the zeros is e^{-T}). The sum of the zeros is given by the negative of the sum of the coefficients of z in numerator and denominator of Eq. (9.89), or

$$\text{Sum of zeros} = 1 + e^{-T} - K(1 - e^{-T}) \tag{9.90}$$

Instability thus occurs for a value of K given by the equation

$$-1 - e^{-T} = 1 + e^{-T} - K(1 - e^{-T})$$ (9.91)

$$K = 2 \frac{1 + e^{-T}}{1 - e^{-T}}$$ (9.92)

This result was derived in the previous section in the discussion preceding Eq. (9.66).

(2) The corresponding root loci in the s plane are readily drawn, as shown in Fig. 9.28 for the primary period strip only. The entire root-locus plot, considering all poles in the s plane, takes the form shown in Fig. 9.29. The horizontal line segments directly connecting the poles in the s plane correspond to the segment of the positive real z axis; the

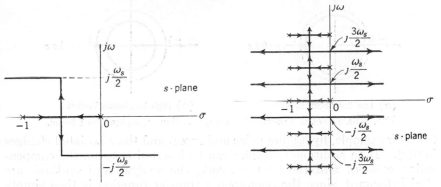

FIG. 9.28. s-plane root locus for primary   FIG. 9.29. Complete s-plane root-locus
strip.   plot.

vertical part of the s-plane locus, to the z-domain circle; and the infinite horizontal lines in the s plane, to the negative real z axis.

(3) If a given transient settling time is specified, the zeros given by the root-locus plot must lie inside a circle determined by the allowable system time constants. Clearly, it is imperative that the circle comprising part of the root locus in the z domain lie inside this specified circle. (In the s plane, the vertical part of the loci must lie to the left of the maximum-time-constant line.) The gain allowable under this specification can be determined either graphically or analytically in the usual manner.

(4) If a minimum relative damping ratio is specified for the poles in the primary period strip of the s plane, the allowable gain can be determined from the z-plane root locus.

(5) The effect of compensation networks can be determined in the z plane, although in the present state of the art considerable trial and error is involved, just as in the case when the Nyquist diagram is used for design. Simple cancellation compensation, involving cancellation of the pole of $G(z)$ at $z = e^{-T}$ and reinsertion of a pole nearer the origin, is readily interpreted. The corresponding operation in the frequency domain is the introduction of a lead network to cancel the pole of $G(s)$

at -1 and add a pole farther from the origin. In terms of the z-domain root locus, the increase in bandwidth has the effect shown in Fig. 9.30. All along the circular part of the locus, the relative stability is improved. However, there is an adverse effect on the velocity constant. As far as the z transform of $G(z)$ is concerned, the effect of moving the pole of $G(s)$ from -1 to $-a$ is equivalent to replacing the sampling period T by aT. The size of the velocity constant to yields system instability decreases. Thus, increasing the bandwidth of the linear system may have either beneficial or adverse effects, depending on the original characteristics of the system and the nature of the specifications. More complex compensation techniques are considerably more difficult to evaluate, primarily as a consequence of the indirect relation between modifications in

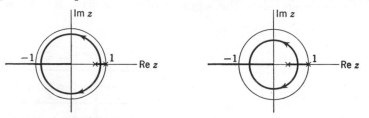

(*a*) Low-bandwidth System   (*b*) High-bandwidth System

FIG. 9.30. Effect of cancellation compensation on z-plane root locus.

$G(s)$ (for example, by adding poles and zeros) and the associated changes in $G(z)$. If an additional sampler can be inserted between the compensation network and the $G(s)$ network, the analysis and synthesis are straightforward, since the open-loop z transfer function is then simply the product of the individual z transfer functions, and the z transfer function of the compensation network can be chosen to control directly the root-locus diagram.

A Logical Synthesis Procedure. Because of the difficulty associated with determining the effects of the introduction of tandem compensation, it is natural to inquire whether sampled-data feedback control systems can be designed by a logical procedure. Attempts to extend the concepts of Guillemin's procedure (Chap. 5) to sampled-data systems introduce several interesting possibilities.

A direct adaptation of Guillemin's procedure leads to design in the following steps:

(1) From the specifications, the nature of the desired system response to a step-function input (or a more general test signal) is determined. An appropriate $C_c(s)$ is determined, where $C_c(s)$ is the Laplace transform of the response. The subscript c denotes the continuous system.

(2) The corresponding $C_c(z)$ is found from the usual partial fraction expansion.

(3) Since $R(z)$ is $z/(z-1)$, the transform of a system function $C_c(z)/R(z)$ can be written.

(4) The relations of Table 9.2 permit determination of appropriate open-loop z transfer functions. If the single-loop unity-feedback system is considered, $G(z)$ is evaluated.

(5) $G(z)/z$ is expanded in partial fractions and $G(s)$ is determined.

(6) Appropriate tandem compensation is synthesized to realize the above $G(s)$.

Such a direct procedure circumvents the difficulties presented by design in terms of the root-locus procedure or the Nyquist diagram. Attempts to apply these six steps encounter one serious difficulty, however. In the first step, a continuous function is selected which meets the specifications. The output of the final sampled-data system is then forced to coincide with the output of this continuous system at the sampling instants. But this similarity between sampled and continuous systems cannot always be achieved. At the present time, there is no simple criterion available for determining the class of continuous systems which can be used as a starting point in the design and which will lead to a physically realizable $G(s)$ for the sampled-data system.

A qualitative explanation of the difficulty here is apparent if the basic system is again considered. In the single-loop unity-feedback configuration, the $G(s)$ network is driven by a sequence of impulses, an impulse arriving each sampling instant. The output $c(t)$ can be considered as the sum of a number of impulse responses for the $G(s)$ system. Thus, the behavior of the output during any sampling period is determined from the behavior in the past. For example, if $G(s) = K/[s(s + a)]$ and $r(t)$ is a unit step function, the first sampling interval displays an output which is simply $(K/a)(1 - e^{-at})$. During the following interval, this response is added to that resulting from the second impulse from the sampler, an impulse which is equal in area to the actuating signal at the time of the sampling. Thus, during the second interval, the total response is also a constant plus a decaying exponential. Thus, if the $G(s)$ system is second-order, the response during the second interval cannot differ markedly from that during the first interval.

The basic philosophy of Guillemin's approach to the synthesis of continuous systems is the idea of forcing the system to behave in the desired manner. The difficulty described above arises because the designer is attempting to make the sampled-data system behave like a continuous system. In actuality, the design of sampled-data systems is in many respects simpler than the corresponding problem for a continuous system if the assumption is made that the characteristics of the sampled-data system can be described by the response at the sampling instants.

A simple example illustrates one possible design procedure which takes advantage of this simplicity.† In the single-loop unity-feedback configuration, $C(z)$ (the z transform of the output) is given by the relation

$$C(z) = \frac{R(z)G(z)}{1 + G(z)} \tag{9.93}$$

If $r(t)$ is a unit step function,

$$C(z) = \frac{G(z)}{1 + G(z)} \frac{z}{z - 1} \tag{9.94}$$

If the desired system is to be second-order, $C(z)$ must take the form

$$C(z) = \frac{a_1 z + a_0}{z^2 + b_1 z + b_0} \frac{z}{z - 1} \tag{9.95}$$

† The author is indebted to Professor G. V. Lago for the discussion here.

(As $z \to \infty$, $C(z)/R(z)$ must approach zero at least as fast as $1/z$ if the corresponding output does not possess a discontinuity at $t = 0$.)

There are four parameters which can be selected arbitrarily in Eq. (9.95). With these four parameters, the response at any four sampling points can be fixed. Clearly, the simplest possible design procedure is to fix these four values. Appropriate values for a feedback control system might be

$$c(T) = 1 \qquad c(2T) = 1.2 \qquad c(3T) = 0.95 \qquad c(\infty) = 1 \quad (9.96)$$

From these values, the coefficients are determined. The steady-state value is established by the final-value theorem, which states that

$$\lim_{t \to \infty} c(t) = \lim_{z \to 1} \left[(z - 1)C(z) \right] \tag{9.97}$$

Hence,

$$\frac{a_1 + a_0}{1 + b_1 + b_0} = 1 \tag{9.98}$$

The first three values are realized by an expansion of $C(z)$ in inverse powers of z:

$$C(z) = \frac{a_1}{z} + \frac{a_0 - a_1(b_1 - 1)}{z^2}$$
$$+ \frac{a_1(b_1 - b_0) + (1 - b_1)[a_0 - a_1(b_1 - 1)]}{z^3} + \cdots \tag{9.99}$$

Combination of Eqs. (9.96), (9.98), and (9.99) yields

$$\begin{array}{ll} a_1 = 1 & b_1 = 0.25 \\ a_0 = 0.45 & b_0 = 0.2 \end{array} \tag{9.100}$$

The corresponding expansion of $C(z)$, the transform of the step-function response, is

$$C(z) = \frac{1}{z} + \frac{1.2}{z^2} + \frac{0.95}{z^3} + \frac{0.973}{z^4} + \frac{1.018}{z^5} + \cdots \tag{9.101}$$

Design along these lines is straightforward. With $C(z)$ determined, $C(z)/R(z)$ is formed and $G(z)$ is evaluated. The corresponding $G(s)$ establishes the required compensation. The entire procedure is a particularly simple application of the philosophy of forcing the system to behave as desired. Since the synthesis is concerned exclusively with the values of the output at the sampling instants, the question arises as to the behavior of the output between these controlled times. If the system is of low order, however, this question is not difficult to answer if the output is considered as the sum of a sequence of impulse responses of the $G(s)$ system, as shown in Fig. 9.31.

The first impulse to excite the $G(s)$ system is of unit area, since at the time of the first sampling the output is zero and the input unity. During the first interval, the response is an exponential approach to a constant value. The output reaches unity at $t = T$. In this simple case, therefore, the second impulse exciting the $G(s)$ system is zero, and the response during the second period is simply the continuation of the response to the first impulse. By $t = 2T$, the output is 1.2; during the next interval, the response to a unit impulse of area -0.2 is added to the original curve. Continuation of this line of reasoning permits construction of the complete output at all times (not only the sampling instants).

Thus, with the system designed by this approach, there is no possibility of high-frequency oscillations between the sampling instants.

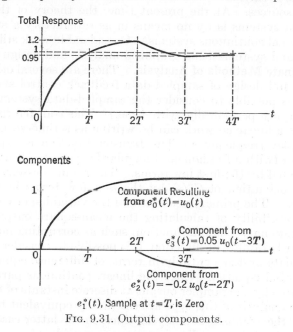

Fig. 9.31. Output components.

There can be no oscillation at a frequency greater than $\omega_s/2$ if, when $G(s)$ is determined from $G(z)$, the system with the smallest possible bandwidth is selected. (It is possible, of course, to select the poles of $G(s)$ to be those of $G^*(s)$ in one of the complementary period strips in the s plane, rather than in the primary period strip, if the high-frequency oscillations are desired.) The response between sampling instants is not necessarily monotonic except in the simple second-order system, but, even if the $G(s)$ is moderately complicated, a plot of $g(t)$ indicates the nature of the response between sampling instants.

Clearly, this concept of summing impulse responses to obtain the total output can be used also as a design procedure for the adjustment of system parameters. For example, if $G(s)$ is $K/[s(s + a)]$, the parameters a and K can be adjusted rapidly by plots of the step-function response of the system as a and K are varied. This viewpoint, considering the actual impulse nature of the input to $G(s)$, is extremely useful as an aid in visualization of system characteristics, even if the design is effected in terms of Nyquist diagrams or root-locus plots.

This section contains a brief description of a variety of methods for the graphical analysis of system stability and the design of sampled-data feedback control systems.   Of the several techniques described, the two most powerful are the Nyquist-diagram analysis, based on a graphical summation of the series for $G^*(s)$ or on a determination of the Nyquist diagram from the z transform, and the root-locus techniques in the z plane. As in any type of feedback control system, the best design of sampled-data systems is carried out with the designer drawing information from all possible sources.   At the present time, the theory of the design of sampled-data systems is by no means in as satisfactory a state as that for conventional continuous systems.   Considerable work still remains in simplifying and systematizing graphical analysis and design procedures.

9.7. Alternate Methods of Analysis.   There are several other methods for analysis and design of sampled-data feedback control systems.   For example, it is possible to consider the sampled-data system as a linear network varying periodically with time.†   The transfer function of a sampler plus a linear network can be written as a time-variant function of the complex frequency s.   The transfer function is expanded in a Fourier series (with a fundamental angular frequency ω_s), and the series is approximated by the first few terms.   The result is essentially equivalent to approximation of $G^*(s)$ by the first few terms in the defining infinite series.   The primary usefulness of the variable-network approach lies in the possibility of calculating the mean-square output when the input is a stationary random function, such as corrupting noise.

In a somewhat different direction, it is possible to consider the analysis of sampled-data systems entirely in terms of difference equations rather than differential equations, since the linear, continuous part of the system is actuated by the sampler output at discrete instants of time.‡   The results of an analysis of this type are essentially equivalent to the results obtained by the z-transform analysis, since, in the latter case, the values of the function at the sampling instants are considered.

If the concept of the difference-equation approach is carried one step further, the sampled-data system can be considered as a system to perform prediction or extrapolation.§   The simple configuration of Fig.

† J. R. Ragazzini and L. A. Zadeh, The Analysis of Sampled-data Systems, *Trans. AIEE*, Vol. 71, Part II, *Applications and Industry*, pp. 229–230, 1952; and L. A. Zadeh, Frequency Analysis of Variable Networks, *Proc. IRE*, Vol. 38, pp. 291–299, March, 1950.

‡ B. M. Brown, Application of Finite Difference Operators to Linear Systems, "Automatic and Manual Control," Proceedings of Cranfield Conference 1951, edited by A. Tustin, pp. 409–418, Butterworths Scientific Publications, London, 1952. The analysis of difference equations by the Laplace transform is described in the book by M. F. Gardner and J. L. Barnes, "Transients in Linear Systems," Vol. I, Chap. IX, John Wiley & Sons, Inc., New York, 1942.

§ C. Holt Smith, D. F. Lawden, and A. E. Bailey, Characteristics of Sampling Servo Systems, "Automatic and Manual Control," Proceedings of Cranfield Conference 1951, edited by A. Tustin, pp. 377–404, Butterworths Scientific Publications, London, 1952.

9.32 serves to illustrate this concept. The sampler monitors the error at regular intervals. This error is transmitted through the holding circuit (if present) to the conventional linear control equipment. The transfer function of the forward loop, other than the sampler, is selected to perform the following function: On the basis of the error samples in the past, the equipment described by $G(s)$ must predict, as well as possible, the value of the input (or desired output) at the next sampling instant. This prediction may be done on the basis of the last sample or a number of the previous samples.†

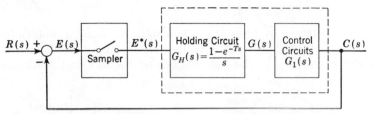

Fig. 9.32. Sampled-data system with holding circuit.

The type of prediction used in a given system is readily determined from the relation between the z transforms of input and output signals. Reference to Table 9.2 indicates that the z transform of the controlled variable for the system of Fig. 9.32 is

$$C(z) = \frac{G(z)}{1 + G(z)} R(z) \tag{9.102}$$

The z transfer function $G(z)/[1 + G(z)]$ is expanded in a power series in inverse powers of z:

$$C(z) = \left(a_0 + \frac{a_1}{z} + \frac{a_2}{z^2} + \cdots\right) R(z) \tag{9.103}$$

In terms of the values of the time functions at the sampling instants, Eq. (9.103) can be written

$$c^*(nT) = a_0 r(nT) + a_1 r[(n - 1)T] + a_2 r[(n - 2)T] + \cdots \tag{9.104}$$

The output at any given sampling instant depends upon the input at the same instant, at one sampling period earlier, at two sampling periods earlier, etc.

In the normal feedback control system, with $G(s)$ possessing at least a double zero at infinity, $G(z)$ tends to zero as z tends to infinity. Under this condition, the output $c^*(nT)$ at any sampling time depends on the input at earlier sampling instants only. In other words, a_0 in Eq. (9.104) is zero. The feedback control system is a predictor, attempting to estimate the desired output on the basis of earlier samples of the input. The

† The view of the design of sampled-data systems as a prediction problem emphasizes the importance of a high sampling frequency. Clearly, if there are significant components of the input at frequencies larger than $\omega_s/2$, prediction is impossible. The value at the next sampling instant may be almost independent of the previous values.

type of prediction being employed can be controlled by the design of $G(s)$, and hence $G(z)$. For example, if only the previous two samples are used, the situation depicted in Fig. 9.33(a) prevails. On the basis of the values of the input at $t = 0$ and $t = T$, the system is to make the best prediction of the value at $t = 2T$. During the interval from T to $2T$, the control circuits bring the output to this predicted value.

The power-series expansion of $G(z)/[1 + G(z)]$ for the system utilizing only two samples as a basis for prediction has the form

$$\frac{G(z)}{1 + G(z)} = \frac{a_1}{z} + \frac{a_2}{z^2} \tag{9.105}$$

Only the two terms are present. The choice of a_1 and a_2 determines the relative weighting of the two samples. If linear extrapolation is used, equal weight is given to the last sample and the last first difference. In

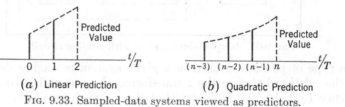

(a) Linear Prediction   (b) Quadratic Prediction

Fig. 9.33. Sampled-data systems viewed as predictors.

other words, passing a straight line through the sample values at 0 and T sec and extrapolating to $2T$ corresponds to making the output at $2T$ equal to the value at T plus the difference between the value at T and that at 0:

$$c(nT) = r[(n-1)T] + \{r[(n-1)T] - r[(n-2)T]\} \tag{9.106}$$

This equation can be rewritten

$$c(nT) = 2r[(n-1)T] - r[(n-2)T] \tag{9.107}$$

With this type of prediction, Eq. (9.105) becomes

$$\frac{G(z)}{1 + G(z)} = \frac{2}{z} - \frac{1}{z^2} \tag{9.108}$$

The design of the system is straightforward. Equation (9.108) is solved for $G(z)$, and the required $G(s)$ function is determined. From Eq. (9.108), $G(z)$ is first found:

$$G(z) = \frac{2z - 1}{z^2 - 2z + 1} \tag{9.109}$$

At this point it is convenient to consider the effect of the holding circuit (if it is to be included). The transfer function of a holding circuit is $(1 - e^{-Ts})/s$. In terms of the z transfer function, the $1 - e^{-Ts}$ factor is equivalent to $(z - 1)/z$. Thus, a new $G_a(z)$ function can be considered,

$$G_a(z) = \frac{z(2z - 1)}{(z - 1)^3} \tag{9.110}$$

After the $G_a(s)$ is found, the $G(s)$ desired is $(1 - e^{-Ts})$ multiplied by $G_a(s)$. The motivation for the removal of the $(z - 1)/z$ factor at this point is merely a desire to simplify the transition from the z to s domains.

The $G_a(s)$ transfer function is found by a partial-fraction expansion of $G_a(z)/z$ followed by multiplication by z:

$$G_a(z) = \frac{z}{(z - 1)^3} + \frac{2z}{(z - 1)^2} \qquad (9.111)$$

The corresponding $G_a(s)$ can be determined by identification of each term in turn. Reference to Table 9.1 simplifies the evaluation. Row f of Table 9.1 gives the transform pair:

$$\frac{z}{(z - 1)^3} + \frac{z/2}{(z - 1)^2} \leftrightarrow \frac{1/T^2}{s^3} \qquad (9.112)$$

If this relation is to be used, Eq. (9.111) is rewritten

$$G_a(z) = \left[\frac{z}{(z - 1)^3} + \frac{z/2}{(z - 1)^2} \right] + \left[\frac{3z/2}{(z - 1)^2} \right] \qquad (9.113)$$

The corresponding $G_a(s)$ consists of two terms:

$$G_a(s) = \frac{1/T^2}{s^3} + \frac{3/(2T)}{s^2} \qquad (9.114)$$

$G(s)$ is the product of this $G_a(s)$ and the factor $1 - e^{-Ts}$:

$$G(s) = \frac{1 - e^{-Ts}}{s} \left[\frac{1/T^2}{s^2} + \frac{3/(2T)}{s} \right] \qquad (9.115)$$

The first factor in Eq. (9.115) is realized by the holding circuit; the second must be the transfer function of the control equipment, the function $G_1(s)$ of Fig. 9.32.

In the above example, the prediction was done on the basis of passing a straight line through the last two samples of the input. A variety of alternate methods are possible. For example, different weights given to the last sample amplitude and the first difference result in different values for the coefficients in the power-series expansion of $G(z)/[1 + G(z)]$. Additional freedom is afforded by the possibility of using more than two samples as a basis for prediction. If three samples are used [see Fig. 9.33(b)], passing a parabola through these three values corresponds to holding constant the second difference,

$$\text{Second difference} = \{r[(n - 1)T] - r[(n - 2)T]\}$$
$$- \{r[(n - 2)T] - r[(n - 3)T]\} \qquad (9.116)$$

The corresponding form of the power series for $G(z)/[1 + G(z)]$ is

$$\frac{G(z)}{1 + G(z)} = \frac{3}{z} + \frac{-3}{z^2} + \frac{1}{z^3} \qquad (9.117)$$

In general, an infinite number of samples may be used, but except in special cases it is impossible to determine a closed-form expression for

$G(z)$ and, hence, the required $G(s)$ transfer function in a form suitable for synthesis. Consideration of the sampled-data system as a predictor is primarily useful, therefore, when the input can be adequately described by the first few differences; *i.e.*, when the input is not changing rapidly and satisfactory prediction can be achieved on the basis of a few samples.

9.8. Continuous Feedback Control Systems with Transportation Lags. This section contains a brief exposition of the basic analysis techniques used when a continuous feedback control system includes a transportation, or distance-velocity, lag. Insertion of this material at this point results in a certain break in the continuity of the chapter. However, the analysis of systems with transportation lags is comparable in several ways to the study of sampled-data systems. In addition, as described

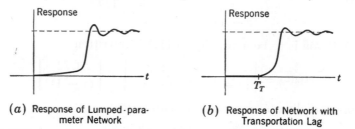

(*a*) Response of Lumped-para-   (*b*) Response of Network with
meter Network   Transportation Lag

FIG. 9.34. Difference between lags of lumped-parameter networks and transportation lags.

in the next section, the presence of a transportation lag in a pulsed system may give rise to several unusual phenomena which are more readily described if the effects of a lag in a continuous system are considered first.

In any linear network consisting of lumped elements only, the response of the system to transient inputs is characterized by the fact that the output starts to respond immediately after the application of the input. The response may not reach an appreciable value until long afterward, but some response appears immediately. As shown in Fig. 9.34(*a*), the step-function response of a typical multisection low-pass filter illustrates this characteristic. Occasionally in feedback systems (*e.g.*, in systems including a human operator within the loop, in process control, and in aircraft control or in systems involving computers within the loop) a somewhat different phenomenon occurs, an ideal time lag, also termed transportation lag or distance-velocity lag. As a result of the distributed nature of the system, the response has the form shown in Fig. 9.34(*b*); the system output remains identically zero until after a given time interval T_T. (The subscript T is used to denote transportation lag.) The transfer function describing the lag alone is of the form $e^{-T_T s}$. The similarity is evident between this function and the transfer functions arising in the analysis of sampled-data control systems.

The block diagram of a typical simple system including a transportation lag is shown in Fig. 9.35. The over-all system function is

$$\frac{C(s)}{R(s)} = \frac{G(s)e^{-T_T s}}{1 + G(s)e^{-T_T s}} \tag{9.118}$$

The characteristics of the system are evident from Eq. (9.118). As a result of the numerator exponential, there is a direct lag of T_T sec between input and output. In addition, the closed-loop performance of the system is affected by the lag because of the factor $e^{-T_T s}$ in the denominator. For example, the stability of such a system is modified by the presence of this factor.

Analytical Stability Analysis. In any analytical stability analysis, the transcendental transfer function has classically been considered by approximating the exponential by a rational algebraic function, after

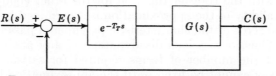

FIG. 9.35. Simple system with transportation lag.

which the usual Routh criterion, root-locus methods, etc., can be applied. A number of approximations have been used, with a few listed below:

(1) The exponential function can be expressed by the limit

$$e^{-T_T s} = \lim_{n \to \infty} \left(\frac{1}{1 + T_T s/n} \right)^n \tag{9.119}$$

If a finite value of n is used, the exponential function is approximated by a pole of order n located at $-n/T_T$ on the negative real axis in the s plane. For example, an n of 3 yields

$$e^{-T_T s} \cong \left(\frac{1}{1 + T_T s/3} \right)^3 \tag{9.120}$$

The corresponding impulse response of the actual function and the approximation are sketched in Fig. 9.36. The approximation is not

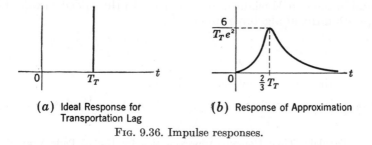

(*a*) Ideal Response for Transportation Lag   (*b*) Response of Approximation

FIG. 9.36. Impulse responses.

particularly good, with the maximum value of the impulse response occurring at $2T_T/3$.

(2) The exponential function can be approximated by the first few terms of the Maclaurin series. The series for either the positive or the negative exponential may be used:

$$e^{-T_T s} = 1 - T_T s + \frac{T_T^2 s^2}{2!} - \frac{T_T^3 s^3}{3!} + \cdots \tag{9.121}$$

$$e^{-T_T s} = \frac{1}{1 + T_T s + T_T^2 s^2/2! + T_T^3 s^3/3! + \cdots} \tag{9.122}$$

Clearly, the approximation is valid when the product $T_T s$ is sufficiently small, but it breaks down far from the origin in the s plane or with large time lags. If Routh's test is applied to the open-loop transfer function, consisting of the approximation derived for the transportation lag in combination with the transfer function for the other components of the system, the validity of the approximation is determined by the values of s at which the zeros of the characteristic polynomial pass into the right-half plane. Thus, one serious disadvantage of any analytical approximation is that the number of terms required for satisfactory approximating accuracy cannot be fixed until the approximation has been used to determine the region of the s plane of interest.

(3) A somewhat better approximation can be achieved without an increase in the complexity of the analytical expression for the open-loop transfer function by the use of a rational algebraic function with both numerator and denominator different from unity. The Padé table for $e^{-T_T s}$ furnishes a particularly simple algebraic function.† The Padé approximation is the rational algebraic function, with numerator polynomial of degree n and denominator of degree m, such that the maximum number of terms in the Maclaurin expansion of the approximating function agree with similar terms in the expansion of the exponential function. In other words, if $e^{-T_T s}$ is to be approximated by the ratio of cubic to quadratic polynomials, there are six coefficients which can be selected arbitrarily:

$$e^{-T_T s} \cong \frac{1 + a_1 s + a_2 s^2 + a_3 s^3}{b_0 + b_1 s + b_2 s^2} \tag{9.123}$$

These six coefficients can be chosen such that at least the first six terms are equal in the two Maclaurin expansions. In this specific example, the appropriate rational algebraic function is

$$e^{-T_T s} \cong \frac{1 - \frac{3}{5} T_T s + \frac{3}{20} T_T^2 s^2 - \frac{1}{60} T_T^3 s^3}{1 + \frac{2}{5} T_T s + \frac{1}{20} T_T^2 s^2} \tag{9.124}$$

The Maclaurin expansion of the fraction is

$$1 - T_T s + \frac{1}{2} T_T^2 s^2 - \frac{1}{6} T_T^3 s^3 + \frac{1}{24} T_T^4 s^4 - \frac{1}{120} T_T^5 s^5 + \frac{1}{800} T_T^6 s^6 - \cdots \tag{9.125}$$

† R. D. Teasdale, Time Domain Approximation by Use of Pade Approximants, 1953 *Convention Record of the IRE, Part 5, Circuit Theory,* pp. 89–94, 1953. A more complete discussion of Padé approximants is given in the book by H. S. Wall, "Continued Fractions," Chap. 20, D. Van Nostrand Company, Inc., New York, 1948. In the author's knowledge, the first extensive application of Padé approximants to network synthesis was made by Dr. M. V. Cerrillo at the MIT Research Laboratory of Electronics.

The first six terms are simply those of the expansion of e^{-T_Ts}; the last term given is the first one to differ.

The Padé table, shown as Table 9.3,† is simply the collection of the approximating functions for numerator and denominator polynomials of various degrees. The rows of the table correspond to fixed degrees for the denominator polynomial; each column gives the approximations for a certain degree of the numerator. In a system such as that shown in Fig. 9.37, for example, in which there is unity feedback and the transportation lag occurs in the forward path, the approximating function can be

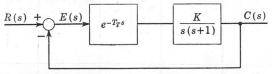

FIG. 9.37. Single-loop system with transportation lag.

used to determine stability through Routh's criterion. The open-loop transfer function for this system is

$$\frac{C(s)}{E(s)} = \frac{K}{s(s+1)} \frac{p(s)}{q(s)} \tag{9.126}$$

Here $p(s)/q(s)$ represents the rational function selected for the approximation. Since the Routh test involves the polynomial $s(s+1)q(s) + Kp(s)$, it is ordinarily desirable to choose $p(s)$ two degrees higher than $q(s)$ in order to meet the approximation requirements with the lowest possible degree for the characteristic polynomial. If the degree of the denominator is selected as unity, the approximation is

$$e^{-T_Ts} \cong \frac{1 - \frac{3}{4}T_Ts + \frac{2}{8}T_T^2s^2 - \frac{1}{24}T_T^3s^3}{1 + \frac{1}{4}T_Ts} \tag{9.127}$$

The resulting open-loop transfer function is the product of this approximating function and $K/[s(s+1)]$. The characteristic polynomial is the sum of the numerator and denominator polynomials of the open-loop transfer function. Routh's test indicates the allowable gain K for a given time lag. As an example, the maximum K with a T_T of 1 sec is found to be 1.14. (The accurate value can be readily determined from plots of open-loop gain and phase versus frequency and is shown below to be the same 1.14.)

(4) Finally, a wide variety of other analytical methods have been used for determining suitable rational algebraic functions to approximate e^{-T_Ts}. Any of the standard methods of network synthesis may be used— e.g., the potential analog method.‡

† O. Perron, "Die Lehre von den Kettenbruchen," p. 424, Chelsea Publishing Company, New York, 1950.

‡ S. Darlington, The Potential Analogue Method of Network Synthesis, *Bell System Tech. J.*, Vol. 30, pp. 315–365, April, 1951.

TABLE 9.3
PADÉ TABLE FOR e^{-x}

$\dfrac{1}{1}$	$\dfrac{1-x}{1}$	$\dfrac{1-x+\dfrac{x^2}{2!}}{1}$	$\dfrac{1-x+\dfrac{x^2}{2!}-\dfrac{x^3}{3!}}{1}$
$\dfrac{1}{1+x}$	$\dfrac{1-\dfrac{1}{2}x}{1+\dfrac{1}{2}x}$	$\dfrac{1-\dfrac{2}{3}x+\dfrac{1}{3}\dfrac{x^2}{2!}}{1+\dfrac{1}{3}x}$	$\dfrac{1-\dfrac{3}{4}x+\dfrac{2}{4}\dfrac{x^2}{2!}-\dfrac{1}{4}\dfrac{x^3}{3!}}{1+\dfrac{1}{4}x}$
$\dfrac{1}{1+x+\dfrac{x^2}{2!}}$	$\dfrac{1-\dfrac{1}{3}x}{1+\dfrac{2}{3}x+\dfrac{1}{3}\dfrac{x^2}{2!}}$	$\dfrac{1-\dfrac{1}{2}x+\dfrac{1}{6}\dfrac{x^2}{2!}}{1+\dfrac{1}{2}x+\dfrac{1}{6}\dfrac{x^2}{2!}}$	$\dfrac{1-\dfrac{3}{5}x+\dfrac{3}{10}\dfrac{x^2}{2!}-\dfrac{1}{10}\dfrac{x^3}{3!}}{1+\dfrac{2}{5}x+\dfrac{1}{10}\dfrac{x^2}{2!}}$
$\dfrac{1}{1+x+\dfrac{x^2}{2!}+\dfrac{x^3}{3!}}$	$\dfrac{1-\dfrac{1}{4}x}{1+\dfrac{3}{4}x+\dfrac{2}{4}\dfrac{x^2}{2!}+\dfrac{1}{4}\dfrac{x^3}{3!}}$	$\dfrac{1-\dfrac{2}{5}x+\dfrac{1}{10}\dfrac{x^2}{2!}}{1+\dfrac{3}{5}x+\dfrac{3}{10}\dfrac{x^2}{2!}+\dfrac{1}{10}\dfrac{x^3}{3!}}$	$\dfrac{1-\dfrac{1}{2}x+\dfrac{1}{5}\dfrac{x^2}{2!}-\dfrac{1}{20}\dfrac{x^3}{3!}}{1+\dfrac{1}{2}x+\dfrac{1}{5}\dfrac{x^2}{2!}+\dfrac{1}{20}\dfrac{x^3}{3!}}$
$\dfrac{1}{1+x+\dfrac{x^2}{2!}+\dfrac{x^3}{3!}+\dfrac{x^4}{4!}}$	$\dfrac{1-\dfrac{1}{5}x}{1+\dfrac{4}{5}x+\dfrac{3}{5}\dfrac{x^2}{2!}+\dfrac{2}{5}\dfrac{x^3}{3!}+\dfrac{1}{5}\dfrac{x^4}{4!}}$	$\dfrac{1-\dfrac{1}{3}x+\dfrac{1}{15}\dfrac{x^2}{2!}}{1+\dfrac{2}{3}x+\dfrac{2}{5}\dfrac{x^2}{2!}+\dfrac{1}{5}\dfrac{x^3}{3!}+\dfrac{1}{15}\dfrac{x^4}{4!}}$	$\dfrac{1-\dfrac{3}{7}x+\dfrac{1}{7}\dfrac{x^2}{2!}-\dfrac{1}{35}\dfrac{x^3}{3!}}{1+\dfrac{4}{7}x+\dfrac{2}{7}\dfrac{x^2}{2!}+\dfrac{4}{35}\dfrac{x^3}{3!}+\dfrac{1}{35}\dfrac{x^4}{4!}}$

There are two primary disadvantages of an analytical approach as outlined:

(1)   The required accuracy of approximation can be determined only after the approximate expression has been used in the analysis.
(2)   Any satisfactory approximation is ordinarily moderately complicated.   The degree of the polynomials involved in the stability analysis rapidly becomes onerous, particularly if the transfer function of the rest of the system is reasonably complex.

Because of these disadvantages, a graphical procedure ordinarily provides a much simpler attack on problems involving transportation lags. The transfer function $e^{-j\omega T_T}$ is readily interpreted in terms of either the Nyquist diagram or the Bode plots without the necessity of any approximation.

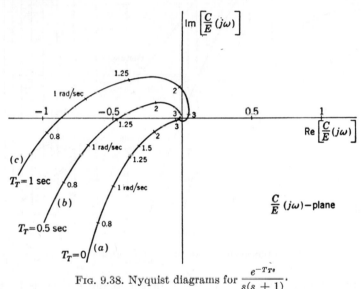

FIG. 9.38. Nyquist diagrams for $\dfrac{e^{-T_T s}}{s(s+1)}$.

Graphical Stability Analysis.   In either the Nyquist diagram or the logarithmic plots, multiplication of a transfer function by $e^{-j\omega T_T}$ represents merely a phase shift varying linearly with frequency.   In terms of the Nyquist diagram, each point on the diagram is rotated through an angle of $-\omega T_T$ rad, where ω is the angular frequency corresponding to the point on the original locus.   Figure 9.38(a) shows the Nyquist diagram of the simple system used in the previous example, with

$$G(s) = \frac{K}{[s(s+1)]}$$

Inclusion of the $e^{-T_T s}$ factor (with T_T equal to 0.5 and 1 sec) changes the diagram to the forms shown in curves (b) and (c), respectively.   The plot spirals inward toward the origin as the frequency increases toward infinity since the added phase shift, $-\omega T_T$ rad, increases without bound.   The form of the diagram indicates that, as either the gain K or the transportation lag is increased, more and more poles of the closed-loop system function move into the right-half plane, as evidenced by the increase in the number of encirclements of the -1 point in the $\dfrac{C}{E}$ $(j\omega)$ plane.

The logarithmic gain and phase plots permit even simpler analysis of the closed-loop system with a transportation lag. The gain curve is unchanged by the introduction of the lag factor, but the phase lag is increased proportional to frequency. Figure 9.39 presents the change

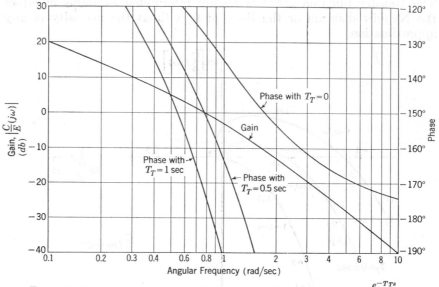

FIG. 9.39. Gain and phase curves for open-loop transfer function $\dfrac{e^{-T_T s}}{s(s+1)}$.

caused by the introduction of the $e^{-T_T s}$ factor in the $K/[s(s+1)]$ transfer function considered previously. The gain K allowable if the system is to be stable is rapidly determined. The gain of the $1/[s(s+1)]$ plot at the frequency at which the phase shift of the total open-loop transfer function is $-180°$ is -1.1 db if T_T is 1 sec. K can then be as high as $+1.1$ db, or 1.14.

The very desirable characteristic of this approach through logarithmic plots to the problem of a transportation lag is that the situation is not particularly complicated by increased complexity in the rest of the open-loop transfer function. The problem with a transportation lag is essentially no more difficult than the analysis of the same system without the lag.

Attempts to apply root-locus techniques to systems with transportation lags† generate very real difficulties similar to those experienced

† Y. Chu, Feedback Control System with Dead-time Lag or Distributed Lag by Root-Locus Method, *Trans. AIEE*, Vol. 70, Part II, pp. 1439–1445, 1951.

with sampled-data systems. The second-order system with an associated lag illustrates the problems. The open-loop transfer function is

$$\frac{C(s)}{E(s)} = \frac{Ke^{-T_T s}}{s(s + 1)} \qquad (9.128)$$

There are poles at the origin and at -1. In the absence of the exponential factor in the numerator, the root locus takes the form shown in Fig. 9.40. With the exponential included, however, the essential singularity at infinity acts as an infinite supply of zeros,† more and more of which move into the finite portion of the plane as the gain is increased. With the increase of the gain from zero, the first noticeable effect is a bending of the locus of Fig. 9.40 toward the right-half plane and a simultaneous arrival of two more zeros in that region in the vicinity of the 0 and -1 points. The locus takes the form shown in Fig. 9.41. Further increases in gain move these two

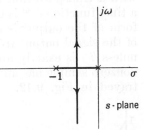

FIG. 9.40. Root locus for system with no transportation lag.

added zeros over into the right-half plane at higher values of frequency and gain, as each crossing corresponds in the Nyquist diagram to an additional encirclement of the -1 point. Accurate construction of the root-locus plots requires consideration of the gain and phase introduced by the factor $e^{-T_T s}$. As pointed out by Chu, the direct approach involves construction of the various phase-angle loci (180°, 170°, 160°, etc.) of the rational algebraic part of the open-loop transfer function. The horizontal lines constituting the phase-angle loci of $e^{-T_T s}$ are superimposed on the plot to obtain the loci along which the over-all transfer function possesses a phase of $\pm 180°$. Clearly, the root-locus diagram is in general considerably more difficult to construct than the logarithmic gain and phase curves.

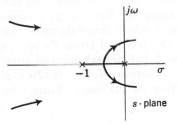

FIG. 9.41. Beginning of root-locus plot with transportation lag present.

9.9. Sampled-data Systems with Transportation Lags. The presence of a transportation lag in a continuous system limits severely the usefulness of root-locus methods of design and increases slightly the degree of difficulty associated with analysis through logarithmic plots. When a transportation lag is present in sampled-data systems, the analysis is complicated in much the same manner. There are, however, certain marked differ-· ences in the effects of lags on the performance of continuous and sampled systems. For example, in a continuous closed-loop system, the introduction of a transportation lag in the forward path increases the

† Zeros of $1 + \dfrac{C}{E}$ (s), or poles of $\dfrac{C}{R}$ (s), the closed-loop system function.

phase lag through the system and hence always tends to decrease the stability margin. The gain allowable if the system is to be stable is decreased. In a sampled-data system, on the other hand, the effect of a transportation lag may be primarily stabilizing. The general characteristics of a sampled-data system with a transportation lag are described in this section through the medium of a simple example considered in more detail by Oldenbourg† and Sartorius.‡

z Transform for Transportation Lags. The z transform of a system with a transportation lag can be determined by physical reasoning. If a time function e^{-at} is delayed by a time T_T, the ordinary Laplace transform of the output is simply $e^{-T_T s}/(s + a)$. However, the z transform of the signal output from the delay line is complicated by the fact that, unless T_T is exactly an integral number of sampling intervals, the first nonzero sample has an amplitude less than unity. The difficulty is portrayed in Fig. 9.42. If T_T lies between the $m - 1$ and m sampling

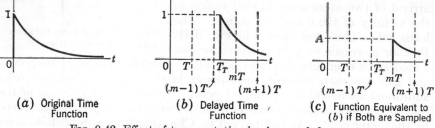

(**a**) Original Time Function   (**b**) Delayed Time Function   (**c**) Function Equivalent to (**b**) if Both are Sampled

FIG. 9.42. Effect of transportation lag in sampled system.

instants, *i.e.*, between $(m - 1)T$ and mT on the time scale, the samples are all zero until the one at mT sec. (The notation of the previous sections of the chapter is still followed here, with T and ω_s representing the period between samples and the angular sampling frequency, respectively.) This first sample has an amplitude A which depends upon the decay of the delayed time function during the interval from T_T sec to mT sec. As far as the samples are concerned, the actual delayed time function cannot be distinguished from the function of Fig. 9.42(*c*), a decaying exponential of amplitude A starting at mT sec. Thus, the z transform of the delayed exponential is

$$G(z) = G_o(z) \frac{1}{z^m} e^{-a(mT - T_T)} \tag{9.129}$$

Here T_T is assumed to lie between $(m - 1)T$ and mT; $G_o(z)$ is the z trans-

† R. C. Oldenbourg, Deviation Dependent Step-by-step Control as Means to Achieve Optimum Control for Plants with Large Distance-Velocity Lag, "Automatic and Manual Control," Proceedings of Cranfield Conference 1951, edited by A. Tustin, pp. 435–447, Butterworths Scientific Publications, London, 1952.

‡ H. Sartorius, Deviation Dependent Step-by-step Control Systems and their Stability, "Automatic and Manual Control," Proceedings of Cranfield Conference 1951, edited by A. Tustin, pp. 421–434, Butterworths Scientific Publications, London, 1952.

form of the original, undelayed exponential; the $1/z^m$ factor represents the delay of everything by mT sec; and the bracketed exponential constant is the amplitude reduction factor A of Fig. 9.42.

The z transform of a step function delayed in the same manner is simply

$$G(z) = G_o(z) \frac{1}{z^m} \qquad (9.130)$$

The amplitude reduction factor is unity. In general, there seems to be no simple way to determine the z transfer function of a tandem combination of a delay line and a group of lumped elements represented by $G_1(s)$. The difficulty arises because the amplitude reduction factors differ from term to term. The only general procedure is to make a partial-fraction expansion of $G_1(s)$, multiply each term individually by $e^{-T_T s}$, and find the corresponding z transfer functions.

A Simple System. The analysis of a simple system illustrates the nature of the effects of a transportation lag on the stability of a sampled-data system. The system to be considered is shown in block diagram form in Fig. 9.43. The conventional part of the system is assumed

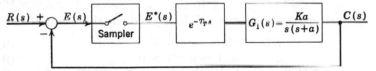

FIG. 9.43. Sampled-data system with transportation lag.

second-order, and the transportation lag is taken less than the sampling period. The maximum gain for system stability is desired as a function of the transportation lag. The realizable velocity constant of this system is to be compared with a similar continuous system with the same transportation lag.

The analysis is initiated with a determination of the open-loop z transfer function $G(z)$, since stability depends on the location of the zeros of $1 + G(z)$. The open-loop transfer function in the s domain is

$$G(s) = e^{-T_T s} \frac{Ka}{s(s + a)} \qquad (9.131)$$

The $G(z)$ is found by first considering only the part of the transfer function associated with the lumped elements.

$$G_1(s) = \frac{Ka}{s(s + a)} = \frac{K}{s} - \frac{K}{s + a} \qquad (9.132)$$

The corresponding $G_1(z)$ can be read directly from Table 9.1.

$$G_1(z) = K\left(\frac{z}{z - 1} - \frac{z}{z - e^{-aT}}\right) \qquad (9.133)$$

$G(z)$ is related to $G_1(z)$ by Eqs. (9.129) and (9.130). In this example, $m = 1$ since the transportation lag is assumed less than a sampling period.

$$G(z) = K\left(\frac{1}{z-1} - \frac{e^{-a(T-T_T)}}{z - e^{-aT}}\right) \tag{9.134}$$

Combining terms gives the open-loop z transfer function:

$$G(z) = K\frac{z(1 - e^{-a(T-T_T)}) + e^{-a(T-T_T)} - e^{-aT}}{(z-1)(z - e^{-aT})} \tag{9.135}$$

The stability is determined by the zeros of $1 + G(z)$. The characteristic polynomial, placing these zeros in evidence, is formed from the sum of the numerator and the denominator of $G(z)$ as given by Eq. (9.135). If this polynomial is denoted $p(z)$,

$$p(z) = z^2 + [K(1 - e^{-a(T-T_T)}) - (1 + e^{-aT})]z + Ke^{-a(T-T_T)} + e^{-aT}(1 - K) \tag{9.136}$$

The system is stable if both zeros of $p(z)$ lie inside the unit circle in the z plane. In terms of the coefficients of the polynomial, these conditions are given by Eq. (9.63), repeated here:

$$|p(0)| < 1 \qquad p(1) > 0 \qquad p(-1) > 0 \tag{9.137}$$

In the present example, these conditions yield the three equations

$$K(e^{-a(T-T_T)} - e^{-aT}) + e^{-aT} < 1 \tag{9.138}$$
$$K(1 - e^{-aT}) > 0 \tag{9.139}$$
$$-K(1 + e^{-aT}) + 2(1 + e^{-aT}) + 2Ke^{-a(T-T_T)} > 0 \tag{9.140}$$

The second equation, (9.139), is obviously satisfied as long as K, a, and T are positive. The first equation, (9.138), can be rewritten

$$K < \frac{e^{aT} - 1}{e^{aT_T} - 1} \tag{9.141}$$

After algebraic manipulation, the third equation, (9.140), can be put in the form

$$K < \frac{2}{1 - 2e^{aT_T}/(e^{aT} + 1)} \tag{9.142}$$

The two equations (9.141) and (9.142) determine the allowable value of the gain constant K. If the two limits on K are plotted as a function of the transportation lag, the curves are as sketched in Fig. 9.44. For very small delays, the inequality of Eq. (9.142) controls the allowable gain; for delays larger than a fixed fraction of T, the gain is limited by Eq. (9.141). If T is 0.1 sec and a is 10/sec, for example, the two inequalities give the same value when T_T is $0.24T$.

This example in itself is not particularly important. The curve of Fig. 9.44, however, does illustrate the rather unusual phenomenon of an increase in the allowable gain with the introduction of a transportation lag. If the K is adjusted to cause oscillations, the system is unstable at a frequency of one half the sampling frequency (and $\frac{3}{2}$, $\frac{5}{2}$, etc., as a result of the periodicity) whenever the transportation lag is small enough that the instability is governed by Eq. (9.142).   With a larger transportation lag, beyond $0.24T$ for the system characterized in Fig. 9.44, the system oscillates primarily because of the phase shift introduced in the delay network, and the frequency of instability decreases with delay.

It is interesting to compare this sampled-data system with a similar continuous system with the same transportation lag and the same second-order transfer function for the linear elements.   The two curves of allowable gain versus transportation lag are shown in Fig. 9.45 for the specific numerical example used previously $(T = 0.1 \text{ sec}, a = 10/\text{sec})$.   Over an appreciable portion of the range of T_T, the sampled-data system permits a high value of gain.   The gain plotted for the continuous system is the velocity constant, while for the sampled-data system the ordinate is the K used previously.   Actually, some care must be taken in interpreting the term "velocity constant" in connection with sampled-data control systems because of the fact that the sampler introduces a gain of

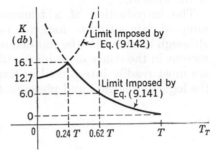

FIG. 9.44. Maximum K for stability in system of Fig. 9.43 with $T = 0.1$ sec and $a = 10/\text{sec}$.

$1/T$ (in this example, 10).   This is clear from the characteristics of the sampler as described in Sec. 9.1.   The $1/T$ factor has been omitted in Fig. 9.45; with the additional 20 db introduced by the sampler (when T is 0.1), the velocity-constant curve for the sampled-data system lies above the curve for the continuous system for all values of the transportation lag larger than a small fraction of the sampling period.

The results described here must be interpreted with some caution. With normal specifications, the sampled-data system is never preferable

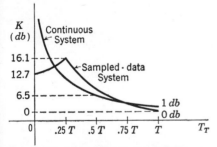

FIG. 9.45. Allowable K for stability in continuous and sampled-data systems.

to a continuous system, whether the system contains a transportation lag or not.   The response of the sampled-data system is always less smooth than that of a continuous system.   In other words, the allowable velocity constant for a system on the border line between stability and instability is here a misleading figure of merit for two reasons: (1) any practical system must possess not only absolute stability, but also relative stability; and (2) the velocity constant measures only the steady-state characteristics but does not indicate either the smoothness or the speed of the initial part of the response.

9.10. Conclusions.   Although the development of techniques for the *synthesis* of sampled-data feedback control systems has lagged far behind analogous developments for continuous systems, many of the *analysis* and *design* methods originally developed for continuous systems can be carried over to the study of sampled-data systems with only slight modifications.   The simplest analysis of sampled-data systems is performed in terms of the Nyquist diagram or the z-domain root-locus plots.   These methods permit both the ready evaluation of the gain to obtain desired relative stability and the study of the effect of the introduction of compensation networks to change the characteristics of the fixed components of the system.

The introduction of a transportation lag in either continuous or sampled-data systems does not present any startlingly new problems, although in each case the root-locus methods lose many of the advantages present in the study of systems without delays.   The effects of the delay are most readily interpreted in terms of either the Nyquist diagrams or the logarithmic gain and phase plots.

CHAPTER 10

NONLINEAR SYSTEMS AND
DESCRIBING-FUNCTION ANALYSIS

One important restriction underlies the theory of feedback systems as presented in the previous chapters: the theory is restricted to the study of linear systems. Particular types of nonlinearities have been considered on occasion, as in Sec. 8.6, which was devoted to the work of Newton on the design of systems subject to saturation. Even there, however, the system design focuses attention on the linear mode of operation: saturation is viewed as an undesirable characteristic which is to be avoided during all except a minor, controlled percentage of the time.

During the past few years, feedback engineers have become increasingly aware that restriction of thinking to linear systems may impose unnecessary burdens on the design in two ways: first, the components used in the feedback control system must be of unnecessarily high quality if they are to operate in a linear fashion when the amplitude and frequency of the input signal vary over wide ranges. If the components are driven into nonlinear regions of operation, linear design predicts the characteristics only approximately and occasionally omits entirely any description of important features of system performance. Second, the restriction to linearity immediately limits narrowly the realizable system characteristics, the type of control systems, and the tasks the control system can be designed to accomplish.

Nonlinearities† in the control system are of two general types: incidental and intentional. Incidental nonlinearities, or unintentional nonlinearities inherent in the system as a result of the limitations of physical equipment, include such phenomena as backlash, saturation, dead zone, or variation of system characteristics with temperature where the temperature depends on the control action. The nonlinearity may have only a minor effect on system performance, as the effect of saturation if the probability of saturation is held low; in other cases, the characteristics of system components change radically with variations in the input signal.

† The term "nonlinearity" or "nonlinear phenomenon" is interpreted in this book as a phenomenon described by a nonlinear differential equation. A nonlinear system is one including one or more components exhibiting nonlinear phenomena. A missile, with the moment of inertia changing during flight as a result of the consumption of fuel, need not be considered a nonlinear system if the fuel consumption can be programed approximately and the inertia considered a function of time alone. In this case, the system is described by a linear differential equation with the coefficients functions of time but not of the dependent variables.

559

Intentional nonlinearities are introduced in order to modify system characteristics. Examples include the nonlinear pitch or yaw dampers so often used in aircraft control systems and the nonlinear controllers designed to realize a relative damping ratio varying with the magnitude of the actuating signal. An extreme case of an intentionally nonlinear system is the on-off or contactor servo, with the control elements designed to apply full torque as soon as the actuating signal exceeds a specified amount.

Nonlinearities can also be classified according to the rate of change of the characteristics of the nonlinear element. *Slow nonlinearities* are those in which the system remains linear over a time interval which is long compared to the response time of the system. *Fast nonlinearities*, on the other hand, are those such as saturation, in which the mode of operation of the system changes rapidly compared to the response time. For example, if a step function is applied, part of the system may saturate until the output is one half the steady-state value, and then the entire system operates in a linear mode during the remainder of the response time. The difficulties associated with the analysis of the two types of systems (with slow and fast nonlinearities) are a magnitude of complexity apart. In the case of a system with a slow nonlinearity, the transfer-function concept is valid and system behavior can be described in terms of poles and zeros which wander slowly around the complex plane. In the case of a system with a fast nonlinearity, such as saturation, the conventional pole-zero, or transfer-function, approach to analysis loses its significance. The describing-function analysis discussed in this chapter is essentially an attempt to approximate a fast nonlinearity by a slow nonlinearity and, in this way, extend the transfer-function concepts to systems with fast nonlinearities.

Techniques for the description of nonlinear systems are still in the early stages of development, with only a limited range of problems susceptible to satisfactory analysis at the present time. The theory of the intentional introduction of nonlinearities into the system is even more decisively incomplete. In certain special problems, a suitable approach is evident and analysis is straightforward. For example,† a suitable linearizing compensation system is readily designed if the differential equation describing the controlled elements takes the form

$$J \frac{d^2e}{dt^2} + B \frac{de}{dt} + B_1 \left(\frac{de}{dt}\right)^3 = T \tag{10.1}$$

where T = restoring torque
$\quad e$ = angular error
$\quad J$ = moment of inertia
$\quad B, B_1$ = constants

† N. Minorsky, Non-linear Control Systems, "Automatic and Manual Control," Proceedings of the Cranfield Conference 1951, edited by A. Tustin, pp. 309–318, Butterworths Scientific Publications, London, 1952. Minorsky discusses the example in connection with the problem of automatic steering of a ship.

If the over-all system is to behave linearly, it is clear that the control system must be designed to yield a T containing a term equal to $B_1(de/dt)^3$. A suitable form for T might be

$$T = B_1 \left(\frac{de}{dt}\right)^3 - Ke \qquad (10.2)$$

The over-all system is then described by the linear differential equation

$$J \frac{d^2e}{dt^2} + B \frac{de}{dt} + Ke = 0 \qquad (10.3)$$

This example illustrates one special technique for handling nonlinear systems. Aside from the fact that such an attack is appropriate only when a simple analytic form exists for describing the nonlinearity, there are certain basic objections to a generalization of this approach:

(1) Linearization of the over-all system means that the components used must be larger than if the system operated in a nonlinear fashion. If the output motor of a servomechanism saturates when the output is driven at the maximum velocity and acceleration, the only way to avoid such saturation and still realize the required velocity is to increase the size of the motor or modify the gear train or mechanical coupling from motor to load. The latter approach eventually fails if the specifications become more and more stringent, however, and a better motor is the only general solution. Unless all components are to be used an excessive percentage of the time at a fraction of the ratings, it is essential that the engineer be able to analyze the effects of nonlinear elements on system performance.

(2) It is certainly not apparent that linearization of the system results in improved performance. Unless the characteristics of the nonlinear system can be determined, there is no indication that the effort expended in linearization is either necessary or desirable. The only obvious characteristic achieved by linearization is a tremendous simplification in analysis.

It is the purpose of this and the following chapter to present the broad outlines of the two general methods which have proved most useful in the study and design of nonlinear feedback control systems. The first method is based on describing functions, first applied to the analysis of feedback control systems in this country by Kochenburger;[†] the second method is based on the phase-plane description of the nonlinear system as suggested first by MacColl.[‡] Regardless of the method used, the ultimate goals are the analysis of the effects of incidental nonlinearities and the synthesis of systems with intentional nonlinearities.

10.1. Characteristics of Nonlinear Systems. The highly developed design and analysis theories for linear systems, in contrast to the rather inadequate state of the art of analysis of nonlinear systems, is a natural result of the well-behaved characteristics of a linear system. Perhaps the most fundamental characteristic of a linear system is the validity of

[†] R. J. Kochenburger, A Frequency Response Method for Analyzing and Synthesizing Contactor Servomechanisms, *Trans. AIEE*, Vol. 69, Part I, pp. 270–284, 1950.

[‡] L. A. MacColl, "Fundamental Theory of Servomechanisms," Appendix, D. Van Nostrand Company, Inc., New York, 1945.

the principle of superposition: if $c_1(t)$ is the response to $r_1(t)$ and $c_2(t)$ to $r_2(t)$, the response to $r_1(t) + r_2(t)$ is $c_1(t) + c_2(t)$. The superposition principle is, of course, simply another way of describing the concept of linearity.   As a consequence of the validity of superposition, certain test signals (*e.g.*, the step function, the impulse function, or the sinusoidal function with variable frequency) can be used to measure system characteristics.   The amplitude of the test signal is immaterial.

The significance of linearity goes even further, however.   If a linear system is excited by a sinusoidal signal, the output is a sinusoidal signal of different phase and amplitude, but of the same frequency.   The output of a linear system cannot contain components at frequencies not present in the input.   Furthermore, the question of stability is clearly defined in linear systems.   The system is either stable or unstable; the driving functions and the initial conditions have no effect on stability. The unexcited stable system eventually comes to rest; the output of the unstable system grows *without bound*, either exponentially or in an oscillatory mode with the envelope of the oscillations increasing exponentially.

All the characteristics mentioned in the preceding two paragraphs, characteristics which permit the systematic analysis and design of linear systems, are absent in the general nonlinear system.   The principle of superposition is not valid; the frequencies present in the output may not be those of the input; the stability of the system may depend on the excitation or initial conditions; and system instability may mean a constant-amplitude output of arbitrary waveform.   With a number of the important features of nonlinear systems considered in detail in this chapter and the following, it is appropriate at this point to describe the general nature of several of these characteristics.[†]

Different Behavior with Different Inputs.   By definition, a nonlinear system is one which may behave quite differently with different input functions.   Consequently, the logical design of a nonlinear system requires a complete description of the input signals.   For example, it is demonstrated in Chap. 7 that the design of a linear system to minimize the mean-square error with random input signals requires a knowledge of the second probability distribution functions of the signal and noise components of the input.   In contrast, the design to yield the nonlinear filter which is optimum on the basis of the mean-square-error criterion theoretically requires knowledge of *all* probability distributions.

This dependence of system behavior on the actual input functions is demonstrated by the jump-resonance phenomenon observed in certain closed-loop systems with saturation.   If $\left| \dfrac{C}{R} (j\omega) \right|$ is plotted as a function of frequency, the curve of Fig. 10.1 results if R, the amplitude of the input, is held constant.   As the frequency is increased from zero, the measured response follows the curve through points A, B, and C, but at C an incremental increase in frequency results in a discontinuous jump

[†] A similar discussion of certain characteristics of nonlinear systems is given by N. Minorsky, *op. cit.*

in the response to point D, after which further increases in frequency lead to values along the curve DEF. If the frequency is decreased, the curve $FEDB'$ is followed, a jump occurs from B' to B, and the gain values continue along the BA curve. The over-all curve exhibits the familiar hysteresis, or jump resonance. Certain conditions under which the jump resonance occurs are described in Sec. 10.5; at this point, it is sufficient to note that in this case the response of the nonlinear system depends not only on the present value of the input, but also on the past history.

Limit Cycles. One of the phe-nomena observed earliest in physi-cal systems and unexplained by linear theory is the existence of limit cycles, oscillations of fixed amplitude and period. Although an unstable linear system always has an unbounded output, the out-put of a physical system is always finite. The oscillations of an elec-tric circuit, for example, may build

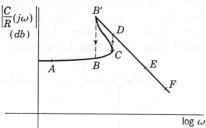

FIG. 10.1. Closed-loop gain characteristic with jump resonance.

up very nearly exponentially until the amplitude reaches a certain level, at which time the rate of growth decreases and eventually the amplitude stabilizes. Van der Pol showed in 1920 that the behavior of an electronic oscillator could be described by a nonlinear differential equation of the form

$$\ddot{q} - \epsilon(1 - q^2)\dot{q} + q = 0 \qquad (10.4)$$

Although the discussion of Sec. 11.5 demonstrates that a system charac-terized by this equation exhibits a limit cycle if ϵ is positive, purely physical reasoning can be used to indicate the plausibility of this result. The equation describes the circuit of Fig. 10.2 if R represents an element with a resistance varying as $-\epsilon(1 - q^2)$. If the amplitude of q is small,

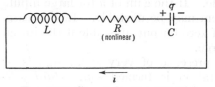

FIG. 10.2. Circuit for Eq. (10.4).

the resistance is approximately $-\epsilon$ and negative. The amplitude of oscillations starts to build up with an exponential envelope. As $|q|$ increases, the resistance varies signif-icantly during a period, until, with $|q|$ very large, the resistance is posi-tive at almost all times. The gen-eral tendency is for the oscillations to die out. An intermediate value of the amplitude of q exists at which the oscillations are stable. (The wave-form of q is, of course, not sinusoidal.)

One important aim of any analysis method for the study of nonlinear systems is the determination of the existence and location of limit cycles. Both the describing-function approach presented in this chapter and the phase-plane analysis developed in Chap. 11 provide techniques for the investigation of limit cycles. In general, in the analysis of feedback control systems, knowledge concerning the existence of a limit cycle is more important than the waveform or exact period of the constant-amplitude oscillation. If the performance of multivibrators, pulse-shaping circuits, etc., is being considered, shaping of the waveform associated with the limit cycle may be the primary purpose of analysis.

Soft and Hard Self-excitations. A third important characteristic of nonlinear systems is the dependence of system stability on the excitation and the initial conditions. The simplest example of this phenomenon is furnished by a system with a dead zone; Fig. 10.3(*a*) is the corresponding block diagram. The input-output characteristic of *n* is shown in part (*b*) of the figure. Clearly, if the system is driven by a signal so small that the input to *n* never exceeds the dead-zone amplitude, the

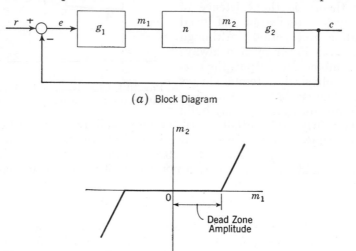

(*a*) Block Diagram

(*b*) Input-output Characteristic of *n*

Fig. 10.3. Feedback control system with dead zone.

output is zero and the system is stable. If the gain of *n* for large inputs is sufficiently high, the over-all system may be unstable. In this case, the system is stable in the vicinity of zero output, unstable if the initial conditions or drive are sufficiently large.

If the system is unstable in the presence of very small signals or disturbances, the resulting self-excitation is termed *soft*. *Hard self-excitation*, as typified by the system with dead zone, means that self-excitation cannot occur with very small disturbances exciting the system from rest; the system must be excited with signals of a certain minimum amplitude or with appropriate initial conditions. Both the phase-plane and describing-function methods of analysis place in evidence the characteristics of soft and hard self-excitation.

Subharmonic Generation. The output of a nonlinear device may contain subharmonics of the input signal. For example, if sinusoidal signals of two angular frequencies ω_1 and ω_2 are added and the sum applied to a nonlinear device, the output contains, in general, components at $m\omega_1 \pm$

$n\omega_2$, where m and n assume all possible integer values and zero. This principle is the basis for the operation of converters and mixers in communication receivers, frequency-demultiplication circuits used to obtain low-frequency signals with the frequency stabilized by a crystal-controlled oscillator, etc.

The possibility of the generation of subharmonics presents certain difficulties in the analysis of nonlinear circuits. Usually the trouble arises because of the question as to whether subharmonic components are possible. In a simple example, if the input signal to a feedback control system is sinusoidal, the presence of significant subharmonics in the output ordinarily results in poor performance characteristics. The analysis of a mechanical circuit containing linear springs and nonlinear dampers illustrates another aspect of the problem. If an analytic form is assumed for the relation between damper force and velocity (for example, force proportional to the square of the velocity), the response of complicated circuits to sinusoidal excitation can be determined point by point with the use of a digital computer. Clearly, it is desirable to be able to terminate the calculations as soon as a steady-state output is reached. A large number of cycles must be evaluated after an apparently steady output is obtained, in order to determine the presence and magnitude of any subharmonic components.

Parametric Excitation. If a parameter of a nonlinear system is varied at an angular frequency ω_1, the system may oscillate at the frequency $\omega_1/2$. Although this direct parametric excitation is not commonly found in feedback control systems, an inverse parametric effect is utilized, as described in Sec. 11.8, to vary the relative stability of the system with changes in the error voltage. The variation in a system parameter is used to absorb the energy of the overshooting oscillation of the step-function response.

Other Phenomena. There are a great many other phenomena peculiar to nonlinear systems, but the above characteristics are the most significant for the control-system engineer. Such phenomena as the synchronization of oscillators and the quenching of oscillations are of only secondary interest in the analysis of these chapters.

Objectives of the Analysis. Thus, the analysis of nonlinear systems presents a twofold problem. First, the analysis must discover such effects as limit cycles, jump resonance, and subharmonic generation. Second, the analysis must indicate the nature of the system response to the actual input functions. There is no single method of attack which is generally applicable. The describing-function approach simplifies the problem by assuming that the input to the nonlinear device is sinusoidal and that the only significant frequency component of the output is that component at the input frequency. The describing-function analysis is applicable to systems of any order; indeed, it usually tends to be more accurate, the higher the order of the system. The second approach, treated in Chap. 11, is based on the phase-plane representation of system characteristics. The method is applicable only to second-order systems or to the approximate investigation of higher-order systems by assuming that the general effects of the nonlinearity can be studied by an approximation of the actual system by a second-order configuration.

10.2. Describing-function Analysis. The fundamental elements of the describing-function approach† to the analysis of nonlinear systems are presented in this section.

Assumptions. The describing-function analysis of nonlinear systems is based on three assumptions:

(1) There is only one nonlinear element in the system. If there are more than one, the part of the system including all nonlinearities is considered as a single nonlinear component. It is theoretically possible to consider systems with more than one isolated nonlinearity, but the analysis becomes unduly complicated except in very special cases (*cf.* Sec. 10.7).

(2) The output of the nonlinear element depends only on the present value and past history of the input. In other words, no time-varying characteristics are included in n, the nonlinear element.

(3) *If the input of n is a sinusoidal signal, only the fundamental component of the output of n contributes to the input.*

The last assumption is the keystone of the describing-function analysis. The significance of this assumption is illustrated by Fig. 10.4, showing the block diagram of a single-loop system with the nonlinear element n and having the linear elements represented by the block g with a transfer function $G(s)$. The input of n is assumed to be sinusoidal. The resulting output is periodic and contains components at the fundamental frequency (the frequency of the input) and, in general, all higher harmonic frequencies.‡ These various frequency components pass through the block g and are then subtracted from the system input to give the actuating signal, the input to n. Assumption (3) states that in this system

---

† Historically, the first exposition in this country of the describing-function method was the MIT Ph.D. thesis of R. J. Kochenburger, which was concerned with the analysis and design of contactor servomechanisms. The work was summarized in the paper, A Frequency Response Method for Analyzing and Synthesizing Contactor Servomechanisms, *Trans. AIEE*, Vol. 69, Part I, pp. 270–284, 1950. The approximation involved is similar to that used by N. Kryloff and N. Bogoliuboff, "Introduction to Non-linear Mechanics," translated by S. Lefschetz, Princeton University Press, Princeton, N.J., 1943.

Apparently independent developments of essentially the same methods were presented in this country by Kochenburger, in the U.S.S.R. by Goldfarb, in Germany by Oppelt, and in England by Tustin. The papers by Goldfarb and Oppelt have been translated and published by the Office of Basic Instrumentation of the National Bureau of Standards as Translation of Papers on Stability of Non-linear Feedback Control Systems, *Natl. Bur. Standards Rept.* 1691, May 29, 1952. The three original papers are: L. C. Goldfarb, On Some Non-linear Phenomena in Regulatory Systems, *Avtomatika i Telemekhanika*, Vol. 8, No. 5, pp. 349–383, 1947, in Russian; W. Oppelt, Locus Curve Method for Regulators with Friction, *J. Inst. Elec. Engrs. (London)*, Vol. 94, Part IIA, Nos. 1 and 2, May, 1947; and A. Tustin, The Effects of Backlash and of Speed-development Friction on the Stability of Closed-cycle Control systems, *J. Inst. Elec. Engrs. (London)*, Vol. 94, Part IIA, No. 1, May, 1947.

‡ Satisfaction of assumption (3) ordinarily requires that no significant subharmonic is generated by n.

the fundamental is the only significant component of the primary feedback (or the system output).

This assumption is justified on two grounds: first, the harmonics of the output of n are ordinarily of smaller amplitude than the fundamental; and, second, in most feedback control systems, the gain of g decreases as the frequency increases, with the result that in transmission through g the higher harmonics are attenuated compared to the fundamental. The assumption is of questionable validity in cases in which the harmonic

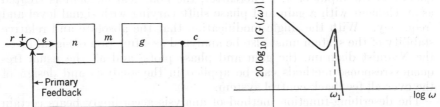

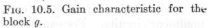

FIG. 10.4. Single-loop system with non-linear element n.

FIG. 10.5. Gain characteristic for the block g.

content of the output of n is high or in which $|G(j\omega)|$, the magnitude of the transfer function of the linear components, has a pronounced peak, as indicated in Fig. 10.5. If this peak occurs at a frequency ω_1, the gain may be larger at ω_1 than at $\omega_1/2$. Consequently, if the fundamental frequency is $\omega_1/2$, the second harmonic of the primary feedback may be larger than the fundamental.

Method of Analysis. If the three basic assumptions listed at the beginning of this section are satisfied, the sinusoidal response characteristics of the nonlinear element can be expressed in terms of a describing function, defined as the ratio of the fundamental component of the output to the amplitude of the input. In the terminology of Fig. 10.6,

$$N = \frac{C_1}{R} \qquad (10.5)$$

FIG. 10.6. Nonlinear element.

Here N is the describing function, R is the amplitude of the sinusoidal input signal $R \sin \omega t$, and C_1 is the amplitude of the output fundamental component $C_1 \sin \omega t$.

In the general case, N is a function of R and ω. If the device is nonlinear, N necessarily depends on R. In addition, if the nonlinear system contains any energy-storage elements, N depends on the frequency. Simple amplifier saturation clearly is described by an N varying with only the amplitude of the input. In contrast, the describing function for a motor with velocity saturation and a load consisting of inertia and damping depends not only on input amplitude, but also on the frequency of the input signal, as a result of the variation of the inertial effect with frequency.

The describing function N may be purely real or may contain a phase shift. N is real if the response characteristic of the nonlinear system is single-valued (*i.e.*, if the output depends only on the present value of the input, not on the past history or the derivatives of the input). Saturation again serves as a particularly simple example. In this case, the fundamental component of the output is always in phase with the input. Backlash and velocity saturation are two examples of simple nonlinearities for which N is complex, as indicated in detail later in this chapter.

The analysis of a nonlinear system is initiated with a determination of the variation of the describing function with the amplitude and frequency of the input of n. Thereafter, the nonlinear element is treated as an element with a gain and phase shift varying with signal level and frequency. With the single modification that the absolute and relative stability of the system must also be analyzed as a function of signal level, the Nyquist diagram, the gain and phase plots, and all the usual frequency-response methods can be applied in the analysis and design of the over-all feedback control system.

The describing-function method of analysis accordingly bears certain sharp distinctions from other conventional approaches to the analysis of nonlinear circuits. For example, vacuum-tube amplifiers, including reactive plate-circuit impedances and driven into the nonlinear region of operation, are classically analyzed by assuming that the plate voltage is sinusoidal, determining the plate current from the known load impedance, and plotting the appropriate operating path on the plate characteristics. This plot determines the waveform of the grid voltage required to give the assumed plate voltage. The difference between this grid-voltage waveform and a sinusoid is used as a measure of the harmonic distortion resulting in the plate voltage if the tube is driven by a sinusoidal signal. Much the same approach is usually used in the study of backlash. The output is assumed sinusoidal, and the corresponding waveform of the position of the motor shaft is calculated.

In both these examples, the waveform of the input signal is determined under the assumption of a sinusoidal output. In the describing-function method, on the other hand, the input to the nonlinear circuit is the starting point of the analysis; it is the waveform at this input which is assumed sinusoidal. The basic assumption is that the output of the nonlinear device is also sinusoidal.

10.3. Calculation of a Describing Function. The first step in the describing-function analysis involves the determination of the describing function for the nonlinear components.† It is assumed that the block diagram of the system is drawn in the form shown in Fig. 10.7: the nonlinear elements, comprising n, are isolated from the linear portions of the system. In general, there may also be linear components in the feedback path or in minor loops within the system; Fig. 10.7 represents a simple system illustrating the general approach. The describing func-

† In addition to those given in the other references throughout this chapter, a number of describing functions are presented by H. D. Greif, Describing Function Method of Servomechanism Analysis Applied to Most Commonly Encountered Nonlinearities, *Trans. AIEE*, Part II, *Applications and Industry*, Vol. 72, pp. 243–248, 1953.

tion N is the ratio of the fundamental component of y to the amplitude of the sinusoidal x:

$$N = \frac{Y_1}{X} \qquad \text{when } x = X \sin \omega t \qquad (10.6)$$

Calculation of the describing function involves a conventional Fourier analysis to obtain the fundamental component of the output. The procedure is illustrated with the nonlinear characteristic of Fig. 10.8. The system possesses a dead zone for inputs from $-D$ to $+D$, has a linear

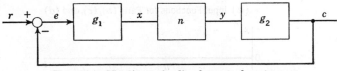

FIG. 10.7. Nonlinear feedback control system.

region of operation for inputs between D and S or $-D$ and $-S$, and exhibits saturation for input magnitudes larger than S.

With a sinusoidal input, the waveform of the output may take any of three forms, as indicated in Fig. 10.9. With the input amplitude less than D, no output results; with X between D and S, the output is similar to the output of a slicer circuit; and, with X larger than S, the peaks of the output are clipped. Since the output is a single-valued odd function of the input, an input signal X sin ωt results in an output of the form

$$y(t) = Y_1 \sin \omega t + Y_3 \sin 3\omega t + Y_5 \sin 5\omega t + \cdots \qquad (10.7)$$

Furthermore, since the nonlinear circuit involves no energy storage, the describing function is independent of frequency and ω can be considered unity.

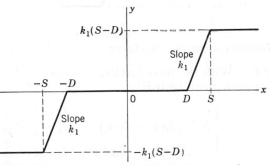

FIG. 10.8. Nonlinear characteristic with dead zone and saturation.

Clearly, the situation shown in Fig. 10.9(b) can be considered at once: with Y_1 equal to zero, N is zero for all X less than D. The describing function with X larger than D is conveniently evaluated if t_1 and t_2 are defined as shown in Fig. 10.10: t_1 is the time when the input equals the dead-zone amplitude and the system starts conducting (the output increases from zero); t_2, the instant when the system starts to saturate. If X lies between D and S, the output is not limited and the value of

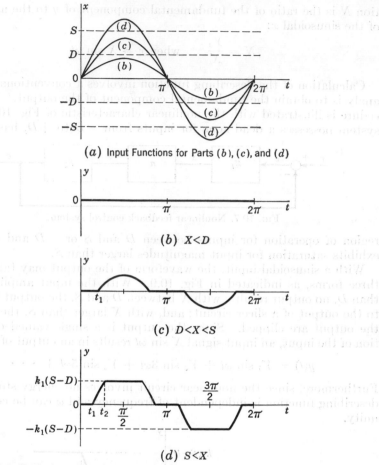

(a) Input Functions for Parts (b), (c), and (d)

(b) $X<D$

(c) $D<X<S$

(d) $S<X$

FIG. 10.9. Variation of output of nonlinear system with amplitude of input.

$\pi/2$ is used for t_2. With the introduction of t_1 and t_2, the output during the first quarter period can be written

$$
y(t) = \begin{cases} 0 & 0 < t < t_1 \\ k_1X \, (\sin t - \sin t_1) & t_1 < t < t_2 \\ k_1X \, (\sin t_2 - \sin t_1) & t_2 < t < \dfrac{\pi}{2} \end{cases} \tag{10.8}
$$

Here k_1 is the incremental gain in the linear region of operation,

$$
k_1 = \frac{dy}{dx} \qquad \text{when } D < x < S \tag{10.9}
$$

Each component of the output is given by the formula for the Fourier coefficients:

$$
Y_k = \frac{4}{\pi} \int_0^{\pi/2} y(t) \sin kt \, dt \qquad k = 1, 3, 5, \ldots \tag{10.10}
$$

Substitution of Eq. (10.8) in (10.10) yields

$$Y_k = \frac{2k_1X}{\pi k} \left\{ \frac{\sin[(k-1)t_2] - \sin[(k-1)t_1]}{k-1} \right.$$
$$\left. + \frac{\sin[(k+1)t_2] - \sin[(k+1)t_1]}{k+1} \right\} \qquad k = 1, 3, 5, \ldots \quad (10.11)$$

The relative magnitude of the fundamental and higher-harmonic components, as found from Eq. (10.11), gives an initial indication as to the applicability of the describing-function approach. The smaller the harmonics at the output of the nonlinear elements, the more easily the basic assumption underlying the use of the describing function is satisfied. In

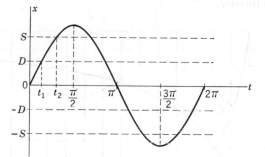

FIG 10.10. Definition of t_1 and t_2.

this case, the amplitude of Y_k drops off roughly as $1/k$, although the braced term does vary with k. With the most troublesome harmonic ordinarily the third, the relative magnitudes of Y_1 and Y_3 are of interest:

$$Y_1 = \frac{2k_1X}{\pi} \left(t_2 - t_1 + \frac{\sin 2t_2 - \sin 2t_1}{2} \right) \qquad (10.12)$$

$$Y_3 = \frac{2k_1X}{3\pi} \left(\frac{\sin 2t_2 - \sin 2t_1}{2} + \frac{\sin 4t_2 - \sin 4t_1}{4} \right) \qquad (10.13)$$

Y_1/X is the describing function, and $|Y_3/Y_1|$ measures the accuracy of the describing-function analysis.

System with Dead Zone, No Saturation. The nonlinear system without saturation is analyzed by substitution of $\pi/2$ for t_2 in Eqs. (10.12) and (10.13):

$$Y_1 = \frac{2k_1X}{\pi} \left(\frac{\pi}{2} - t_1 - \frac{\sin 2t_1}{2} \right) \qquad (10.14)$$

$$Y_3 = -\frac{2k_1X}{3\pi} \left(\frac{\sin 2t_1}{2} + \frac{\sin 4t_1}{4} \right) \qquad (10.15)$$

The describing function is Y_1/X:

$$N = \begin{cases} 0 & \dfrac{X}{D} < 1 \\[2ex] \dfrac{2k_1}{\pi} \left(\dfrac{\pi}{2} - t_1 - \dfrac{\sin 2t_1}{2} \right) & \dfrac{X}{D} > 1 \end{cases} \qquad (10.16)$$

In Eq. (10.16), t_1, the instant during the first quarter cycle at which conduction starts, is given by the relation

$$t_1 = \arcsin \frac{D}{X} \tag{10.17}$$

Figure 10.11 is a plot of N as a function of the ratio X/D. The describing function is zero for inputs too small to drive the system into conduction. As X is increased beyond D, N increases monotonically until, with X much larger than D (corresponding to essentially no dead zone), the describing function equals the gain of the linear portion of the input-output characteristic.

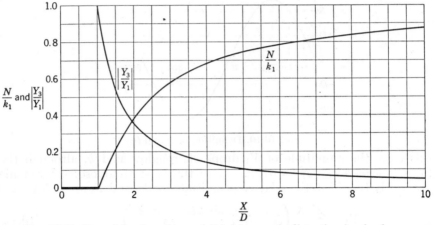

Fig. 10.11. Describing function and third-harmonic distortion for dead zone.

The third-harmonic distortion of the output waveform is measured by the ratio of Eq. (10.15) to (10.14):

$$\frac{Y_3}{Y_1} = -\frac{1}{6} \frac{2 \sin 2t_1 + \sin 4t_1}{\pi - 2t_1 - \sin 2t_1} \tag{10.18}$$

The magnitude of the ratio is plotted in Fig. 10.11 as a function of X/D. As X increases above D, the relative magnitude of the third harmonic falls rapidly, with $|Y_3/Y_1|$ less than 0.36 for all values of X larger than $2D$. Since the gain is small with $X < 2D$, the closed-loop system in most cases is definitely stable and the third-harmonic distortion is not significant. When the gain is high and a greater tendency for oscillation exists, the relative amplitude of the third harmonic is small and the describing-function analysis depicts more accurately the behavior of the nonlinear element.

  System with Saturation, No Dead Zone.   If there is no dead zone ($t_1 = 0$), Eqs. (10.12) and (10.13) become

$$Y_1 = \frac{2k_1X}{\pi}\left(t_2 + \frac{\sin 2t_2}{2}\right) \tag{10.19}$$

$$Y_3 = \frac{2k_1X}{3\pi}\left(\frac{\sin 2t_2}{2} + \frac{\sin 4t_2}{4}\right) \tag{10.20}$$

The describing function and relative third harmonic are

$$N = \frac{2k_1}{\pi}\left(t_2 + \frac{\sin 2t_2}{2}\right) \tag{10.21}$$

$$\frac{Y_3}{Y_1} = \frac{1}{6}\frac{2\sin 2t_2 + \sin 4t_2}{2t_2 + \sin 2t_2} \tag{10.22}$$

In these equations, t_2 is defined in terms of X and the saturation level S:

$$t_2 = \arcsin \frac{S}{X} \tag{10.23}$$

The variation of N and $|Y_3/Y_1|$ with X/S is shown in Fig. 10.12. The describing function is k_1 for all signal inputs less than the saturation

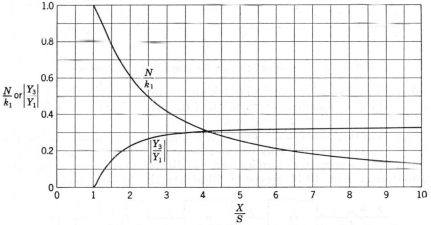

Fig. 10.12. Describing function and third-harmonic distortion for saturation.

level and then falls off rapidly as the amplitude increases further. N approaches zero as X tends to infinity because the output becomes a square wave of a peak-to-peak amplitude $2k_1S$. The amplitude of the fundamental component of the square wave is finite $(4k_1S/\pi)$, but the input is infinite. The relative amplitude of the third harmonic increases to a maximum value of $\frac{1}{3}$ for small t_2 (when the input is large enough that the output is essentially a square wave).

System with Saturation and Dead Zone. If both saturation and dead zone are present, the variation of N with X is a combination of the curves of Figs. 10.11 and 10.12. The actual curve depends on the ratio S/D, but, in general, N is zero for X less than D, increases with X to a maximum value occurring when X is slightly larger than S, then falls again toward zero because of the saturation. Figure 10.13 indicates the variation of N with the ratio X/D for various values of S/D.

Thus, calculation of the describing function entails a straightforward determination of the fundamental component of the output of the non-linear device. If desired, the amplitude of the third harmonic can also be determined in order to estimate the accuracy of the describing-function analysis. In any but the simplest cases, however, the calculation of N

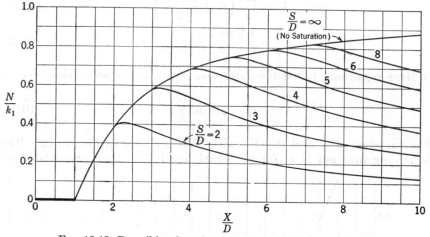

FIG. 10.13. Describing function for saturation and dead zone.

and $|Y_3/Y_1|$ is tedious, particularly if the nonlinear characteristic is not single-valued. Machine computation of the describing function is essential in more complicated situations.

10.4. Stability Analysis. The describing function, obtained for the known nonlinearity either by calculation or by analog or digital computation, can be used to determine the stability of the system. The configuration of Fig. 10.14 serves to illustrate the general techniques of

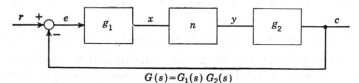

$$G(s)=G_1(s)\,G_2(s)$$

FIG. 10.14. Single-loop system to illustrate stability analysis.

stability analysis. The stability of this system is established by the open-loop gain: the gain from a given point (such as the input of n) around the loop and back to the same point. If the nonlinear device can be adequately characterized by the describing function N, the loop gain is simply $-NG(j\omega)$, where N generally depends on both frequency and the signal level at the input of n. Thus, the study of stability involves an investigation of the zeros of $1 + NG(j\omega)$, or the values of frequency and amplitude which satisfy the equation

$$-N = \frac{1}{G(j\omega)} \tag{10.24}$$

Nonlinear systems for which N is independent of frequency are considered in this section.

Nyquist-diagram Analysis. The stability, as a function of the signal amplitude at the input of n, is investigated by a modification of the

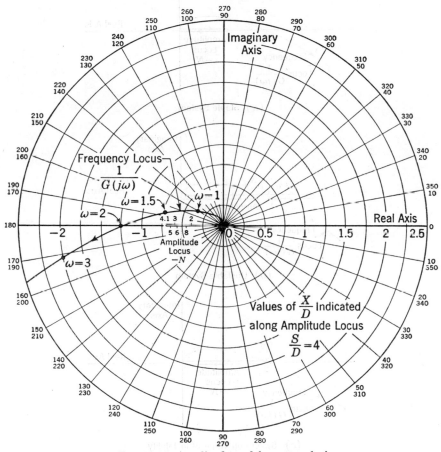

FIG. 10.15. Amplitude and frequency loci.

Nyquist diagram. Two loci are drawn in the complex plane: the inverse Nyquist diagram [the plot of the imaginary versus the real part of $1/G(j\omega)$], and the variation of $-N$ with the amplitude of the input signal of the nonlinear device. The former is the *frequency locus*, the latter the *amplitude locus*. Figure 10.15 shows the nature of the frequency locus for

$$G(s) = \frac{16}{s(s+1)(s+4)} \tag{10.25}$$

The figure also includes the amplitude locus for the nonlinearity described in the preceding section: the system with dead zone and saturation, and here with S/D equal to 4.† The two loci of Fig. 10.15 show independently the variation of the characteristics of the frequency-dependent and amplitude-dependent parts of the system. Along the frequency locus,

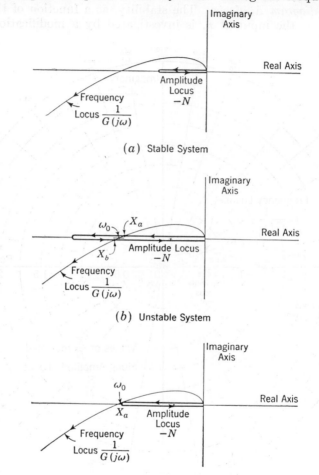

(a) Stable System

(b) Unstable System

(c) System on Verge of Instability

FIG. 10.16. Stability analysis of nonlinear system.

various values of ω are marked, and, along the amplitude locus, the values of X/D, the ratio of the amplitude of the input and the dead-zone amplitude, are shown.

The stability of the system depends on the relative location of the two loci. The three parts of Fig. 10.16 demonstrate the possible situations. The arrow on the amplitude locus corresponds to the direction

† The amplitude locus actually lies entirely on the negative real axis since N is purely real. For clarity, it is shown slightly off the axis.

of increasing amplitude. In part (a) of the figure, the loci correspond to a system which is stable regardless of signal amplitude. The gain of the nonlinear device is never large enough to result in a loop gain of unity when the phase shift is 180°.

The two loci of Fig. 10.16(b), however, depict the characteristics of a system which is unstable for all values of X between X_a and X_b. With values of X less than X_a or larger than X_b, the system is stable. If the system is at rest, slight disturbances do not lead to instability. If the disturbance or input is sufficiently large to cause a signal at the input of n with the frequency ω_0 and the amplitude X_a, sustained oscillations occur. A slightly larger signal results in a loop gain greater than unity, and the oscillations increase until X_b is reached, at which time equilibrium again exists and sustained oscillations of amplitude X_b and frequency ω_0 are observed. A still larger signal results in a stable system, with a decay of the oscillation amplitude back to X_b. Thus, the two intersections, at amplitudes of X_a and X_b, represent unstable and stable equilibrium conditions, respectively.

In Fig. 10.16(c), the two loci touch at only one point, and the system is on the border line between stability and instability. The system possesses an unstable equilibrium point for sustained oscillations with the frequency ω_0 and amplitude X_a. Any amplitude decrease (e.g., as a result of random noise) results in the oscillations dying out and the system coming to rest. The condition depicted in Fig. 10.16(c) is of more academic than practical interest, however, since physically the parameters of the system are never known accurately and vary slightly with changes in ambient temperature, drift in supply voltages, tube aging, and so forth. In addition, the describing-function analysis involves an approximation of the actual characteristics of the nonlinear elements.

In the study of feedback control systems, the engineer is as interested in relative stability as in absolute stability. A system exhibiting the characteristics shown in Fig. 10.16(c) is ordinarily as unsatisfactory for control purposes as one described by part (b) of the figure. Whether the stable system represented by part (a) of the figure possesses satisfactory relative stability is determined by the relative position of the frequency and amplitude loci. The constant-M circles (loci of constant closed-loop gain) can be constructed in the plane of the open-loop transfer function in the usual way,[†] with the exception that the -1 point of the conventional analysis is replaced by the appropriate point on the amplitude locus. The closed-loop system possesses an M_p[‡] which is a function of the value of the amplitude of the signal at the input of the nonlinear device. Actually, the value of M_p for a constant X does not correspond to the conventional maximum of the closed-loop system function, but, rather, the M_p determined by the graphical construction is the maximum value of the closed-loop gain as a function of frequency, where the gain curve is determined by varying the input amplitude R with fre-

[†] G. S. Brown and D. P. Cambell, "Principles of Servomechanisms," pp. 176–182, John Wiley & Sons, Inc., New York, 1948.

[‡] M_p is the maximum value of the closed-loop gain as a function of frequency.

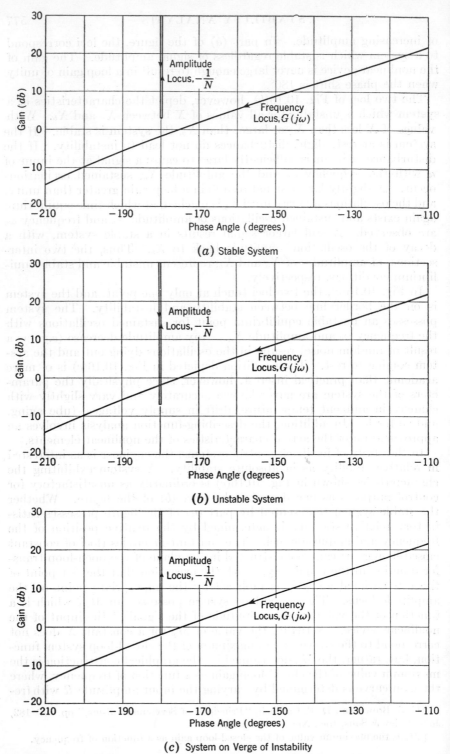

(a) Stable System

(b) Unstable System

(c) System on Verge of Instability

FIG. 10.17. Gain-phase plots corresponding to Fig. 10.16.

quency in such a way as to hold X constant. The relation between open-loop and closed-loop characteristics is discussed in more detail in the next section.

Analysis in Gain-phase Plane. Exactly the same stability analysis can be carried out in the gain-phase plane (in terms of Nichols charts). The loci previously considered are shown in Fig. 10.17, with the frequency locus now plotted as gain versus phase. Again here, it is immaterial whether the loci of $1/G(j\omega)$ and $-N(X)$ or those of $G(j\omega)$ and $-1/N(X)$ are plotted, although the latter form is more familiar. For the describing function of the system with dead zone and saturation (S/D equal to 4),

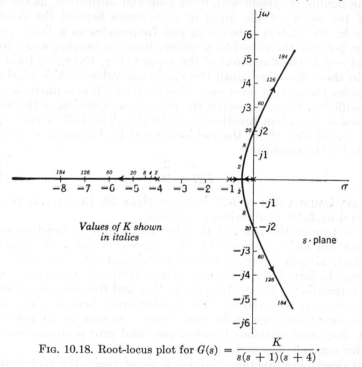

Fig. 10.18. Root-locus plot for $G(s) = \dfrac{K}{s(s+1)(s+4)}$.

the amplitude locus lies entirely along the vertical 180° line. The points of instability are the intersections of the two loci. The three parts of Fig. 10.17 correspond, respectively, to the three relative positions shown in Fig. 10.16. Again the stable and unstable (convergent and divergent) equilibrium points are apparent from the direction of the amplitude locus at the intersection.

Root-locus Analysis. In the special cases in which the describing functions are purely real and independent of frequency, the significance of the describing function is clearly indicated by the root-locus plots for the system. Figure 10.18 shows the root loci for the $G(s)$ previously considered,

$$G(s) = \frac{K}{s(s+1)(s+4)} \qquad (10.26)$$

The entire open-loop transfer function, evaluated at real frequencies, is

$$-NG(j\omega) = \frac{-KN}{j\omega(j\omega + 1)(j\omega + 4)} \tag{10.27}$$

The behavior along the $j\omega$ axis is identical with that of a system without the nonlinearity and with a gain of KN. Accordingly, the real-frequency behavior of the system for any given amplitude of the input of n can be determined by locating the poles of the closed-loop system function at the appropriate point on the root loci.†

In the nonlinear system with dead zone and saturation, as the amplitude of the signal at the input of n increases beyond the dead-zone magnitude, the system behaves at real frequencies as a linear system, with the poles of the closed-loop system function moving away from 0, -1, and -4 in the directions of the arrows (Fig. 10.18). Motion continues in these directions until the maximum value of N is reached, at which point the motion reverses. Clearly, the system is unstable only if KN is sufficiently large to cause the maximum excursion of the poles of the closed-loop system function to lie in the right half of the s plane. In the case of Fig. 10.18, the loci indicate that the nonlinear system is unstable for the conditions

$$\omega = 2 \tag{10.28}$$
$$KN = 20 \tag{10.29}$$

If the maximum value of KN is larger than 20, the system possesses stable and unstable equilibrium conditions.

This picture of the poles of the closed-loop system function moving along the root loci as the gain of the nonlinear device varies provides a particularly simple interpretation of the significance of the describing function. Unfortunately, however, there does not appear to be any simple correlation between this pole motion and the corresponding transient response of the system. The trouble arises because the pole-zero concepts essentially refer to linear systems. As soon as the poles are in motion, the usual relations between pole and zero positions and overshoot, for example, are no longer valid.

If the describing function contains a phase angle, the root-locus plot for $G(s)$ must be modified. Not only the loci for a 180° angle of $G(s)$, but also the loci for angles of 170°, 160°, etc., must be plotted, since the poles of C/R are determined by the condition

$$NG(s) = -1 \tag{10.30}$$

Thus, the root-locus plot presents essentially the same limited information as the Nyquist diagram or the gain-phase plot, but, if N is complex, the added difficulty of construction discourages the use of root-locus methods.

† The root-locus diagram of Fig. 10.18 might be considered as plots with the gain KN as a parameter. Rigorously, however, the describing function has no significance at points in the s plane off the $j\omega$ axis. Thus, the figure should be interpreted as a means for characterizing the behavior of the system only when the input of n is sinusoidal.

10.5. Closed-loop Describing Functions. The describing function measures the sinusoidal gain of the nonlinear components as a function of the amplitude of the input of the nonlinear part of the system. Frequently, it is desirable to obtain the correlation between this describing function and the frequency characteristics of the closed-loop system with a constant amplitude of the input of the over-all system. A typical problem is depicted in Fig. 10.19: with the describing function (N) and the conventional transfer function [$G(s)$] known, the ratio $\dfrac{C}{R}$ ($j\omega$) is to be obtained as a function of ω *and with the input amplitude R fixed.*

The difficulties arise because for a given R and ω the amplitude of the actuating signal E depends on N, but N is in turn determined by E. As a result of this interdependence of N and E, the calculation of the closed-loop frequency response for a fixed R may be a complicated procedure. Indeed, in certain cases (notably, when saturation is present) the closed-loop response may be a multivalued function of frequency. This phenomenon is illustrated in detail by the following example, in which the parameter values are purposely chosen to yield the multivalued response.

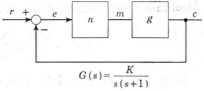

$$G(s) = \frac{K}{s(s+1)}$$

Fig. 10.19. Nonlinear single-loop system.

Regardless of the nature of $\dfrac{C}{R}$ ($j\omega$) for constant R, the characteristic can be determined by a graphical calculation yielding both N and E. From the known describing function, the amplitude of the output of the nonlinear component is plotted as a function of E; superimposed on the same graph is a plot of that amplitude of the output of n which satisfies the closed-loop equation of the system [the relation between E and R established by N and $G(j\omega)$ and the closing of the loop]. The intersections of the two curves give the appropriate E and N.

The method is illustrated with the analysis of the system shown in Fig. 10.19,† a system which also exhibits the unusual phenomenon of a multivalued closed-loop frequency characteristic. (The primary significance of the example lies in the general approach, however, rather than the specific results.) The nonlinear device is assumed to possess only saturation, with the result that the describing function is as shown in Fig. 10.12. The equation describing the closed-loop nature of the system is

$$E(s) = \frac{1}{1 + \dfrac{KN}{s(s+1)}} R(s) \tag{10.31}$$

The use of the describing function N is only valid when $s = j\omega$.

† The analysis presented here is identical in approach to that of E. Levinson, Some Saturation Phenomena in Servomechanisms with Emphasis on the Tachometer Stabilized System, *Trans. AIEE*, Vol. 72, Part II, *Applications and Industry*, pp. 1–9, March, 1953.

In terms of the real-frequency variable and E and R (the amplitudes of the sinusoidal actuating signal and input), Eq. (10.31) can be written

$$E = \left| \frac{j\omega(1 + j\omega)}{j\omega(1 + j\omega) + KN} \right| R \qquad (10.32)$$

Here R, ω, and K are known constants, and N and E are to be determined. The equation is manipulated into a form in which NE, the output of the nonlinear components (if the validity of the describing function is assumed), is given as a function of E. Clearing of fractions and squaring in Eq. (10.32) yields

$$[(KN - \omega^2)^2 + \omega^2]E^2 = \omega^2(1 + \omega^2)R^2 \qquad (10.33)$$

Algebraic manipulation of the expression gives

$$NE = \frac{\omega^2 E}{K} \pm \frac{\omega}{K} \sqrt{(1 + \omega^2)R^2 - E^2} \qquad (10.34)$$

Plots of the left and right sides of Eq. (10.34) are shown in Fig. 10.20.†

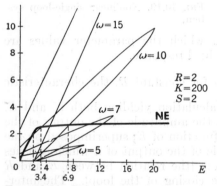

FIG. 10.20. Determination of closed-loop gain. (*From E. Levinson, Some Saturation Phenomena in Servomechanisms with Emphasis on the Tachometer Stabilized System, Trans. AIEE, Vol. 72, Part II, Applications and Industry, p. 5, March, 1953.*)

The left side, NE, is simply the amplitude of m as determined from the describing function; the right side, a function of the specified variables K, ω, and R and the independent variable E, expresses the amplitude of m required by the closed-loop nature of the system. The intersections of the two curves give the values of N and E satisfying the equation with the known characteristics of the nonlinear components. The possibility of three pairs of values for E and N, each pair satisfying Eq. (10.34), is presented by the curves of Fig. 10.20. For example, at a frequency of 10 rad/sec and with the given input amplitude of 2, the following three sets constitute approximate solutions of the equation:

$$
\begin{array}{lll}
E = 2   & NE = 2   & N = 1 \\
E = 3.4 & NE = 2.4 & N = 0.71 \qquad (10.35) \\
E = 6.9 & NE = 2.5 & N = 0.36
\end{array}
$$

† The curves for the expression on the right side of Eq. (10.34) are taken directly from the article by Levinson, *op. cit.*, p. 5. The curve of NE versus E is derived from Fig. 10.12 and is plotted for a maximum value of N equal to unity (that is, k_1 of Fig. 10.12 made unity). Any flat gain present in n is included in the value used for K. In the specific case shown, K is 200 and S, the saturation level, is 2.

The feasibility of several solutions is readily substantiated by a qualitative consideration of the system.   The gain of the nonlinear device is high when the actuating signal is small; this high gain, itself, tends to cause a high loop gain and a small actuating signal.   When the actuating signal is large, on the other hand, N is small (the output limited by the saturation), and the loop gain is low.

The multivalued response is expressed in terms of the curves of closed-loop gain versus frequency, as shown in Fig. 10.21.   The phenomenon exhibited by the curves is termed jump resonance or bending resonance and is similar to a hysteresis effect.   As the frequency is increased with the input to the closed-loop system held constant, the output gain and phase vary along the curve shown from A to B to C.   At very low frequencies, the actuating signal is small as a result of the high gain of the

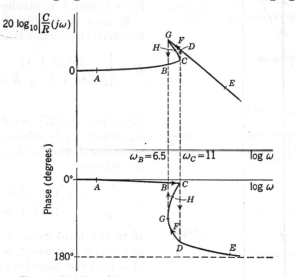

FIG. 10.21. Closed-loop gain and phase curves.

linear components, described by $G(j\omega)$.   If the frequency is slowly increased, the actuating signal never builds up appreciably, and, within the region of ω yielding multiple solutions for E, the smallest value is realized.   As the frequency is increased just beyond ω_C, the output jumps discontinuously to the value at D.   The actuating signal is now single-valued and large.   Further increases in frequency correspond to output values falling along the curve from D to E.

If the frequency response is measured by slowly decreasing the applied frequency, the path $EDFGBA$ is followed.   The actuating signal is large at the time the frequency reaches ω_C and, as the frequency is further decreased, stays at the larger of the two stable values until G, beyond which the solution for N and E is again single-valued.   The closed-loop response characteristics depend on the direction of change in frequency. The unstable region of the response from C to H to G cannot be observed experimentally.

The multivalued nature of the closed-loop system function is also readily deduced from the root-locus plot. Figure 10.22 is a sketch indicating the nature of the root-locus plot for the same example, with

$$NG(s) = \frac{KN}{s(s + 1)} \quad (10.36)\dagger$$

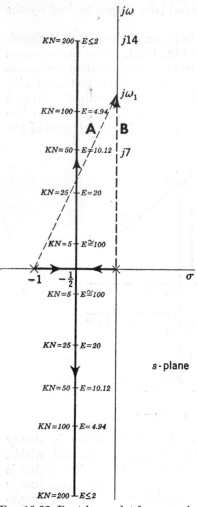

Along the locus the appropriate values of KN are indicated, as well as the value of E required with K equal to 200 to give the corresponding N (the relation between N and E is shown in Fig. 10.12 with $S = 2$, $k_1 = 1$, and X equivalent to E).

E may be readily determined at any given frequency from the relation

$$E = \left| \frac{j\omega(j\omega + 1)}{j\omega(j\omega + 1) + KN} \right| R$$

$$(10.37)\ddagger$$

Equation (10.37) states that, if a frequency ω_1 is selected, the corresponding E can be determined from the relation

$$E = \frac{\omega_1 \sqrt{1 + \omega_1^2}\, R}{|j\omega_1(j\omega_1 + 1) + KN|} \quad (10.38)$$

Fig. 10.22. Root-locus plot for example. (Not drawn to scale.)

Here the numerator, a constant for any given frequency, is the product of R and the magnitudes of the vectors **A** and **B** of Fig. 10.22. The denominator is the product of the lengths of the vectors from the two poles of the closed-loop system function to the point on the $j\omega$ axis under consideration. In order to find these poles, a short trial-and-error procedure is required, since two conjugate points on the root locus must be located such that the E given by Eq. (10.38) corresponds to the E marked along the locus at these points. In this manner, it can be demonstrated that, in the system used here as an example and with an input amplitude

---

† Again, use of the describing function is permissible only when $s = j\omega$. Thus, the root-locus plot characterizes the system only along the $j\omega$ axis, not throughout the s plane.

‡ Here, as throughout this section, E and R are the amplitudes of the sinusoidal signals $e(t)$ and $r(t)$.

of 2, the closed-loop response is multivalued in the frequency range from about 6.5 to 11 rad/sec. For example, at a frequency of 10 rad/sec, one value of actuating signal (an E of 2) is determined by the linear system, with N equal to unity and E small enough that the system does not saturate. Two additional values occur when N is less than unity.

This phenomenon of jump resonance is well known in nonlinear mechanics and is frequently observed experimentally in high-gain servomechanisms. In this example, the equation involved is similar to the Duffing equation,[†] and the phenomenon can be predicted. The general conditions under which jump resonance occurs, particularly in higher-order systems, are not clear at the present time. Even the examination of a single system is difficult because of the complexity of the expressions which must be plotted.

10.6. Frequency-dependent Describing Functions. The nonlinearities (saturation and dead zone) considered in the preceding sections result in a particularly simple analysis as a consequence of the real and frequency-independent nature of the describing function. As a result of this simplification, the describing function can be determined analytically and interpreted simply in terms of the root-locus plots. The analysis of systems with more complex nonlinearities is illustrated in this section by the consideration of velocity saturation in a single-loop system.[‡]

TABLE 10.1

Parameter	Armature-controlled d-c motor	Two-phase motor	Hydraulic motor
m	Armature voltage	Control-phase voltage	Control-valve position or pump displacement ratio
c	Output velocity	Output velocity	Output velocity
R_1	Armature resistance	Series resistance	Leakage and hydraulic flow resistance
$1/R_2$	Viscous mechanical damping	Viscous mechanical damping	Viscous mechanical damping
C_J	Output inertia	Output inertia	Output inertia

The block diagram of the system is shown in Fig. 10.23(a).[§] The equivalent circuit of part (b) of the figure is used to represent the nonlinear element, which may be an armature-controlled d-c motor, a two-

[†] J. J. Stoker, "Non-linear Vibrations in Mechanical and Electric Systems," Interscience Publishers, Inc., New York, 1950.

[‡] The discussion in this section follows that of R. J. Kochenburger, Limiting in Feedback Control Systems, *Trans. AIEE*, Vol. 72, Part II, *Applications and Industry*, pp. 180–194, 1953. Kochenburger also discusses the characteristics of acceleration limiting.

[§] In all figures of this section, the nonlinearity drives the output directly. If output displacement rather than velocity is of interest, the block g can be separated into a block g_1 preceding n and a block g_2, with a transfer function $1/s$, between n and the output. For stability analysis, it is immaterial whether g appears in one or two sections.

phase motor, or a hydraulic motor. The significance of the parameters in the equivalent circuit is indicated in Table 10.1. The limiting circuit enclosed by the dashed lines represents the effect of saturation. If the limiting characteristic is sharp (the output a linear function of the input up to a critical value, beyond which the output is constant and independent of the input), R_3 is zero. Although physical limiting always involves a small but nonzero R_3, the customary assumption that R_3 is zero is made here. The limiting circuit is effective whenever $|c|$ is greater than C_L.

The complexity of the circuit arises because the limiting does not simply clip the top and bottom of the waveform of the velocity which

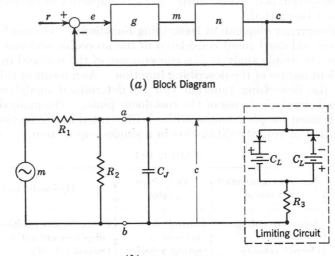

(a) Block Diagram

(b) Equivalent Circuit

FIG. 10.23. Velocity limiting.

would exist without the limiting. The schematic of Fig. 10.24(a) is an equivalent circuit for the simpler situation; here the analysis involves a determination of c_0 from linear analysis, the evaluation of the effects of clipping, and the insertion of an additional integration (if required) to revert to consideration of output displacement rather than velocity. The saturation can be separated from the energy storage as indicated by the block diagram of Fig. 10.24(b). The waveforms of parts (c) and (d) of Fig. 10.24 describe the system. The limiting starts as soon as c_0 exceeds a specified level and continues until c_0 again drops below this level.

That this is not a realistic description of velocity limiting is clear from physical considerations. The limitation on the output velocity has a direct interrelation with the energy storage in the inertia. The actual waveforms are those of Fig. 10.25, where c_0 is again the voltage equivalent of the output velocity in the absence of limiting. During the first half cycle shown, limiting starts when c_0 equals C_L. Once the limiting circuit is conducting, the capacitor voltage (the velocity of the inertia) is constant at the value C_L. Hence, the capacitor draws no current, and

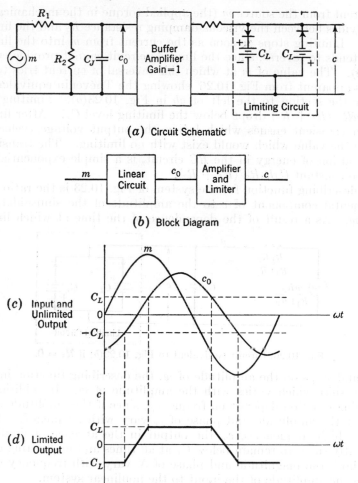

(a) Circuit Schematic

(b) Block Diagram

(c) Input and Unlimited Output

(d) Limited Output

FIG. 10.24. Limiting simplified to simple clipping.

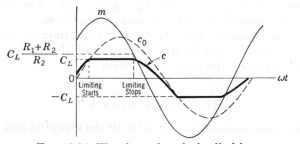

FIG. 10.25. Waveforms in velocity limiting.

the current from the source m (the applied torque in the mechanical system) divides between the viscous-damping resistance R_2 and the limiting circuit.   Limiting stops as soon as the current from m into the limiting circuit tends to reverse, since the limiting circuit cannot provide current (torque).   The value of m at which this reversal of current tries to take place is apparent from Fig. 10.26, showing the Thévenin equivalent circuit for the section to the left of ab in Fig. 10.23(b).   Limiting stops when $mR_2/(R_1 + R_2)$ drops below the limiting level C_L.   After limiting stops, a transient ensues which brings the output voltage (velocity) c back to the value which would exist with no limiting.   The transient, a redistribution of energy in the RC circuit, is a simple exponential with the time constant $C_J R_1 R_2/(R_1 + R_2)$.

The describing function for the system of Fig. 10.23 is the ratio of the fundamental component of c to the amplitude of the sinusoidal input signal m.   As a result of the dependence of the time at which limiting

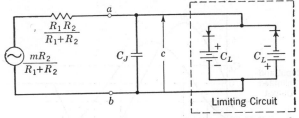

Fig. 10.26. Circuit equivalent to Fig. 10.23(b) if $R_3 = 0$.

starts and stops on the amplitude of m, the describing function involves a phase shift which varies with the amplitude of m.   In addition, the describing function depends on frequency, since if the amplitude of m is constant the amplitude and phase of c_0 vary with frequency.   At sufficiently high frequencies, c_0, the output in the absence of limiting, is sufficiently small to remain below C_L at all times and no limiting occurs. Thus, both the magnitude and phase of N vary with frequency as well as with the amplitude of the input to the nonlinear system.

The calculation of the describing function is complicated by the dependence on frequency.   The most satisfactory procedure involves analog simulation of the equivalent circuit of Fig. 10.23(b).   The results of such an analysis are presented in Fig. 10.27.   The describing function is plotted versus frequency with the ratio of the input amplitude to the limiting level as a parameter.   If M, the amplitude of the sinusoidal input, is less than C_L, no limiting occurs and the output velocity is related to the input by the transfer function

$$\frac{C(s)}{M(s)} = \frac{R_2}{R_1 + R_2} \frac{1}{Ts + 1} \tag{10.39}$$

Here T is the time constant associated with the charging and discharging of C_J, or

$$T = \frac{R_1 R_2}{R_1 + R_2} C_J \tag{10.40}$$

With M/C_L equal to 2 (6 db), the describing function is reduced for all frequencies below the value at which M is 6 db greater than C_0, the amplitude of the sinusoidal c_0. Beyond this frequency, c_0 never exceeds the limiting value and the describing function is identical with the real-frequency value of the transfer function of the linear circuit. For frequencies at which the system is limiting, the phase lag of the describing function is less than that of the linear circuit. This phase-lead effect of

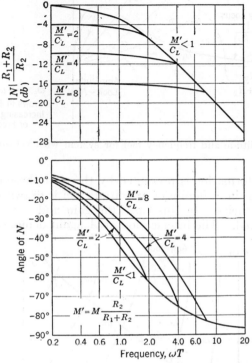

FIG. 10.27. Describing function for velocity limiting. (*From R. J. Kochenburger, Limiting in Feedback Control Systems, Trans. AIEE, Vol. 72, Part II, Applications and Industry, p. 186, 1953.*)

velocity saturation is clear from Fig. 10.25, where it is apparent that the fundamental component of c leads c_0.

The curves of Fig. 10.27 characterize the nonlinearity of velocity saturation and, when combined with the transfer function of the linear components, suffice to determine the stability of the system. The stability can be studied in terms of either the Nyquist diagram or a plot of gain versus phase. The Nyquist-diagram approach involves a frequency locus for $1/G(j\omega)$ [where $G(s)$ is the conventional transfer function of the linear components in tandem with n] and an amplitude locus of $-N$. This amplitude locus varies with frequency as shown in Fig. 10.28, which also includes a possible frequency locus. Sustained oscillations are indicated by the intersection of the loci at point A, for at this intersection the frequency parameter along the frequency locus has the same value as the frequency for the intersecting amplitude locus. The sustained oscillations are stable in this case, since a decrease in amplitude (corresponding to motion toward point B) makes the system unstable and oscillations build up; an increase in amplitude (motion toward point C) results in a stable system, the oscillations dying down.

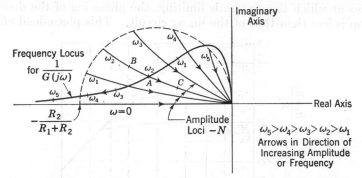

FIG. 10.28. Amplitude and frequency loci for system with velocity limiting. (Not drawn to scale.)

The same information is presented by the gain-phase curves shown in Fig. 10.29. Again, a family of amplitude loci is drawn for a number of different frequencies. In this case, the gain and phase of $-1/N$ and $G(j\omega)$ are plotted. The intersection at A again demonstrates the exist-

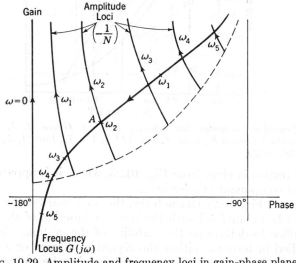

FIG. 10.29. Amplitude and frequency loci in gain-phase plane.

ence of sustained oscillations with a frequency ω_2 and an amplitude determined from the amplitude locus at the intersection. In a more general case, both stable and unstable equilibrium points may exist, as illustrated by Fig. 10.30, showing amplitude loci similar to those of Fig. 10.29 but a more complex frequency locus. In this case, the intersection at A

corresponds to stable equilibrium, while that at B represents unstable equilibrium.

Closed-loop Characteristics.   The amplitude loci for a fixed value of the reference input amplitude R can be obtained in the manner described in Sec. 10.5.   The general characteristics of these loci can be deduced directly from qualitative considerations.   In particular, it is informative

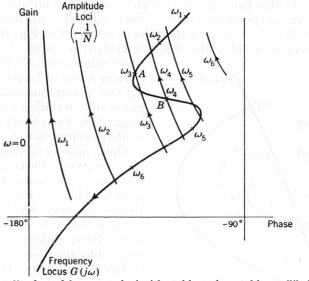

FIG. 10.30. Amplitude and frequency loci with stable and unstable equilibrium points.

to determine approximately the open-loop gain-phase curve for a constant input amplitude.   With a given R there is no limiting at very low frequencies (because of the high loop gain) or at very high frequencies (because of the attenuation in the nonlinear system).   The frequencies at which limiting starts and stops can be determined from an analysis of the linear system.   For example, in the system of Fig. 10.31, at very low frequencies, E, the amplitude of the sinusoidal actuating signal, is given by

$$E = \left| \frac{1}{1 + NG(j\omega)} \right| R \quad (10.41)$$

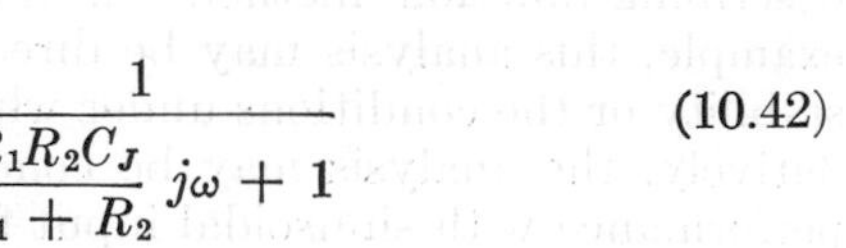

If velocity limiting is again considered and the equivalent circuit of Fig. 10.23(b) is used, N, in the absence of limiting, is given by Eqs. (10.39) and (10.40):

FIG. 10.31. System with velocity limiting.

$$N = \frac{R_2}{R_1 + R_2} \frac{1}{\dfrac{R_1 R_2 C_J}{R_1 + R_2} j\omega + 1} \quad (10.42)$$

Thus, E is related to R by the known values of $G(j\omega)$, R_1, R_2, and C_J.

The transitions between linear operation and limiting occur when the amplitude of output velocity equals C_L, the limiting value:

$$C_L = |NG(j\omega)|E \qquad (10.43)$$

The three equations above give two frequencies, ω_1 and ω_2, between which the system is limiting with the specified input amplitude. For all frequencies in this band, a positive phase shift and an attenuation are introduced in the open-loop gain function as a result of the limiting. The gain-phase characteristic with the form of curve (a) of Fig. 10.32 for the linear system then takes the shape indicated by curve (b). A larger input signal results in limiting over a wider range of frequencies (ω_1' to ω_2') and a larger maximum positive phase shift resulting from the limiting. The two effects are demonstrated in curve (c) of Fig. 10.32.

Thus, velocity limiting bends the gain-frequency locus around the constant-M contours, shown as the dashed lines of Fig. 10.32. Although for very small amplitudes of input the system may have very poor relative stability, as the signal amplitude increases, the relative stability improves. If the input signals are adequately approximated by sinusoidal functions, the characteristics are favorable if, with small input signals, a given percentage error is less significant.

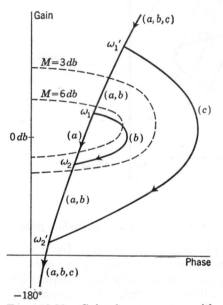

Fig. 10.32. Gain-phase curves with velocity limiting and for constant input amplitudes. (Arrows in direction of increasing frequency.)

10.7. Describing Functions in Design. One of the most important aspects of describing-function analysis is the possibility of adapting the methods to the logical design of compensation networks for nonlinear feedback control systems. The analysis techniques described in this chapter constitute valuable tools in design, but ultimately the complete design theory must include procedures which transcend strict analysis and permit the logical selection of system components to meet performance specifications.

The preceding sections demonstrate the direct application of the describing-function methods in the analysis of a given system. For example, this analysis may be directed toward determination of system stability or the conditions under which sustained oscillations exist; alternatively, the analysis may be concerned with an evaluation of system performance with sinusoidal input functions. The simplest extension of these analysis techniques to design is considered in Secs. 10.5 and 10.6. From either the Nyquist diagram or the gain-phase plots, the relative stability of the system can be determined as a function of the signal level at either the input of the nonlinear device or the input of the closed-loop system.   The familiar problem of the adjustment of loop gain to obtain suitable relative stability can be solved in terms of the graphical presentation.   In addition, conventional techniques can be used to shape the frequency locus in such a way as to improve relative stability and dynamic performance.   The only difference between the conventional Nyquist-diagram analysis and the describing-function analysis is that, in the latter case, the -1 point moves with changes in the signal level.

A more elegant design problem involves the determination of *nonlinear elements* appropriate for insertion in either a linear or a nonlinear system to improve over-all dynamic performance.   Perhaps the major difficulty in such a design lies in the problem of phrasing the specifications in a form amenable to analytical design techniques.   The marked dependence of the performance characteristics of nonlinear systems on the particular input signals means that, in general, the specifications must include precise descriptions of input and desired output.   The usefulness of the

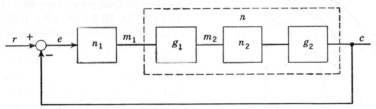

Fig. 10.33. System with two nonlinearities.

describing-function approach depends, in the present state of the art, on the ability of the designer to reinterpret these specifications in terms of sinusoidal response characteristics.

A particularly simple problem, and yet one of considerable practical interest, is the design of nonlinear networks to compensate for undesired nonlinearities in the system.†   The procedure for determining the describing function of the required nonlinearity is straightforward in a number of important cases.   The system of Fig. 10.33 can be used to illustrate one possible sequence of steps in the design of the nonlinearity n_1 to compensate for the nonlinearity n_2 in the presence of the linear components g_1 and g_2.   The Nyquist-diagram approach is used in the description which follows, although the gain-phase plot is equally appropriate.

(1)   The first step entails a determination of N_2, the describing function of the given nonlinear element n_2. N_2 in general depends on the frequency as well as the amplitude of the signal at the input of n_2.

(2)   The second step in the design requires an evaluation of the describing function N, representing all elements in the block including g_1, n_2, and g_2. N depends on both the frequency and the amplitude of

† Haas describes the broad outlines of a procedure similar to that of the following two paragraphs. See V. G. Haas, Jr., Coulomb Friction in Feedback Control Systems, *Trans. AIEE*, Vol. 72, Part II, *Applications and Industry*, pp. 119–126, 1953.

the fundamental component of the signal m_1. The signal m_1 is not sinusoidal, since it is the output of the nonlinearity n_1. As indicated below, the analysis here assumes that g_1 provides adequate low-pass filtering to make m_2 essentially sinusoidal.

(3)   A family of curves is plotted, each curve representing the variation of $-1/N$ with frequency for a given amplitude of m_1. These loci might take the form shown in Fig. 10.34.

(4)   With the known part of the system now analyzed, the desirable characteristics of n_1 can be determined. If the over-all system is to be linear, n_1 must have a describing function N_1 with an amplitude locus which essentially counteracts the amplitude variation of the frequency loci. In other words, if relative stability is of paramount interest, the amplitude locus for N_1 must be such that the " -1 point" for each of the curves of Fig. 10.34 lies in the same position relative to the curve

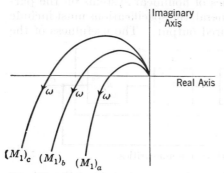

FIG. 10.34. Frequency loci for various amplitudes of m_1. (Plots of $-1/N$.)

(e.g., the M_p values should be the same for all amplitudes, where M_p is the maximum value of the closed-loop gain-frequency curve). If the loci of Fig. 10.34 are all roughly the same shape and represent magnifications of a single locus, the determination of a real N_1 which effects this equalization is not difficult, but, if the loci differ widely not only in gain but also in shape, N_1 must involve a frequency dependence in order to compensate for the nonlinearity of n_2. The determination of N_1 then becomes difficult.

There are two additional difficulties associated with this approximate linearization of a nonlinear system. First, the realization of a nonlinear element with a specified describing function (in this case, N_1) may be difficult in complex cases, even if the describing function is real and independent of frequency. Second, the assumption that the over-all open-loop transfer function is $N_1(E)G_1(j\omega)N_2(M_2,\omega)G_2(j\omega)$ implies two conditions: if e is sinusoidal, g_1 provides adequate filtering to make m_2 sinusoidal, and, if m_2 is sinusoidal, g_2 provides the filtering to make e sinusoidal. In other words, both g_1 and g_2 must have the characteristics of low-pass filters. The problem here is much the same as that which arises in sampled-data feedback control systems, where the z transfer function of two tandem networks is not the simple product of the two z transfer functions unless the two networks are separated by a sampler. Here, the describing function of the two networks in tandem must, in general, be evaluated by viewing the over-all nonlinear system as a single nonlinearity, since the higher harmonics in the output of n_1 affect the fundamental component of the output of n_2. Thus, in general, the design of the nonlinearity n_1 either must involve consideration of the harmonic content of the output of g_2 and the allowable harmonic content in

m_1 if m_2 is to be essentially sinusoidal or must be carried out by considering the actual waveforms throughout the system.

The primary justification for a linearization as described above lies in the resulting simplification in the analysis. A much more significant problem concerns the selection of n_1 to give an over-all *nonlinear* system with desirable characteristics. In the present state of the art, very little is known about the design of systems intentionally nonlinear, and the solution of individual problems depends largely upon the ingenuity of the designer. The describing-function approach provides a useful analytical tool in a wide variety of situations.

The design of integral compensation for a conditionally stable system illustrates certain aspects of the application of describing functions in design problems.†

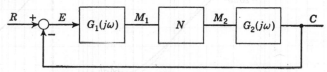

Fig. 10.35. Block diagram of tandem system.

The block diagram of the basic system is shown in Fig. 10.35: here $G_2(j\omega)$ is the transfer function for the controlled system, $G_1(j\omega)$ represents the passive integral-compensation network, and N is the describing function for the nonlinear system. The two transfer functions are‡

$$G_1(j\omega) = K\frac{j\omega + 50}{j\omega + 1} \tag{10.44}$$

$$G_2(j\omega) = \frac{j\omega + 15}{j\omega(j\omega + 4)(j\omega + 200)(j\omega + 400)} \tag{10.45}$$

The nonlinear system is assumed to include saturation and possess a maximum gain of unity ($N = 1$) when the amplitude of the sinusoidal input to n is less than the saturation level. Figure 10.12, with k_1 equal to unity, is a plot of the describing function.

The effects of the nonlinearity are illustrated by the plots of gain and phase versus frequency as shown in Fig. 10.36, or by the root locus, which takes the form indicated by Fig. 10.37.§ With the velocity constant between 64 and 95 db, the system is stable, but, as the gain is decreased, the system becomes unstable. If, for example, the velocity constant is

† The example follows that described by R. J. Kochenburger, Limiting in Feedback Control Systems, *Trans. AIEE*, Vol. 72, Part II, *Applications and Industry*, pp. 180–194, 1953.

‡ The numbers here are chosen to simplify the explanation and do not correspond to any physical system. For example, the poles and zeros of $G_1(j\omega)$ and $G_2(j\omega)$ are purposely selected widely separated to facilitate visualization of the form of the gain curves and root locus.

§ For the determination of Fig. 10.37, $j\omega$ in Eqs. (10.44) and (10.45) is replaced by s. The pole positions of Fig. 10.37 are only significant in that they yield the correct behavior along the $j\omega$ axis, since N is defined for $s = j\omega$ only.

made 80 db for small signals (with N equal to unity), the gain falls as the signal level increases as a result of the decrease in N. When N has decreased by 16 db, the system is unstable, the amplitude of oscillations grows, and N continues to fall. The intersection of the $j\omega$ axis and the root locus (at point A) is an unstable equilibrium point, with the stable equilibrium point B corresponding to an oscillatory amplitude sufficient to make the value of N 60 db below unity.

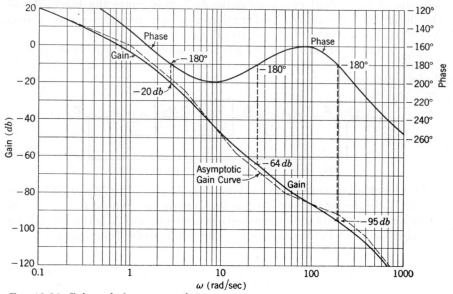

FIG. 10.36. Gain and phase curves for

$$NG_1(s)G_2(s) = \frac{KN(s+15)(s+50)}{s(s+1)(s+4)(s+200)(s+400)}.$$

$$\left(\text{Plotted for } K_v = 1, \text{ where } K_v = \frac{KN \times 15 \times 50}{4 \times 200 \times 400}.\right)$$

The assumption is made that with small signals the system behaves properly and possesses suitable relative stability even though it is conditionally stable. The instability of the system for larger signal amplitudes can be considered to be a consequence of the phase lag introduced by the integral-compensation network. If the compensation can be made operative only when the signal level is small, this instability can be avoided. It is clear that one method for accomplishing such nonlinear compensation is to realize the integral compensation by a subsidiary feedback loop around N (Fig. 10.38). When N is small, the gain of this minor loop is low and the transfer function M_2/M_1 approaches K_2N; $H_1(j\omega)$ does not affect the characteristics of the over-all system.

A variety of values might be used for $H_1(j\omega)$, K_1, and K_2. The over-all transfer function of the subsidiary closed-loop system and the amplifier with gain K_1 is

$$\frac{M_2}{E}(j\omega) = \frac{K_1K_2N}{1 + K_2NH_1(j\omega)} \qquad (10.46)$$

If this transfer function is to realize the integral compensation

$$K \frac{(j\omega + 50)}{(j\omega + 1)}$$

when N is unity, the denominator of $H_1(j\omega)$ must be $j\omega + 50$. Of the variety of numerators which can be chosen, the simplest is $j\omega K_H$. Then

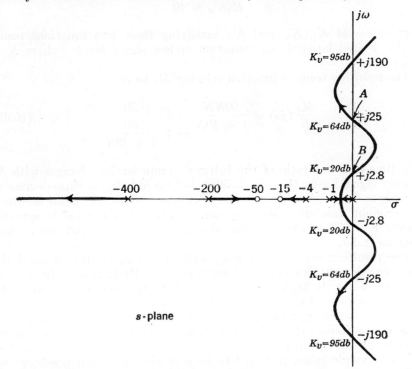

FIG. 10.37. Root-locus plot for conditionally stable system. (Not drawn to scale.)

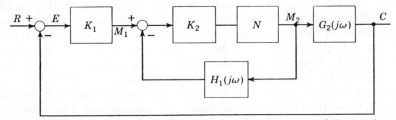

FIG. 10.38. Integral compensation introduced by minor loop around the nonlinearity.

K_1, K_2, and K_H are determined by equating the transfer function M_2/E for the system of Fig. 10.35 with the expression of Eq. (10.46), describing the system of Fig. 10.38:

$$\frac{K_1 K_2 N}{1 + K_2 N \dfrac{K_H j\omega}{j\omega + 50}} = KN \frac{j\omega + 50}{j\omega + 1} \qquad \text{when } N = 1 \qquad (10.47)$$

At zero frequency, Eq. (10.47) reduces to the relation

$$K_1K_2 = 50K \tag{10.48}$$

Substitution of Eq. (10.48) into (10.47) and cancellation of common factors yield the additional condition

$$K_2K_H = 49$$

Any values of K_1, K_2, and K_H satisfying these two equations result in the desired integral compensation at low signal levels (where N is unity).

The resulting transfer function relating M_2 to E is

$$\frac{M_2}{E}(j\omega) = \frac{50KN}{1 + 49N}\frac{j\omega + 50}{j\omega + \dfrac{50}{1 + 49N}} \tag{10.49}$$

The time-constant ratio of the integral compensation changes with N. For low signal levels, the ratio is 50:1, but, as N falls, the ratio decreases, varying as $1 + 49N$. For a value of N down 16 db (the point at which the original, tandem system becomes unstable), the ratio is approximately 8.8. The corresponding phase lag is reduced and the system remains stable.

The resulting nonlinear system, with the compensation around the nonlinear element, is still conditionally stable. Reduction of the tandem gain, K_1 in Fig. 10.38, leaves the value of the time-constant ratio of the integral-compensation network at 50 for small signals and, hence, causes the system to become unstable. The introduction of the subsidiary feedback loop stabilizes the system for all signal levels, but does not remove the conditional stability.

This example is not intended to be a specific, practical problem, but rather to illustrate the possibilities of using the describing-function approach in the design of nonlinear systems. Certainly, in this problem the validity of the describing-function analysis of the subsidiary closed-loop system is open to serious question, since the open-loop transfer function actually is that of a high-pass filter. The basic assumption underlying the describing-function analysis, the assumption of the insignificance of the higher harmonics, is of dubious validity. Thus, the describing-function approach, although not an ultimate or complete design procedure, indicates methods for minimizing the deleterious effects of nonlinearities or for actually utilizing the nonlinearity to improve system performance characteristics.

10.8. Limitations and Disadvantages of Describing-function Analysis. The examples of the preceding sections of this chapter illustrate the general characteristics of the describing-function analysis of nonlinear systems. It is appropriate at this point to summarize the classes of problems amenable to this type of analysis and the difficulties encountered in such an analysis.

Problems Amenable to Analysis. The describing-function analysis is often termed sinusoidal analysis. As a consequence of the restriction of consideration to sinusoidal signals for the characterization of the non-linear components, there are certain classes of problems amenable to analysis and other classes for which this approach gives incomplete or unsatisfactory results. For example, the describing-function method is appropriate for the determination of both the existence of sustained oscillations and the approximate amplitude and period (or frequency), but not the waveform.

Although the greater part of the mathematical work in nonlinear mechanics has been concerned with the establishment of the existence or nonexistence of limit cycles (*i.e.*, the possibility of sustained oscillations), the engineer is perhaps more often interested in the performance of a nonlinear system which is known to be stable. In so far as a describing-function analysis indicates the sinusoidal response characteristics of the system, the available information about system performance is roughly similar to that present in the Nyquist diagram or gain and phase plots of a linear system. The relative stability of the system is indicated as a function of the level of the signal input of the nonlinear device. Sufficient information is presented to permit evaluation of the effects of the introduction of compensation networks in closed-loop systems.

Although in many simple cases the Nyquist diagram of a linear system defines the nature of the system transient response, the describing-function analysis does little more than indicate the general characteristics of the transient response of a nonlinear system. The weak correlation between frequency and time domains in the study of linear systems is made even more unsatisfactory by the variation of the sinusoidal characteristics with signal level and the difficulty of determining the appropriate variation of sinusoidal amplitude to correspond to a given transient input. In special cases where the describing function is purely real and independent of frequency, the gain of the nonlinear device varies only with the amplitude of the input and this variation can be interpreted as motion of the poles of the closed-loop system function along the root loci. This interpretation, discussed in Sec. 10.4, may in certain cases indicate the nature of the step-function response of the nonlinear closed-loop system, but there is no evident, concise correlation between time and frequency domains. Thus, the describing-function analysis indicates transient response only in so far as it demonstrates approximately the relative stability and bandwidth.

Likewise, describing-function analysis is not readily applicable to the study of the response of a nonlinear system to random input functions. As stated in Sec. 8.7, on the basis of the minimization of the mean-square error as a design criterion, the optimum filter is nonlinear unless the signal and noise are both normally distributed. Marked improvement in filtering can be realized in many simple cases by the introduction of non-linear elements. More generally, however, the inclusion of any but the simplest nonlinearities results in tremendous complication of the analysis.

Difficulties in the Analysis. There are three primary difficulties which arise in an analysis based on describing functions. The first is the computational difficulty associated with the determination of the describing function for a wide range of amplitudes and frequencies. All but the simplest problems require either analog- or digital-machine aids to computation. The problem is particularly suited for study with an analog computer, if the nonlinearity can be suitably instrumented.†

The second difficulty, also computational, is present in certain cases in which the response desired is that of the closed-loop system excited by sinusoidal input signals of a constant amplitude. The interdependence of the describing function N and the amplitude of the actuating signal is demonstrated in detail in Sec. 10.5, where it is shown that the jump resonance sometimes observed in systems with saturation can be explained from the fact that a single value of reference input may correspond to more than one amplitude of actuating signal.

The third and most basic difficulty is related to the inaccuracy of the method and, in particular, to the uncertainty throughout the analysis about the accuracy. There is no simple method for evaluating the accuracy of the describing-function analysis of a nonlinear system and no definite assurance that the results derived with the describing function are even approximately correct. Indeed, the analysis may not indicate limit cycles actually present. Johnson's work,‡ described briefly in the next section, is directed toward determining the second term of a series for which the result of the describing-function analysis comprises the first term. With the additional term, the results of the describing-function analysis can be partially corrected and an idea of the accuracy obtained. Johnson's results, however, give only a second approximation to the correct answer. Furthermore, in all but the simplest cases, calculation of this second term of the series is laborious.

From these comments on the absence of any indication of accuracy, it should not be inferred that the accuracy of the describing-function analysis is necessarily poor. The accuracy achieved in a number of cases reported in the literature§ is actually rather startling. For example, in Johnson's analysis of the second-order system with backlash, the frequency of oscillation is determined within 0.97 per cent and the amplitude within 2.50 per cent. In a wide variety of systems, the errors introduced by the approximations of the describing-function approach are small compared to the probable errors in the description of the nonlinear characteristics: for example, errors resulting from inaccurate

† Two examples are given in the papers: V. B. Haas, Jr., Coulomb Friction in Feedback Control Systems, *Trans. AIEE*, Vol. 72, Part II, *Applications and Industry*, pp. 119–125, 1953; R. J. Kochenburger, Limiting in Feedback Control Systems, *Trans. AIEE*, Vol. 72, Part II, *Applications and Industry*, pp. 180–194, 1953.

‡ E. C. Johnson, Sinusoidal Analysis of Feedback-control Systems Containing Nonlinear Elements, *Trans. AIEE*, Vol. 71, Part II, *Applications and Industry*, pp. 169–181, 1952.

§ Johnson considers the cases of a contactor servomechanism, a system with velocity limiting, and one with backlash; Haas reports on a system with coulomb friction; and Kochenburger, in his two papers, describes contactor servos and systems with torque, velocity, and acceleration saturation.

evaluation of coulomb-friction forces or approximation of a physically saturating element by one which exhibits a sharp transition from linear operation to perfectly limited operation. Evaluation of the importance of the errors introduced by the describing-function analysis must be tempered by consideration of the primary objectives of the analysis in the study of feedback control systems. In the vast majority of cases, the designer desires a rough measure of the effects of certain nonlinearities and a quick method for evaluating the effects of additional linear or nonlinear components introduced within the loop.

10.9. Accuracy Analysis. The value of any approximate method of analysis is limited by the confidence the designer has in the results. At the present stage of development, the validity of the describing-function method is primarily based on intuition and experimental results. Intuition indicates that in a wide variety of feedback control systems the higher harmonics generated by a nonlinear element are of only secondary importance both because of the small amplitude of the harmonics and because of the attenuation of the harmonic components by the linear part of the feedback loop. Experimental results for a variety of non-

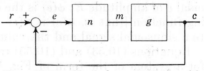

Fig. 10.39. Single-loop system with one nonlinearity.

linearities tend to bear out this intuitive evaluation. Indeed, the correlation between experimental and theoretical results is in many cases better than the accuracy of the design data.

Extension of the describing-function methods requires, however, a more quantitative analysis of the accuracy to be expected. Such an analysis is available in Johnson's work,[†] based on the earlier studies of Bulgakov.[‡] The essential features and results of this work are summarized in this section. For simplicity, the analysis is restricted to consideration of the configuration of Fig. 10.39, a single-loop, single-nonlinearity system with a describing function which is purely real and a function of only the amplitude of the input signal of the nonlinear device. The more general case of multiple nonlinearities, each with a complex frequency-dependent describing function, is considered in Johnson's paper. If the unexcited system (with r equal to zero) is considered, further simplification results, and, for the ordinary stability analysis, there is no significant loss of generality, since stability depends on the gain around the loop.

Basic Problem. If these assumptions are made, the equations describing the behavior of the system of Fig. 10.39 are

$$q_2(p)c - q_1(p)m = 0 \tag{10.50}$$
$$m = n(e) \tag{10.51}$$
$$e = -c \tag{10.52}$$

[†] Johnson, *op. cit.*

[‡] B. V. Bulgakov, Periodic Processes in Free Pseudo-linear Oscillatory Systems, *J. Franklin Inst.*, Vol. 235, pp. 591–616, June, 1943, and On the Method of Van der Pol and Its Applications to Non-linear Control Problems, *J. Franklin Inst.*, Vol. 241, pp. 31–54, January, 1946.

Here $q_1(p)$ and $q_2(p)$ are polynomial functions of the operator $p = d/dt$. $G(s)$, the transfer function of the linear components, is $C(s)/M(s)$, or $q_1(s)/q_2(s)$. Equation (10.51) states that m, the output of the nonlinear device, is a function of the input e.

If Eq. (10.52) is used to eliminate c, system behavior is described by the two equations

$$-q_2(p)e - q_1(p)m = 0 \tag{10.53}$$
$$m = n(e) \tag{10.54}$$

Equation (10.54), describing the nonlinear characteristic, can be written in terms of the describing function N,

$$m - N(E)e = \phi(e) \tag{10.55}\dagger$$

In this equation, $N(E)$ is the describing function evaluated for a sinusoidal e of amplitude E; $\phi(e)$ is the error introduced by use of the describing function [that is, $\phi(e)$ is $n(e) - N(E)e$]. As yet, e is not restricted to a sinusoidal signal and the value of E is unspecified.

Equations (10.53) and (10.55) represent the general nonlinear problem for a system of the form of Fig. 10.39. The periodic solutions desired are obtained by a perturbation procedure, as described below. This derivation requires the assumption that all derivatives of $\phi(e)$ exist for values of e covering the range of interest.

In order to obtain a solution by the perturbation procedure, an additional parameter μ is introduced as a multiplier of the error function ϕ. The equations then become

$$-N(E)e + m = \mu\phi(e) \tag{10.56}$$
$$+q_2(p)e + q_1(p)m = 0 \tag{10.57}$$

The desired solution for either e or m is a power series in the parameter μ. For example, e is to be determined in the form

$$e = e_0 + e_1\mu + \frac{e_2}{2!}\mu^2 + \frac{e_3}{3!}\mu^3 + \cdots \tag{10.58}$$

The correct value of e is then found by substituting μ equal to unity, with the result

$$e = e_0 + e_1 + e_2 + e_3 + \cdots \tag{10.59}$$

Here each of the component functions $(e_0, e_1, \ldots)$ is a function of time. The frequency of the periodic solution is also represented by a power series in μ,

$$\omega = (1 + \lambda)\omega_0 \tag{10.60}$$

where

$$\lambda = \lambda_1\mu + \frac{\lambda_2}{2!}\mu^2 + \frac{\lambda_3}{3!}\mu^3 + \cdots \tag{10.61}$$

---

† Actually, since the describing function is not defined as yet in this development, this equation represents an arbitrary separation of the nonlinear characteristic into two components.

Again, the correct value of ω is found by substituting $\mu = 1$:

$$\omega = \left(1 + \lambda_1 + \frac{\lambda_2}{2!} + \frac{\lambda_3}{3!} + \cdots\right)\omega_0 \qquad (10.62)$$

This form for the solution is particularly appropriate because, as established in the following discussion, the first-order solution, found by letting μ equal zero, is identical with the amplitude and frequency given by the describing-function analysis. This first approximation is

$$e = e_0 \qquad \text{and} \qquad \omega = \omega_0 \qquad (10.63)$$

The added terms ($e_1, e_2, \ldots$ and $\lambda_1, \lambda_2, \ldots$) for the solution in this form give higher-order approximations to the correct periodic solution for e. Thus, stability analysis involves the determination of the two power-series equations (10.58) and (10.61) from the system equations (10.56) and (10.57).

The First Approximations. The first approximations, e_0 and ω_0, are the solutions when the parameter μ is zero. But with a zero value for μ, the system equations (10.56) and (10.57) become

$$-N(E)e + m = 0 \qquad (10.64)$$
$$q_2(p)e + q_1(p)m = 0 \qquad (10.65)$$

The two equations have a nonzero, periodic solution only if the determinant is zero. In other words, it must be possible to find a value of E, denoted E_0, and a value of frequency, ω_0, such that the determinant (with p replaced by $j\omega$) is zero when evaluated at E_0 and ω_0:

$$-[q_2(j\omega_0) + N(E_0)q_1(j\omega_0)] = 0 \qquad (10.66)\dagger$$

Division by $-q_2(j\omega_0)$ yields the relation

$$1 + N(E_0)G(j\omega_0) = 0 \qquad (10.67)$$

Equation (10.67) defines the determination of E_0 and ω_0; this determination can be effected graphically as described in the preceding sections of this chapter. The amplitude locus $-N(E)$ and the frequency locus $1/G(j\omega)$ are plotted, with the intersections determining E_0 and ω_0. The corresponding values of e_0 and m_0 are

$$e_0 = E_0 \cos \omega_0 t \qquad (10.68)$$
$$m_0 = E_0 N(E_0) \cos \omega_0 t \qquad (10.69)$$

---

† Equation (10.66) can be derived using the Laplace-transform theory, which may be familiar to servo engineers. Equations (10.64) and (10.65), when transformed, become

$$-N(E)E(s) + M(s) = 0$$
$$q_2(s)E(s) + q_1(s)M(s) = I(s)$$

$I(s)$ represents initial conditions. Elimination of $M(s)$ yields

$$E(s) = \frac{I(s)}{q_2(s) + Nq_1(s)}$$

If $e(t)$ is to have a periodic component, $E(s)$ must have simple poles on the $j\omega$ axis at $\pm j\omega_0$. Hence, Eq. (10.66) must be satisfied.

The analysis to this point is simply a rephrasing of the details of the describing-function method. Clearly, the describing-function analysis is accurate only if the higher-order correction terms (e_1, e_2, . . . and λ_1, λ_2, . . .) are truly negligible.

The remainder of this section is devoted to an evaluation of these higher-order terms. Since the terms e_1 and λ_1 are the coefficients of μ in the power series for e and ω, these terms are found by differentiating the system equations (10.56) and (10.57) with respect to μ and setting μ equal to zero. At this stage, the necessity for the infinite series for ω is made apparent, for, if ω is not defined in terms of the series, the frequency of the periodic solutions obtained for e_1 and m_1 is different from ω_0. In order that the second-order approximation for e may be written as $e_0 + e_1$, e_0 and e_1 must have the same period. Thus, it is necessary to define a new time variable τ such that

$$(1 + \lambda)t = \tau \tag{10.70}$$

where
$$\lambda = \lambda_1 \mu + \frac{\lambda_2}{2!} \mu^2 + \frac{\lambda_3}{3!} \mu^3 + \cdots \tag{10.71}$$

The frequency ω, corresponding to the variable τ, is related to ω_0, corresponding to t, by

$$\omega = (1 + \lambda)\omega_0 \tag{10.72}$$

λ_1, λ_2, . . . are chosen to make the periods of e_0, e_1, e_2, . . . identical when measured in terms of the time variable τ. For the first-order solution, $t = \tau$ and $\omega = \omega_0$; hence, e_0 and m_0 can be written in terms of τ directly from Eqs. (10.68) and (10.69):

$$e_0 = E_0 \cos \omega_0\tau \tag{10.73}$$
$$m_0 = E_0 N(E_0) \cos \omega_0\tau \tag{10.74}$$

The First Frequency Correction. The second terms in the two power series (for e and ω) are determined by differentiation of the original system equations with respect to μ and substitution of μ equal to zero. Differentiation of (10.56) and (10.57) yields

$$-N(E) \frac{\partial e}{\partial \mu} + \frac{\partial m}{\partial \mu} = \phi(e) + \mu \frac{\partial \phi(e)}{\partial e} \frac{\partial e}{\partial \mu} \tag{10.75}$$

$$q_2(p) \frac{\partial e}{\partial \mu} + e \frac{dq_2(p)}{dp} \frac{\partial p}{\partial \mu} + q_1(p) \frac{\partial m}{\partial \mu} + m \frac{dq_1(p)}{dp} \frac{\partial p}{\partial \mu} = 0 \tag{10.76}$$

With $\mu = 0$, the following relations are apparent from the form of the power series [Eq. (10.58)]:

$$(e)_{\mu=0} = e_0 \qquad \left(\frac{\partial e}{\partial \mu}\right)_{\mu=0} = e_1$$

$$(m)_{\mu=0} = m_0 \qquad \left(\frac{\partial m}{\partial \mu}\right)_{\mu=0} = m_1 \tag{10.77}$$

In addition, the operator $p = d/dt$ is related to p', defined as $d/d\tau$, by

$$p = p'(1 + \lambda) \tag{10.78}$$

Hence,

$$(p)_{\mu=0} = p'$$
$$\left(\frac{\partial p}{\partial \mu}\right)_{\mu=0} = \lambda_1 p' \tag{10.79}$$

Substitution of Eqs. (10.77) and (10.79) in (10.75) and (10.76) gives

$$-N(E_0)e_1 + m_1 = \phi(e_0) \tag{10.80}$$

$$q_2(p')e_1 + q_1(p')m_1 = -\lambda_1 p' \left\{ \left[\frac{dq_2(p)}{dp}\right]_{p=p'} e_0 + \left[\frac{dq_1(p)}{dp}\right]_{p=p'} m_0 \right\} \tag{10.81}$$

The solution sought for these two equations is periodic with a frequency of ω_0 in the time variable τ. The conditions for the existence of such a solution can be derived by expressing $\phi(e_0)$ as a Fourier series with the fundamental frequency ω_0. The expansion is possible since e_0 is periodic with the same fundamental period. (It is assumed at this point that the nonlinear device generates no subharmonics.) Then,

$$\phi(e_0) = \frac{1}{2} \sum_{k=-\infty}^{\infty} \Phi_k e^{jk\omega_0\tau} \tag{10.82}$$

where
$$\Phi_k = \frac{1}{\pi} \int_{-\pi}^{\pi} \phi(e_0) e^{-jk\omega_0\tau} \, d(\omega_0\tau) \tag{10.83}$$

In this Fourier series, Φ_1 and Φ_{-1} are zero as a consequence of the definition of ϕ. In the derivation of Eq. (10.55), ϕ is defined as the output of the nonlinear device minus the describing function times the input. With e_0 sinusoidal, the fundamental component of the output is absorbed completely in $N(E_0)E_0 \cos \omega_0\tau$, and $\phi(e_0)$ contains only d-c and higher-harmonic components.

From Eqs. (10.73) and (10.74), the values of e_0 and m_0 are also expressed in terms of $e^{\pm j\omega_0\tau}$,

$$e_0 = \frac{E_0}{2} (e^{j\omega_0\tau} + e^{-j\omega_0\tau}) \tag{10.84}$$

$$m_0 = \frac{E_0}{2} N(E_0)(e^{j\omega_0\tau} + e^{-j\omega_0\tau}) \tag{10.85}$$

After substitution of Eqs. (10.82), (10.84), and (10.85), the differentiated system equations (10.80) and (10.81) become

$$-N(E_0)e_1 + m_1 = \frac{1}{2} \sum_{k=-\infty}^{\infty} \Phi_k e^{jk\omega_0\tau} \tag{10.86}$$

$$q_2(p')e_1 + q_1(p')m_1$$

$$= -\frac{\lambda_1 E_0}{2} \left\{ \left[\frac{dq_2(p)}{dp} \right]_{p=j\omega_0} j\omega_0 e^{j\omega_0 \tau} - \left[\frac{dq_2(p)}{dp} \right]_{p=-j\omega_0} j\omega_0 e^{-j\omega_0 \tau} \right.$$

$$\left. + \left[\frac{dq_1(p)}{dp} \right]_{p=j\omega_0} j\omega_0 N(E_0) e^{j\omega_0 \tau} - \left[\frac{dq_1(p)}{dp} \right]_{p=-j\omega_0} j\omega_0 N(E_0) e^{-j\omega_0 \tau} \right\} \quad (10.87)\dagger$$

For simplicity, the coefficients A and $\bar{A}$ (the conjugate of A) are introduced to represent the coefficients of $e^{j\omega_0 \tau}$ and $e^{-j\omega_0 \tau}$, respectively, in the right side of Eq. (10.87). The equations can then be written

$$-N(E_0)e_1 + m_1 = \frac{1}{2} \sum_{k=-\infty}^{\infty} \Phi_k e^{jk\omega_0 \tau} \quad (10.88)\star$$

$$q_2(p')e_1 + q_1(p')m_1 = A e^{j\omega_0 \tau} + \bar{A} e^{-j\omega_0 \tau} \quad (10.89)\star$$

These two equations determine e_1 and m_1, each periodic with a frequency ω_0. This periodicity alone is sufficient to establish the value of λ_1. If m_1 is eliminated between the two equations, an equation for e_1 alone results:

$$[-q_2(p') - q_1(p')N(E_0)]e_1$$

$$= -[A e^{j\omega_0 \tau} + \bar{A} e^{-j\omega_0 \tau}] + \frac{q_1(p')}{2} \sum_{k=-\infty}^{\infty} \Phi_k e^{jk\omega_0 \tau} \quad (10.90)$$

The bracketed factor multiplying e_1 is the system determinant, which goes to zero at $p' = j\omega_0$ [cf. Eq. (10.66)]. Consequently, on the right side of Eq. (10.90) there can be no term representing an oscillation of frequency ω_0. Hence, A must be equal to zero if e_1 is to be periodic with a frequency of ω_0.‡ Accordingly, if the value of A from Eq. (10.87)

† The derivation of (10.87) from (10.81) requires that $p'e^{j\omega_0 \tau}$ be recognized as $j\omega_0 e^{j\omega_0 \tau}$. The operator p' signifies differentiation with respect to τ. For the same reason, $[dq_2(p)/dp]_{p=p'} e^{j\omega_0 \tau}$ is equivalent to $[dq_2(p)/dp]_{p=j\omega_0} e^{j\omega_0 \tau}$.

‡ The condition that A must be zero may be more apparent if the Laplace-transform equivalent of Eq. (10.90) is considered,

$$[-q_2(s) - q_1(s)N(E_0)]E_1(s)$$

$$= -\left[\frac{A}{s - j\omega_0} + \frac{\bar{A}}{s + j\omega_0} \right] + \frac{q_1(s)}{2} \sum_{k=-\infty}^{\infty} \frac{\Phi_k}{s - jk\omega_0}$$

$$E_1(s) = \left[\frac{1}{-q_2(s) - q_1(s)N(E_0)} \right] \left[-\frac{A}{s - j\omega_0} - \frac{\bar{A}}{s + j\omega_0} + \frac{q_1(s)}{2} \sum_{k=-\infty}^{\infty} \frac{\Phi_k}{s - jk\omega_0} \right]$$

If $e_1(\tau)$ is to be periodic, there can be no terms of the form $\tau \cos \omega_0 \tau$. Hence, $E_1(s)$ can have no multiple-order poles on the $j\omega$ axis. The first term in brackets of the expression for $E_1(s)$ introduces simple poles at $s = \pm j\omega_0$, as a result of Eq. (10.66). Consequently, the second term cannot include poles at these points. If Φ_1 were other than zero, it would be possible for the pole represented by $-A/(s - j\omega_0)$ to be is set equal to zero,

$$-\frac{\lambda_1 E_0}{2}\left\{\left[\frac{dq_2(p)}{dp}\right]_{p=j\omega_0} j\omega_0 + \left[\frac{dq_1(p)}{dp}\right]_{p=j\omega_0} j\omega_0 N(E_0)\right\} = 0 \quad (10.91)$$

Equation (10.91) can be written

$$\frac{j\omega_0\lambda_1 E_0}{2} D'(E_0,j\omega_0) = 0 \qquad (10.92)$$

Here $D'(E_0,j\omega_0)$ is the derivative of the system determinant evaluated at E_0 and ω_0 and cannot be zero, as noted in the last footnote. Hence,

$$\lambda_1 = 0 \qquad (10.93)^\star$$

Thus, the periodicity condition for e_1 and m_1 is alone sufficient to demonstrate that the first frequency correction is zero.

First Amplitude Correction and Second Frequency Correction. Equations (10.88) and (10.89) represent the two simultaneous inhomogeneous equations determining e_1 and m_1, the first amplitude corrections. If the values determined above ($A = \bar{A} = 0$) are substituted, the two equations can be written

$$-N(E_0)e_1 + m_1 = \frac{1}{2}\sum_{k=-\infty}^{\infty}\Phi_k e^{jk\omega_0\tau} \qquad (10.94)$$

$$q_2(p')e_1 + q_1(p')m_1 = 0 \qquad (10.95)$$

The solutions sought (e_1 and m_1) are periodic, with a frequency of ω_0. The expression for e_1, alone, is given by Eq. (10.90) with A equal to zero; the corresponding equation for m_1 can be found by elimination of e_1 in (10.94) and (10.95):

$$[-q_2(p') - q_1(p')N(E_0)]e_1 = \frac{q_1(p')}{2}\sum_{k=-\infty}^{\infty}\Phi_k e^{jk\omega_0\tau} \qquad (10.96)$$

$$[-q_2(p') - q_1(p')N(E_0)]m_1 = -\frac{q_2(p')}{2}\sum_{k=-\infty}^{\infty}\Phi_k e^{jk\omega_0\tau} \qquad (10.97)$$

The coefficient of either m_1 or e_1 is the system determinant, with a zero at $p' = j\omega_0$. The right side of each equation represents a periodic func-

---

canceled by the pole introduced by the summation term; however, with Φ_1 zero, A must also be zero.

For the same reason, $-q_2(s) - q_1(s)N(E_0)$ must have only simple zeros at $\pm j\omega_0$. Hence, if this expression is denoted $D(E_0,s)$, $D'(E_0,j\omega_0)$ must not be zero. Furthermore, the assumption is implied throughout the remainder of the discussion that this determinant $D(E_0,j\omega)$ is not zero at the higher harmonics of ω_0, since the second term in the equation above introduces simple poles at these frequencies, and a zero value of D would result in multiple-order poles.

tion with components at frequencies of $0, 2\omega_0, 3\omega_0, \ldots$. The resulting forms for the periodic components of e_1 and m_1 are

$$e_1 = B \cos \omega_0 \tau + \tfrac{1}{2} \sum_{k=-\infty}^{\infty} E_{1k} e^{jk\omega_0 \tau} \tag{10.98}$$

$$m_1 = BN(E_0) \cos \omega_0 \tau + \tfrac{1}{2} \sum_{k=-\infty}^{\infty} M_{1k} e^{jk\omega_0 \tau} \tag{10.99}$$

The evaluation of the coefficients B, E_{1k}, and M_{1k} is effected directly from Eqs. (10.96) and (10.97). If Eq. (10.96), for example, is solved by the Laplace transform, $E_1(s)$ can be written

$$E_1(s) = \left[\frac{q_1(s)}{2} \sum_{k=-\infty}^{\infty} \frac{\Phi_k}{s - jk\omega_0} \right] \frac{1}{D(E_0, s)} \tag{10.100}$$

$E_1(s)$ has simple poles on the $j\omega$ axis at the points

$$s = 0, \pm j\omega_0, \pm j2\omega_0, \pm j3\omega_0, \ldots \tag{10.101}$$

The poles at $\pm j\omega_0$ are the result of the zero value of $D(E_0, \pm j\omega_0)$; all the other poles are generated in the bracketed expression of Eq. (10.100). The amplitudes of the periodic terms in $e_1(\tau)$ are determined by the residues at these poles. The residue at the pole $s = +j\omega_0$ is

$$K_{j\omega_0} = \left[\frac{q_1(j\omega_0)}{2} \sum_{k=-\infty}^{\infty} \frac{\Phi_k}{j\omega_0 - jk\omega_0} \right] \frac{1}{D'(E_0, j\omega_0)} \tag{10.102}$$

Here $D'(E_0, j\omega_0)$ is written for $[dD(E_0, s)/ds]_{s=j\omega_0}$. The residue at each of the other poles is given by

$$K_{jk\omega_0} = \frac{q_1(jk\omega_0)}{2} \Phi_k \frac{1}{D(E_0, jk\omega_0)} \tag{10.103}$$

Thus, the forms of e_1 and m_1 are as given in Eqs. (10.98) and (10.99) with

$$E_{1k} = \begin{cases} 0 & k = 1 \\ \dfrac{q_1(jk\omega_0)\Phi_k}{D(E_0, jk\omega_0)} & k \neq 1 \end{cases} \tag{10.104}$$

$$M_{1k} = \begin{cases} 0 & k = 1 \\ \dfrac{-q_2(jk\omega_0)\Phi_k}{D(E_0, jk\omega_0)} & k \neq 1 \end{cases} \tag{10.105}$$

What is the significance of Eq. (10.98)? In the analysis of this section, the original simultaneous equations describing system behavior are being solved by determining successive terms in the infinite series for e and m. The first terms of the series give e_0 and m_0, purely sinusoidal signals which are determined by the describing-function analysis. The second terms of the series are e_1 and m_1, given by Eqs. (10.98) and (10.99). Each correction is composed of two components: an additional fundamental component [$B \cos \omega_0\tau$ or $BN(E_0) \cos \omega_0\tau$]† and the higher harmonics generated by passing the first approximation (e_0) through the nonlinear device. The harmonic components can be calculated directly from Eqs. (10.104) and (10.105).‡ The calculation must be preceded by the determination of Φ_k, each coefficient in the Fourier series for $\phi(e_0)$. These coefficients, as well as $N(E_0)$, can be found by evaluating the Fourier series for the *exact* output of the nonlinear device when the input is e_0, since $\phi(e_0)$ is the error between the actual output and that given by describing-function analysis. Once this single Fourier series is determined, all harmonic components of e_1 and m_1 can be found immediately from the known transfer function $G(s)$ evaluated at $s = jk\omega_0$.

The determination of the fundamental component of the first correction involves the evaluation of B, which is related to the residue given by Eq. (10.102). It is more convenient to determine B (and also λ_2) from the requirement that the second correction term be periodic. This second correction is found in a manner similar to that used for the first correction. Now the original equations (10.56) and (10.57) are differentiated twice with respect to μ, and then μ is set equal to zero. Again the requirement of periodicity is imposed (no terms of the form $\tau^n \cos \omega_0\tau$, where n is a nonzero integer). The resulting periodicity equation is

$$E_0B \left[\frac{dN(E)}{dE} \right]_{E_0} + j \, \frac{\lambda_2\omega_0E_0}{2} \, \frac{N(E_0)G''(j\omega_0)}{G(j\omega_0)}$$

$$= -\frac{E_{10}}{2} \left[\frac{d\Phi_0}{dE} \right]_{E_0} \cdots \sum_{k=2}^{\infty} \left\{ \left[\frac{d\Phi_k}{dE} \right]_{E_0} \operatorname{Re} E_{1k} + \frac{jk}{E_0} \Phi_{1k} \operatorname{Im} E_{1k} \right\} \quad (10.106)$$

The two equations derived from the real and imaginary parts of this equation suffice to determine the values of B and λ_2.

† Bulgakov shows that this additional fundamental component can be assumed in phase with the first approximation. *Cf.* B. V. Bulgakov, Periodic Processes in Free Pseudo-linear Oscillatory Systems, *J. Franklin Inst.*, Vol. 235, pp. 591–616, June, 1943.

‡ Equations (10.104) and (10.105) actually can be written by inspection if the physical significance of these terms is appreciated. E_{1k} is the amplitude of the kth harmonic at the input terminals of n when the output of n is assumed to be the exact output resulting from excitation of n by the first approximation e_0. This excitation causes a harmonic component of amplitude Φ_k at a frequency $k\omega_0$ in the output of n. This harmonic component is transmitted from the output of n to the input through the gain $-G(jk\omega_0)$. The loop is closed through the nonlinear device with a gain $N(E_0)$. Hence,

$$E_{1k} = \frac{-G(jk\omega_0)}{1 + N(E_0)G(jk\omega_0)} \Phi_k \qquad k \neq 1$$

This equation is equivalent to (10.104). A similar line of reasoning indicates that

$$M_{1k} = \frac{1}{1 + N(E_0)G(jk\omega_0)} \Phi_k \qquad k \neq 1$$

Clearly, the evaluation of B, even in the simple single-loop, single-nonlinearity feedback control system of Fig. 10.40, requires machine calculation. Determination of B from Eq. (10.106) involves the quantities listed in Table 10.2.

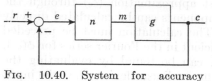

FIG. 10.40. System for accuracy analysis.

Conclusions. The analysis presented in this section is directed toward estimation of the errors involved in the use of describing functions in the analysis of nonlinear systems. The results of the somewhat extended analysis are contained in Eqs. (10.93) and (10.106), the former stating that the first frequency correction is zero, the latter yielding the values of the second frequency correction and the fundamental component of the first amplitude correction. The results afford a method for evaluating the accuracy of the first approximation (given by the describing function) or, alternatively, for improving the accuracy of the describing-function

TABLE 10.2
DETERMINATION OF B

Evaluated from the describing-function analysis	E_0	Amplitude of the first approximation for e_0
	$E_0 N(E_0)$	Amplitude of the first approximation for m_0
	ω_0	Frequency of the first approximation
Evaluated from the transfer function of the linear components	$\dfrac{G'(j\omega_0)}{G(j\omega_0)}$	Value at $s = j\omega_0$ of the logarithmic derivative of the transfer function of the linear components
	$q_1(jk\omega_0)$	Value at $s = jk\omega_0$ of the numerator polynomial of $G(s)$
	$D(E_0,jk\omega_0)$	System determinant, or $-q_1(jk\omega_0)\left[N(E_0) + \dfrac{1}{G(jk\omega_0)}\right]$
Evaluated from Fourier analysis of output of nonlinear device	$\Phi_0,\ \Phi_2,\ \Phi_3,\ \ldots$	D-C and higher harmonics of the *exact* output of the nonlinear device when the input is $E_0 \cos \omega_0\tau$
Evaluated from Eq. (10.104)	$E_{10},\ E_{12},\ E_{13},\ \ldots$	D-C and higher-harmonic amplitudes of the first correction e_1
Evaluated from the nonlinear characteristic (these are the parameters determined with most difficulty)	$\left(\dfrac{d\Phi_0}{dE}\right)_{E_0},\ \left(\dfrac{d\Phi_2}{dE}\right)_{E_0},\ \ldots$ $\left(\dfrac{dN(E)}{dE}\right)_{E_0}$	Derivatives with respect to E of the harmonic components of the exact output of the nonlinear device when the input is $E \cos \omega_0\tau$.

analysis in the determination of the amplitude and frequency of a periodic solution. In Johnson's example of a second-order system with backlash, introduction of the corrections e_1 and λ_2 decreases the frequency error from -0.97 to -0.23 per cent and the amplitude error from -2.50 to -0.28 per cent.

For the design engineer, the results of this section are of only occasional usefulness. From the viewpoint of the designer of feedback control systems, the primary significance of the describing-function analysis lies in the possibility of controlling, at least roughly, the relative stability of a nonlinear system by the conventional design procedures (gain adjustment and introduction of linear compensation networks) or improving the dynamic performance of a linear or nonlinear system by the introduction of nonlinear components. In the majority of problems, the describing functions are employed to yield rapidly an evaluation of a system or a determination of the general effects of nonlinearities of specific types. The engineer is interested more often in determining the characteristics of a stable system than in evaluating the frequency and amplitude of oscillation of an unstable system.

Thus, from the viewpoint of the engineer, a complete evaluation of the describing-function analysis should answer such questions as the following:

(1) Under what conditions might the describing-function analysis indicate stability, while the actual system is unstable? Johnson states that experience indicates that such failures occur when the amplitude and frequency loci approach one another and then separate without intersecting. The engineer would prefer a more quantitative criterion, if possible.

(2) Under what conditions does the separation of the two loci indicate the relative stability of the system, particularly with transient input signals?

The work of Johnson, although it does not provide the answers for such questions, does present a theoretical basis for the describing-function approach and reconfirms the recorded correlations between experimental results and describing-function studies.

10.10. Concluding Comments. The breadth of the subject of the analysis and design of nonlinear systems prevents any single general method for the solution of all problems. Very simple systems can be studied by the phase-plane methods described in the next chapter. More complex systems can often be considered with the use of describing functions. The difficulty in the analysis of nonlinear systems arises because of the inability to describe systems in terms of the poles and zeros of the transfer functions. The position of a pole moving rapidly through a region of the complex-frequency plane no longer has the usual significance in terms of transient or frequency response.

The describing-function analysis replaces these rapidly moving poles and zeros by critical frequencies which move slowly. The equivalence is valid at a point on the $j\omega$ axis (*i.e.*, at a sinusoidal frequency). The poles and zeros move with changes in the amplitude of the signal input of the nonlinear device. Absolute and relative stability can be evaluated as a function of signal level by letting the test point on the $j\omega$ axis, the test frequency, vary from zero to infinity.   The approximation of rapidly moving poles and zeros by slowly moving critical frequencies is effected by neglecting all harmonic components except the fundamental in the output of the nonlinear device.   Accordingly, validity of the approximation depends directly on the harmonic distortion of this output and the extent of low-pass filtering in the linear components between output and input terminals of the nonlinear device.   In a great many feedback control systems, the accuracy of the describing-function analysis is well within the accuracy with which the component characteristics are known.

CHAPTER 11

PHASE-PLANE ANALYSIS

The describing-function analysis of feedback control systems represents an adaptation of linear techniques to the study of nonlinear systems. In contrast, the phase-plane method† of describing the characteristics of nonlinear systems involves an approach radically different from that of conventional linear analysis. It is the intent of this chapter to present the basic theory underlying the phase-plane methods and to illustrate this theory with a few simple examples taken from the automatic-control field.

The phase-plane analysis, as used in the study of feedback control systems, is concerned with the characteristics of the solution of the differential equation

$$\ddot{x} + a(x,\dot{x})\dot{x} + b(x,\dot{x})x = 0 \qquad (11.1)‡$$

Here $a(x,\dot{x})$ and $b(x,\dot{x})$ are functions of the signal and its derivative. The phase plane is the plot of $\dot{x}$ as a function of x, the curves in the phase plane indicating the time variations of x and $\dot{x}$. The initial conditions $x(0)$ and $\dot{x}(0)$ locate a point in the phase plane; the path through this point indicates the behavior of the system at all later times. For example, if the path tends to infinity, the system is unstable, while if the path approaches the origin, the system comes to rest.

As a result of the form of Eq. (11.1), the range of applicability of phase-plane methods is severely limited by three fundamental restrictions:

(1) The phase plane is useful for the analysis of second-order systems only. The effects of nonlinearities in more complex systems can ordinarily be studied only by reducing the system to second order. Attempts have been made to extend the analysis to higher-order systems, but as yet there has been no significant result of general applicability.

(2) The phase plane can be used to study only the transient performance of a system subject to initial conditions but otherwise unexcited.

† The best reference for engineers on the techniques of phase-plane analysis is probably the Princeton translation of the book by A. A. Andronow and C. E. Chaikin, "Theory of Oscillations," Princeton University Press, Princeton, N.J., 1949. The major portion of the material presented in the first five sections of this chapter is based on this book.

‡ Throughout this chapter, x is considered as a general variable dependent on time t; $\dot{x}$ is the first derivative dx/dt; and $\ddot{x}$, the second derivative d^2x/dt^2. As indicated in subsequent sections, application of this analysis to feedback control systems may call for the identification of x with $c(t)$, $e(t)$, or one of the other variables.

Here again, there have been several attempts to extend the theory to the study of sinusoidally excited systems, but again with no general results. In a feedback control system such as that shown in Fig. 11.1, if x refers to the actuating signal $e(t)$, the admission of initial values of e and $\dot{e}$ permits the study of the response of the over-all system to either a step-function or a ramp-function input. The differential equation of the forward part of the system is

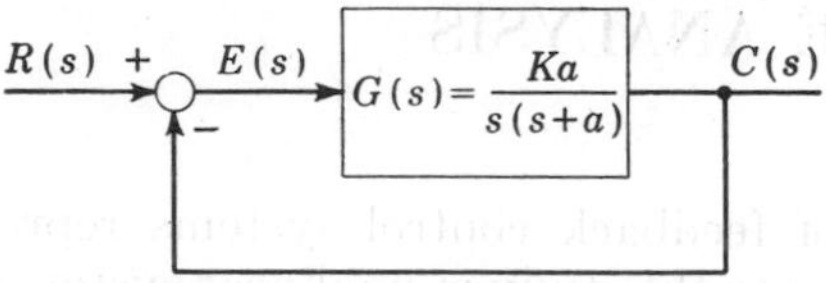

$$aKe = \ddot{c} + a\dot{c} \qquad (11.2)$$

$c(t)$ is given in terms of $r(t)$ and $e(t)$ by

Fig. 11.1. Simple second-order feedback control system.

$$c = r - e \qquad (11.3)$$

Substitution of this relation in Eq. (11.2) yields

$$\ddot{e} + a\dot{e} + aKe = \ddot{r} + a\dot{r} \qquad (11.4)$$

If $r(t)$ is a unit step function, $\ddot{r}$ and $a\dot{r}$ are both zero for positive time. The step-function response of the system is described by the equation

$$\ddot{e} + a\dot{e} + aKe = 0 \qquad (11.5)$$

The initial conditions are

$$e(0) = 1 \qquad \dot{e}(0) = 0 \qquad (11.6)$$

If $r(t)$ is a unit ramp function $r(t) = t$, the behavior is described by the same equation [(11.5)] in a new variable,

$$x = e - \frac{1}{K} \qquad (11.7)$$

The initial conditions are

$$x(0) = -\frac{1}{K} \qquad \dot{x}(0) = 1 \qquad (11.8)$$

The new variable x is introduced in order to allow consideration of an equation in which the dependent variable tends to a steady-state value of zero. Thus, both step-function and ramp-function responses can be obtained, but the sinusoidal response of the system cannot be studied.

(3) The third basic restriction relates to the admissible types of non-linearities. Equation (11.1) indicates that only signal-dependent non-linearities are allowed. The coefficients of $\dot{x}$ and x can be functions of x and $\dot{x}$, but not of time explicitly. Time-dependent systems, or systems with parameters varying with time, have been studied by Zadeh[†] and Kirby and Giulianelli.[‡] In this chapter, such systems are excluded.

[†] L. A. Zadeh, Frequency Analysis of Variable Networks, *Proc. IRE*, Vol. 38, pp. 291–299, March, 1950.

[‡] M. J. Kirby and R. M. Giulianelli, Stability of Varying-element Servomechanisms with Polynomial Coefficients, *Trans. AIEE*, Vol. 70, Part II, pp. 1447–1450, 1951.

Thus, the phase-plane methods of analysis which are described in this chapter are directly applicable to the study of the transient performance of simple systems characterized by signal-dependent nonlinearities, such as backlash, saturation, etc.   The qualitative effects of similar nonlinearities in higher-order systems can often be ascertained by approximation of the complex system by a simpler configuration.   Because the concepts associated with the use of the phase plane are unfamiliar to many engineers, the first two sections of this chapter illustrate the investigation of simple linear systems and the consideration of nonlinear systems is deferred until later sections.

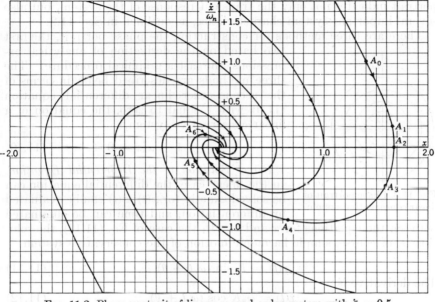

Fig. 11.2. Phase portrait of linear second-order system with ζ = 0.5.

11.1. Construction of the Phase Portrait.   The unexcited linear second order system is described by the equation

$$\ddot{x} + 2\zeta\omega_n\dot{x} + \omega_n^2 x = 0 \tag{11.9}$$

The state of the system at any time is fixed by the values of x and $\dot{x}$: for example, if $x(0)$ and $\dot{x}(0)$ are known, the solution for all positive time is completely determined.   This dependence of the future state of the system on the initial conditions can be portrayed graphically in the *phase plane*, the $x\dot{x}$ plane.†   The *phase portrait* is the totality of *paths* in the phase plane, each path describing the variation of x and $\dot{x}$ with time. Figure 11.2 is the phase portrait for a linear system with a relative damping ratio of 0.5.   As an example, if the initial conditions are

† Throughout this chapter, the plane with $\dot{x}$ as ordinate and x as abscissa is termed the $x\dot{x}$ plane or the plane with $\dot{x}$ plotted versus x.   Such a notation is consistent with the usual description of the plane with rectangular coordinates as the xy plane.

$\dot{x}(0) = 1.03\ \omega_n$ and $x(0) = 1.4$, the system is initially in a state corresponding to point A_0. As time progresses, the point describes the path through A_1, A_2, etc. The projection from this moving point onto the horizontal axis is the variation of x with time; the projection on the vertical axis, the variation of $\dot{x}$. Time appears in the phase portrait only implicitly as a parameter changing value along any path.

Clearly, there is only one path through each point in the phase plane since the solution to Eq. (11.9) is uniquely determined by specification of both x and $\dot{x}$ at any one instant of time. The phase portrait for the linear system is, thus, a collection of noncrossing paths describing system behavior after all possible initial conditions. The nature of the phase portrait indicates not only the transient response of the system, but also several important system characteristics, as outlined in Sec. 11.2.

There are three methods for constructing the phase portrait, the first two based on the derivation of analytical expressions, the last a graphical procedure. The three methods are described below in terms of the second-order linear differential equation (11.9) with ζ equal to zero, the equation of a linear conservative system,[†]

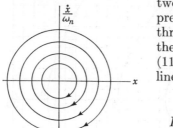

FIG. 11.3. Phase portrait of linear conservative system.

$$\ddot{x} + \omega_n^2 x = 0 \qquad (11.10)$$

Direct Solution of the Differential Equation.
In the linear case, the differential equation can be solved exactly for $x(t)$, $\dot{x}(t)$ can be evaluated by differentiation, and time can be eliminated between the equations for x and $\dot{x}$. In the case of Eq. (11.10), the solution is, of course, simple harmonic motion of the conservative system:

$$x(t) = K \sin (\omega_n t + \theta) \qquad (11.11)$$

The derivative is

$$\dot{x}(t) = \omega_n K \cos (\omega_n t + \theta) \qquad (11.12)$$

Time is eliminated to give the single equation relating x and $\dot{x}$:

$$\frac{\dot{x}^2}{\omega_n^2} + x^2 = K^2 \qquad (11.13)$$

Equation (11.13) describes the phase portrait. The paths are ellipses with axes K and $K\omega_n$. Normalization of the velocity by plotting $\dot{x}/\omega_n$ rather than $\dot{x}$ results in a portrait (Fig. 11.3) which is a family of circles of radius K. The given initial conditions specify a particular circle, and, thereafter, the point moves around this circle forever.

The same procedure, involving exact solution of the differential equation, can occasionally be used in the analysis of nonlinear systems also. The simple system of Fig. 11.4 illustrates this concept. The viscous-friction force of a linear system is proportional to the velocity. *Coulomb*

---

† A conservative system is one in which there is no dissipation of energy.

friction,[†] in contrast, is a frictional force independent of the magnitude of the velocity and always opposing the velocity. The force-velocity relationship is shown in Fig. 11.5. The differential equation describing system behavior is

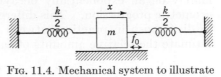

FIG. 11.4. Mechanical system to illustrate coulomb friction. (f_o represents the coulomb friction.)

$$m\ddot{x} + kx \pm f_o = 0 \quad (11.14)$$

k is the effective spring-constant restraining motion, and the sign associated with f_o in the equation is the same as that of $\dot{x}$. It is convenient to normalize the equation by defining the variables ω, a, and u:

$$\omega = \sqrt{\frac{k}{m}} \qquad (11.15)$$

$$a = \frac{f_o}{m\omega^2} \qquad (11.16)$$

$$u = \begin{cases} x - a & \dot{x} < 0 \\ x + a & \dot{x} > 0 \end{cases} \qquad (11.17)$$

The differential equation then becomes

$$\ddot{u} + \omega^2 u = 0 \qquad (11.18)$$

The corresponding phase portrait for the $u\dot{u}$ plane is just that of the linear conservative system considered previously. In the $\dot{x}/\omega$ vs. x plane,

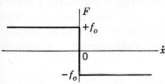

FIG. 11.5. Coulomb-friction force as a function of velocity.

the phase portrait is conveniently found in two parts, one for the upper-half plane ($\dot{x}/\omega > 0$), the other for the lower-half plane ($\dot{x}/\omega < 0$). Since x is related to u by a simple translation, the portrait in the upper half of the $\dot{x}/\omega$ vs. x plane is a family of semicircles centered about $x = -a$. The center for the lower-half-plane semicircles is, correspondingly, $x = +a$. The phase portrait is sketched in Fig. 11.6.

The phase portrait presents at once the nature of the response of the system. The response to an initial displacement and zero initial velocity is shown in Fig. 11.7, with the corresponding motion in the phase plane indicated in Fig. 11.6. The response is characterized by the following features:

(1) Each section (*e.g.*, 0 to π, or π to 2π, on the ωt scale) is a half sinusoid, centered about either $+a$ or $-a$ values of x.

(2) The absolute values of successive extrema (maxima or minima) form an arithmetic progression with a difference of $2a$. This is in direct

[†] I. A. Greenwood, Jr., J. V. Holdam, Jr., and D. MacRae, Jr., "Electronic Instruments," MIT Radiation Laboratory Series, Vol. 21, pp. 357–359, McGraw-Hill Book Company, Inc., New York, 1948.

contrast to the nature of the response of a system with viscous damping only, in which the magnitudes of the successive extrema fall approximately on an exponentially decaying curve and, consequently, form a geometric progression. This difference between system responses is used to distinguish in practice between viscous and coulomb friction and to estimate the relative amounts of each.

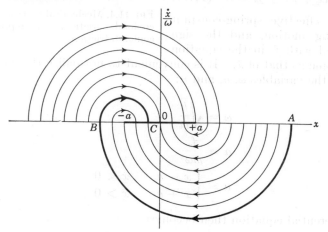

FIG. 11.6. Phase portrait of system of Fig. 11.4.

(3) As soon as the response has an extremum inside the interval $-a \leq x \leq +a$, all motion stops. The system may come to rest anywhere within this interval. The possibility of large steady-state errors can be eliminated if dither is used, the system output oscillated at a high frequency and low amplitude. The phase portrait of Fig. 11.8 demonstrates the feasibility of this method of reducing static errors. Although

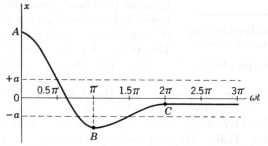

FIG. 11.7. Time response for system with coulomb friction.

all semicircles hit the axis normally, the larger the circle, the more slowly it breaks away from the vertical as it leaves the x axis. Consequently, a slight $\dot{x}$ disturbance, alternately positive and negative, makes the system, initially at A, tend toward the origin. A slight negative disturbance, $\overline{AB}$, results in the system returning to rest at C, while a positive disturbance, $\overline{AD}$, is followed by a return to E. Since $\overline{AC}$ is greater than

$\overline{AE}$, alternating positive and negative disturbances bring the system toward the origin.

Solution of the Differential Equation for $\dot{x}$ as a Function of x.   In certain systems, rather than solving the original second-order differential equation, it is simpler to determine the differential equation for $\dot{x}$ in terms of x, with t not appearing explicitly.   The procedure is more readily visualized if the variable y is defined

$$y = \dot{x} \tag{11.19}$$

With this definition, the original differential equation (11.10) can be written

$$\dot{y} + \omega_n^2 x = 0 \tag{11.20}$$

The equation is divided, term by term, by y or $\dot{x}$:

$$\frac{\dot{y}}{\dot{x}} + \omega_n^2 \frac{x}{y} = 0 \qquad (11.21)$$

But $\dot{y}/\dot{x}$ is $(dy/dt)/(dx/dt)$, which is simply dy/dx.   Hence, Eq. (11.21) can be written as a first-order differential equation for y as a function of x.

$$\frac{dy}{dx} + \omega_n^2 \frac{x}{y} = 0 \qquad (11.22)$$

Even if the original differential equation is very difficult to solve, this first-order equation may be solvable, with the solution giving directly the equation for the phase paths. (In the simple linear conservative

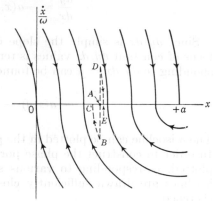

FIG. 11.8. Effect of slight velocity disturbances within the coulomb-friction zone.

case, represented by the above equations, the construction of the phase portrait is so straightforward that any method appears satisfactory.) Equation (11.22) leads to a solution identical with that obtained by the first method,

$$\frac{y^2}{\omega_n^2} + x^2 = K^2 \tag{11.23}$$

With the introduction of the y notation, the vertical axis of the phase plane is y rather than $\dot{x}$.

Determination of the Isoclines.†   The third method of determining the phase portrait is the most useful in the study of nonlinear systems.   Even if the differential equations of the first two methods cannot be solved, the phase portrait can be constructed graphically by an investigation of the slopes of the phase paths.   The procedure described in connection with the second method is used to obtain the first-order differential equa-

† A. A. Andronow and C. E. Chaikin, "Theory of Oscillations," pp. 248–250, Princeton University Press, Princeton, N.J., 1949.

tion for y in terms of x. In the general system, the original differential equation is of the form

$$\ddot{x} + a(x,\dot{x})\dot{x} + b(x,\dot{x})x = 0 \tag{11.24}$$

Substitution of y for $\dot{x}$ yields

$$\dot{y} + a(x,y)y + b(x,y)x = 0 \tag{11.25}$$

Division by $y = \dot{x}$ gives

$$\frac{\dot{y}}{\dot{x}} + a(x,y)\frac{y}{y} + b(x,y)\frac{x}{y} = 0 \tag{11.26}$$

If $\dot{y}/\dot{x}$ is replaced by dy/dx, Eq. (11.26) can be written

$$\frac{dy}{dx} = -a(x,y) - b(x,y)\frac{x}{y} \tag{11.27}$$

Since dy/dx is simply the slope of the paths in the phase plane, the locus of constant dy/dx values is termed an isocline. The isocline corresponding to $dy/dx = \alpha$ can be found from the equation

$$-a(x,y) - b(x,y)\frac{x}{y} = \alpha \tag{11.28}$$

The α isocline can be plotted in the phase plane by the use of Eq. (11.28). In order to construct the phase portrait, a large number of isoclines are plotted, corresponding to various slopes of the phase paths. If these isoclines are drawn sufficiently close together, the phase paths can be sketched.

The procedure is illustrated by the previous example of the linear conservative system. The expression for dy/dx is found from Eq. (11.22):

$$\frac{dy}{dx} = -\omega_n^2 \frac{x}{y} \tag{11.29}$$

If the normalized phase plane is used (with y/ω_n as the ordinate y_1), dy_1/dx is given by

$$\frac{dy_1}{dx} = -\frac{x}{y_1} \tag{11.30}$$

The α isocline is determined by the relation

$$-\frac{x}{y_1} = \alpha \tag{11.31}$$

The isoclines (shown in Fig. 11.9) constitute a family of straight lines passing through the origin in the phase plane and with a slope $-1/\alpha$.

The path from any given point can be constructed in the following manner. Point A in Fig. 11.10 lies on the isocline corresponding to an α of -1. The motion of the path away from A is then downward and to the right. The $\alpha = -1.33$ isocline is the next intercepted by a path moving in this direction. From point A a line segment of slope -1.17 (the average of -1 and -1.33) is drawn to the $\alpha = -1.33$ isocline to establish the point B. From point B the process is repeated, with the next line segment possessing a slope of -1.67, the average of -1.33 and -2. The phase path is the connection of these various line segments.

The accuracy of the method depends on the number of isoclines drawn and can be made as high as desired. There are certain difficulties which occasionally arise in this method of construction. It is shown in succeeding sections that one important aspect of nonlinear systems is often the existence of closed paths. The approximation inherent in construction of the phase portrait by the isocline method makes it difficult in some cases to determine whether the phase path is closed or whether it is simply approaching the origin very slightly during each revolution. However, this is not a serious defi-

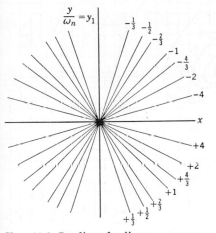

FIG. 11.9. Isoclines for linear conservative system for various values of $\alpha = dy_1/dx$.

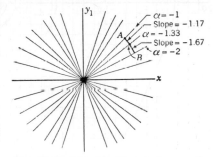

FIG. 11.10. Construction of phase path from isoclines.

ciency of the method in most practical situations. The absence of any method for determining the accuracy achieved by a selected number of isoclines is disturbing, but again, in most engineering problems, if the phase portrait is not changed significantly by increasing the number of isoclines, the accuracy of the original portrait is sufficient.

11.2. Interpretation of the Phase Portrait. What characteristics of system behavior can be obtained from the phase portrait? Certain interpretations of importance in the analysis of feedback control systems are summarized in this section.

Response to Initial Conditions. The phase portrait, as indicated in the preceding section, portrays the response of the unexcited system to any initial conditions. Figure 11.11 is the portrait for a second-order linear system with a relative damping ratio of 0.5. The response of the system to the initial conditions $x(0) = 1$ and $\dot{x}(0) = 0$ is found by following the path from point A_0 through points A_1, A_2, etc., in toward the origin. If the initial conditions are changed to zero initial value and an initial rate of change of $0.5\omega_n$, the response is given by the B path. In a similar fashion, any initial value and initial rate of change can be considered. The response is always obtained as the variation of $\dot{x}$ (or y) with x, rather than the variation of either x or $\dot{x}$ with time.

If the phase portrait is drawn for $y = \dot{x}$, the motion in the phase plane is always to the right in the upper-half plane (since with $\dot{x} > 0$, x is increasing with time) and to the left in the lower-half plane. All paths

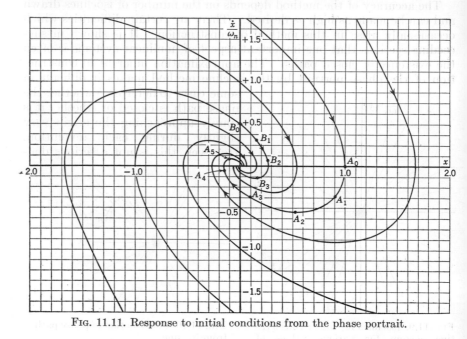

Fig. 11.11. Response to initial conditions from the phase portrait.

cross the x axis normally because, with $\dot{x} = 0$, x is not changing. Thus, the response is obtained by locating the point corresponding to the specified initial conditions and then following the path through this point.

Total Energy. The total energy stored in the system is also available from the phase portrait. If the phase portrait describes a second-order linear differential equation, the total stored energy is proportional to the square of the radial distance to the point in the normalized phase plane (with the ordinate y/ω_n, or $\dot{x}/\omega_n$). This interpretation of energy is clarified if the differential equation is considered to describe the circuit of

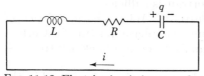

Fig. 11.12. Electric circuit for second-order system.

Fig. 11.12. The variable x is then the charge q; the variable $\dot{x}$, the current i. The equation is written

$$L\frac{di}{dt} + Ri + \frac{1}{C}q = 0 \qquad (11.32)$$

Division by L puts the equation in the form previously considered,

$$\frac{di}{dt} + \frac{R}{L} i + \frac{1}{LC} q = 0 \tag{11.33}$$

The total stored energy is simply $\frac{1}{2} Li^2 + \frac{1}{2} q^2/C$. If i is replaced by y and q by x, the stored energy is

$$\mathcal{E} = \frac{1}{2} Ly^2 + \frac{1}{2C} x^2 \tag{11.34}$$

With ω_n^2 equal to $1/LC$, Eq. (11.34) becomes

$$\mathcal{E} = \frac{1}{2C} \left(\frac{y^2}{\omega_n^2} + x^2 \right) \tag{11.35}$$

The stored energy corresponding to any point in the phase plane is $1/(2C)$ times the square of the radial distance from the origin to the point under consideration.

In the conservative system, the normalized phase portrait is a family of circles centered at the origin. The stored energy along any path remains constant, oscillating between the magnetic and the electric fields, if the electric system of Fig. 11.12 is considered with R equal to zero. The phase portrait of the dissipative system (R of Fig. 11.12 positive) is shown in Fig. 11.11. The stored energy is continually decreasing with time as a consequence of the dissipation. Similar interpretation of the stored energy can often assist in the investigation of nonlinear systems, as indicated in subsequent sections.

Time from Reciprocal Plots. Although appearing only implicitly as a parameter in the phase portrait, time can be determined explicitly and x can be plotted as a function of time from the appropriate phase path. The variation of time along a path can be found by two methods in addition to the obvious procedure involving solution of the differential equation.

The first and more familiar method is based on the relation between time and the plot of $1/y$ as a function of x. By definition,

$$y = \frac{dx}{dt} \tag{11.36}$$

dt can be written

$$dt = \frac{1}{y} dx \tag{11.37}$$

Integration yields

$$t = \int \frac{1}{y} dx \tag{11.38}$$

Thus, if $1/y$ is plotted as a function of x, the integral under the curve between any two points is the time required for the state of the system to change from one point to the other. This procedure essentially amounts to a graphical solution of the differential equation.

The determination of time is illustrated by a simple example, involving the linear system with a relative damping ratio of 0.5. In the phase portrait of Fig. 11.13, the time for the system to move from A to B is to be determined. The exact solution can be found since in this simple

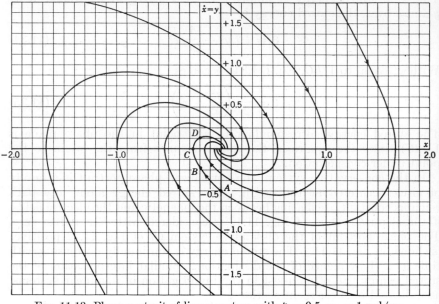

FIG. 11.13. Phase portrait of linear system with $\zeta = 0.5$, $\omega_n = 1$ rad/sec.

linear case the differential equation can be solved directly. If ω_n is considered to be unity, the solution is

$$x(t) = Ke^{-\frac{1}{2}t} \sin\left(\frac{\sqrt{3}}{2} t + \theta\right) \tag{11.39}$$

K and θ are determined from the initial conditions. If t is made zero when the system is at point A,

$$x(t) = -\frac{1}{\sqrt{3}} e^{-\frac{1}{2}t} \sin\frac{\sqrt{3}}{2} t \tag{11.40}$$

The time in transition from A to B is found by substituting -0.2 for x in Eq. (11.40). The result is a value of approximately 0.55 sec.

The graphical solution is readily determined. In Fig. 11.14, $1/\dot{x}$ is plotted as a function of x in the interval A to B. The integral under the curve can be evaluated with a planimeter, but simple approximation of the area with rectangles yields sufficient accuracy for most purposes. The approximate value of time obtained from Fig. 11.14 is 0.56 sec.

The graphical integration presents difficulties if y passes through zero in the interval of interest. For example, the evaluation of the transition time between points A and D of Fig. 11.13 requires a determination of the area under a curve of the shape shown in Fig. 11.15.   The magnitude of the area of region I corresponds to the length of the time interval required for the state of the system to move from A to C; that of region II, the time from C to D.   Even with the integrand unbounded, the integral exists, although it is not readily evaluated graphically unless the time for the state of the system to pass through a small interval about C is neglected.

Time Geometrically.   An alternate method for the determination of time is based upon an approximation of the phase path by a series of arcs of circles centered on the x axis.   If the section of the path from

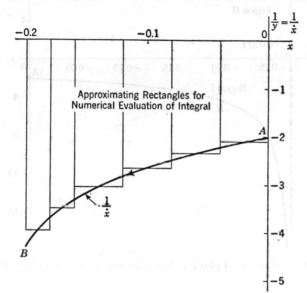

FIG. 11.14. Determination of time from reciprocal plot.

A to B (Fig. 11.16) can be considered to be a segment of a circle with center at x_0, the time interval corresponding to a section within AB is found as follows.   A perpendicular is dropped from A to the x axis.   The line segment AD is drawn, making an angle ϵ with the vertical.   From D, the line segment DC is drawn such that DC also makes an angle ϵ with the vertical.   The time from A to C is given by $2\epsilon\tau$,† where ϵ is measured in radians and τ is the ratio of the y and x scale factors,

$$\tau = \frac{\text{value of } x \text{ corresponding to one division}}{\text{value of } y \text{ corresponding to one division}} \qquad (11.41)$$

The application of this technique is illustrated by the example used previously, the calculation of the time required for the state of the system to change from A to B in Fig. 11.13.   The AB section of the phase

† K. V. Diprose, Discussion on nonlinear problems, "Automatic and Manual Control," Proceedings of Cranfield Conference 1951, edited by A. Tustin, p. 304, Butterworths Scientific Publications, London, 1952.

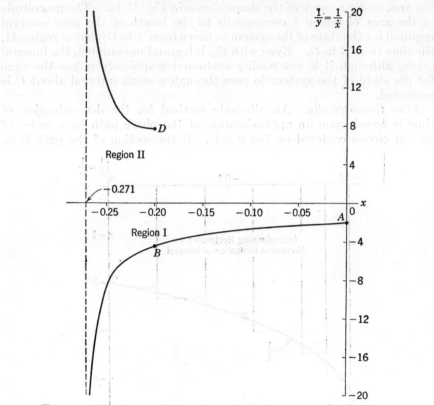

FIG. 11.15. Reciprocal plot for time calculation, A to D in Fig. 11.13.

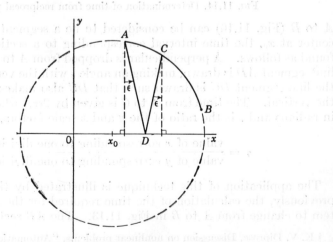

FIG. 11.16. Determination of time geometrically.

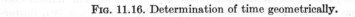

path is redrawn to a larger scale in Fig. 11.17. Trial and error with a compass indicates that the section from A to A_1 can be approximated by the arc of a circle centered on the x axis. From A_1, another circle suffices up to A_2, and a last circle completes the approximation.

With points A_1 and A_2 determined, the next step is the determination of the ϵ angle for each of the three segments. In the first segment, the

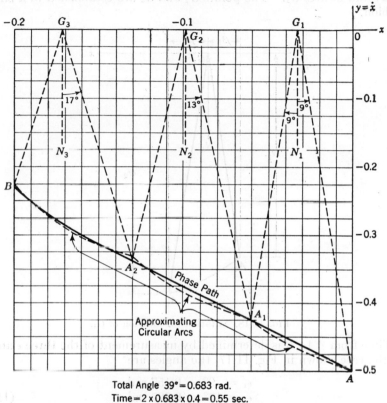

Total Angle 39° = 0.683 rad.
Time = 2 × 0.683 × 0.4 = 0.55 sec.
FIG. 11.17. Geometrical evaluation of time in portrait of Fig. 11.13.

point G_1 must be found such that $\underline{/AG_1N_1} = \underline{/A_1G_1N_1}$. G_1 is readily determined from the equality of these two angles (or the corresponding tangents). If the notation of Fig. 11.18 is used,

$$\frac{\beta_2}{\alpha_2} = \frac{\beta_1}{\alpha_1} \qquad (11.42)$$

A somewhat more convenient relation is

$$\frac{\beta_2}{\beta_1 + \beta_2} = \frac{\alpha_2}{\alpha_1 + \alpha_2} \qquad (11.43)$$

In the case of Fig. 11.17,

$$\beta_1 + \beta_2 = 0.06 \quad = \text{magnitude of the change in } x \text{ from } A \text{ to } A_1$$
$$\alpha_1 = 0.425 = \text{magnitude of } \dot{x} \text{ at } A_1 \quad\quad (11.44)$$
$$\alpha_2 = 0.50 \quad = \text{magnitude of } \dot{x} \text{ at } A$$

Substitution of the values of Eq. (11.44) into Eq. (11.43) yields a β_2 of 0.324 and locates G_1. The points G_2 and G_3 are established in a similar fashion.

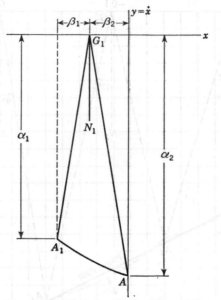

FIG. 11.18. Notation for location of G_1.

Time from A to B is determined by measurement of the three ϵ angles. In the case shown in Fig. 11.17, the angles are

$$\epsilon_1 = 9° = 0.157 \text{ rad}$$
$$\epsilon_2 = 13° = 0.227 \text{ rad} \quad\quad (11.45)$$
$$\epsilon_3 = 17° = 0.297 \text{ rad}$$

The τ factor, given by Eq. (11.41), is in this case

$$\tau = \frac{0.02}{0.05} = 0.4 \quad\quad (11.46)$$

The time intervals are simply $2\epsilon\tau$:

$$T_1 = 2\epsilon_1\tau = 2 \times 0.157 \times 0.4 = 0.126 \text{ sec}$$
$$T_2 = 2\epsilon_2\tau = 2 \times 0.228 \times 0.4 = 0.182 \text{ sec}$$
$$T_3 = 2\epsilon_3\tau = 2 \times 0.298 \times 0.4 = 0.238 \text{ sec}$$

Starting from A, the system reaches A_1 in 0.126 sec, A_2 in 0.182 additional sec, and B 0.238 sec later. The total time from A to B is the sum of the three intervals, or 0.55 sec.

The validity of this method of time measurement is established heuristically along the following line of argument. If the segment of the phase path is an arc of a circle centered on the x axis, the time to traverse from A to B in Fig. 11.19 is equal to $\theta\tau$, where θ is the arc length in radians, or the central angle subtending the arc, and τ is the scaling factor. The relation $T = \theta\tau$ follows from the study of the linear conservative system for which the phase portrait was shown to be a family of concentric circles. The time to traverse any circle is simply one period, or 2π sec in the normalized plane. The velocity along the circle is constant (since the motion is simple harmonic), with the result that time is given by the central angle subtending the traversed arc. The translation of the circle along the x axis simply corresponds to a shift in the reference used for the measurement of x. In the unnormalized plane, the expression for time is multiplied by τ, since if the x scale were

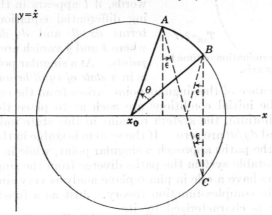

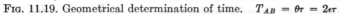

FIG. 11.19. Geometrical determination of time. $T_{AB} = \theta\tau = 2\epsilon\tau$

expanded tremendously a given θ would correspond to a very short time interval.

Once the relation between time and θ is established, the relation between time and ϵ follows directly. Figure 11.19 demonstrates that ϵ is the angle ACB, where C is the intersection of the vertical from B and the circle. But this angle ACB, or ϵ, is one half the arc length θ, by a basic plane-geometry theorem, which states that the angle inscribed in a circle is one half the enclosed arc length. Thus, the time interval from A to B is $2\epsilon\tau$.

This method for the determination of time is particularly useful in the regions of the phase portrait in the vicinity of the x axis. It is shown below that if the phase plane is a plot of $\dot{x}$ versus x the paths always cross the x axis vertically. Thus, in the vicinity of the x axis, the paths always can be approximated by a large circle centered on the axis. If A is within this circular region, the time required for the system state to change from A to the point B on the axis is proportional to the angle AB makes with the vertical. Figure 11.20 indicates the construction here. The time from A to B is again simply $2\epsilon\tau$. This method of determining time avoids any difficulty with integration under curves tending to infinity.

Singular Points. The singular points in the phase plane are of fundamental importance in the analysis of the characteristics of nonlinear systems. If a second-order system can be described in terms of two variables x and y, the differential equations describing the system are of the form

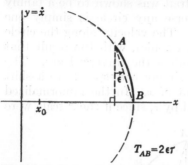

$$\frac{dx}{dt} = P(x,y) \qquad (11.47)$$

$$\frac{dy}{dt} = Q(x,y) \qquad (11.48)$$

FIG. 11.20. Determination of time to a point on the x axis.

If the system is autonomous (in other words, if t appears in the two describing differential equations only in the terms dx/dt and dy/dt), the points where $\dot{x}$ and $\dot{y}$ vanish are called *singular points*. At a singular point, the system is in a *state of equilibrium.*

The significance of the singular points arises from the equilibrium condition. If the initial conditions are such as to place the system in a state of equilibrium, the system remains in this state indefinitely, since both dx/dt and dy/dt are zero. If the system is stable in the conventional linear sense, the paths approach a singular point, while in the phase portrait of an unstable system the paths diverge from the singularity. The singular points have a role in phase-plane analysis very similar to that of singularities in complex-function theory. Just as a function of a complex variable is characterized by its singularities, the singular points in the phase plane are the source of many of the distinguishing features of the phase portrait, or the basic characteristics of the nonlinear differential equation.

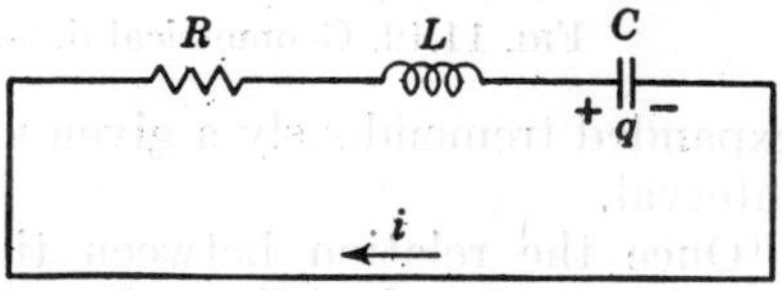

FIG. 11.21. Electric circuit for second-order system.

The simple second-order linear system of Fig. 11.21 illustrates the determination of the singular points. The system is described by the differential equation

$$L\frac{d^2q}{dt^2} + R\frac{dq}{dt} + \frac{1}{C}q = 0 \qquad (11.49)$$

Equation (11.49) can be written as two simultaneous first-order equations in the manner of Eqs. (11.47) and (11.48):

$$\frac{dq}{dt} = i \qquad (11.50)$$

$$\frac{di}{dt} = -\frac{R}{L}i - \frac{1}{LC}q \qquad (11.51)$$

The phase portrait is a plot of i versus q. Since the singular points are located where dq/dt and di/dt are both zero, there is only the one singular point, at $i = q = 0$. In a more comprehensive example, the singular points, determined by simultaneous solution of the two equations $P(x,y) = 0$ and $Q(x,y) = 0$, may be several in number. The system may be in equilibrium in a variety of different states. In the example of Sec. 11.1 involving the analysis of a system with coulomb friction, it is found that the entire x axis from $-a$ to $+a$ represents equilibrium. In the following sections, however, consideration is given to only the cases in which the singular points are isolated.

11.3. Types of Singular Points. The origin is the only singular point in the phase portrait of the linear system of Fig. 11.21. This singular point may exhibit a number of different characteristics with variations of the coefficients in the differential equations (11.50) and (11.51). The singular points of a nonlinear system are conveniently studied in terms of the system description by two first-order equations:

$$\frac{dx}{dt} = P(x,y) \tag{11.52}$$

$$\frac{dy}{dt} = Q(x,y) \tag{11.53}$$

The singular points are given by the simultaneous solution of the two equations

$$P(x,y) = 0 \tag{11.54}$$
$$Q(x,y) = 0 \tag{11.55}$$

If the singular points are isolated, the behavior of the phase portrait in the vicinity of the singular points is readily determined from the nature of the functions $P(x,y)$ and $Q(x,y)$.† If the singular point is assumed to lie at $x = a$ and $y = b$, $P(x,y)$ and $Q(x,y)$ are expanded about these points, with the result that Eqs. (11.52) and (11.53) become

$$\frac{dx}{dt} = a_1(x - a) + a_2(y - b) + a_3(x - a)^2 + a_4(x - a)(y - b)$$
$$+ a_5(y - b)^2 + \cdots \tag{11.56}$$
$$\frac{dy}{dt} = b_1(x - a) + b_2(y - b) + b_3(x - a)^2 + b_4(x - a)(y - b)$$
$$+ b_5(y - b)^2 + \cdots \tag{11.57}$$

The assumption is made here that P and Q can each be expanded in this form. The higher-order terms not shown have no constant, linear, or quadratic components. The nature of the singular point is determined entirely by a_1, a_2, b_1, and b_2, for, if a sufficiently small region in the

† N. Minorsky, "Introduction to Nonlinear Mechanics," pp. 42–48, J. W. Edwards, Publisher, Inc., Ann Arbor, Mich., 1947.

vicinity of the singular point is considered, the linear terms predominate in the series.†

Such a simplification of P and Q is nothing more than a linearization of the nonlinear system. Within a small enough region (here chosen around the singular point), the system behaves linearly. The describing equations are

$$\frac{dx}{dt} = a_1(x - a) + a_2(y - b) \tag{11.58}$$

$$\frac{dy}{dt} = b_1(x - a) + b_2(y - b) \tag{11.59}$$

What is the nature of the phase portrait in this region? The characteristics are readily found if attention is focused on one of the two variables. If x is chosen, y is eliminated between the two equations, and the solution for $x(t)$ is determined. No loss of generality occurs if a and b are both considered zero, since the singularity can be shifted to the origin by simple changes of variables, $x - a = u$ and $y - b = v$.

As the first step, the Laplace transform of Eqs. (11.58) and (11.59) is taken:

$$sX(s) - x(0) = a_1X(s) + a_2Y(s) \tag{11.60}$$

$$sY(s) - y(0) = b_1X(s) + b_2Y(s) \tag{11.61}$$

$Y(s)$ is eliminated, with the result

$$X(s) =$$
$$\frac{(s - b_2)x(0) + a_2y(0)}{s^2 - (a_1 + b_2)s + (a_1b_2 - a_2b_1)} \tag{11.62}$$

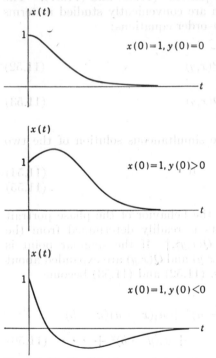

The nature of the behavior of $x(t)$ depends upon the two zeros of the denominator, or characteristic, polynomial. If the coefficients are all real, six situations may exist:

FIG. 11.22. Possible forms of response with two zeros of characteristic polynomial negative real.

(1) The zeros are both real and both in the left half of the s plane. In this case, the time response $x(t)$ resulting from specified initial conditions may take three general forms, as shown in Fig. 11.22. If there is an initial value $x(0)$ but $y(0)$ is zero, the response displays the conventional overdamped characteristic. A positive initial value $y(0)$ causes a

† The assumption is made here that a_1 and a_2 (or b_1 and b_2) are not zero simultaneously.

response in which a maximum is attained at a positive value of time. A large negative value of $y(0)$ causes a single overshoot, as shown in the last part of the figure. The corresponding phase portrait thus takes the form sketched in Fig. 11.23. After a finite amount of rotation, all paths head in directly toward the origin. Such a singular point is termed a *stable node,* "stable" indicating that the paths converge toward the singular point and "node" indicating the direct nature of the approach.

(2) The zeros are conjugate complex and in the left-half plane. The response is oscillatory, with $x(t)$ a damped sinusoid for any initial con-

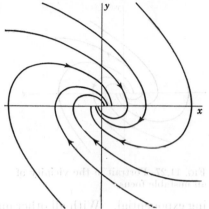

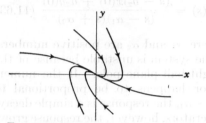

FIG. 11.23. Portrait in the vicinity of a stable node.

FIG. 11.24. Portrait in the vicinity of a stable focus.

ditions. The nature of the phase portrait is indicated by Fig. 11.24. The paths again approach the origin, but in a manner quite different from that exhibited in the case of real zeros. The spiraling nature of the paths gives rise to the term *stable focus* for this type of singularity.

(3) The zeros are conjugate and lie on the $j\omega$ axis. With this location of the zeros, $x(t)$ exhibits simple harmonic motion, with the oscillatory

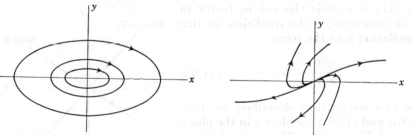

FIG. 11.25. Portrait in the vicinity of a center.

FIG. 11.26. Portrait in the vicinity of an unstable node.

amplitude dependent on the initial conditions. The phase portrait, as sketched in Fig. 11.25, is a family of ellipses about the singular point. The neighborhood of the singular point exhibits the same characteristics as the entire phase portrait of the linear conservative system discussed in Sec. 11.1. The singularity is termed a *center.*

(4) The zeros are both real and both in the right half of the s plane. The singular point is unstable, with the corresponding $x(t)$ growing as

the sum of two positive exponentials. The singularity is termed an *unstable node*, and the phase portrait takes the form shown in Fig. 11.26.

(5) The zeros are conjugate complex and in the right-half plane. The time function is again oscillatory, but in this case with an envelope which grows exponentially with time. With the phase portrait spiraling outward from the singular point (Fig. 11.27), the singularity is an *unstable focus*.

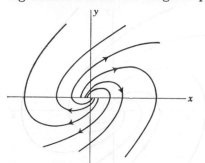

FIG. 11.27. Portrait in the vicinity of an unstable focus.

(6) The zeros are real, with one in the left-half plane and one in the right-half plane. In this case, Eq. (11.62) becomes

$$X(s) = \frac{(s - b_2)x(0) + a_2 y(0)}{(s - \alpha_1)(s + \alpha_2)} \quad (11.63)$$

Here α_1 and α_2 are positive numbers. The system is unstable because of the right-half-plane pole. If the numerator happens to be proportional to $s - \alpha_1$, the response is a simple decaying exponential. With all other numerators, however, the response grows without limit. The condition under which the unstable mode is not excited is a relation between $x(0)$, $y(0)$, and the coefficients of the system; specifically, the relation is of the form

$$\frac{y(0)}{x(0)} = -K_1 \quad (11.64)$$

Here K_1 depends on a_1, a_2, b_1, and b_2. The decaying exponential is never excited, and the response simply grows exponentially if the numerator of Eq. (11.63) cancels the $s + \alpha_2$ factor in the denominator. The condition for this cancellation is of the form

$$\frac{y(0)}{x(0)} = K_2 \quad (11.65)$$

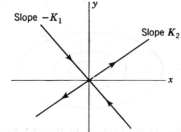

FIG. 11.28. Separatrices for a saddle-point singularity.

The two separatrices described by Eqs. (11.64) and (11.65) are shown in the phase plane of Fig. 11.28. The general shape of the remainder of the phase portrait can be sketched from the known behavior of the sum of a growing and a decaying exponential and is shown in Fig. 11.29. A singularity of this type is called a *saddle point*.

Thus, the nature of the singular point and the behavior of the phase portrait in the vicinity of the singular point are determined by the zeros of the characteristic polynomial or, more basically, by the coefficients a_1, a_2, b_1, and b_2 of Eqs. (11.58) and (11.59). In particular, the type of singularity depends on the values of the two coefficients of the characteristic polynomial: $-(a_1 + b_2)$ and $a_1b_2 - a_2b_1$. The picture of Fig. 11.30† is useful in clarifying these relations: if $-(a_1 + b_2)$ is plotted as the ordinate, and $a_1b_2 - a_2b_1$ as the abscissa, the plane can be divided into regions corresponding to the various types of singularities. The dividing line between the node and focus regions is the parabola

$$(a_1 + b_2)^2 = 4(a_1b_2 - a_2b_1) \tag{11.66}$$

Of particular interest in the analysis of feedback control systems is the special case in which the variable y is simply the time derivative of x.

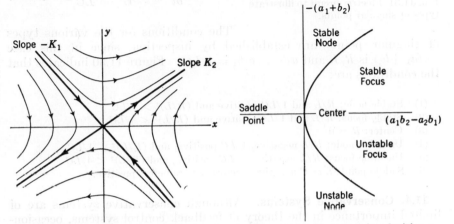

FIG. 11.29. Portrait in the neighborhood of a saddle point.

FIG. 11.30. Types of singularities.

In this case, all singular points fall on the x axis, since the condition $dx/dt = 0$ implies $y = 0$. Equation (11.58) indicates that for this situation

$$a_1 = 0$$
$$a_2 = 1 \tag{11.67}$$

The characteristic polynomial then becomes $s^2 - b_2s - b_1$. The values of b_1 and b_2 determine the nature of the singular points. It can be shown that Eqs. (11.64) and (11.65) become, respectively,

$$\frac{y(0)}{x(0)} = -\alpha_2 \tag{11.68}$$

$$\frac{y(0)}{x(0)} = \alpha_1 \tag{11.69}$$

The phase portrait in the vicinity of a saddle point is of the form shown in Fig. 11.29, but the line of slope K_2 now always lies in the first and third quadrants, that of slope $-K_1$ always in the second and fourth quadrants.

† A. A. Andronow and C. E. Chaikin, "Theory of Oscillations," p. 193, Princeton University Press, Princeton, N.J., 1949.

The concepts of this section are illustrated by consideration of the linear second-order system of Fig. 11.31. The simultaneous first-order differential equations describing system behavior were found in the preceding section to be

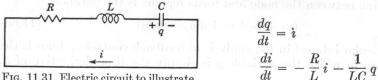

$$\frac{dq}{dt} = i \qquad (11.70)$$

$$\frac{di}{dt} = -\frac{R}{L}i - \frac{1}{LC}q \qquad (11.71)$$

Fig. 11.31. Electric circuit to illustrate types of singular points.

The conditions for the various types of singular points are established by inspection, since in this case $-(a_1 + b_2)$ is R/L and $a_1 b_2 - a_2 b_1$ is $1/LC$. Figure 11.30 indicates that the conditions are:

(1) Stable node: R/L and $1/LC$ positive and $(R/L)^2 > 4/LC$
(2) Stable focus: R/L and $1/LC$ positive and $(R/L)^2 < 4/LC$
(3) Center: $R = 0$
(4) Unstable node: R/L negative, $1/LC$ positive, and $(R/L)^2 > 4/LC$
(5) Unstable focus: R/L negative, $1/LC$ positive, and $(R/L)^2 < 4/LC$
(6) Saddle point: L or C negative, the other parameters positive.

11.4. Conservative Systems. Although conservative systems are of limited importance in the theory of feedback control systems, occasionally a physical system is adequately approximated by considering it conservative. In addition, there are a number of physical systems for which the general characteristics of the system behavior can be deduced from an analysis based on an assumption of no dissipation. Also, an investigation of the characteristics of conservative systems serves as a useful introduction to the analysis of more general systems.

The conservative system is defined by the equation

$$\frac{\dot{x}^2}{2} + V(x) = h \qquad (11.72)$$

If x is a displacement, Eq. (11.72) states that the kinetic energy $\dot{x}^2/2$ plus the potential energy $V(x)$ is equal to a constant h, independent of time. [The usual definition of kinetic energy, $mv^2/2$, where v is the velocity of the mass m, is obtained if Eq. (11.72) is multiplied throughout by m. The form of (11.72) is for a normalized mass m of unity.] The potential energy $V(x)$ is a general real function of the variable x. The *linear* conservative system is obtained if $V(x)$ is simply proportional to x.

The differential equation describing system behavior can be obtained directly from Eq. (11.72). Differentiation of the equation with respect to time yields

$$\dot{x}\ddot{x} + V'(x)\dot{x} = 0 \qquad (11.73)$$

Division by $\dot{x}$ leads to the differential equation

$$\ddot{x} + V'(x) = 0 \tag{11.74}$$

Here $V'(x)$ is the derivative of $V(x)$ with respect to the argument x.

Singular points. The singular points are determined by rewriting the differential equation in terms of y, defined as $\dot{x}$. The two first-order differential equations are

$$\dot{x} = y \tag{11.75}$$
$$\dot{y} = -V'(x) \tag{11.76}$$

The singular points (located where $\dot{x}$ and $\dot{y}$ are both zero) are on the x axis at the real zeros of $V'(x)$.

Types of Singular Points. The nature of the singular points can be found from the analysis described in Sec. 11.3. For Eqs. (11.75) and (11.76), three of the parameters used in the last section are completely determined. The fourth, b_1, depends on the $V'(x)$ function. For the singular point at x_0,

$$a_1 = 0 \qquad b_1 = -V''(x_0) \tag{11.77}$$
$$a_2 = 1 \qquad b_2 = 0$$

Since both a_1 and b_2 are zero, Fig. 11.30 indicates that the singular point is either a center or a saddle point: a center if $V''(x_0)$ is positive [*i.e.*, if x_0 is a minimum of $V(x)$], a saddle point if $V''(x_0)$ is negative [x_0 a maximum of $V(x)$], and a degenerate type of saddle point if $V''(x_0)$ is zero. Consequently, if the degenerate saddle points are excluded, the centers and saddle points alternate along the x axis.

Simple Isoclines. The construction of the phase portrait is simplified if the general nature of the portrait is determined before accurate construction is initiated. In most systems, the isoclines for zero and infinite slopes of the phase paths are readily evaluated. The isocline equation is determined by dividing $\dot{y}$ [Eq. (11.76)] by $\dot{x}$ [Eq. (11.75)]:

$$\frac{dy}{dx} = -\frac{V'(x)}{y} \tag{11.78}$$

The locus of infinite dy/dx is the x axis; that for zero dy/dx consists of all vertical lines through the singularities, the real zeros of $V'(x)$.

Symmetry. In the analysis of many systems, the existence of symmetry in the phase portrait can be established directly from the equations describing system behavior. In the case of the conservative system, for example, Eq. (11.72), expressing the conservation of energy, can be written

$$\frac{y^2}{2} + V(x) = h \tag{11.79}$$

Clearly, if a positive value of y satisfies this equation, the negative y of the same magnitude must also. The phase portrait must be symmetrical about the x axis. The only difference in the phase portraits of upper- and lower-half planes is that motion is to the right when y is positive, to the left with y negative. Thus, it is unnecessary to determine the portrait in the lower-half plane.

Neighborhood of the Singular Points.† Another source of information about the general nature of the phase portrait is the behavior of the portrait in the immediate neighborhood of each singular point. In the conservative system, the singular points are the real zeros of $V'(x)$. A singular point x_0 may be of three types, depending on whether $V''(x_0)$ is positive, negative, or zero.

If $V''(x_0)$ is positive, x_0 is a center. The nature of the phase portrait in the immediate vicinity of x_0 is determined from a plot of $V(x)$ as a function of x. Figure 11.32 illustrates the nature of such a plot.

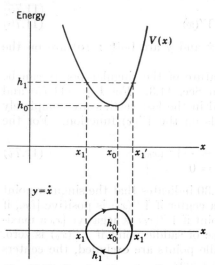

FIG. 11.32. Construction of paths near a center.

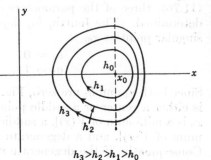

FIG. 11.33. Portrait of conservative system in neighborhood of a center.

Equation (11.72), expressing the conservation of energy, is the basis for the construction of the portrait. Each path in the phase plane is essentially a path of constant total energy. The path corresponding to the total energy h_0 is simply the point x_0, since for all other values of x the potential energy is greater than this total energy. The path corresponding to the total energy h_1 cuts the x axis at x_1 and x_1', the two values of x for which $V(x) = h_1$. For values of x between x_1 and x_1', a positive kinetic energy satisfies Eq. (11.72) and the y value is real. The value of y reaches a maximum at x_0 since there the kinetic energy is a maximum. In addition, the study of the isoclines revealed that the h_1 path has a zero slope when $x = x_0$ and an infinite slope at x_1 and x_1'. The general form of the h_1 path can now be sketched without calculation and is shown in Fig. 11.32. In an exactly similar manner, the family of paths about the center at x_0 can be constructed on the basis of the plot of $V(x)$ as a function of x and the conservation-of-energy relation of Eq. (11.72). The phase portrait in the neighborhood of a minimum of $V(x)$ has the form shown in Fig. 11.33.

If $V''(x_0)$ is negative (x_0 a saddle point), the phase portrait around x_0 is constructed in the same fashion. The form of $V(x)$ in the neighborhood

† Andronow and Chaikin, *op. cit.*, pp. 64–69.

of x_0 is shown in Fig. 11.34. The h_0 path is first drawn, where h_0 is the potential energy at the singular point. On either side of the singular point, the potential energy is less than the total energy and the y values are real. The corresponding h_0 paths are shown in Fig. 11.34. The h_1 path, a typical path corresponding to an energy less than h_0, exists only outside the interval $x_1 < x < x_1'$ and appears in two parts on the phase portrait. The h_2 path, representing an energy greater than h_0, exists for all x, but never intersects the x axis since the kinetic energy is never zero. The entire phase portrait in this vicinity has the form shown in Fig. 11.35 and exhibits the usual behavior of a saddle-point type of singularity.

In the special case when $V''(x_0)$ is zero, a degenerate saddle point exists. The phase portrait, constructed in the usual manner, has the form shown in Fig. 11.36. The singular point is unstable, but exhibits a behavior somewhat different from that of the conventional saddle point.

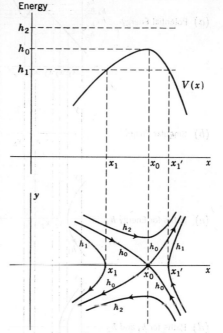

FIG. 11.34. Construction of portrait near a saddle point.

Sketch of the Over-all Phase Portrait. The phase portrait is particularly easy to construct in the case of conservative systems. The first step is

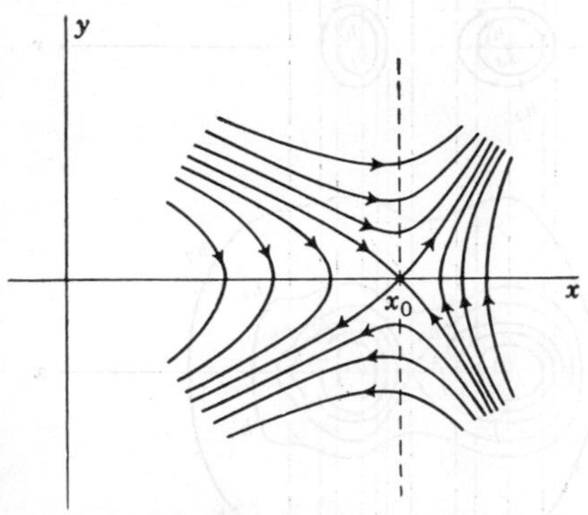

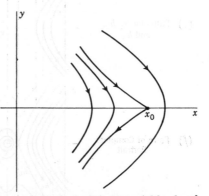

FIG. 11.35. Portrait in the neighborhood of a saddle point.

FIG. 11.36. Portrait in the neighborhood of a degenerate saddle point.

a plot of the potential energy function $V(x)$ as a function of x. Figure 11.37(a) shows a curve sufficiently complex to illustrate the general pro-

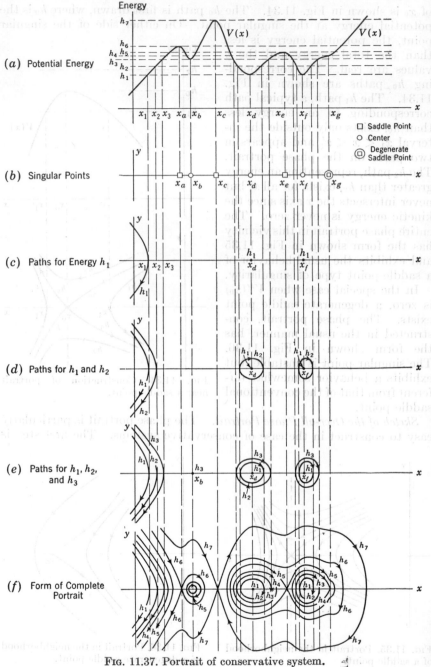

(a) Potential Energy

(b) Singular Points

□ Saddle Point
○ Center
◎ Degenerate Saddle Point

(c) Paths for Energy h_1

(d) Paths for h_1 and h_2

(e) Paths for h_1, h_2, and h_3

(f) Form of Complete Portrait

FIG. 11.37. Portrait of conservative system.

cedure. Rough construction of the phase portrait is effected in the following steps.

(1)   The singular points are located in the phase plane at x_a, x_b, . . . , x_g, as indicated in Fig. 11.37(b).

(2)   The nature of each singular point is determined: *i.e.*, whether a saddle point or a center. In Fig. 11.37(b), the saddle points are marked by □, the centers by 0, and the degenerate saddle point by ◐.

(3)   The path corresponding to the lowest energy of interest is constructed as outlined in the preceding discussion. In the example considered here, h_1 is taken as the lowest energy. One path corresponding to h_1 is located entirely to the left of x_1. In addition, x_d and x_f correspond to the energy h_1.

(4)   A slightly larger energy h_2 is considered, and the corresponding paths are drawn, as indicated in Fig. 11.37(d).

(5)   The energy h_3 is the next value of interest. There are four paths corresponding to h_3: a path entirely to the left of x_3, closed paths around x_d and x_f, and the isolated point x_b. These are shown in part (e) of the figure.

(6)   Continuation of this process produces the phase portrait shown in Fig. 11.37(f).

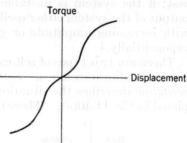

Fig. 11.38. Output torque-displacement characteristic.

11.5. Limit Cycles. The importance of the singular points as indications of the basic characteristics of the phase portrait is demonstrated by the conservative systems considered in the previous section. In the example of Fig. 11.37, the general nature of the phase portrait can be sketched as soon as the location and types of the various singular points are known. In the analysis of nonlinear systems, in general, the singular points alone are not sufficient to determine the stability of the system. One example[†] illustrates this inadequacy. If the output torque-displacement characteristic has the form shown in Fig. 11.38, the system may be stable near the origin, where the gain is low, and be unstable for larger displacements with the higher gain. For small disturbances, the system is stable, but large disturbances cause the amplitude of oscillation to increase to a steady value.

A description of the behavior of the dissipative nonlinear system must include not only the location and type of each singular point, but also a description of the limit cycles. A *limit cycle* is an isolated closed path in the phase portrait. In a sense, one of the basic purposes of nonlinear analysis is the determination and location of limit cycles, for the limit cycles describe the oscillations of a nonlinear system.

The existence of a limit cycle corresponds to a system oscillation of

† W. E. Scott, Discussion on nonlinear problems, "Automatic and Manual Control," Proceedings of Cranfield Conference 1951, edited by A. Tustin, p. 327, Butterworths Scientific Publications, London, 1952.

fixed amplitude and period. The limit cycle may be either stable or unstable, depending on whether the paths in the neighborhood converge toward the limit cycle or diverge away from it. The portrait of the system discussed in connection with Fig. 11.38, for example, has a stable singular point surrounded by an unstable limit cycle (since within this closed path the paths must converge toward the singular point), which is in turn surrounded by a stable limit cycle. The nature of the corresponding phase portrait is indicated in Fig. 11.39. This possibility of oscillations of fixed amplitude is a distinguishing characteristic of non-linear systems. A linear system is either stable or unstable; if it is stable, any initial condition results in the system eventually coming to rest; if the system is unstable, the output of the system either oscillates with increasing amplitude or grows exponentially.†

There are two types of self-excitation of nonlinear systems. *Soft self-excitation* describes the situation depicted in Fig. 11.40(a). There is one

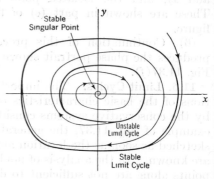

(a) Portrait with Soft Self-excitation

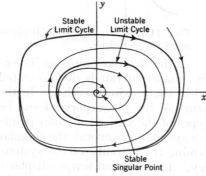

(b) Portrait with Hard Self-excitation

FIG. 11.39. Possible portrait for system with characteristic of Fig. 11.38.

FIG. 11.40. Portraits illustrating soft and hard self-excitations.

limit cycle, enclosing a single unstable singular point. Any slight disturbance moving the state of the system away from the equilibrium state results in subsequent divergence of the path out to the limit cycle. The term *hard self-excitation* refers to a limit cycle enclosing either a stable limit cycle or a stable singular point. In this situation, with one example shown in Fig. 11.40(b), the generation of oscillations depends on the initial conditions. In the case of Fig. 11.40(b), for example, if the system is at rest at the singular point, an impulse or disturbance is required

† The discussion of Sec. 11.3 demonstrated that an unstable linear system might not exhibit unbounded output if the initial conditions are properly adjusted to avoid excitation of the nonlinear mode. Any slight change in the initial conditions, however, results in an unbounded output.

to move the state of the system outside the unstable limit cycle before the steady oscillations can be observed.

In the general system, there is no clear-cut way to determine the limit cycles, or even whether a limit cycle exists. The basic method for proving the existence of a limit cycle involves establishment of the convergent properties of the paths outside the limit cycle and the divergent properties inside. For example, if it can be shown that outside a circle C_1 centered about the origin all paths are converging (the radial distance to the point moving along the path is decreasing), and that inside a smaller circle C_2 (cf. Fig. 11.41) the paths are diverging, a limit cycle must exist within the region bounded by C_1 and C_2. Frequently, the required convergence and divergence properties can be demonstrated from physical reasoning based on consideration of the change of stored energy with time.†

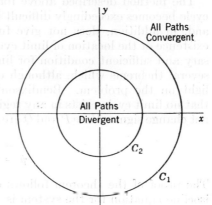

FIG. 11.41. Method for establishing existence of a limit cycle.

The details of the method are illustrated with Van der Pol's equation

$$\ddot{x} - \epsilon(1 - x^2)\dot{x} + x = 0 \quad (11.80)$$

The corresponding first-order equations are

$$\dot{x} = y \quad (11.81)$$
$$\dot{y} = \epsilon(1 - x^2)y - x \quad (11.82)$$

The time derivative of the square of the radial distance from the origin is

$$\frac{dr^2}{dt} = \frac{d}{dt}(x^2 + y^2) = 2x\dot{x} + 2y\dot{y} \quad (11.83)$$

Substitution of Eqs. (11.81) and (11.82) in (11.83) leads to the relation

$$\frac{1}{2}\frac{dr^2}{dt} = \epsilon y^2(1 - x^2) \quad (11.84)$$

The sign of dr^2/dt changes as $|x|$ passes through unity. If ϵ is positive, paths far from the origin are converging, since $|x|$ is greater than unity almost all the time. Equations (11.81) and (11.82) indicate further that

† A number of examples can be found to illustrate this method for establishing the existence of limit cycles. Two examples of interest to control-system engineers are: B. G. Farley, General Considerations Concerning Non-linear Circuits and Negative Resistance, "The Transistor," Selected material on transistors prepared by Bell Telephone Laboratories, pp. 237–248, Western Electric Company, Inc., New York, 1951; and L. L. Rauch, Oscillation of a Third Order Nonlinear Autonomous System, "Contributions to the Theory of Nonlinear Oscillations," edited by S. Lefschetz, Annals of Mathematics Studies, No. 20, pp. 39–88, Princeton University Press, Princeton, N.J., 1950.

the system has only one singular point, located at the origin. The tests of Sec. 11.3 demonstrate that the singular point is an unstable node or focus if ϵ is positive. This is apparent from the differential equation (11.80) directly, since linearization in the vicinity of the singular point results in the equation

$$\ddot{x} - \epsilon\dot{x} + x = 0 \qquad (11.85)$$

Positive ϵ means negative damping, hence instability. Consequently, the paths diverge from the origin, but converge in from infinity. At least one limit cycle must exist.

The method described above for establishing the existence of a limit cycle becomes exceedingly difficult in many cases of practical importance and, in addition, does not give full information concerning either the existence or the location of limit cycles. Unfortunately, no simple necessary and sufficient condition for limit cycles can be written. There are several theorems which, although of limited applicability, do shed some light on the problem. Bendixson's first theorem, for example, states that no limit cycle exists in any region within which $\partial P/\partial x + \partial Q/\partial y$ does not change sign. Here P and Q are defined as in Eqs. (11.47) and (11.48):

$$\dot{x} = P(x,y) \qquad (11.86)$$
$$\dot{y} = Q(x,y) \qquad (11.87)$$

The proof of the theorem follows directly from Gauss's theorem. The isocline equation for the system is

$$\frac{dy}{dx} = \frac{Q}{P} \qquad (11.88)$$

Equation (11.88) can be rewritten

$$P\,dy - Q\,dx = 0 \qquad (11.89)$$

This equation describes the relation which must exist along any path in the phase plane. Gauss's theorem states that

$$\iint_D \left(\frac{\partial P}{\partial x} + \frac{\partial Q}{\partial y}\right) dx\,dy = \oint_{C_o} (P\,dy - Q\,dx) \qquad (11.90)\dagger$$

The surface integral over the complete domain D is related to the line integral around C_o, the closed path which is the boundary of the region. If a limit cycle C_o is assumed bounding the region D, the right side of Eq. (11.90) is zero since the integrand is zero everywhere on C_o. Consequently, the left side of the equation must be zero, with the resulting condition that $\partial P/\partial x + \partial Q/\partial y$ must change sign within D. The application of this theorem in a simple example is again illustrated by con-

---

$\dagger$ The relation is valid if P and Q and the derivatives are continuous in the domain D and if C_o is sectionally smooth. Cf. R. Courant, "Differential and Integral Calculus," Vol. II, pp. 384–389, Blackie & Son, Ltd., Glasgow, 1936.

sideration of Van der Pol's equation (11.80).   From (11.81) and (11.82),

$$P(x,y) = y \tag{11.91}$$
$$Q(x,y) = \epsilon(1 - x^2)y - x \tag{11.92}$$

Differentiation yields

$$\frac{\partial P}{\partial x} + \frac{\partial Q}{\partial y} = \epsilon(1 - x^2) \tag{11.93}$$

Clearly, no limit cycle can exist entirely within the strip in the phase plane bounded by the lines $x = 1$ and $x = -1$.   A limit cycle may pass through this strip, but none can exist in the interior within which the damping is always positive.

There are other theorems which aid the analyst in determining the existence of limit cycles.[†]   For example, Poincaré has shown that within any limit cycle the number of node, focus, and center types of singularities must exceed the number of saddle points by one.   A second example is Bendixson's second theorem, which states that, if a path stays inside a finite region D and does not approach a singular point, it must either be a limit cycle or approach a limit cycle asymptotically. These theorems, however, do not furnish any straightforward, universally applicable procedure for establishing the existence of limit cycles.

11.6. Implicit Polynomial Factoring.   The system of Fig. 11.42 for the implicit determination of the zeros of a polynomial[‡] illustrates the application of several of the concepts of the preceding sections to the analysis of a nonconservative nonlinear system of a

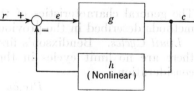

FIG. 11.42. System for determining zeros of a polynomial.

particularly simple type.   The g components comprise a high-gain electromechanical system with the transfer function

$$G(s) = \frac{Ka}{s(s + a)} \tag{11.94}$$

The h section is a nonlinear system to generate the actuating signal $e(t)$.

The operation of the system is as follows: the input $r(t)$ is maintained zero.   The high gain of the block g results in the actuating signal e being held close to zero.   The feedback system generates the error function desired by the polynomial under investigation.   For example, if a zero of the polynomial $x^2 + x + 1$ is to be found, the desired operator h is one which forms the function $-(c^2 + c + 1)$.   The difference between

† N. Minorsky, "Introduction to Non-linear Mechanics," pp. 75–79, J. W. Edwards, Publisher, Inc., Ann Arbor, Mich., 1947.

‡ I. A. Greenwood, Jr., J. V. Holdam, Jr., and D. MacRae, Jr., "Electronic Instruments," MIT Radiation Laboratory Series, Vol. 21, pp. 15–21, McGraw-Hill Book Company, Inc., New York, 1948.

zero (the value of r) and the primary feedback is applied to the high-gain amplifier g to modify the output in such a way as to force e toward zero.

The differential equations describing system operation are readily formulated in terms of the output $c(t)$. The forward path is described by the relation

$$\ddot{c} + a\dot{c} = Kae \qquad (11.95)$$

The actuating signal is the negative of the primary feedback,

$$e = -h(c) \qquad (11.96)$$

Here $h(c)$ is the operation on c performed by the feedback block. Substitution of Eq. (11.96) in (11.95) yields the nonlinear second-order differential equation

$$\ddot{c} + a\dot{c} + Kah(c) = 0 \qquad (11.97)$$

The corresponding pair of first-order equations in terms of c and $\dot{c}$ are

$$\frac{dc}{dt} = \dot{c} \qquad (11.98)$$

$$\frac{d\dot{c}}{dt} = -a\dot{c} - Kah(c) \qquad (11.99)$$

The general characteristics of the phase portrait are derived using the methods described in the previous sections.

Limit Cycles. Bendixson's first theorem immediately establishes that there are no limit cycles in the phase plane. For the system under consideration,

$$P(c,\dot{c}) = \dot{c} \qquad (11.100)$$

$$Q(c,\dot{c}) = -Kah(c) - a\dot{c} \qquad (11.101)$$

$$\frac{\partial P}{\partial c} + \frac{\partial Q}{\partial \dot{c}} = -a \qquad (11.102)$$

The function $\partial P/\partial c + \partial Q/\partial \dot{c}$ is simply the constant $-a$ and is negative everywhere in the phase plane.

Singular Points. The singular points, located where dc/dt and $d\dot{c}/dt$ are both zero, are the real zeros of $h(c)$. Since these singular points are the states of equilibrium of the system, it is clear that $h(c)$ should be proportional to the polynomial under investigation if the steady-state value of $c(t)$ is to be a zero of this polynomial. The discussion is simplified at this point if a specific polynomial is considered:

$$p(x) = x^2 - x - 2 \qquad (11.103)$$

The appropriate value of $h(c)$ is

$$h(c) = K_h(c^2 - c - 2) \qquad (11.104)$$

K_h is a positive or negative constant. In this specific case, the singular points are the real zeros of the polynomial, or $c = 2$ and $c = -1$.

Nature of the Singular Points. The type of each singular point is determined by reference to Fig. 11.30. In the system under consideration, Eqs. (11.100) and (11.101) indicate that

$$a_1 = 0 \qquad b_1 = -Kah'(c_o)$$
$$a_2 = 1 \qquad b_2 = -a \qquad (11.105)$$

$h'(c_o)$ is the derivative, evaluated at the singular point, of $h(c)$ with respect to c. Figure 11.30 indicates that the singular point is either a

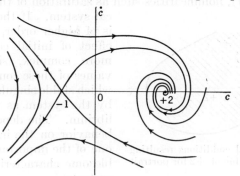

(*a*) Portrait with +2 the Stable Zero

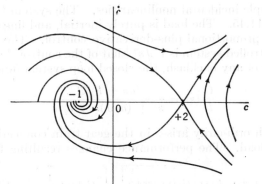

(*b*) Portrait with −1 the Stable Zero

FIG. 11.43. Phase portraits for system of Fig. 11.42 with polynomial $p(x) = x^2 - x - 2$.

stable node or focus or a saddle point: a stable singularity if $aKh'(c_o)$ is positive, an unstable saddle point if $aKh'(c_o)$ is negative. Clearly, then, the zeros of the polynomial are alternately stable and unstable. In the specific example considered here,

$$aKh'(c_o) = aKK_h(2c_o - 1) \qquad (11.106)$$

If aKK_h is positive, +2 is the stable singular point, −1 the unstable one; while, if aKK_h is negative, −1 is the stable singularity and +2 the unstable singular point. The general nature of the phase portrait in each case is shown in Fig. 11.43.

Significance of Initial Conditions. The sketches of Fig. 11.43 indicate clearly the importance of the initial conditions in the performance of this nonlinear system. If aKK_h is positive (the circuit arranged to determine the zero at $+2$), the system approaches the desired value in the steady state only if the initial conditions lie within the shaded region of Fig. 11.44. An initial state of the system outside this domain results in an unbounded output, or, in a practical system, an output which is determined by the large-signal nonlinearities not described in the differential equation (11.97), nonlinearities such as saturation of the electromechani-

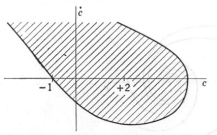

cal system. If the polynomial $p(x)$ is of higher order, the study of the effect of initial conditions is even more complex, since the specific values of these conditions determine which stable singular point is selected by the system as the point of equilibrium. The dependence of system behavior on the initial conditions is one of the important and often troublesome characteristics of nonlinear systems.

FIG. 11.44. Initial conditions resulting in steady-state value of $+2$ for portrait of Fig. 11.43(a).

11.7. Backlash. Consideration of a simple second-order servomechanism with backlash serves to illustrate the use of the phase plane in the analysis of simple incidental nonlinearities. The system to be studied is shown in Fig. 11.45. The load is purely inertial, and linear stabilization is realized by proportional-plus-derivative control. The transfer function of the controlled system is $1/Js^2$, that of the control elements, $as + b$. In the absence of any backlash, the closed-loop system function is simply

$$\frac{C}{R}(s) = \frac{(as + b)/J}{s^2 + (a/J)s + b/J} \tag{11.107}$$

The backlash ordinarily arises in the gear train connecting the output motor to the load. The performance changes resulting from the addi-

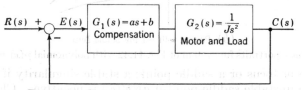

FIG. 11.45. Simple system for study of backlash.

tion of backlash depend markedly upon whether the major portion of the output inertia is on the motor or the load side of the backlash. The two situations are considered in turn in this section.

Inertia at Motor Side of Backlash. If the inertia is entirely at the motor end of the backlash (*e.g.*, in the case where the motor inertia is much larger than the load inertia referred to the motor shaft), the block diagram of the system takes the form shown in Fig. 11.46. The break in the output line is used to indicate the backlash. The signal to the left of the backlash is termed c_m, the output, c. The gear ratio is lumped in with the g_1 and g_2 blocks, with the result that, if the backlash tends to zero, c tends to c_m.

The phase plane used in the analysis of the system is the plot of $\dot{c}$ versus c (or, equivalently, $\dot{e}$ versus e could be used). The phase portrait

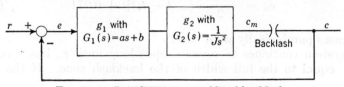

FIG. 11.46. Inertia on motor side of backlash.

of the linear system is known and here assumed to be of the form shown in Fig. 11.47, with the relative damping ratio of the system equal to 0.5. A single path is considered, with the initial conditions assumed to be $\dot{c}(0) = 0.5\omega_n$ and $c(0) = 0$. It is further assumed that at zero time the gears are making contact in the direction of motion. Motion starts from point A and travels along the phase path shown until, at time t_B, point

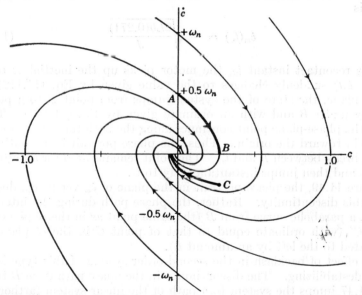

FIG. 11.47. Phase portrait with backlash between inertia and output shaft. (ζ of linear system equal to 0.5.)

B is reached. At this instant, the output is 0.271 and the velocity is changing sign. As $\dot{c}_m$ tends to reverse, the gears open as a result of the backlash. The loop is opened and the system shown in Fig. 11.48 controls the response $c_m(t)$. With the actuating signal remaining constant at -0.271, the waveform of c_m is determined from the differential equation and boundary conditions

$$J\ddot{c}_m = a\dot{e} + be \qquad (11.108)$$
$$c_m(t_B) = 0.271 \qquad (11.109)$$
$$\dot{c}_m(t_B) = 0 \qquad (11.110)$$

The solution to Eq. (11.108), with $\dot{e} = 0$ and $e = -0.271$, is

$$c_m = \frac{-0.271}{2} [\omega_n(t - t_B)]^2 + 0.271 \qquad (11.111)$$

c_m decreases parabolically with time.

The system continues to operate open-loop until c_m has traversed a distance equal to the full width of the backlash zone. If the angular

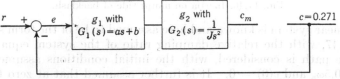

FIG. 11.48. System of Fig. 11.46 operating open-loop.

width of this zone is L, the velocity $\dot{c}_m$ at the time the gears make contact again is

$$\dot{c}_m(t_C) = -\sqrt{\frac{2Lb(0.271)}{J}} \qquad (11.112)$$

At this recontact instant t_C, the motor picks up the inertialess output shaft. $\dot{c}(t)$ suddenly changes to the value given by Eq. (11.112). In the $c\dot{c}$ plane, the state of the system jumps from point B to a point C directly under B and with an ordinate given by Eq. (11.112). Thereafter, the phase-plane point continues along the path through C and converges in toward the origin. Thus, the phase portrait is discontinuous, with a break between B and C. The point remains at B for a finite time $t_C - t_B$ and then jumps instantaneously to C.

Figure 11.49, the phase portrait in the plane of $\dot{c}_m$ versus c_m, does not show this discontinuity. Rather, the phase path during the interval t_B to t_C is a parabolic curve from B (the same point as in the $c\dot{c}$ plane) to a point C' (with ordinate equal to that of point C in the $c\dot{c}$ plane, but translated to the left by an amount L).

The effect of backlash in the second-order system of this type is definitely destabilizing. The discontinuity in the phase path from B to C in Fig. 11.47 jumps the system to a path of the linear system farther from the origin. It is not difficult to demonstrate the possibility of a limit cycle in the phase portrait. The magnitude of the vertically downward jump from B to C is proportional to the square root of the magnitude of the output at B. Thus, as B moves along the x axis, the corresponding C point moves as shown in Fig. 11.50. Clearly, the effect of backlash tends to be more destabilizing the smaller the amplitude of the output. If the backlash zone is sufficiently wide, a critical value of B exists, B_c, above which the diminished effect of backlash results in the output decreasing each cycle. This value of B_c lies on the limit cycle, which has the shape shown in Fig. 11.51. The extent of the divergence of the output waveform from a sinusoid depends upon the relative damping ratio of the linear system.

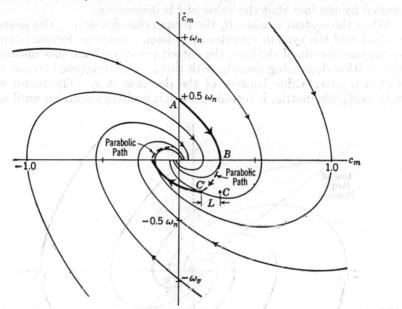

FIG. 11.49. Phase portrait in $c_m - \dot{c}_m$ phase plane.   (ζ of linear system equal to 0.5.)

Inertia at Output Side of Backlash. If the inertia is predominantly at the load end of the backlash, the performance of the system is markedly different from that described above. The backlash zone causes a loss of contact at the instant when the torque transmitted through the output shaft tends to reverse, since the motor is assumed to be inertialess and

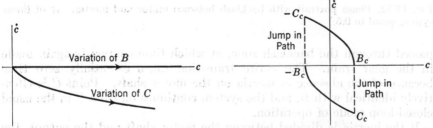

FIG. 11.50. Motion of C point with   FIG. 11.51. Limit cycle with backlash
changes in B.   between inertia and output.

developing a torque proportional to $a\dot{e} + be$. Thus, if the initial state of the system is again assumed at A [with $c(0) = 0$ and $\dot{c}(0) = 0.5\omega_n$], motion is along the linear phase portrait until point B of Fig. 11.52 is reached, at which time

$$a\dot{e} + bc = 0 \tag{11.113}$$

In this case, it is assumed that initially the gears are making contact in a direction opposite to that assumed in the study of the system with the inertia entirely at the motor shaft. This change is necessary because in the region from A to B of Fig. 11.52 the torque is negative, as demonstrated by the fact that the value of $\dot{c}$ is decreasing.

When the system reaches B, the torque changes sign. The gears lose contact and the system operates open-loop. Since no torque is applied to the pure inertia of the load, the output velocity $\dot{c}$ continues unchanged, the position decreasing linearly with time. The developed torque starts with a positive value because of the decrease in c. The motor shaft, with negligible inertia, is forced through a positive excursion until c_m has

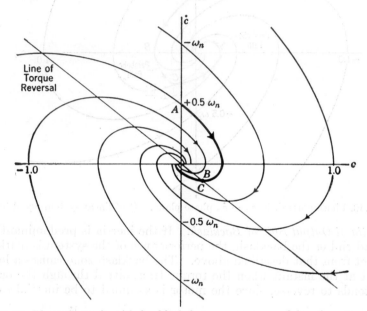

Fig. 11.52. Phase portrait with backlash between motor and inertia. (ζ of linear system equal to 0.5.)

passed through the backlash zone, at which time contact is again made in the gear train. The entire transition takes essentially zero time because of the absence of inertia on the motor shaft. Point C is effectively identical with B, and the system continues on from C in the usual closed-loop mode of operation.

If the inertia is divided between the motor shaft and the output, the system is analyzed in exactly the manner described above. The break in gear contact resulting from the backlash occurs at the instant when the torque transmitted through the shaft reaches zero. With the break in contact, the system operates open-loop and can be analyzed to find c_m and c as functions of time. The remaking of contact is characterized by instantaneous changes in both $\dot{c}_m$ and $\dot{c}$, the value of $\dot{c}$ (equal to $\dot{c}_m$) after recontact being determined by the conservation of momentum.

11.8. Introduction of Nonlinear Elements.   The examples of the previous sections illustrate the application of the phase-plane methods in the analysis of the effects of nonlinearity in simple feedback control systems.   The phase plane is directly useful in the study of nonlinearity if the significant characteristics of the control-system performance can be adequately described by a second-order differential equation of the form

$$\ddot{x} + a(x,\dot{x})\dot{x} + b(x,\dot{x})x = 0 \qquad (11\ 114)$$

The phase plane provides a useful tool also in the design of systems; in particular, the phase portrait indicates in a number of important cases the type of nonlinearities which can be introduced intentionally to improve system performance characteristics.   The remainder of this chapter includes a brief description of certain aspects of this application of phase-plane analysis.

The design of nonlinear elements to improve system performance is complicated by one characteristic of nonlinear systems: since the principle of superposition is not valid, a given nonlinear element may improve the system performance with one type of input signal while causing a marked deterioration of performance with a different input.   A wide variety of feedback control systems in normal operation experience input signals which predominantly fall into one of the following categories:

(1)   Step functions
(2)   Ramp functions
(3)   Sinusoidal functions
(4)   Random functions

A nonlinearity designed to improve the step-function response of the system may have an adverse effect in a similar system with input signals which are close to sinusoidal.

The phase-plane methods are particularly useful in the design of systems with step-function and ramp-function inputs.   A sinusoidally excited system is ordinarily more readily designed and analyzed by the describing-function approach, although some work has been done on determining the performance characteristics of a sinusoidally excited second-order system by use of a three-dimensional (x, y, and t) phase space.[†]   Such an analysis, involving considerable computational effort, can yield the limit cycles, the conditions for the existence of subharmonic oscillations, etc.   The design of nonlinear systems for the optimum transmission of random functions with known probability distributions remains at the present time a problem without an adequate engineering solution.

The simplest application of phase-plane methods in the design of nonlinear elements for second-order systems is based upon the familiar possibility of improving the system step-function response by making the damping vary with the magnitude of the error.   In a linear system, the limitation on the speed of the step-function response is related to the

† D. Young, H. L. Turritin, H. A. Miller, and P. N. Hess, Analysis of Non-linear Systems, *Minneapolis-Honeywell Aero Rept. AD 5042-TR2*, Sec. I, *Second Interim Report on Non-linear Mechanics*, September 1, 1952.

allowable overshoot.　The response curves sketched in Fig. 11.53 indicate the variation of the response with the relative damping ratio ζ. Evidently, the high response speed associated with low values of ζ can be approached without the undesirable overshoot if ζ can be made to

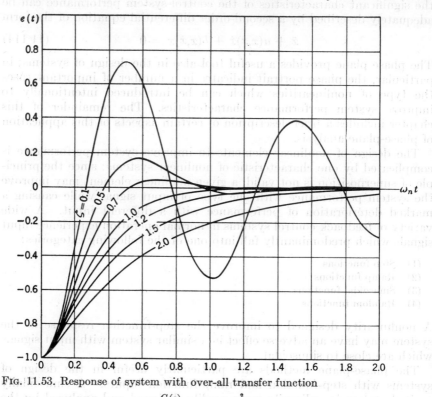

FIG. 11.53. Response of system with over-all transfer function

$$\frac{C(s)}{R(s)} = \frac{\omega_n^2}{s^2 + 2\zeta\omega_n s + \omega_n^2}$$

Error versus time for various damping ratios and with a unit step function as the input.

increase as the actuating signal decreases.　One possible differential equation is

$$\ddot{e} + \frac{2\zeta_o\omega_n}{1 + a|e|}\,\dot{e} + \omega_n^2 e = 0 \tag{11.115}$$

Here e is the actuating signal and ζ_o, ω_n, and a are constants.　For very small actuating signals, the relative damping ratio is ζ_o, which is selected larger than unity; as $|e|$ increases, the relative damping ratio decreases.

The design of such a system involves two problems: the selection of a, and the realization of the circuits to accomplish the desired nonlinear operations.　The selection of a is effected by use of the phase portrait, constructed in the usual manner as outlined in the preceding sections of this chapter.　In the normalized phase plane ($a\dot{e}/\omega_n$ versus ae), the isocline equation is

$$y = \frac{-x}{\alpha + \dfrac{2\zeta_o}{1 + |x|}}$$ (11.116)

where y is $a\dot{e}/\omega_n$, x is ae, and α is the slope in the xy plane,

$$\alpha = \frac{dy}{dx}$$ (11.117)

The phase portrait, constructed by the method of isoclines (Sec. 11.1), is shown in Fig. 11.54 for a ζ_o equal to 2.† With this normalization, the

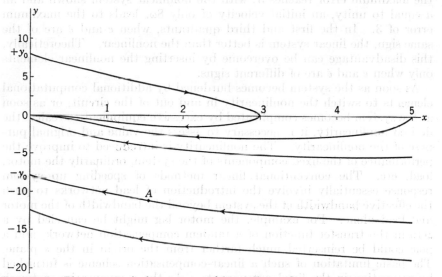

FIG. 11.54. Phase portrait for system with nonlinear damping. ($\zeta_0 = 2$.) (*From D. McDonald, Nonlinear Techniques for Improving Servo Performance, Proc. Natl. Electronics Conf. 1950, Vol. 6, p. 404, 1951.*)

phase paths are independent of a. The portrait is shown in the first and fourth quadrants only, since the isoclines equation (11.116) indicates that α is unchanged if y is replaced by $-y$ and x by $-x$. The portrait in the second and third quadrants is obtained by reflecting the portrait shown about both axes. The path followed, for example, by a point starting at A is found by continuing along the path through A until the y axis is reached at $-y_o$. At this point, a jump is made to $+y_o$ and the path shown is followed, with the vertical axis now $-y$ and the horizontal axis $-x$.

Inspection of the phase portrait indicates at once the criteria for the selection of the parameter a. The complete portrait reveals that the sys-

† D. McDonald, Nonlinear Techniques for Improving Servo Performance, *Proc. Natl. Electronics Conf.*, Vol. 6, pp. 400–421, 1950. The article contains a discussion of the type of nonlinearity described in this section and includes the derivation of Eq. (11.116) and a more detailed discussion of the characteristics summarized here.

tem is undesirably sluggish for step-function inputs smaller than about two units on the x scale (or ae scale) and that it overshoots radically if the input amplitude is larger than 10 units. On the basis of the probable range of actual unnormalized input amplitudes and the allowable range in overshoot, the optimum a is selected to give the fastest response.

This very simple system illustrates one serious difficulty encountered in the design of nonlinear systems. Although the response to step functions of the proper range of amplitudes is improved by the division of the relative damping ratio by $1 + a|e|$, the response to an initial value of $\dot{e}$ may be made worse. For example, in a linear system, if the relative damping ratio is 2, an initial $\dot{e}$ as large as $13.8\omega_n$ can be applied before the maximum error reaches 3; with the nonlinear system shown and an a equal to unity, an initial velocity of only $8\omega_n$ leads to the maximum error of 3. In the first and third quadrants, when e and $\dot{e}$ are of the same sign, the linear system is better than the nonlinear. Theoretically, this disadvantage can be overcome by inserting the nonlinear elements only when e and $\dot{e}$ are of different signs.

As soon as the system becomes burdened by additional computational elements to switch the nonlinearity in and out of the circuit, or as soon as the system becomes complicated by excessive equipment to realize the desired nonlinearity, it is necessary to assess the value and original purpose of the nonlinearity. The nonlinearity is introduced to improve the performance of the fixed components of the system, ordinarily the motor, load, etc. The conventional linear methods of speeding up system response essentially involve the introduction of lead networks to push the effective bandwidth of the system beyond the bandwidth of the motor and load alone. For example, the motor lag might be canceled by a zero in the transfer function of a tandem compensation network, and a pole could be reinserted much farther from the origin in the s plane. The basic limitation of such a linear-compensation scheme is furnished by saturation in the fixed components. As the compensation network approaches more nearly an ideal derivative network, the motor is driven harder and harder. If the actuating signal undergoes a sudden change, the input to the motor contains a sharp pulse. A limiting bandwidth is soon reached, beyond which it is not practicable to attempt to equalize the system.

One escape from this difficulty is offered by the use of larger motors, driven in normal operation over a smaller percentage of full range. In an attempt to avoid this introduction of additional weight, space requirements, cost, etc., nonlinear elements present promising possibilities. Clearly, however, if the equipment associated with the introduction of the nonlinearity is excessive, the advantages of nonlinear elements are sharply reduced and such possibilities as employing larger motors or switching to hydraulic motors must be considered.

In addition, the extent of the equipment necessary for the introduction of the nonlinearity discussed above as well as the complexity of the required analysis leads directly to the questions: Does the system designed with such a nonlinearity approach the optimum system for the given input signals? Since, at least theoretically, any sort of nonlinearity can be introduced and the system made to behave in a tremendous variety of quite different manners, is the approach based on a modification of the linear system the optimum? Is it correct to assume that the optimum system is one in which ζ is varied according to the signal [in the manner illustrated above or in any other nonlinear fashion, such as by multiplication of ζ by $1/(1 + ae^2)$] or in which ω_n is changed with the instantaneous amplitude of the actuating signal? The answer to all these questions is definitely in the negative. The discussion of the next section is a very brief summary of work done in the past few years in attempts to approach the optimum system.

11.9. Optimization of Feedback Control Systems. The optimum system is determined by the nature of the input signals. Principal efforts thus far in the feedback-control field have been directed toward the determination and realization of the optimum system with the input a step function.† In this special case, the feedback control system is asked to change the output as rapidly as possible from an initial value (which can be assumed zero) to a desired value. The response of the system can be evaluated by a consideration of the $e\dot{e}$ phase plane. (Strictly, this is the phase plane only if the system is second order or less; for higher-order equations, it is a section of the phase space.) With the actuating signal given a certain initial

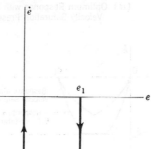

FIG. 11.55. Phase path of ideal system.

value, the system is to return the actuating signal to zero as rapidly as possible.

The best system is clearly one which moves the system along the path shown in Fig. 11.55. The acceleration is infinitely large and negative, and then switches instantaneously to an infinite and positive value until e and $\dot{e}$ are both zero. Since the area under the reciprocal plot, $1/\dot{e}$ versus e, is zero, no time is required for the reduction of e to zero. Although such a system is ideal, it is clearly unobtainable. Some practical limitations must be imposed; the desired optimum system is the system which is best within these practical constraints.

The constraints usually considered are the saturation limits of the equipment. In Sec. 8.6, the description of Newton's method introduced the concept of a number of saturation points throughout the system, points at which saturation might occur as a result of demands for exceptional system performance. Newton's method represents a design of the optimum system with random input functions under the assumption that it is desirable to limit the probability that saturation may occur. In a

† R. S. Neiswander, and R. H. MacNeal, Optimization of Nonlinear Control Systems by Means of Nonlinear Feedbacks, *AIEE Tech. Paper* 53-252, April, 1953. This paper contains a considerably more extensive discussion of the optimization problem for systems with step-function excitation than is possible in this section.

sense, the optimization to be considered in this section is in direct contrast to Newton's approach, since here the system is to be optimized in the presence of saturation, even if the resulting optimum system saturates 95 per cent of the time. Again in Secs. 10.3 and 10.5, the characteristics of saturation were considered, but there primarily from an analysis viewpoint. The effects of torque, velocity, and acceleration saturation were studied, but the applications of these results were primarily in design by extended analysis, design by analysis of a number of different systems and selection of the final system on the basis of known characteristics of various circuits and configurations.

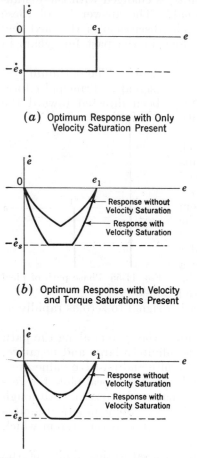

(a) Optimum Response with Only Velocity Saturation Present

(b) Optimum Response with Velocity and Torque Saturations Present

(c) Optimum Response with Velocity, Torque, and Torque-rate Saturations Present

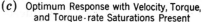

Fig. 11.56. Effect of saturation on optimum response.

The practical limitations to be considered in this section are of the following nature:

(1) Velocity saturation
(2) Torque saturation (or acceleration saturation if the load is purely inertial)
(3) Torque-rate saturation, a limitation on the rate at which the torque can be changed

All these saturation levels are assumed symmetrical (e.g., the same magnitude of torque results in saturation whether the torque is positive or negative). The effect of each of these limitations on the ideal phase-plane trajectory after a step disturbance is shown in Fig. 11.56. If velocity saturation only is present, the paths in the phase plane are confined to a horizontal strip bordered by the lines $\dot{e} = \pm \dot{e}_s$, where $\dot{e}_s$ is the magnitude of velocity at which saturation occurs. The optimum path is shown in Fig. 11.56(a): the system velocity changes instantaneously to the saturation value $-\dot{e}_s$, continues at this velocity until the actuating signal is reduced to zero, and returns to a state of equilibrium instantaneously. The time required to return the system to equilibrium is no longer zero, but, rather, is given by the area under the curve of $1/\dot{e}$ versus e. In this simple case, the specific value is

$$T = \frac{e_1}{\dot{e}_s} \qquad (11.118)$$

The consideration of velocity saturation still leaves the designer with an impractical "best" system, since the acceleration cannot be made infinite in any system with load inertia. Acceleration is always limited as a result of the limitations on the torque available from the power element. This torque saturation is equivalent to acceleration saturation if the output load is purely inertial, but depends on velocity, position, etc., with more general loads. For the purpose of simplifying this discussion, the simple system of Fig. 11.57 is considered, with the developed torque proportional to the acceleration of both the output and the actuating signal. The effect of acceleration saturation can be interpreted as a limitation on the permissible shape of the phase paths. With a maximum acceleration value of $\ddot{e}_s$, $d\dot{e}/de$ is limited to the value $\ddot{e}_s/\dot{e}$. In other words, the paths may be vertical as they cross the e axis (where $\dot{e} = 0$), but as the magnitude of $\dot{e}$ increases, the magnitude of $d\dot{e}/de$ must decrease.

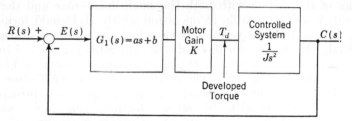

FIG. 11.57. Simple system to illustrate optimization.

With acceleration saturation, the optimum response is as shown in Fig. 11.56(b). If the initial value e_1 is sufficiently small that the velocity magnitude never reaches $\dot{e}_s$, the path is the combination of two parabolas.[†] The acceleration is negative and at maximum magnitude until the error is reduced to one half the initial value, after which maximum deceleration is applied to bring the system to rest at the instant e reaches zero. Any other path results in a longer time interval before the actuating signal is reduced to zero. The effect of velocity saturation, also shown in Fig. 11.56(b), is to clip off the bottom of the curve.

The final type of saturation considered involves a limitation of the rate at which the torque can reverse. The response of that path of Fig. 11.56(b) which exhibits no velocity saturation requires that the torque developed by the motor change instantaneously from maximum negative to maximum positive (at the time when e is $e_1/2$). In practice, full torque reversal requires a finite time, and the reversal must be initiated slightly sooner than indicated by Fig. 11.56(b). The optimum response is shown in Fig. 11.56(c) for the system with and without velocity saturation. It is clear that the inclusion of torque-rate saturation results in a slower optimum response since the value of $1/\dot{e}$ is larger during the time of torque reversal.

Consideration of the phase-plane paths of Fig. 11.56 leads directly to the conclusion that the relay system is the optimum. The best per-

† D. McDonald, Nonlinear Techniques for Improving Servo Performance, *Proc. Natl. Electronics Conf.*, Vol. 6, pp. 400–421, 1950.

formance is realized by the application of full torque, first in one direction and then in the opposite direction. The optimum performance can be realized by a relay system with the relays controlled by an appropriate computer.[†] The principal disadvantage of the relay-controlled system is a practical one derived from the difficulty associated with realization of the switching at exactly the proper instant to cause the path followed after switching to head directly for the origin. As a consequence of this difficulty, attributed to imperfect control intelligence (in the terminology of Neiswander and MacNeal), the optimum system in practice is one which operates linearly in a small neighborhood around the origin in the phase plane. Even if the phase path after switching is not directed exactly toward the origin, the path is captured by this domain of linear operation and moves toward the origin in the fashion described previously in the analysis of linear systems.

Design of the system with both the small linear zone and the region of saturated operation leads to operation which McDonald terms dual-mode.[‡] There are clearly two ways in which dual-mode operation may be realized. In the simpler method, the saturation is achieved by over-driving the physical components (*e.g.*, overdriving the motor of Fig. 11.57 to cause torque saturation). The existence of very small error signals then leads to unsaturated operation. There are three primary disadvantages associated with this scheme for achieving dual-mode operation. First, the linear mode may extend over parts of the entire phase plane, since the signal at the motor input passes through zero at the time the torque is reversing. This linear band of operation must be much narrower than the band corresponding to torque reversal in the phase plane. Otherwise, the actual trajectories deviate widely from the optimum trajectories unless the linear band is carefully designed.[§] The second disadvantage is derived from the difficulty of realizing physical equipment with sharp saturation characteristics. In most saturating elements, there exists a wide region of nonlinear but nonsaturating performance between the linear and saturation regions. The third disadvantage stems from the large amplification required to obtain the saturation.

The second method for realizing dual-mode operation involves the modification of a relay system by the addition of a third relay position, corresponding to linear operation.[‖] The instrumentation of such a system is more complex than that of the type described above, but complete freedom is theoretically available in the selection of the boundary between

---

[†] A computer here is interpreted as any device which computes the required switching time on the basis of the actuating signal. The simplest computer is a simple passive network; more complicated computers measure e and $\dot{e}$ and determine the instant at which the system reaches the switching point.

[‡] D. McDonald, "Multiple Mode Operation of Servomechanisms," *Cook Research Laboratories Bull.* S-3, Cook Electric Company, Chicago, Ill., 1951.

[§] R. S. Neiswander and R. H. MacNeal, *op. cit.*

[‖] K. C. Mathews and R. C. Boe, The Application of Nonlinear Techniques to Servomechanisms, *Proc. Natl. Electronics Conf.*, Vol. 8, pp. 10–21, 1953.

the two regions. The desire for simplicity of instrumentation generally limits this boundary rather severely, however. Figure 11.58 shows one suggested boundary to control the switching into the linear mode of operation. The system is switched when the magnitude of e is less than a specified value at the time $\dot{e}$ is zero.† The nonzero height of the region is a result of the inaccuracy in the determination of the time at which $\dot{e}$ is zero.

Design of the optimum system is illustrated by the simple configuration shown in Fig. 11.59. The load consists only of inertia, and only the saturation mode of operation is of concern. It is assumed that the linear mode is properly designed and that the boundary between modes is suitably established. The only saturation considered is the limitation of torque. Since the constant, maximum torque is proportional to output acceleration, the phase portrait for the saturating system consists of two families of parabolas, shown in Fig. 11.60, one family corresponding to full positive torque, the other to full negative torque. If initial conditions start the system at point A, the phase path follows the trajectory

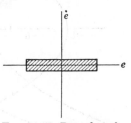

FIG. 11.58. Boundary for switching into linear mode of operation.

through B and C. The optimum switching point is at D, at which time full torque in the opposite direction is applied and the system follows the parabola DEF toward the origin. The desired phase portrait is shown in Fig. 11.61. Design of the system is basically the design of a computer to switch the system whenever a path reaches either of the two parabolic sections marked $ABCD$ in Fig. 11.61. If a definite effort is made to switch as close to the $ABCD$ lines as possible, the computer must measure e and $\dot{e}$ and determine the required switching instants.‡ A fair approximation to the required switching instant can be obtained with a passive

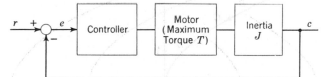

FIG. 11.59. Simple system to illustrate design of nonlinear controller.

network driven by the actuating signal e and yielding an output which is a specified linear combination of e and $\dot{e}$. If the network elements are made dependent on e (e.g., by the use of saturable reactors), an excellent approximation can be realized.§

† Basic Research in Nonlinear Mechanics as Applied to Servomechanisms, *Cook Research Laboratories Interim Progress Rept. PR* 16-5, Contract No. AF33(038)-21673, Cook Electric Company, Chicago, Ill., December 10, 1952.

‡ Mathews and Boe, *op. cit.* This article contains a description of a suitable computer.

§ P. E. Kendall, "Linear Compensation of Saturating Servomechanisms," Ph. D. thesis, Purdue University, Lafayette, Ind., 1953.

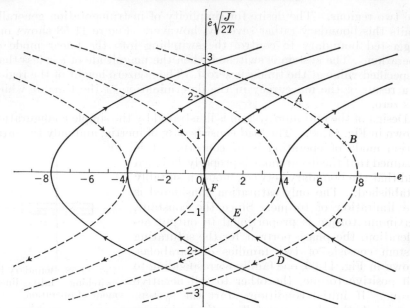

FIG. 11.60. Phase paths with full positive torque (dashed lines) or full negative torque (solid lines). *(From D. McDonald, Nonlinear Techniques for Improving Servo Performance, Proc. Natl. Electronics Conf. 1950, Vol. 6, p. 410, 1951.)*

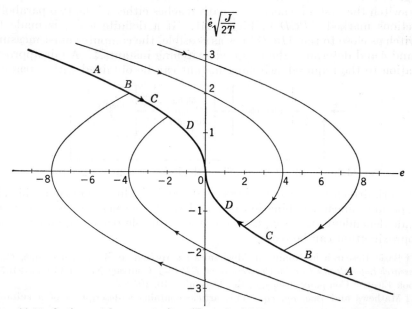

FIG. 11.61. Optimum phase portrait. *(From D. McDonald, Nonlinear Techniques for Improving Servo Performance, Proc. Natl. Electronics Conf. 1950, Vol. 6, p. 413, 1951.)*

The example described above is perhaps oversimplified, with the result that undue emphasis is placed on the difficulties of mechanization of the required nonlinearity. In the more general case, the determination of the required nonlinear characteristic is in itself complex. The general procedure† for the design of a dual-mode feedback control system is initiated with a design of the linear system and a determination of the optimum response of the system when saturated. These optimum saturation responses are then modified to take into consideration both system time lags and effects of the nonlinear, nonsaturated region between linear and saturated operation. In any but the simplest cases, the computations involved require the use of digital or analog computational aids. The complexity of the calculations is not a severe limitation of this method, however. Indeed, it is not surprising that optimization of a complex control system should involve considerable complexity, even when the optimization is considered only for the response of systems to step-function inputs.

11.10. Concluding Comments. The phase-plane methods are useful in the analysis of the effects of nonlinear elements on the step-function and ramp-function responses of second-order feedback control systems.‡ From such an analysis, a qualitative description of the effects of similar nonlinearities in higher-order systems can often be deduced. Perhaps even more important are the concepts associated with the phase-plane methods of analysis: in particular, the concepts of phase paths, singular points, and limit cycles in the performance of nonlinear systems.§ These concepts not only serve as useful tools in the analysis of nonlinear systems, but also provide a picture of the problems associated with the optimization of control systems excited by step-function signals. This optimization problem is amenable to solution in a wide variety of cases with physical constraints in the form of saturation levels throughout the system. Procedures for the optimization of systems sinusoidally excited or subject to random disturbances are not evident at the present time and do not seem subject to study in the phase plane.

† Neiswander and MacNeal, *op. cit.*

‡ Numerous additional applications are described in the literature. For example, the analysis of a control system in which the rate of change of the error is proportional to the trigonometric sine of the integral of the actuating signal is described in an article by P. Zilczer, H. Levenstein, and B. Farber, Application of Non-linear Differential Equations to the Analysis of an Unusual Feedback Problem, *Airborne Electronics*, 1953, pp. 137–140, Abstracts of paper delivered at 1953 National Conference on Airborne Electronics, IRE, Dayton, Ohio, 1953. A system designed to respond in an optimum fashion with ramp-function input is described by A. M. Hopkin, A Phase-plane Approach to the Compensation of Saturating Servomechanisms, *Trans. AIEE*, Vol. 70, Part I, pp. 631–639, 1951.

§ Jones, for example, has applied the linearization described in Sec. 11.3 to the study of the types of singular points in the analysis of higher-order feedback control systems. *Cf.* R. W. Jones, Stability Criteria for Certain Non-linear Systems, "Automatic and Manual Control," Proceedings of the Cranfield Conference 1951, edited by A. Tustin, pp. 319–324, Butterworths Scientific Publications, London, 1952.

INDEX

Aaron, M. R., 279
Abscissa of absolute convergence, 35
Acceleration constant, from closed-loop
    poles and zeros, 283–284
    constrained in optimization, 487–488
    definition of, 80–82
    insignificance of, 284
    (*See also* Error coefficients)
Active systems, analysis of (*see* Signal-
    flow diagrams)
Admittance, of active structures, 131
    input, 131–132
    in terms of return difference, 131
Ahrendt, W. R., 3, 143
A-c systems, compensated by frequency
    transformation, 401–406
    compensation for, 392–393, 397–409
    ideal, 398–400
    general description of, 390–392
    mechanical networks for, 394
    narrow-band, 400–401
    RC compensation of, 407–409
    tandem compensation of, 397–409
Amplitude-density spectrum, 440
Amplitude loci for nonlinear systems,
    575–579
Amplitude-modulated wave, transform
    of, 53
Amplitude modulation, suppressed-car-
    rier, 390–391
Amplitude spectrum, 439
Analogy, electrical-mechanical, 395
Analyticity, 6
Andronow, A. A., 613, 619, 635, 638
Approximation, in frequency domain,
    345–348
    Linvill's procedure for, 360–375
    of gain characteristic, 356
    impulse method of, 379–390
    of phase characteristic, 358–360
    with rational algebraic functions,
    548–550
    in time domain, 375–390
    of transportation lag, 547–553
    with triangles, 396–397
Asymptotes, for linear factor, accuracy
    of, 351
    for phase-angle loci, 246–247
    for root loci, 227–228

Asymptotic frequency plots for gain,
    265, 348–356
Autocorrelation function, definition of,
    429
    of derivative, 432–433
    measurement of, 445–453
    of periodic signals, 431–432
    properties of, 431–433
    significance of, 429–430
    of sum of two signals, 435–437
    in terms of probability distributions,
    430

Backlash, 610–611, 648–652
Bailey, A. E., 542
Bandwidth, conservation of, 405
    definition of, 77
    relation of, to K_v, 293–294
    to rise time, 77, 80
    of second-order system, 293
Barnes, J. L., 44, 228, 397, 503, 542
Bending resonance, 562–563, 583
Bendixson's first theorem, 644–646
Bendixson's second theorem, 645
Berkeley, E. C., 449
Blanton, H. E., 392
Blasingame, B. P., 375
Block diagrams, 98–99
    compared to signal-flow diagrams, 159
    importance of, 88
    manipulation of, 98
Bode, H. W., 128, 129, 141, 143, 162,
    346, 405, 460, 470
Bode diagrams, for sampled-data sys-
    tems, 532–533
    with transportation lag, 551–552
Boe, R. C., 660, 661
Bogoliuboff, N., 566
Bollay, N., 221
Boonton, R. C., Jr., 493
Boothroyd, A. R., 31
Bower, J. L., 343
Boxcar generator, 507–508
Brainerd, H. B., 447
Branch point, definition of, **7**
    order of, 7
    pole-type, 8
    zero-type, 8